Classroom-Relevant Research in the Language Arts

Coordinated by
Harold G. Shane, University Professor of Education
James Walden, Professor of Education
Indiana University, Bloomington

Foreword by Donald R. Frost

LANGUAGE
LANGUAGE
LANGUAGE
LANGUAGE
LANGUAGE
LANGUAGE

Association for Supervision and Curriculum Development
1701 K St., N.W., Washington, D.C. 20006

Stock number: 611-78140
Library of Congress Catalog Card Number: 78-56931
ISBN 0-87120-090-2

Contents

Foreword

PERIODIC reviews of language arts research long have been a characteristic of the publications program with which the Association for Supervision and Curriculum Development seeks to serve its members. It is of interest to note that this is the fifth publication of this kind to appear in 23 years.

During an era of renewed interest in skills development, the present publication is especially timely because of its extensive substantive content and its focus on studies and writing that have direct relevance for the classroom. It also is important because of the new areas of study such as visual literacy which are introduced for the first time.

An examination of the four earlier ASCD publications which emphasized communication skills (1955, 1963, 1967, 1971) brings to mind how fortunate our Association is in being able to draw upon professional resource persons for the tasks of preparing or reviewing its publications. Their names provide a roster of educational leadership as listed in these four past publications: May Hill Arbuthnot, Jeanne Chall, Mildred Dawson, Gertrude Hildreth, William S. Gray, Gordon Mackenzie, Laura Zirbes, John I. Goodlad, Ruth Strickland, and many more. Linguists such as Albert H. Marckwardt and Sumner Ives along with James Squire and Eldonna Evertts were a few of many who helped ensure the authenticity of our 1967 review of linguistics as a new force in the language arts.

I feel that we have been fortunate, indeed, as an organization to have had the support, the dedication, and the talent of friends such as these both within and from outside the ranks of our membership in ASCD.

Because of the timeliness and relevancy of the content, I enthusiastically recommend that every teacher and professor of language arts, supervisor, director, principal, and superintendent read this new edition. It is a valuable reference on the latest in language research and indicates direction in improving instructional programs to ensure quality learning in the language arts.

DONALD R. FROST, *President, 1978-79*
Association for Supervision and
Curriculum Development

Acknowledgments

IN A world sorely beset by problems, it is important to bear in mind that our planet will continue to provide a benign home for humans only if we can more fully accept both our individual and our shared responsibility for the general welfare. This concern must be reflected in policies that do not serve the interests of some while ignoring the rights of others.

Of great importance in a mutual attack on the present crisis of crises is skill in communicating effectively with one another. We need to know how to speak clearly, to write lucidly, to listen intelligently, and to recognize the power of language for good or for evil as words are used to explain or heal, to mislead or harm. In fine, there is an even greater need for teachers to understand communication skills than was the case nearly a quarter-century ago when the Association for Supervision and Curriculum Development distributed the first of its five publications directly concerned with language development and research in the language arts.

I had the privilege of preparing that first manuscript with the cooperation of some of the most distinguished specialists of the era; Roma Gans, Leland Jacobs, Helen Robinson, Ruth Strickland, and Viola Theman among them. Now the fifth review of classroom-relevant research appears, and James Walden and I have the opportunity to acknowledge the help of a variety of new contributors to this 1978 résumé of significant studies that have surfaced since he and I, with Ronald Green, coordinated *Interpreting Language Arts Research for the Teacher* in 1971.

Among the colleagues at Indiana University, Bloomington, who cheerfully and effectively contributed chapters are Professors Harry Gradman, Robert Lafayette, Milton Marten, and Dennis Pett. Students in Dr. Walden's doctoral seminar—Kevin Sue Bailey, Dixie Bjurstrom, Peter Connallon, Nelly Ferriera, Joanne Gentry, and Linda Lotto—prepared drafts of six chapters. Appreciation also is due Dolores MacNaughton of the University of Calgary for preparing the chapter on language and critical thinking and Kathryn R. Akural, who collaborated with Dr. Walden in writing the epilog.

The project secretary, Velma Trussell, very much merits our warm thanks. Not only did she produce the typescript expertly; her careful, patient reading and checking saved Dr. Walden and me much time and effort. He and I also express our gratitude for the work of our project assistant and professional colleague, Patricia Love Staver, who spent many hours on manuscript production and bibliographic checks.

As always, it is important to acknowledge the interest, advice, care, and technical skill with which Robert R. Leeper performed his usual editorial alchemy on the present manuscript. Appreciation also is due to Lana Pipes and to the ASCD staff who helped with the various production stages, from in-depth editing to checking proof: Nancy Olson, Production Manager; Myra K. Taub; Teola T. Jones; Elsa Angell; and Patsy Connors.

HAROLD G. SHANE
Indiana University

1. Introduction: The Language Arts— Relevance in Retrospect

Harold G. Shane

ALL human institutions have a need for traditions. Indeed, whole-some traditions often provide a foundation supporting these institutions—a base that gives them cumulative meaning and integrity, in the original Latin sense of "wholeness" and "completeness."

Over the years, the Association for Supervision and Curriculum Develop-ment has developed many *cumulative* traditions. Among them were belief in process during the 1950's, faith in humanistic educational practices and goals during the 1960's, and an active approach to resolving social issues in the 1970's. There has also been a tradition reflected in guides to current research: in mathe-matics, science, and the social studies, for example; and, of course, in the realm of the language arts.

Classroom-Relevant Research in the Language Arts is the fifth in a series that began in 1954 with exploratory work on *Research Helps in Teaching the Language Arts.* In the process of introducing the 1978 review, it is of historical value and interest to note how ASCD language publications reflect social and educational change.

Impact of Change

Let us look briefly at how changing times have left their mark on research as a whole and then take note of the ways in which studies in the language arts have mirrored the transition through which the schools have passed in a quarter-century that has been crowded with problems and crises.

Research as a reflection of changes in school or society. A backward glance to the world of 80-odd years ago provides evidence as to changing research techniques and their foci. The first "modern" research, for example—a study based on a random sample—was done in the field of spelling by Joseph M. Rice, a physician. Writing in 1897 on "The Futility of the Spelling Grind," he re-flected a new viewpoint, namely that drill often could be futile since leading

1

adults in U.S. communities—including school board members—did badly in the elementary school spelling quizzes he administered (10).[1]

The impact of the scientific movement and of the growing veneration of science was illustrated in 1910 when E. L. Thorndike (13) devised a scale to appraise handwriting. A few years later, in 1915, Leonard P. Ayres was to prepare an influential spelling scale. Research was also beginning on so-called scientific word lists (later voiced by Dick and Jane!), and in the 1920's Pressey's first teaching machine made its debut: a bit of candy reinforced learning and provided literal "feedback" for an expected answer! More thoughtful, speculative inquiries and early research were to be done in the twenties, notable among them Piaget's classic (1926) *The Language and Thought of the Child* (9).

Other illustrations of how changing times shaped research and publications[2] are too numerous to mention in the space available here, and in any case a few exemplars make the point:

Publication	*Probable Causal Factors*
George S. Counts, *Dare the Schools Build a New Social Order?* 1932 (3)	Social unrest associated with the Great Depression
Wilford M. Aiken, *The Story of the Eight Year Study*, 1935-1942 (1)	Educational debate between progressives and essentialists
Educational Policies Commission, *The Purposes of Education in American Democracy*, 1938 (5)	A response to social concerns in a world troubled by economic problems and gathering war clouds
Allison Davis and John Dollard, *Children of Bondage*, 1940 (4)	Early prescient inquiry into cultural bias and how it had operated to the particular detriment of the black child in an economically depressed era
Erik Erickson, *Childhood and Society*, 1950 (6); and Hans Selye, *The Stress of Life*, 1953 (11)	Growing awareness of inner focus, social forces, and the dangerous stress or tension they can create
Rudolph Flesch, *Why Johnny Can't Read*, 1955 (7)	Epitome of the widespread criticism of public education that began in the late 1940's and exploded in the 1950's

Literally dozens of other key education-related writings reflecting changing ideas, concerns, mores, growing social insights, technological change, environ-

---

[1] Numbers in parentheses are coded to match the list of references at the end of each chapter.

[2] For a summary of influential writings and research reports, 1897-1970, see Chapter 3 in Shane et al., *Guiding Human Development* (12: 73-92).

mental dangers, and resource depletion can be listed. McLuhan's *Global Village* (1965), Harrington's *The Other America: Poverty in the United States* (1965), the Coleman "Equality" Report (1966), the Herndon-Holt-Kozol (1967-70) brand of sharp and sometimes moving critiques of school practices, Barry Commoner's and Ralph Nader's current concern for environment and consumer respectively are all cases in point. Such writings and research are powerfully mediated by the developments woven on the looms of humankind's history.

The language arts as "mirrors of transition" since 1954. The ASCD language arts research reviews began in 1954—five in all, counting the present 1978 review. Taken together, these monographs provide an interesting reflection of changing forces, stresses, and intellectual break-throughs during more than two decades of change in the communication skills field. Let us reminisce about a few of the developments of these decades.

Research in the mid-fifties. When it appeared in 1955, *Research Helps in Teaching the Language Arts* proved to be a highly classroom-and-method centered booklet. The hundreds of teachers who were asked what questions *they* would like to see treated in the first of the *Research Helps . . .* publications raised approximately 1,300 of them—some 700 even after duplicate questions were eliminated. Virtually all of these queries zeroed in on the teaching of reading, writing, and spelling: How can reading readiness be developed? What are effective ways of developing word attack skills? What are the relative merits of cursive as opposed to manuscript writing? What should the teacher know about handedness? What are the best word lists for use in individualized spelling programs?

Neither teachers' questions nor published studies were much concerned a quarter-century ago with such matters as, for instance, ethnicity, sexism in readers, or the concepts of visual literacy. The distribution of research and writings also is intriguing in retrospect. Nearly 200 references that were located in 1954 dealt with reading problems in their many forms. With regard to creative writing, grammar, foreign language, and oral English, references were few indeed; the review cited 24, 15, 17, and 14 items, respectively.

Changes in language arts research by the early 1960's. A great deal of water poured over the social and educational spillways in the eight years that elapsed between that first ASCD language arts research booklet and its 1963 successor, *Improving Language Arts Instruction Through Research.*

The critical comments of Bestor, Flesch, and Rickover had led to various curriculum changes such as an infusion of the "new math." Charles C. Fries' (8) ideas regarding structural grammar had attracted scholarly interest. Furthermore, the influence of transformational-generative grammar was increasing rapidly as a result of Noam Chomsky's slender but respected book, *Syntactic Structures* (2). Finally, by 1963, the term "excellence" had become a catchword—at least partly as a result of the Woods Hole Conference out of which had come Jerome Bruner's "sense of the meeting" report, *The Process of Education.*

ASCD's *Improving Language Arts . . .* report reflected at least some of these changes and was virtually double the length of the first review (from 80 to 153 pages) as a result. The questions of 387 classroom teachers who were polled during the early 1960's reflected the criticisms of U.S. schooling, a growing interest in the importance of research, and concern over, for instance, sexism in readers. References also suggested the proliferation of research underway and foreshadowed the explosion of studies that the use of computers and ERIC-type centers would encourage later in the decade.

Linguistics leaves its imprint on practice. The third ASCD research publication in the language arts field, *Linguistics and the Classroom Teacher* (1967), grew out of the "English Reformation"—almost a revolution—that resulted from the impact of linguistics in the mid-sixties. In its 120 pages, 329 references were cited; and, because of almost endemic confusion over the meanings and implications of linguistics, the monograph was analogous to a small textbook dealing with backgrounds, terminology, pertinent research, and classroom strategies on which the "new English" impinged. It even included a six-page glossary that bristled with such terms as *allomorph, idiolect, suprasegmental,* and *tagmemics!* Once again new threads woven into language instruction were depicted in the changing patterns of the era.

The 1971 report. *Interpreting Language Arts Research for the Teacher* was published by ASCD in 1971. This time the venture was a team project involving 15 contributors who cited 1,168 references. Twenty years of cumulative change in communications skills now sprawled over so wide a range as to require a cooperative approach to the report, which now included chapters on the mass media and linguistics, and in which research germane to reading and to writing was subdivided into elementary and secondary school summaries.

Looking Toward Yesterday and Tomorrow

The present review of the literature and related research is a product of the many educational mutations that have occurred with the passage of time. Directly or obliquely, it reports studies and writings that have been influenced by the many elements of the language arts heritage which have accumulated since the first slim "research helps" booklet was written. Among these elements are the Great Debate over school practices which began around 1950 and the curriculum reform movement later in the decade. These were followed in the early and mid-sixties by quests for "excellence" and for "relevance"; by social-humanistic insights related to such matters as the culture of poverty, ethnicity, and liberation movements; and, of course, by the innovative scholarship that gave the profession its clearer grasp of such fields of study and inquiry as linguistic science and visual literacy.

Classroom-Relevant Research, in keeping with earlier monographs, looks to tomorrow as well as to yesterday. In its pages appear, with a few exceptions, writings published since 1970—studies that probably foreshadow practices of from five to ten years hence. Furthermore, the present ASCD publication has a selective quality. In the interests of (a) efficient use of the reader's time and (b) economy during a time of sky-high printing costs, the contributing authors have been urged to choose what they deem the most *pertinent* of current studies rather than to take the comprehensive approach followed in 1971 when more than 1,100 references confronted the reader!

To summarize, the five ASCD language arts research publications that have appeared since 1955 are documents which serve to footnote the ways in which education has been impacted by change. Among the dozens of powerful forces or developments mediating school practices for the past quarter-century are the following particularly important ones:

1. *Upward and downward extension* of the responsibilities delegated to education —from early childhood to senior learners

2. *Automation and expanding urban areas* as technological changes uprooted and transplanted families to megalopolitan centers

3. *A new examination of educational goals* as citizens deliberated such questions as who shall be educated, what should be taught, and how to teach it

4. *Clearer conceptions of the meaning of a more responsible society* in which compensatory education and alternative forms of schooling began to find a place

5. *Principles of social justice* such as integration as a means of reducing economic disparities and educational inequities

6. *Greater emphasis on the learner* without disregarding the importance of what was to be learned

7. *Improved perspectives with regard to the nature and cause of cross-cultural problems* both at home and in a transnational context

8. *Innovative practices in education:* flexible scheduling, modules, team teaching, computer-assisted instruction, and the like

9. *Wider recognition by educators of the need for curriculum change* as a result of such factors as the curriculum reform movement beginning in the fifties and the focus on protecting the human environment in the late sixties

10. *An increasing interest in the significance of the future for education* and the growing impact of change agencies such as foundations, government-sponsored research projects, and regional laboratories

11. *The increased use of technology* such as third generation computers adaptable to sophisticated research in education

12. *The substantial expansion of the "education business"* including the widespread application of instructional systems technology.

Plan of the 1978 Research Review

Because it is a relatively new language-related field, *visual literacy* is the topic of the next chapter. As a realm permeating all chapters, *critical thinking* is the focus of Chapter Three.

Chapters Four and Five, respectively, treat *foreign languages* and the teaching of *English as a second language. Listening* is examined in Chapter Six. *Reading* long has been the subject of research and conjecture, and three chapters—Seven, Eight, and Nine—are required to review the literature of the seventies in this field.

Composition and *creative writing* are treated in Chapter Ten, *spelling* and *handwriting* in Chapter Eleven, and *literature* in Chapter Twelve. The *Epilog* that brings *Classroom-Relevant Research* to a close looks to the future for research in the language arts.

References for each chapter appear at the end of that chapter. Reference numbers in parentheses in the text are coded to coincide with the numbering of each chapter's reference list. When numbers are separated by a colon, the second number refers to the page on which a citation appears. For example, "Cochran (2: 3)" indicates a citation from page three of the second entry in a given chapter reference list.

References

1. AIKIN, WILFORD M. *The Story of the Eight Year Study.* New York: Harper & Bros., 1942.

2. CHOMSKY, NOAM. *Syntactic Structures.* The Hague, Netherlands: Mouton and Company, 1957.

3. COUNTS, GEORGE S. *Dare the Schools Build a New Social Order?* New York: The John Day Company, 1932.

4. DAVIS, ALLISON, and JOHN DOLLARD. *Children of Bondage.* Washington, D.C.: American Council on Education, 1940.

5. Educational Policies Commission. *The Purposes of Education in American Democracy.* Washington, D.C.: National Education Association, 1938.

6. ERIKSON, ERIK. *Childhood and Society.* New York: W. W. Norton & Co., 1950.

7. FLESCH, RUDOLPH. *Why Johnny Can't Read.* New York: Harper & Bros., 1955.

8. FRIES, CHARLES C. *The Structure of English*. New York: Harcourt, Brace and World, Inc., 1952.

9. PIAGET, JEAN. *The Language and Thought of the Child*. New York: Harcourt Brace & Company, 1926.

10. RICE, JOSEPH M. "The Futility of the Spelling Grind." *Forum Magazine* 163: 172, 409-19; April-June 1897.

11. SELYE, HANS. *The Stress of Life*. New York: McGraw-Hill Book Co., 1953.

12. SHANE, HAROLD G., et al. *Guiding Human Development*. Worthington, Ohio: Charles H. Jones Publishing Co., 1971.

13. THORNDIKE, E. L. *Educational Psychology*. Three volumes. New York: Teachers College Press, 1913.

2. Visual Literacy
Dennis W. Pett

ON THE motion picture screen we see:

Orange leaves glowing in the evening sun . . . a slow dissolve. . . .

Wintry blasts shaking snow-laden branches . . . a slow dissolve. . . .

A violet crocus pushing through melting snow. . . .

We know tacitly as we watch that several months have elapsed; we can "read" or interpret what the film seeks to tell us. This is one aspect of visual literacy. The concepts are old. Art teachers have been teaching youngsters to "read" and appreciate master works of art for many years. Film writers have delved into the meanings created by optical effects and by dynamic editing. Communication researchers have studied the effects of media on children and adults.

However, the term "visual literacy" in the broad field of communications skills is a relatively new one, having come into common use as recently as 1969 when the first national conference on visual literacy was held in Rochester, New York. Since that time a growing number of conferences and publications have been devoted to the topic.

Four important questions to consider in relation to visual literacy are:

1. What is visual literacy—how is it defined?

2. Why is visual literacy important—what contributions can it make to education?

3. What does research contribute to visual literacy—what directions has research taken and what directions may it take in the future?

4. How are visual literacy programs implemented?

Each of the four queries will be considered in turn as we explore this recently opened territory in the realm of language arts-communication skills.

8

What Is Visual Literacy?

In mid-1976 about 75 educators spent a week at Lake Okoboji, Iowa, probing and brainstorming about "visual literacy." As one might expect, in view of the newness of the field, virtually each person had his or her own definition of the term, but two key things stand out in many of the definitions. *First,* there is such a thing as visual languaging. *Second,* visual literacy refers to a person's ability to understand and evaluate this language as well as his or her ability to use visual languaging to communicate.

Cochran (2:3) pointed out that originally and traditionally literacy was identified with literature and the abilities related to written communication. However, literacy—including visual literacy—now has come to be associated with the total body of skills needed for effective communication in any medium. There are similarities, for instance, between verbal and visual languages. Visual language uses visual symbols in a linear manner and, as in written language, visual elements can be combined in many ways to say different things. Words do not have meanings except for the meaning each individual ascribes to them. Similarly, as Wendt (31) indicated, meanings reside not in pictures themselves, but in what we bring or ascribe to them. Turbayne (29: 241) said it in another way: what we *see* are sense data, what we *perceive* are mind facta. When we look at a so-called visual illusion it is the mind that is deluding us.

About 1950, Henry Smith of Indiana University, Bloomington, developed pictorial materials to show how visual elements are used as subjects and as modifiers comparable to nouns and adjectives. Since that time Fransecky and Debes (9) as well as others have pointed out linkages between the grammars of visual and verbal language. Debes (4) has developed a hierarchy of visual skills ranging from distinguishing light from dark to being able to apply the grammar and syntax of visual language in the interpretation or creation of visual messages. In the same vein, Randhawa (25) has suggested the need for a preliminary taxonomy of visual literacy analogous to Bloom's taxonomy in the cognitive domain. Since there is ample evidence that visual languaging not only exists but also is a skill that can be learned, let us examine more closely the matter of its importance.

Why Is Visual Literacy Important?

I can't believe I ate the whole thing.

Plop, plop, fizz, fizz. . . .

Try it, you'll like it.

It's the real thing.

At present most people in the United States would recognize these lines from well-known and oft-repeated commercials. The average person watches over 20 hours of television a week. As Hattersley (15) pointed out, since TV is a dominant and powerful visual form, we need to know what it *is,* what it *does,* and *how* it does it. We need a knowledge of visual conventions and experience in reading visuals. Visual communication on television includes hidden symbolic or implied information. Visual literacy can help us cope with this kind of communication (17).

Peters (23: 197ff.) indicated that one limiting factor in the use of educational films has been the lack of filmic knowledge by students. Therefore he contended that we need to see and to understand the nature and significance of thoughts expressed visually. Early films simply recorded a stage production—a camera record of what an audience at a play would see. As film making increased in sophistication, moving cameras, juxtaposition of images to create new meanings, optical effects, and other techniques began to create a film language which eventually developed a complex vocabulary and elaborate syntax. Since communication takes place when the sender and receiver are in agreement on the symbols and on the arrangement, there is need for planned learning experiences that will enable both young and old to become more literate in the language of films.

McLuhan and Fiore (19: 8ff.) noted more than a decade ago that ". . . media work us over completely. Their influence is so pervasive that no part of us is left untouched, unaffected, unaltered." Their observation underscores the point that visual media are an important part of our lives and an irrefutable reason for emphasizing visual literacy in the curriculum.

As children grow, it is important to replace the passive reception of visual impressions with the active use of the eye and mind to communicate visually (12: 237-39). Under these circumstances it is encouraging to note that technological advances have made it possible for preschool children to use cameras to communicate with photographs and for school-age children to make Super-8 films and videotapes.

People are influenced by television in two languaging forms—the visual and the verbal. They appear intuitively to know something about how it works, judging by the widespread ability of Americans to interpret TV messages. This knowledge provides a base for educating both children and adults in the more refined forms of personal communication through such media as photography (15: 6ff.).

Another benefit in using photography and other visual media as a part of one's personal resources in communication is the motivating effect of such media on children who have difficulty with verbal communication. As Hedges (16) has indicated, photography also can be used to build better self-concepts.

The beginning sensations of the newborn are predominantly tactile as they move through the very early stages of development. Infants soon reach a point, however, where what they see becomes a source of the primary sensations that contribute to the learning of language. Randhawa (24) pointed out that children have a greater capacity to process visual than auditory inputs, and that a young child can describe what is seen through nonverbal inputs better than through verbal descriptions.

Some interesting relationships are being established between verbal and visual performance. In a presentation at the 1975 meeting of the Association for Educational Communications and Technology, Debes (3: 1-16) spoke about some recent changes in scores on the Stanford-Binêt tests. Current scores rise rapidly to about 110 at age 1½, then increase more slowly to 111 at age 5½. The scores then drop back to near 100 when boys and girls are 8½ years old. Today's children under 5½ apparently know more than their counterparts of 20 years ago. However, as one might expect from the ages of the children sampled, item analysis shows that the questions associated with the increased IQ scores are nonverbal items. The higher scores are recorded at an age when television is a dominant influence, and the subsequent drop occurs at a time when verbal activities are being emphasized in school.

As of 1977 certain scholastic achievement test scores have been declining slightly each year for 14 years, according to the College Entrance Examination Board's Special Advisory Panel. Perhaps much of what children and youth have been learning through visual means is not related to our predominantly verbal tests. In any case, Debes (5: 40ff.) has concluded on the basis of considerable evidence that we should be able to provide visual learning opportunities that will help young learners achieve at a superior level. Methodically fostering visual literacy presumably would improve verbal literacy also.

For some time it has been recognized that the hemispheres of the brain are generally specialized for different functions. The left hemisphere seems to deal primarily with verbal and mathematical functions; the right hemisphere primarily with spatial functions. Both hemispheres seem to deal with sequencing. It makes sense to be providing learning environments in which both halves of the brain can develop fully.

What Does Research Contribute to Visual Literacy?

Clarence Williams (32) was one of the first persons to summarize some of the research findings in visual literacy. He presented them in the form of nine propositions:

1. Early visual deprivation can relate to later visual problems.
2. Visual enrichment in early life increases success in visual tasks in later life.
3. A good program of visual enrichment can probably increase learning.

4. Ability to sequence visual stimuli is related to experience of the learner.

5. The development of the glance curve is related to sequencing experiences.

6. Hierarchical potential in a scene or pictorial sequence is related to experiences, sequencing ability, and development of verbal literacy.

7. Ability in the development of visual metaphoric communication is related to the development of verbal literacy.

8. There is a range of visual literacy sophistication related to experience and opportunities.

9. The ability to go back and forth between visual and verbal metaphors is related to visual and verbal development.

Research that relates to the concept of visual literacy falls into several major categories.

Seeing and learning from pictures. In an article in *Art Quarterly* in 1950, Gaffron (10) pointed out that skill in reading pictures is a learned phenomenon and in the western world observers tend to read pictures from left to right. For instance, a study by Brandt (1) indicated that the first point of fixation when looking at a picture is in the upper left quadrant, and 60 percent of the viewing time is spent looking at the upper half of a picture.

The works of Haber (13) and others have indicated that the recognition memory scores for a large number of pictures shown at intervals is very high. In one study viewers recalled 85 to 95 percent of 2,560 slides shown at ten-second intervals. Haber took note of a difference in the form of visual and verbal memory. Images of pictures are stored in pictorial form, he indicated, and words are taken out of pictorial form and stored and recalled as words.

Hanes (14: 19ff.) emphasized the diversity that exists in research on learning from pictures as it relates to the developmental aspects of children. He listed three variables that interact in the process of perceptual learning: (a) learner characteristics, (b) stimulus attributes, and (c) the requirements of the learning task.

Visual-verbal learning. People process visual and verbal stimuli differently. In *The Bisected Brain,* Gazzaniga (11) discussed in detail the function of the halves of the brain. The two halves are connected by a bundle of nerve fibers. When intact, the "two brains" exchange information and work together. The left half, however, is primarily related to verbal-mathematical behavior while the right is primarily related to visual-spatial behavior. This division of functions may be illustrated by considering the Japanese languages Katakana and Konji. Katakana is a verbal language where visual letters represent sounds as in English; Konji is a visual language and symbols represent concepts. If the left brain of a person who is competent in both these languages is damaged, he or she can still use and process Konji although Katakana abilities are lost (5: 20ff.).

Young children, at very early ages, have a greater capacity for processing visual input than verbal input. Perhaps for this reason, media communicators "talk" to children with visual language before the verbal vocabulary is significantly developed. This seems to have resulted in a generation with different skills from those attained by persons who did not grow up with television as a commonplace in their lives. Debes (5) noted a study that showed great differences in sequencing abilities between children and pre-TV era adults: the former were appreciably more skilled in reading visual signs.

Still on the theme of visual learning, an investigation of a group of third-grade children with reading difficulties showed that nearly all the children had a high degree of three-dimensional capacity. Reading problems were inversely proportional to three-dimensional visualization ability. In another study, children with a balance of visual and verbal opportunities in the first grade outdid their peers and four years later continued to excel in academic achievement (5: 10ff.).

In a study of emotionally disturbed children, Strandberg and Griffith (28) compared the subjects' verbal responses to pictures of specified objects with verbal responses to pictures the children took at home. Three interesting results occurred:

1. Verbal language responses were longer and grammatically more complex when the children were talking about pictures taken at home.

2. Training in picture sequencing increased the length and complexity of verbal language responses.

3. The children's verbal language behavior was more spontaneous when they were describing pictures taken at home.

There seems to be a motivational factor related to the use of pictures in conjunction with verbal tasks. This is related to the improvement in self-concept that has been noted by several writers. Nuell and Fryrear (22) worked on a photo project with a group of subjects ages 13-16 who scored below the fiftieth percentile on the Coopersmith Behavioral Rating Form and the Tennessee Self-Concept Scale. Subjects used simple, inexpensive cameras to take pictures that were then organized into scrapbooks. Post-test scores showed significant increases in self-concept scores. As Myra Ross (27) concluded in working with filmic media, film making is an "effective, exciting, and innovative way of changing self-concept."

If visual languaging is a different skill from verbal languaging, then we need to understand ways to test—to measure—visual abilities.

Measuring visual abilities. Visual testing can be divided into two general categories. The first consists of tests that measure various aspects of visual perception; an example of these are figure drawing tests reviewed by McWhinnie

(20) in 1971. In his review of research he listed six uses for such tests in art education and psychology:

1. To measure nonverbal aspects of intelligence
2. To provide nonverbal measures of emotional and personality disorders
3. To assess perceptual style
4. To measure perception growth in art
5. To measure cross-cultural aspects of perceptual style and intelligence
6. To measure children's growth and development in art.

Of great concern to proponents of visual literacy is a second category of tests—those used to measure the nonverbal components of a wide variety of subject matter. Although films, videotapes, and other visual media have been used to assess achievement of a variety of educational objectives, most appraisals continue to be made with conventional paper and pencil tests—tests that depend on verbal responses. Ellison (7) noted that tests should be designed to fit the instructional methodology, content, and performance expectations. Among 16 advantages he listed for nonverbal tests, three seem particularly important: (a) they can measure objectives not easily measured by paper and pencil tests, (b) they reduce dependence on reading as the means of producing test stimuli, and (c) for some objectives they can be superior to paper and pencil tests for measuring achievement. Despite the widely expressed need for ways of measuring nonverbal learning and the advantages that have been cited for nonverbal tests, there actually is little literature related to this area.

A variety of research efforts have contributed to the visual literacy area, but as Fork and Jonassen (8: 2ff.) have pointed out, there is as yet no generally accepted base for conducting visual literacy research. One must infer that a framework is needed; a framework that will encompass both relevant practical and important theoretical dimensions of the field.

In the meantime two areas of research seem particularly promising for further study:

1. We need to know more about how children learn from pictures and how this relates to the various stages of their development.

2. We need to find better ways to test and measure visual languaging abilities at a variety of age levels.

How Are Visual Literacy Programs Implemented?

The real value of visual literacy is attained only if it can be more completely woven into the curriculum. Unfortunately, well-conceived visual literacy programs are by no means widely implemented or even accepted in theory. On the other hand, a few outstanding programs have begun to demonstrate what the integration of visual literacy concepts into curricula can accomplish. A primary goal of such programs, according to Debes (3: 15ff.), is to help children grow in the ability to visualize ideas, organize them, think of ways to express them visually, and encode them in sequential, visual metaphors.

Books such as Meiselas' *Learn To See* (21), McKim's *Experiences in Visual Thinking* (18), and Dondis' *A Primer of Visual Literacy* (6) provide promising suggestions for content that might be incorporated into visual literacy programs. Some examples of programs that have been developed are described in a Kodak publication, *Visual Literacy Programs That Work* (30). Ventures in this new literacy concept have been introduced at the Garfield Elementary School in Montebello, California, where seven- and eight-year-olds are using cameras to develop skills in conceptualization, design, and language development. At Willowbrook High School in Villa Park, Illinois, students have used photography to communicate how they feel about themselves and their world. Another illustration is the "Media Now" course developed at the Southwest Iowa Learning Resources Center; this course has as its major objectives the improvement of young adolescents' mass media knowledge and techniques, an increase in their abilities to produce visual communications, a decrease in their susceptibility to persuasion by the mass media, and an increase in positive attitudes toward media. The James Russell Lowell Elementary School in San Diego also has introduced visual literacy instruction as a means of helping children with reading problems. Results thus far are encouraging—both self-concept and reading skills have been improved.

One more example is provided by Milford, Ohio, where visual communication is part of the regular curriculum from first through twelfth grades. This program reflects the belief that visual skills are basic to effective participation in today's society. An example of one course in the curriculum is the tenth-grade course with the simple title, "Media."

Four areas are emphasized: (a) the analysis of visual-aural messages; (b) the development of general understanding of the mechanics and operation of various media; (c) the comparative strengths and weaknesses of visual and print media; and (d) a look into possible future uses of film and television.

In view of its brief history, the field of visual literacy seems to be faring reasonably well. Nonetheless, its full potential has yet to be determined as a means of developing in U.S. children better means of understanding themselves and communicating with accuracy, empathy, and insight.

References

1. BRANDT, HERMAN F. *The Psychology of Seeing.* New York: The Philosophical Library, 1945.

2. COCHRAN, LIDA. "What Is Visual Literacy?" *AECT Research and Theory Division Newsletter* 5(3): 2; November 1976.

3. DEBES, JOHN L. "The Eyeful Power." Presentation at the National Convention of the Association for Educational Communications and Technology, Dallas, Texas, April 1975.

4. DEBES, JOHN L. "The Loom of Visual Literacy—An Overview." In: Clarence M. Williams and John L. Debes, editors. *Proceedings of the First National Conference on Visual Literacy.* New York: Pitman Publishing Corporation, 1970.

5. DEBES, JOHN L. *Superminds: New Potentials for Educating Children Through Visual Literacy.* (Pamphlet.) Stillman, Oklahoma: Oklahoma State Visual Literacy Conference, 1974.

6. DONDIS, DONIS. *A Primer of Visual Literacy.* Cambridge, Massachusetts: The MIT Press, 1973.

7. ELLISON, JOHN W. "Visual Tests: An Alternative." *Educational Technology* 13: 50-52; May 1973.

8. FORK, DONALD J., and DAVID JONASSEN. "Search for a Paradigm: A Theoretical Approach to the Study of Visual Literacy." *Visual Literacy Newsletter* 5(5): 2; July 1976. (Washington, D.C.: Center for Visual Literacy, Gallaudet College.)

9. FRANSECKY, ROGER B., and JOHN L. DEBES. *Visual Literacy: A Way To Learn—A Way To Teach.* Washington, D.C.: Association for Educational Communications and Technology, 1972.

10. GAFFON, MERCEDES. "Right and Left in Pictures." *Art Quarterly* 13: 4; Autumn 1950.

11. GAZZANIGA, MICHAEL S. "The Split Brain in Man." *Scientific American* 217: 24-29; August 1967.

12. GERACI, A. JOHN. "The Use of Photography To Stimulate Visual Literacy." In: Clarence M. Williams and John L. Debes, editors. *Proceedings of the First National Conference on Visual Literacy.* New York: Pitman Publishing Corporation, 1970.

13. HABER, RALPH NORMAN. "How We Remember What We See." *Scientific American* 222: 104-12; May 1970.

14. HANES, MICHAEL. "The Research on How Children Learn from Pictures." *Viewpoints* (Bulletin of the School of Education, Indiana University) 49: 11-20; March 1973.

15. HATTERSLEY, RALPH. "What Is Visual Literacy?" *35mm Photography,* Summer 1976.

16. HEDGES, ROBERT E. "Photography and Self-Concept." *Audiovisual Instruction* 17: 26-28; May 1975.

17. MACOMBER, PHILLIP A. "Non-Verbal Aspects of Television." In: Clarence M. Williams and John L. Debes, editors. *Proceedings of the First National Conference on Visual Literacy.* New York: Pitman Publishing Corporation, 1970. pp. 147-51.

18. McKim, Robert H. *Experiences in Visual Thinking.* Monterey, California: Brooks/Cole Publishing Company, 1972.

19. McLuhan, Marshall, and Quentin Fiore. *The Medium Is the Massage.* New York: Bantam Books, 1967.

20. McWhinnie, Harold J. "Review of Recent Literature on Figure Drawing Tests as Related to Research Problems in Arts Education." *Review of Educational Research* 41: 131-42; April 1971.

21. Meiselas, Susan, editor. *Learn To See.* Cambridge, Massachusetts: Polaroid Corporation, 1974.

22. Nuell, Lon R., and Jerry L. Fryrear. "A Photographic Approach to Self-Concept Modification in Juvenile Delinquents." *Visual Literacy Newsletter* 5: 8; September 1976. (Washington, D.C.: Center for Visual Literacy, Gallaudet College.)

23. Peters, J. M. L. "The Necessity of Learning How To See a Film." *Audiovisual Communication Review* 3: 197-205; Summer 1955.

24. Randhawa, B. S. "Intellectual Development and the Ability To Process Visual and Verbal Information." *Audiovisual Communication Review* 19: 298-312; Fall 1971.

25. Randhawa, Bikkar S. "Visual Literacy: Prospectus for the Future." *AECT Research and Theory Division Newsletter* 5: 14; November 1976.

26. Rheinish, Robert K. "A Study of the Development of Children's Perceptions of Selected Film Conventions." Unpublished doctoral thesis, Indiana University, Bloomington, 1971.

27. Ross, Myra M. "Development of Self-Concept and Self-Image Through Film-Making." In: Clarence M. Williams and John L. Debes, editors. *Proceedings of the First National Conference on Visual Literacy.* New York: Pitman Publishing Corporation, 1970. pp. 158-60.

28. Strandberg, Twila, and Jerry Griffith. "Study of the Effects of Training in Visual Literacy on Verbal Language Behavior." *Journal of Communication Disorders* 3: 252-63; 1969.

29. Turbayne, Colin Murray. *The Myth of Metaphor.* Columbia: University of South Carolina Press, 1962.

30. *Visual Literacy Programs That Work.* Rochester, New York: Eastman Kodak Company, 1976.

31. Wendt, Paul R. "The Language of Pictures." In: S. I. Hayakawa, editor. *The Use and Misuse of Language.* Greenwich, Connecticut: Fawcett Publications, Inc., 1962. pp. 175-83.

32. Williams, Clarence M. "Nine Visual Literacy Propositions and Some Related Research." In: Clarence M. Williams and John L. Debes, editors. *Proceedings of the First National Conference on Visual Literacy.* New York: Pitman Publishing Corporation, 1970. pp. 60-69.

3. Language Development and Critical Thinking

Dolores MacNaughton

LANGUAGE arts and the ability to think critically probably are intimately related. The power to use language also is as uniquely human as psychologist David Krech pointed out many years ago (18: 374). In short, cognition and the spoken word are as closely related as two sides of the same coin. This chapter reviews research related to critical thinking, with particular heed given to its relation to vocabulary development.

Research Bearing on Vocabulary Development

Critical thinking and vocabulary. Several theoretical opinions and research findings suggest that cognitive processes are fused with language processes. Vygotsky, the distinguished Russian scholar, pointed out that "the speech structures mastered by the child become the basis of his thinking" (28: 51). In the same vein, Piaget's studies (23, 24) suggested language is a mode for symbolizing thought, while Carroll (6) concluded that we can think of language as a system of responses that facilitates thinking. Wilkinson subsequently stated that language profoundly transforms thought by helping it to attain a more advanced level (31: 79). Finally, Cazden (7) proposed that internal language processes are exemplified in thought which is vital to cognitive development.

Several studies which are also relevant to the topic of critical thinking and vocabulary were reported by the American Council on Education (Dressel and Mayhew, 11). Selected committee members examined the relationship of critical thinking ability in social science and the learner's knowledge of terminology necessary for success in understanding social science. The Test of Critical Thinking in Social Science and the Vocabulary Test were administered to college students to test the hypothesis that a knowledge of terminology is essential for critical thinking but not sufficient *of itself* to ensure success in critical thinking. The results of the investigation supported the generalization that knowledge of the vocabulary used in the content of the social science area is not per se a guarantee of success in critical thinking.

A study by MacNaughton (20: 81) led to the conclusion that a significant relationship does exist between each of three components of critical thinking (inference, deduction, interpretation), as measured by the Watson-Glaser Thinking Appraisal, and listening vocabulary and reading vocabulary respectively, as measured by the Durrell Listening Reading Series. Additional results of this study indicated that both listening vocabulary and reading vocabulary are effective predictors of each of the three components of critical thinking, but that listening vocabulary is the most effective predictor of all.

A number of other educators have expressed opinions about the relationship of critical thinking and vocabulary. As early as 1910, Dewey (10) stated that oral and written speech can be perfected as tools for assisting thought. Anderson (2) asserted that an impoverished vocabulary is a barrier to critical thinking, and that appropriate language expressions lead to the fostering of critical thought. Anderson's claim was disputed by D'Angelo (8) when he suggested that a poor vocabulary is not necessarily a barrier to critical thinking. A student can possess a simple vocabulary, he argued, and still correctly apply different thinking skills.

It would appear that the literature and research have little that is conclusive to contribute to the relationship of critical thinking and vocabulary. However, a profound interest in the topic has been expressed by educators who have theorized about how cognitive processes relate to language processes.

Studies with an Indirect Bearing on the Language Arts

Critical thinking and intelligence. One of the concerns of educators who have investigated critical thinking has been its relationship to intelligence. Do tests of intelligence and critical thinking—both closely linked to language—measure the same traits? Or is critical thinking independent of intelligence? Evidence can be adduced from a number of studies to support the hypothesis that performance on intelligence tests will be related, but not highly, to performance on critical thinking tests (Dressel and Mayhew, 11; Furst, 13; Glaser, 14; Westbrook and Sellers, 30). Critical thinking thus appears to be at least partially independent of what is commonly measured as "general intelligence."

Can critical thinking be taught? A review of several studies supports the suggestion that critical thinking skills can be taught. As an illustration, a classical experiment was reported by Glaser in 1941 (14). The results of the investigation indicated that the students who were taught by methods dealing specifically with concepts of critical thinking made significantly greater gains on the Watson-Glaser Tests of Critical Thinking than did the students who studied regular subject content.

A cooperative study of evaluation in general education (Dressel and

Mayhew, 11) involving college students appeared to support the conclusion that explicit attention to critical thinking can result in much richer and more varied approaches to teaching and also can encourage greater student growth in critical thinking.

Livingston's study (19) led to the conclusion that students' critical thinking ability improved as a result of instruction in general semantics, and somewhat later Rodunsky (25) suggested that the use of an inductive-approach social studies unit is likely to result in critical thinking growth. Bibb (4) developed instructional materials which he suggested could be used to teach various categories of critical thinking skills related to the teaching of English, while Hall (16) indicated that students of teachers trained in methods of teaching critical thinking achieved a significant gain in critical thinking ability.

When current evidence is examined, it sometimes supports the proposition that educators can teach critical thinking skills. At the same time, it should be kept in mind that other studies (Harris, 17; Massialas, 21; Witt, 32) indicated inconclusive results when methods of teaching critical thinking were examined. Apparently, the jury is still out and it must be concluded that there is a need for further research which investigates the concept of critical thinking in relation to successful instructional strategies.

Critical thinking and aptitude. It should be noted that many aptitude tests have been developed as tests of *scholastic* ability. Such tests commonly are used in appraising fundamental intellectual abilities such as verbal reasoning, numerical ability, and abstract reasoning rather than specialized learning abilities such as art and music. The following two paragraphs concern themselves with thinking and aptitude as determined through the use of scholastic aptitude tests.

A 1950 study by Furst (13: 616) tested the hypothesis: "Performance on various specialized tests of critical thinking will become more independent of scholastic aptitude as a result of a relatively prolonged period of instruction in thinking skills." Since the correlations between tests of critical thinking and tests of scholastic aptitude changed only slightly after a two-year period of instruction in critical thinking skills, Furst suggested there was little support for the hypothesis that such interrelations will tend to decrease as a result of instruction in thinking skills. Furst also concluded that tests of critical thinking measure characteristics of student behavior which are not highly related to measures of scholastic aptitude. He further suggested that students at all levels of scholastic aptitude may be able to develop to a relatively high degree those various skills measured in his study as aspects of critical thinking.

The results of previously mentioned studies sponsored by the American Council on Education (Dressel and Mayhew, 11) indicated that critical thinking scores in that era did not correlate highly with scholastic aptitude scores. These results led the committee to conclude that critical thinking ability is not completely dependent on scholastic aptitude. MacNaughton (20) reported that a significant relationship existed between each of three critical thinking components—inference, deduction, interpretation—and three scholastic aptitude measures—verbal reasoning, spelling, grammar—as measured by the Differential Aptitude Tests.

The conclusions of the studies cited suggest that the ability to become proficient in the use of critical thinking skills is not completely dependent on scholastic aptitude. Patently, in view of the limited number of studies on the topic, the relationship of critical thinking ability and aptitude is open to further investigation.

Critical thinking and academic achievement. Particularly since the 1977 report on academic score decline was published by the College Entrance Examination Board, there has been even greater interest in achievement in the United States and Canada. Several studies of critical thinking have investigated its relationship to academic achievement. The purpose of these investigations has been to identify those academic areas which seem to reflect the use of critical thinking skills. A survey of the literature and research reveals varying conclusions and opinions as to the relationship.

On the one hand, Glaser (14) concluded that a low correlation exists between academic achievement scores and critical thinking, nor did Burns (5) detect any significant relationship between the two variables. Smith (27) reported that critical thinking ability and academic achievement in science tend to reflect each other with respect to the achievement of males but not females. This does not jibe with findings by Denny (9) that critical thinking correlated with knowledge of science for both males and females. MacNaughton (20) added to the evidence in a 1976 inquiry which suggested that a significant relationship exists between critical thinking and the language arts academic achievement measure.

Investigations and opinions as to the relationship between the ability to read and the ability to think critically also do not seem to agree in their conclusions. Betts (3) inferred from his survey of the literature that only a low positive relationship, if any, exists between reading ability and critical thinking ability. Moreover, Watson and Glaser (29) suggested that many persons who are superior readers may score relatively low in critical thinking. Conversely, Haas (15) reported that a positive relationship between measures of critical thinking and reading ability exclusive of rate *does* exist. More recently, Harris (17) indicated that reading ability is a consistent significant concomitant of critical thinking competencies.

It would appear that interested students should examine the original research data cited in past investigations. And quite obviously additional research is needed to identify those academic areas which reflect the use of critical thinking skills, since research results to date appear to be inconclusive.

Does critical thinking vary with sex differences? A realm of inquiry which has received considerable attention has been the assessment of whether the critical thinking ability of females differs from the critical thinking ability of males. The following research data present some of the conclusions that have been reached on the topic. Edwards (12) indicated that in high school science, males think more critically than females, and Smith (27) came to an analogous conclusion that in the sciences males in grades eleven and twelve think more critically than do females in those grades. However, Alston (1) suggested in a doctoral study that the critical thinking ability of male and female teachers does not vary significantly. Nixon (22) came to the same decision, as did Burns (5) after a study of male and female undergraduates. With respect to children and adolescents, Harris (17) suggested that males and females in grade five do not differ in their ability to think critically, and MacNaughton (20) indicated that males and females in grade nine differ only in the "interpretation" component of critical thinking, in regard to which males think more critically than females. Only Schafer's (26) doctoral research, which focused on teachers, indicated that female teachers think more critically than male teachers.

Whatever the persuasion of the reader may be, there is no conclusive evidence to support any one theory as to whether males and females differ in their ability to think critically!

In conclusion. References extending back at least to 1910 show that the topic of critical thinking long has been one of educational interest. However, there continues to be a need for more comprehensive understanding of the concept of critical thinking. Once obtained, such knowledge can then be used to provide a framework for the development of instructional methods and materials to be used in teaching critical thinking skills.

Insofar as the language arts are concerned, classroom-relevant research distinctly suggests that time spent on vocabulary development is a good means of increasing pupils' potential ability to engage in the symbol manipulation involved in critical thought processes.

References

1. ALSTON, D. N. "An Investigation of the Critical Reading Ability of Classroom Teachers in Relation to Selected Background Factors." Unpublished doctoral dissertation, Florida State University, Tallahassee, 1969.

2. ANDERSON, H. A. "Critical Thinking Through Instruction in English." *English Journal* 36: 73-80; 1947.

3. BETTS, E. A. "Research on Reading as a Thinking Process." *Journal of Educational Research* 50: 1-15; 1956.

4. BIBB, T. C. "Toward a Theory of the Development and Improvement of Critical Thinking Skills in a Classroom in English." Unpublished doctoral dissertation, Northwestern University, Evanston, Illinois, 1973.

5. BURNS, R. L. "The Testing of a Model of Critical Thinking Ontogeny Among Central Connecticut State College Undergraduates." Unpublished doctoral dissertation, University of Connecticut, Storrs, 1974.

6. CARROLL, J. B. *Language and Thought.* Englewood Cliffs, New Jersey: Prentice-Hall, Inc., 1964. p. 4.

7. CAZDEN, C. B. "Some Implications of Research on Language Development for Preschool Education." In: R. D. Hess, editor. *Early Education.* Chicago: Aldine Publishing Co., 1968.

8. D'ANGELO, E. *The Teaching of Critical Thinking.* Amsterdam: B. R. Gruner N. V., 1971.

9. DENNY, L. L. "The Relationships Between Teaching Method, Critical Thinking, and Other Selected Teacher Traits." Unpublished doctoral dissertation, University of Missouri, Columbia, 1968.

10. DEWEY, J. *How We Think.* New York: D. C. Heath & Co., 1910.

11. DRESSEL, P., and L. B. MAYHEW, directors. *General Education: Explorations in Evaluation.* Final Report of the Cooperative Study of Evaluation in General Education. Washington, D.C.: American Council on Education, 1954.

12. EDWARDS, T. B. "Measurement of Some Aspects of Critical Thinking." *Journal of Experimental Education* 18: 263-72; 1950.

13. FURST, E. J. "Relationship Between Tests of Intelligence and Tests of Critical Thinking and of Knowledge." *Journal of Educational Research* 43: 614-25; 1950.

14. GLASER, E. M. *An Experiment in the Development of Critical Thinking.* Contribution to Education No. 843. New York: Bureau of Publications, Teachers College, Columbia University, 1941.

15. HAAS, M. G. "A Comparative Study of Critical Thinking, Flexibility of Thinking, and Reading Ability Involving Religious and Lay College Seniors." Unpublished doctoral dissertation, Fordham University, Bronx, New York, 1963.

16. HALL, W. C. "A Descriptive Study of Modified Teacher Instructional Methods, Attitudes, and Role Perceptions, and Student Critical Skills and Attitudes Through an Application of the Hilda Taba Teaching Strategies in Metropolitan Nashville Public Schools, 1973-74." Unpublished doctoral dissertation, George Peabody College for Teachers, Nashville, Tennessee, 1975.

17. HARRIS, N. E. "A Study of Certain Critical Thinking Skills Among Fifth Graders in the Area of Propaganda in Advertising." Unpublished doctoral dissertation, Boston University School of Education, Boston, Massachusetts, 1975.

18. KRECH, DAVID. "Psychoneurobiochemeducation." *Phi Delta Kappan* 50: 370-75; March 1969.

19. LIVINGSTON, H. "Investigation of the Effect of Instruction in General Semantics on Critical Reading Ability." *California Journal of Educational Research* 16: 93-96; 1965.

20. MACNAUGHTON, D. E. "The Relationship Between Critical Thinking and Selected Variables." Unpublished doctoral dissertation, University of Calgary, Alberta, Canada, 1976.

21. MASSIALAS, B. G. "Description and Analysis of a Method of Teaching a High School Course in World History." Unpublished doctoral dissertation, Indiana University, Bloomington, 1961.

22. NIXON, J. T. "The Relationship of Openness to Academic Performance, Critical Thinking, and School Morale in Two School Settings." Unpublished doctoral dissertation, George Peabody College for Teachers, Nashville, Tennessee, 1973.

23. Piaget, J. "The Genetic Approach to the Psychology of Thought." *Journal of Educational Psychology* 52: 275-81; 1961.

24. PIAGET, J. *Six Psychological Studies.* New York: Random House, 1967.

25. RODUNSKY, S. "Change in Critical Thinking Scores Effected by a Fenton Inquiry Sequence." Unpublished master's thesis, University of Calgary, Alberta, Canada, 1969.

26. SCHAFER, P. J. "An Inquiry into the Relationship Between the Critical Thinking Ability of Teachers and Selected Variables." Unpublished doctoral dissertation, University of Pittsburgh, Pennsylvania, 1972.

27. SMITH, P. M. "Critical Thinking and the Science Intangibles." *Science Education* 47: 405-408; 1963.

28. VYGOTSKY, L. S. *Thought and Language* (1934, translated by E. Haufmann and G. Vakar). Cambridge, Massachusetts: The MIT Press, 1962.

29. WATSON, G., and E. M. GLASER. *Watson-Glaser Critical Thinking Appraisal Manual.* New York: Harcourt, Brace & World, 1964.

30. WESTBROOK, B. W., and J. R. SELLERS. "Critical Thinking, Intelligence, and Vocabulary." *Education and Psychological Measurement* 27: 443-46; 1967.

31. WILKINSON, A. *The Foundation of Language.* London, England: Oxford University Press, 1971.

32. WITT, M. "Developing Reading Skills and Critical Thinking." *Social Education* 25: 239-42; 1961.

4. Research in the Realm of Second Language Instruction

Robert C. Lafayette

THE famous German poet, novelist, and playwright Johann von Goethe once said, "He who knows no foreign language has never really learned his own." Ironically, if declines in foreign language enrollments in the United States are any indicator, either the great majority of Americans are not familiar with the statement or—if they are—they probably do not believe it. Throughout the history of American education, foreign languages, except Latin and Greek, have almost always been electives and subject to the vagaries of educational and social pressures at a given time.

Trends in the Past Decade

Enrollment. Due to Sputnik and to the National Defense Education Act of 1958, foreign languages enjoyed a significant period of growth during the early sixties. National enrollment statistics (57) tell us that in 1968 nearly five million students in the public secondary schools were enrolled in foreign language instruction. That represented 27.1 percent of the total public secondary school population. By 1974, enrollment in foreign languages had plummeted by some 700,000 while the total enrollment increased by approximately 3½ million; thus only 19.2 percent of secondary school students in the United States were receiving language instruction. The decline can be attributed to a variety of factors. Conjecture suggests that they include a divisive war in Vietnam, student rejection of traditional content during the late sixties and early seventies, the recession of the early seventies, and a lack of insight as to the value of foreign language. Chastain (10: 37) said, "If the economy worsens, society's interests will turn inward, and language learning will be less important than at present." However, the middle seventies, reinforced by the Bicentennial, have witnessed significant social developments, the most important of which has been the increased interest in ethnicity and cultural pluralism, intensified in part by the growing impact of Spanish-speaking Americans. This in turn has fostered, and in certain states introduced, bilingual education in American schools. The trend,

25

in addition to expanding international business and travel, promises to have a powerful impact on the future of foreign language instruction.

Research trends. Paradoxically, during a period of declining enrollments, the profession experienced a substantial proliferation of professional literature. In 1968, the American Council on the Teaching of Foreign Languages (ACTFL) issued the first volume of the *ACTFL Review of Foreign Language Education,* edited by Birkmaier (4). Subsequently, the Council has sponsored yearly volumes edited by Lange (34, 35, 36) and Jarvis (23, 24, 25, 26); each contains more than 1,000 references concerning contemporary trends in foreign language teaching.

Since 1968, foreign language education has also experienced considerable diversification of both curriculum and instruction. As they began to dispel the impression that their foreign language programs catered only to above-average students, the schools made substantial strides in meeting the needs of a much larger student population by emphasizing basic communication skills and the cultural importance of language instruction, in addition to experimenting with various aspects of individualized instruction.

Paralleling present trends in educational research, the great majority of recent research studies in foreign language teaching have been descriptive in nature. In a recent compilation of 300 studies done since 1970, Frechette (17) identified 204 of these as "descriptive." Within this category, 96 were of the interrelationship type, including case studies, correlational studies, and comparative studies. The remainder of these descriptive studies were for the most part surveys and growth or trend studies. Experimental research characterized by rigorous control over variables was found in less than 100 of the studies compiled.

Instructional Strategies

The eclectic movement. Unlike the decade of the sixties which was dominated by audio-lingual approaches that stressed habit formation through mimicry, memorization, and pattern drill, thus far the seventies can best be characterized as the decade of eclecticism. In fine, there is virtually no consensus among language teachers as to which methods are best. This is due in part to the lack of any persuasive research signaling the superiority of audio-lingualism. Chastain and Woerdehoff (11), Smith (54), Mueller (42), and Von Elek and Oskarsson (61) all conducted studies comparing the audio-lingual method with variants of a cognitive approach emphasizing understanding, meaning, and explicit explanation of linguistic forms. In no case did the results favor the audio-lingual method, and only Smith (54) found that no significant difference appeared to exist between the two. The other scholars concluded that a cognitive approach was the superior method.

Naturally, this finding was not entirely acceptable to the mass of foreign language teachers, many of whom had been trained within the narrow confines of audio-lingualism. This led to uncertainty, which in turn resulted in the classroom teacher's turning to eclecticism—using either an audio-lingual approach (often modified by some basic cognitive procedures) or a cognitive approach influenced by remnants of audio-lingualism.

Divergent methodologies. Eclecticism did not deter certain individuals from developing and advocating highly specific approaches to language teaching, but none seems to have had any significant impact on the profession as a whole. It is important, nonetheless, to mention a few because they may signal a return to more structured methodologies. Gattegno (18), advocating the "Silent Way" approach, claimed that learning is not primarily imitation or drill. Rather, the mind draws on everything it has already acquired, including its experience in learning its native language. The method gets its name from the notion that the teacher must stop interfering or sidetracking the learner's activity. Gattegno proposed that students should do 90 percent or more of the talking in chorus or individually in response to the teacher's gestures.

"Community Language Learning," described by La Forge (32), involves a simple mechanical classroom procedure. The learners, seated in a closed circle, talk with one another in the foreign language, tape-record what they say, play it back, write it down, and identify its component parts. Teachers or resource persons help them produce the utterance in the foreign language and eventually help them to analyze what was said.

Individuals interested in information about other unique approaches to foreign language teaching may consult Diller (14) or Stevick (56), both of whom provide excellent overviews of specific methodologies.

Many language teachers share the conviction that language learning must occur within a meaningful context; thus the current emphasis on meaningful dialogs, including functional practice or drills. Both Oller and Obrecht (45) and Jarvis (22) concluded that it is undesirable for students to practice structural patterns in drills that are devoid of a meaningful or communicative context.

These studies paved the way for a significant movement in foreign language teaching, "communicative competence." Savignon defined communicative competence as "the ability to function in a truly communicative setting—that is, in a dynamic exchange in which *linguistic competence* must adapt itself to the total informational input, linguistic and paralinguistic, of one or more interlocutors" (49: 8). In her experiment Savignon compared the effect of three treatments on tests of linguistic and communicative competence in three beginning college French classes. All three groups met for four 50-minute periods per week for the same basic course of instruction. Experimental group 1 spent an additional 50-minute period learning to communicate, experimental group 2 devoted the hour to studying aspects of French culture in English, and the third group, the control group, used the time to practice French structure in the language laboratory. Results showed no significant differences among the three groups on standardized tests of linguistic competence in listening and reading or on course examinations and final grades. The communicative skills experimental group, however, scored significantly better on communication tests designed by the experimenter.

In an analogous study, Joiner (27) contrasted communicative practice involving transmission of new information with meaningful practice composed of drills and question-answer exercises where no real information was transmitted. Results showed that students involved in the communicative treatment scored significantly higher on an oral communication test. Similar to the findings of Savignon, the treatments did not significantly affect scores on other language skills.

Bartz (3) and Schulz (50) examined the relationships between linguistic and communicative tests in the four skills in German and French respectively. Although both found significant positive relationships between the two, they concluded that serious attention should be paid to teaching and testing linguistic and communicative competence separately.

In discussing the implications of communicative competence for the design of foreign language teaching syllabi, Valdman (58) favored the use of the term "approximative communicative competence" because sociolinguists who originally introduced the term "communicative competence" meant it to include not only the ability to communicate a message but also the ability to apply all the various social rules of language use, a goal usually beyond the expectations of American foreign language courses. Valdman claimed that if approximative communicative competence is to be an important goal in the American classroom, then the present syllabus must undergo a thorough revision. He suggested that revisions should be guided by the following principles: (a) drastic reduction of the number of features introduced; (b) use of cyclical rather than linear ordering; (c) reduction of the complexity of material presented; (d) reduction of variants and alternants; (e) tolerance of learner errors.

Individualized instruction. Individualized instruction has had a significant impact on American education during the 1970's, and among all the different subject matter areas in today's curriculum, foreign language is probably the most involved. The professional literature is replete with articles on the topic; in fact *Foreign Language Annals,* the official organ of the American Council on the Teaching of Foreign Languages, included a special feature on individualized instruction in every issue for a period of three years. In addition to several books of edited readings, Disick (15), Grittner and LaLeike (19), Logan (39), and Steiner (55) provide classroom teachers with excellent books on the classroom implementation of individualized instruction. All four offer very practical suggestions which are not limited to teachers interested in this mode of instruction.

Unfortunately, interest in individualized instruction has not been accompanied by definitive research efforts. In a two-year study in beginning and intermediate German courses at the University of California at Berkeley, Clausing, Mueller, and Stein (12) reported that the performance of individually instructed students was significantly better on all written tests than that of students in a basic course for which the same textbook was used. The oral performance of the individualized instruction group also was found to be equal to that of students in the basic course.

La Charité and Mueller (29) reported that a flexible individualized instruction program in beginning French at the University of Kentucky has resulted in better student attitudes toward language learning, a significant increase in enrollment (about 40 percent) without any decrease in results as measured by Modern Language Association cooperative tests, and a higher retention of those students who begin the program.

One of the significant developments emanating from the interest in individualized instruction among foreign language teachers has been a considerable influx of individualized materials into the textbook market. Bull et al. (6), for instance, made use of a modified programmed instruction approach in their Spanish texts. The Center for Curriculum Development (9) and La Grone and Romera-Navarro (33) maintained standard texts but provided sets of individualized materials as an option. Valette and Valette (60), in their teacher's edition, suggested various modifications of the basic text to meet different student goals.

Curricular Changes

Culture concepts. During the past ten years classroom teachers and textbook publishers have been endeavoring to place a greater emphasis on the teaching of language in the context of its culture. In the past, culture had been treated primarily in a historical, geographic, and artistic manner. As a result of the more recent approach, there is a better balance at present between culture as the history of civilization and the attention paid to the customs, daily activities, and social structures of a people. Nostrand (43) suggested the use of a thematic approach for grouping the various patterns of a culture into 10-12 major categories such as love, religion, and individuality. Santoni (48), on the other hand, argued for a contextual approach because he saw significant cultural differences reflected in linguistic differences.

Although no significant research exists in the area of teaching culture, teachers should be aware of three books—Altman and Hanzeli (2), Lafayette (31), and Seelye (52)—that contain numerous practical suggestions for teaching culture in the classroom. The latter suggests seven basic objectives for teaching culture and provides many useful ideas.

The emphasis on culture is also evident in recently released foreign language texts and supplementary materials. Valdman, MacMillin, La Vergne, and Belasco (59), Valette and Valette (60), and *Voix et Visages de la France* (9), for example, all include culture sections. In the teacher's edition, Valdman et al. (59) include a cultural guide treating specific cultural traits. Valette and Valette (60) presented three principal cultural themes in their second level text: (a) attitudes, values, and behavior of contemporary French youth; (b) aspects of life in France; and (c) the diversity of the French-speaking world.

In addition to basic texts reflecting the impact of culture, a multitude of supplementary materials deal with the subject. Among them is the series in French, German, Italian, and Spanish published by National Textbook Company; this series concerns the use of newspapers and magazines in the teaching of contemporary culture. For more information see Culver (13), Jorstad (28), Rallo (46), Schulz (51), and Seelye and Day (53).

Programs for early adolescents. A second curricular change in language teaching has occurred at the junior high/middle school level of instruction. Partly due to the rapid disappearance of FLES (Foreign Languages in the Elementary School) programs throughout the country and also to the exploratory nature of middle school education, the profession has witnessed a rapid development of exploratory foreign language programs. Fearing and Grittner (16) identified four types of programs: (a) the "Language Potpourri" where three to five languages are offered for limited periods during the academic year; (b) the "General Language Course" which focuses on the nature of language; (c) the "Single Language Exploratory Offering"; and (d) the "Required Elective Program" in which students are required to study for a semester one of the languages offered in high school. Adcock (1) reported the results of a national survey showing that, of the four, Language Potpourri is the type most frequently adopted. Detailed descriptions of exploratory courses can be found in Bourque and Chehy (5) and in Morrow (40).

The minicourse. In an attempt to diversify the curriculum and to retain advanced students, some foreign language programs have introduced the concept of minicourses, courses shorter than the established length of the normal academic unit. In a national survey, Lafayette (30) identified the basic minicourse characteristics as follows:

1. The majority of programs limit their minicourse sequences to advanced levels of instruction.

2. The length of minicourses ranges from one to 18 weeks, the most popular length corresponding to the length of a grading period.

3. The content of minicourses varies from specific skill-oriented courses to sophisticated literary offerings, with the greatest concentration being in the area of culture.

Lafayette concluded that the most significant change brought about by minicourses has been the broadening of content at advanced levels of instruction.

Foreign languages in the elementary school. Professional literature indicates that foreign languages in the elementary schools (FLES) are in decline, especially in communities where a foreign language is not in daily use. Two longitudinal studies done in Britain and Japan provide relevant data. Both indicate that younger children are no better at a foreign language than are older children. After a ten-year study of British children beginning the study of French at age eight, Burstall concluded, "Pupils taught French from the age of eight did not show any substantial gains in achievement, compared with those who had been taught French from the age of eleven. By the age of sixteen, the only area in which the pupils taught French from the age of eight consistently showed any superiority was that of listening comprehension" (7: 248).

The findings of Oller and Nagato (44) are strikingly similar. After a six-year study of Japanese girls, they found that students with six years of English prior to entering junior high school were overtaken by those who began English in junior high by the time they reached the eleventh grade. In both studies it was pointed out that FLES and non-FLES students are often integrated once they reach the eighth or ninth grade. This evidence notwithstanding, Lee (37) suggested that the value of an educational activity is not to be seen only in its results as measured several years later.

Bilingualism. Although FLES is almost dead in non-bilingual communities, foreign language instruction in bilingual settings is very much alive. In some of these settings the target language not only is taught as an end in itself but is used along with the native language as a vehicle of instruction.

Since the passage of the Bilingual Education Act (Title VII, 1967-68) of the Elementary and Secondary Education Act of 1965, bilingual programs in the United States have grown rapidly. In 1973, almost 130,000 pupils participated in 209 programs funded under Title VII. This fostered state and local support such as that of the 1975 Illinois General Assembly, which appropriated $6,000,000 for bilingual education. The U.S. Supreme Court has also influenced the situation with its 1974 *Lau* vs. *Nichols* decision, which affirmed the right of students whose native language is other than English to an appropriate educational program. In practice, the *Lau* decision has mandated linguistically comprehensible education for children of limited English-speaking ability.

Today, several states (Massachusetts, Illinois, Wisconsin, Texas, Florida) have legislation making bilingual education mandatory whenever there are concentrations of children of limited English-speaking ability.

Although the majority of the state or federal bilingual programs are transitional in nature—that is, designed to prepare the non-English-speaking learner to become a full participant in the English-speaking classroom—the very presence of these programs has influenced the monolingual population to want to participate. Adcock (1) mentioned the Milwaukee Public Schools' Spanish K-6 bilingual/bicultural program, which is open to both Spanish-dominant children and English-dominant children whose parents would like to have them develop skills in two languages as well as an appreciation for more than one culture. Adcock also described the Cincinnati Public Schools' K-6 bilingual/bicultural program in French, German, and Spanish for students who almost exclusively speak English. The presence of the latter program is highly significant in that it was not established to meet the language needs of a bilingual community.

The Learner

In addition to fostering curricular and instructional changes, the decade of the 1970's has witnessed an increasing interest in identifying student learning styles. This trend no doubt has been engendered partially by the individualized instruction movement within the foreign language teaching profession. By asking students to think aloud while doing exercises for their French class, Hosenfeld (21) found important differences between what teachers think the students are learning from working on a particular exercise and what is actually going on in the students' minds. For instance, in completing grammar exercises, students paid little attention to the context if it was not necessary to complete the task.

In the area of cognitive style mapping, Lepke (38), using the Cognitive Preference Inventory developed by Hill (20), found that there is a demonstrable and significant relationship between learning style and foreign language achievement. A very simple and useful instrument for identifying learning styles in foreign language learning has been developed by Reinert (47). Entitled the *Edmonds Learning Style Identification Exercise* (ELSIE), the instrument can be administered, scored, and used for preliminary evaluation by a classroom teacher in less than a half hour. Research data gathered with this instrument clearly show that differences between individuals are far more extensive and much deeper than heretofore assumed. By analyzing data from the components of the instrument (visualization, written word, listening, and activity), the teacher can adapt classroom procedures to individual student needs.

The Teacher

What are some implications of research for the classroom practice of foreign language teachers? Moskowitz (41) studied the classroom interaction of 11 teachers who were identified as outstanding in a survey of former students and compared these with a group of 11 "typical" foreign language teachers. The Flint system of interaction analysis as well as anecdotal records were used to collect data during four different lessons for each teacher. Data from 88 observations enabled Moskowitz to identify some of the characteristics that typify the classroom interaction of *outstanding* foreign language teachers as distinct from a *heterogeneous* group of foreign language teachers. Included below are fewer than half of the traits enumerated:

1. The target language dominates the classroom interaction, whether the teacher or the students are speaking.

2. The teachers have an excellent command of the target language.

3. The amount of teacher talk is less.

4. The teachers use more indirect behaviors (those which encourage and reinforce student participation), whether communicating in the foreign language, English, or nonverbally.

5. There is more laughter in their classes.

6. The teachers personalize the content more.

7. Students exhibit more outward signs of enthusiasm to participate.

8. Student behavior is criticized very little.

9. Fewer routine tasks are carried out by the teachers.

10. There is a greater amount of warmup questions, review, and focusing on the skill of speaking.

11. There are a greater number of different activities per lesson.

12. When correcting student errors, the teachers do so gently.

13. Students assist the teacher more in setting up and running equipment (41: 156-57).

The aspect of teaching which was overlooked is the role of culture in the classes of the teachers observed.

According to Carroll, high-quality foreign language instruction includes:

1. Setting up pleasant and interesting learning conditions in which students feel they are making progress toward their goals and having their efforts rewarded

2. Making the instruction as meaningful as possible by making the foreign language come alive in meaningful communication situations

3. Making sure students understand what they are to learn

4. Trying to predict the effect of instructional presentations on students' minds

5. Intellectualizing foreign language learning tasks in early stages by providing explanations of material to be learned

6. Providing ample and varied opportunities to practice and perfect what has been learned (8: 143).

Although the inherent value of foreign language learning to American education may not as yet be fully appreciated, in the seventies teachers are working successfully to meet the varied needs of all students. In doing so, they are helping to enhance the importance of foreign languages throughout American education.

References

1. ADCOCK, DWAYNE. "Foreign Languages in Elementary and Emerging Adolescent Education." In: Gilbert A. Jarvis, editor. *An Integrative Approach to Foreign Language Teaching: Choosing Among the Options.* ACTFL Review of Foreign Language Education, Volume 8. Skokie, Illinois: National Textbook Company, 1976. pp. 289-325.

2. ALTMAN, HOWARD B., and VICTOR E. HANZELI, editors. *Essays on the Teaching of Culture.* Detroit: Advancement Press of America, Inc., 1974.

3. BARTZ, WALTER H. "A Study of the Relationship of Certain Learner Factors with the Ability To Communicate in a Second Language (German) for the Development of Measures of Communicative Competence." Unpublished doctoral dissertation, Ohio State University, Columbus, 1974.

4. BIRKMAIER, EMMA M., editor. *Foreign Language Education: An Overview.* ACTFL Review of Foreign Language Education, Volume 1. Skokie, Illinois: National Textbook Company, 1968.

5. BOURQUE, JANE, and LINDA CHEHY. "Exploratory Language and Culture: A Unique Program." *Foreign Language Annals* 9: 10-16; February 1976.

6. BULL, WILLIAM E., LAUREL A. BRISCOE, ENRIQUE E. LAMADRID, CARL DELLACCIO, and MARGARET J. BROWN. *Spanish for Communication.* Boston: Houghton Mifflin Company, 1975.

7. BURSTALL, CLARE. "Primary French in the Balance." *Foreign Language Annals* 10: 245-52; May 1977.

8. CARROLL, JOHN B. "Learning Theory for the Classroom Teacher." In: Gilbert A. Jarvis, editor. *The Challenge of Communication.* ACTFL Review of Foreign Language Education, Volume 6. Skokie, Illinois: National Textbook Company, 1974. pp. 113-50.

9. CENTER FOR CURRICULUM DEVELOPMENT. *Voix et Visages de la France.* Chicago: Rand McNally and Company, 1974.

10. CHASTAIN, KENNETH. *Developing Second-Language Skills: Theory to Practice.* Second edition. Chicago: Rand McNally College Publishing Company, 1976.

11. CHASTAIN, K., and F. J. WOERDEHOFF. "A Methodological Study Comparing the Audio-Lingual Habit and the Cognitive Code-Learning Theory." *Modern Language Journal* 52: 268-79; May 1968.

12. CLAUSING, GERHARD, KLAUS A. MUELLER, and ANNELIESE S. STEIN. "Individualized German Instruction at the College Level—A Follow-Up Report." *Foreign Language Annals* 7: 237-42; December 1973.

13. CULVER, ANKE. *The Magazine: German Mini-Culture Unit.* Skokie, Illinois: National Textbook Company, 1976.

14. DILLER, KARL C. "Some New Trends for Applied Linguistics and Foreign Language Teaching in the United States." *TESOL Quarterly* 9: 65-73; March 1975.

15. DISICK, RENEE S. *Individualizing Language Instruction: Strategies and Methods.* New York: Harcourt Brace Jovanovich, Inc., 1975.

16. FEARING, PERCY, and FRANK GRITTNER, editors. *Exploratory Foreign Language Programs in the Middle School.* Curriculum report prepared in ACTFL Preconference Workshop for Foreign Language Consultants and Supervisors, Denver, Colorado, November 27, 1974. ERIC ED 104 174

17. FRECHETTE, ERNEST A. "Directions of Research in the 1970's." In: Gilbert A. Jarvis, editor. *An Integrative Approach to Foreign Language Teaching: Choosing Among the Options.* ACTFL Review of Foreign Language Education, Volume 8. Skokie, Illinois: National Textbook Company, 1976. pp. 351-95.

18. GATTEGNO, CALEB. *Teaching Foreign Languages in Schools: The Silent Way.* New York: Educational Solutions, 1972.

19. GRITTNER, FRANK M., and FRED H. LALEIKE. *Individualized Foreign Language Instruction.* Skokie, Illinois: National Textbook Company, 1973.

20. HILL, JOSEPH E. *Personalizing Educational Programs and Utilizing Cognitive Style Mapping.* Bloomfield Hills, Michigan: Oakland Community College, 1971.

21. HOSENFELD, CAROL. "Learning About Learning: Discovering Our Students' Strategies." *Foreign Language Annals* 9: 117-30; April 1976.

22. JARVIS, GILBERT A. "A Comparison of Contextualized Practice with Particularized Referents vs. Practice with Generic Meaning in the Teaching of Beginning College French." Unpublished doctoral dissertation, Purdue University, Lafayette, Indiana, 1970.

23. JARVIS, GILBERT A., editor. *The Challenge of Communication.* ACTFL Review of Foreign Language Education, Volume 6. Skokie, Illinois: National Textbook Company, 1974.

24. JARVIS, GILBERT A., editor. *An Integrative Approach to Foreign Language Teaching: Choosing Among the Options.* ACTFL Review of Foreign Language Education, Volume 8. Skokie, Illinois: National Textbook Company, 1976.

25. JARVIS, GILBERT A., editor. *The New Freedom in Foreign Language Education.* ACTFL Review of Foreign Language Education, Volume 7. Skokie, Illinois: National Textbook Company, 1975.

41. MOSKOWITZ, GERTRUDE. "The Classroom Interaction of Outstanding Foreign Language Teachers." *Foreign Language Annals* 9: 135-57; April 1976.

42. MUELLER, T. "The Effectiveness of Two Learning Models: The Audio-Lingual Habit Theory and the Cognitive Code-Learning Theory." In: P. Pimsleur and T. Quinn, editors. *The Psychology of Second Language Learning*. London: England: Cambridge University Press, 1971. pp. 113-22.

43. NOSTRAND, HOWARD LEE. "Empathy for a Second Culture: Motivations and Techniques." In: Gilbert A. Jarvis, editor. *Responding to New Realities*. ACTFL Review of Foreign Language Education, Volume 5. Skokie, Illinois: National Textbook Company, 1974. pp. 263-327.

44. OLLER, JOHN W., JR., and NAOKO NAGATO. "The Long-Term Effect of FLES: An Experiment." *Modern Language Journal* 58: 15-19; January-February 1974.

45. OLLER, J. W., JR., and D. H. OBRECHT. "Pattern Drill and Communicative Activity: A Psycholinguistic Experiment." *International Review of Applied Linguistics* 6: 165-74; May 1968.

46. RALLO, JOHN A. *The Newspaper: Italian Mini-Culture Unit*. Skokie, Illinois: National Textbook Company, 1976.

47. REINERT, HARRY. "One Picture Is Worth a Thousand Words? Not Necessarily!" *Modern Language Journal* 10: 160-68; April 1976.

48. SANTONI, GEORGES V. "Langue et culture en contexte et contraste." *French Review* 59: 255-65; February 1976.

49. SAVIGNON, SANDRA J. *Communicative Competence: An Experiment in Foreign Language Teaching*. Philadelphia: Center for Curriculum Development, Inc., 1972.

50. SCHULZ, RENATE A. "Discrete-Point versus Simulated Communication Testing: A Study of the Effect of Two Methods of Testing on the Development of Communicative Proficiency in Beginning College French Classes." Unpublished doctoral dissertation, Ohio State University, Columbus, 1974.

51. SCHULZ, RENATE A. *The Newspaper: French Mini-Culture Unit*. Skokie, Illinois: National Textbook Company, 1976.

52. SEELYE, H. NED. *Teaching Culture*. Skokie, Illinois: National Textbook Company, 1974.

53. SEELYE, H. NED, and LAWRENCE DAY. *The Newspaper: Spanish Mini-Culture Unit*. Skokie, Illinois: National Textbook Company, 1974.

54. SMITH, PHILIP D. *A Comparison of the Cognitive and Audiolingual Approaches to Foreign Language Instruction: The Pennsylvania Foreign Language Project*. Philadelphia: Center for Curriculum Development, Inc., 1970.

55. STEINER, FLORENCE. *Performing with Objectives*. Rowley, Massachusetts: Newbury House Publishers, Inc., 1975.

56. STEVICK, EARL W. *Memory, Meaning, and Method: Some Psychological*

Perspectives on Language Learning. Rowley, Massachusetts: Newbury House Publishers, Inc., 1976.

57. "Summary Comparisons, by Region, of PSS Enrollment and Foreign Language Enrollments Grades 7-12." Fall 1968, 1970, and 1974. A survey conducted for the U.S. Office of Education by the Modern Language Association of America, 1976.

58. VALDMAN, ALBERT. "Communicative Competence and Its Implications for the Design of Foreign Language Teaching Syllabi." *Foreign Language Annals* 11: 5; October 1978.

59. VALDMAN, ALBERT, GUY MACMILLIN, MARCEL LA VERGNE, and SIMON BELASCO. *Son et Sens.* New edition. Glenview, Illinois: Scott, Foresman and Company, 1977.

60. VALETTE, JEAN-PAUL, and REBECCA M. VALETTE. *French for Mastery 1* and *French for Mastery 2.* Lexington, Massachusetts: D. C. Heath and Company, 1975.

61. VON ELEK, TIBER, and MATS OSKARSSON. *Teaching Foreign Language Grammar to Adults.* Research Bulletin No. 10. Gothenburg, Sweden: Gothenburg School of Education, 1972.

5. English as a Foreign Language (EFL)
Harry L. Gradman

THE combination of recent U.S. court decisions, increased numbers of non-native speakers of English, and expanded overseas job possibilities in the face of decreased domestic opportunities has intensified interest in the teaching of English as a second or foreign language. While not a new field of instruction, its importance has been enhanced because of the 1974 *Lau-Nichols* (27) decision. Essentially, the U.S. Supreme Court stated in that decision that students are entitled to education in a language they understand.

EFL Instruction

While it is not clear at present how these children whose native language is not English can best be taught, some language specialists contend they should undergo intensive English language training so that they can understand the materials being presented to their English-speaking classmates. Others contend they should be taught by teachers proficient both in the students' native language and in English. Regardless of the view one accepts, English as a second language is in the process of becoming an integral part of the curriculum.[3]

The increased need for teaching English as a second language. One reason for teaching English as a second language is the increasing number of American public school children who are not native speakers of English.

With the close of the Vietnam War, a large number of refugees from southeast Asia, many of whom knew little or no English, came to this country. The host communities in which they have settled are recognizing that new instructional programs must be devised. In response to this need, materials such

[3] So recent is the work in establishing needs in this area that the National Center for Education Statistics is only now in the process of compiling data on the availability of teacher training in English as a second language, both for the purpose of contributing to a report to the President and Congress on the state of bilingual education, and for suggesting program evaluation and funding.

39

as those provided for Vietnamese by the Center for Applied Linguistics (44) were rushed into print, and workshops were rapidly set up in order to provide necessary assistance for teachers beleaguered by new students, none of whom could communicate in English.

Because of changes in immigration laws, new arrivals in the United States are quite different from many of the past half-century. Many new residents either do not speak English or they have dependents who do not speak English. Since the value of the American dollar has changed in relationship to currencies of other countries, foreigners now find it less costly to visit at length, or to study, in the United States. As a result of increases in the number of foreign visitors and students, many of whom bring dependents, there is a need to help those who speak little or no English. Of particular note is the increased number of foreign students from the oil-rich countries, ranging from the Middle East to Venezuela. They and their dependents must learn the language in order to profit fully from the investment made in their education in this country.

The impact on many school systems of children who speak little or no English has been monumental. Consider, for example, the school system which serves Bloomington, Indiana, the location of Indiana University. For the past two years, one school in the University district has seen a sudden and unexpected enrollment approaching 150 non-native speakers of English. In a school of just under 750 students, the problems and adjustments have been substantial; nor is the situation unique.

Finally, the job market itself has played an important role in the increased interest in English as a second or foreign language. While employment prospects for teachers in the United States have at times been difficult, opportunities for teachers abroad, particularly in developing areas around the world, have been increasing. English-speaking teachers experienced with non-native speakers have become sought after, are paid good wages, and have opportunities for world travel. As one result, programs preparing multi- or bilingual teachers find their enrollments increasing yearly.

Linguistics and EFL. Several influential linguists of the structuralist era, such as C. C. Fries, also participated directly in the formalization of the audio-lingual method of language teaching with English as the foreign language tool. In some ways EFL has been the testing ground for the application of linguistics to language teaching methodology. Similarly, second language acquisition theory, such as it is, has been advanced especially within the past decade or so by researchers with a particular focus on English as a foreign language—for example, Corder (8), Oller (30, 31, 32), Richards (36, 37), Selinker (38, 39), and Spolsky (41, 42), to name a few.

Research Related to EFL

Perhaps of most interest with regard to foreign language teaching is work recently done in four areas: (a) second language acquisition, (b) contrastive and error analysis,[4] (c) sociolinguistics, and (d) language testing. In no area, however, has research been exhaustive or even extensive. Research direction and methodology have changed almost as drastically as the theory of linguistics itself. For example, just as first language acquisition studies have begun to focus on process and creativity, characterized by a universal developmental sequence (McNeill, 28, 29; Brown, 4, 5; Slobin, 40), so too have studies of second language learners necessarily required observation, via the case study approach, without preconceived notions as to the deficiency model of the learner.

Children and second languages. Children seem to acquire second or third languages in much the same way they do their first language. Studies of children performing in foreign languages indicate many structures similar to those employed by native speakers learning those same languages.

It has also been suggested that adults, too, may learn a second language in the same manner as children. Corder (8), for example, postulated a similar model of language acquisition for first and second language learners. Selinker (39) suggested the term "interlanguage" to characterize the relationships experienced by second language learners. Presumably they go through stages similar to those encountered in first language acquisition. Richards (36, 37) supported Selinker's notion by citing examples of similar performance by second language learners from a variety of different native language backgrounds. He suggested, as have others (for example, Selinker, 39; Corder, 8; Gradman, 20; Gradman and Gaies, 23), that many errors exhibited by second language learners can be attributed to strategies common to language learners. These include such things as overgeneralization and simplification, and not the interference of a first language. In a case study of an adult learning English as a foreign language, Hanania (25) added further supportive evidence of such a notion, as did Hanania and Gradman (26).

Adult studies. The number of studies of adults acquiring second languages is even smaller than the number of studies of children learning second languages. Also, since such studies often require the collection of data over a period of time, the results are necessarily slow in coming. Suffice it to say that recent studies show interesting similarities in language acquisition, regardless of the native language background or number of languages being acquired.

---

[4] Contrastive analysis requires the examination of second language errors in terms of the student's native language, whereas error analysis involves the examination of second language errors from a variety of potential influences.

These studies have created a renewed interest in an area now generally characterized as "error analysis." Put quite simply, error analysis is an expansion of the once more popular differential analysis technique known as "contrastive analysis" (see footnote 4 for definitions). Formerly it was popular to compare the native language of the students with the target or second language—the language to be learned—in an attempt to predict errors that would be made by second language learners. With evidence from recent language acquisition studies, as well as with other considerations of the merits of the contrastive analysis hypothesis (Gradman, 19, 22; Oller, 30; Selinker, 38), the focus has shifted to studies of errors made by second language learners without preconceived frameworks for collection of data as restrictive as those of the contrastive analysis hypothesis.

Once again, not only do the results tend to support notions about the similarities between first and second language acquisition, but they also reemphasize a difficulty quite often overlooked in the reporting of second language acquisition research: *methods of linguistic analysis are not necessarily secure enough for the accurate reporting of actual language performance.* As helpful as linguistic models may be for the formulation of psycholinguistic models, the tools for analysis are not precise enough for totally accurate characterization of the real linguistic performance of second language learners. Inferences are made which seem reasonable, given the limitations of the tools, but it should be remembered that linguistic research in second language learning remains to a large degree speculative.

Sociolinguistic inquiries. Sociolinguistic studies have had their greatest impact on attempts to point out and characterize the wide range of factors that influence the acquisition of second languages. One of these factors, recognized for some time now, is that the *attitudes* of language learners toward the target language (and the target language community!) affect the likelihood of success in second language learning (Gardner and Lambert, 18; Ervin-Tripp, 13). In general, a person who identifies with the target language community and its culture sees the acquisition of a second language as a means of enhancing that identification. If one has an "instrumental" or "utilitarian" concept, learning may be slower. In other words, the second language is learned less rapidly when merely seen as useful in education or employment than when the learner has "cultural rapport."

Attitudes of parents toward the languages being learned seem to influence their children. Hence it often is the parents' orientation, as transmitted to children, that initially influences their learning of a second language (Aguirre-Carrasco, 2; Abbashar, 1). At the same time, it must be made clear that learners of second languages have been successful with either type of orientation predominating (Spolsky, 41; Gardner, 17; Gardner and Lambert, 18; Anisfeld and

Lambert, 3). In short, a number of studies have shown a relationship between interest, motivation, and the grades earned in EFL classrooms (Politzer, 34; Pimsleur, 33).

Should dialects be legitimatized? We lately have been reminded that problems of teaching the so-called standard dialect to speakers of other dialects is not unique to the United States, and that solutions offered in other settings may be appropriate for this country as well. Now and throughout history, as Fishman and Lueders-Salmon (14) pointed out, it has not been unusual for school children to learn to read and write in a language different from that used at home. Apparently, the solutions others have reached suggest that rather than trying to eradicate dialects, it would be better to try legitimatizing dialects in practice as well as in theory—and for students and teachers alike. We are reminded, too, that properly implemented immersion programs, such as those that have been carried out in Canada and to a lesser extent in the United States, show a high degree of success when the child who speaks a different language or dialect from the target is not ostracized through sometimes well-meaning but usually embarrassing attention (Cohen and Swain, 7).

Language testing. An interesting intersection between language theory and language teaching is found in the area of language testing. Diagnosis and evaluation are indispensable to the proper placement and advancement of language students. Recent research in language testing has been as impressive for what it has shown us about language behavior itself as for what it has shown us about language testing. We have seen, for instance, that the "cloze" or structured "fill-in" type test seems to be a good predictor of overall language abilities (Oller and Conrad, 32). These so-called "reduced redundancy" techniques, where a part of the message is obscured, either aurally or in writing, indicate that the more advanced the language learner, the better he or she can make predictions as to the message, and consequently the less ideal the conditions for language behavior need to be (Spolsky et al., 42; Gradman, 21; Gradman and Spolsky, 24). Several writers have suggested that native and non-native speakers alike can communicate with essentially the same amount of background interference, thus arguing against the notion that language learning must take place under particularly sterile laboratory conditions (Gaies, Gradman, and Spolsky, 15; Gradman and Spolsky, 24).

Interest also has shifted to functionally-oriented language tests, as opposed to the more discrete [5] tests of the fifties and early sixties. Dictation tests in language, for instance, are reported to be useful because they reflect the degree to which the second language learner is able to process and replicate a native

[5] Discrete-point language tests focus on only one identifiable linguistic problem in each test item.

speaker's words and phrases (Oller, 31). Subjective tests, such as the oral interview or written composition, are thought to provide better samples of one's language abilities than tests of particular sounds and grammatical points, the understanding and analysis of which remain in considerable dispute among linguists and applied linguists alike.

Summary. This résumé of research has reflected a notion that has begun to permeate advanced studies in the area of English as a foreign language, and —indeed—in all second language acquisition. The notion is this: there are far too many limitations in current research to make a compelling case for any one "best" procedure. Current work, either cited or ongoing, as suggested in an article by Tarone, Swain, and Fathman (43), has yet to come of age. They pointed out that (a) the linguistic scope of current studies is limited, (b) information on cognitive processes and learning strategies is at best limited, (c) we are just beginning to identify the role of individual variables in second language learning as well as the role of social and environmental variables, (d) there is no standard methodology for data analysis, and (e) very few studies have been replicated.

They identified more specifically reasons supporting Chomsky's skepticism during the sixties over the rush to apply linguistic theory before it was verified through research and practice. He reminded us, "It is possible—even likely—that principles of psychology and linguistics, and research in these disciplines, may supply insights useful to the language teacher. But this must not be demonstrated, and cannot be presumed. It is the language teacher himself who must validate or refute any specific proposal. There is very little in psychology or linguistics that he can accept on faith" (6: 45).

Yet this is one of the reasons language learning research is so exciting. It remains an area where the probing of the practitioner is crucial at all levels: selection, presentation, evaluation, and research. Ultimately, it is likely to be the EFL teacher who will validate the theory of second language learning.

References

1. ABBASHAR, ABDEL WAHAB. "Attitudinal and Aptitudinal Factors and Their Relationship to Learning English as a Foreign Language." Unpublished doctoral dissertation, Indiana University, Bloomington, 1977.

2. AGUIRRE-CARRASCO, OSCAR. "Linguistic, Motivational, and Orientational Factors Contributing to Overall Achievement in the Acquisition of English as a Foreign Language." Unpublished doctoral dissertation, Indiana University, Bloomington, 1973.

3. ANISFELD, M., and W. E. LAMBERT. "Social and Psychological Variables in Learning Hebrew." Journal of Abnormal and Social Psychology 63: 524-29; 1961.

4. BROWN, ROGER. "Development of the First Language in the Human Species." *American Psychologist* 28: 97-106; February 1973.

5. BROWN, ROGER. *A First Language: The Early Stages.* Cambridge, Massachusetts: Harvard University Press, 1973.

6. CHOMSKY, NOAM. "Linguistic Theory." In: Robert G. Mead, Jr., editor. *Language Teaching: Broader Contexts.* Working Committee Reports. Middlebury, Vermont: Northeast Conference on the Teaching of Foreign Language, 1966. pp. 43-49.

7. COHEN, ANDREW D., and MERRILL SWAIN. "Bilingual Education: The Immersion Model in the North American Context." *TESOL Quarterly* 10: 45-73; March 1976.

8. CORDER, S. PIT. "The Significance of Learner's Errors." *International Review of Applied Linguistics* 5: 161-69; 1967.

9. DULAY, HEIDI C., and MARINA K. BURT. "Goofing: An Indicator of Children's Second Language Strategies." *Language Learning* 22: 235-49; 1972.

10. DULAY, HEIDI C., and MARINA K. BURT. "Natural Sequences in Child Second Language Acquisition." *Language Learning* 24: 37-53; 1974.

11. DULAY, HEIDI C., and MARINA K. BURT. "Should We Teach Our Children Syntax?" *Language Learning* 23: 245-58; 1973.

12. ERVIN-TRIPP, SUSAN. "Is Second Language Learning Like the First?" *TESOL Quarterly* 8: 111-27; 1974.

13. ERVIN-TRIPP, SUSAN. "On Becoming a Bilingual. " In: A. S. Dil, editor. *Language Acquisition and Communicative Choice: Essays by Susan M. Ervin-Tripp.* Stanford, California: Stanford University Press, 1973. pp. 111-26.

14. FISHMAN, JOSHUA A., and ERIKA LUEDERS-SALMON. "What Has the Sociology of Language To Say to the Teacher? On Teaching the Standard Variety to Speakers of Dialectal or Sociolectal Varieties." In: A. S. Dil, editor. *Language in Sociocultural Change: Essays by Joshua A. Fishman.* Stanford, California: Stanford University Press, 1972. pp. 340-55.

15. GAIES, STEPHEN J., HARRY L. GRADMAN, and BERNARD SPOLSKY. "Toward the Measurement of Functional Proficiency: Contextualization of the 'Noise Test.' " *TESOL Quarterly* 11: 51-57; March 1977.

16. GARDNER, ROBERT C. "Attitudes and Motivation: Their Role in Second-Language Acquisition." *TESOL Quarterly* 2: 141-50; 1968.

17. GARDNER, ROBERT C. "Motivational Variables in Second-Language Acquisition." *Canadian Journal of Psychology* 13: 266-72; 1959.

18. GARDNER, ROBERT C., and WALLACE E. LAMBERT. *Attitudes and Motivation in Second-Language Learning.* Rowley, Massachusetts: Newbury House Publishers, 1972.

19. GRADMAN, HARRY L. "The Limitations of Contrastive Analysis Predictions." *Working Papers in Linguistics* 3: 11-15; 1971.

20. GRADMAN, HARRY L. "Reduced Redundancy and Error Analysis, Part Two: A Study of Selected Performances on the Contextualized Noise Test." In: Robert

St. Clair and Beverly Hartford, editors. *Error Analysis and Language Testing. Lektos,* Special Issue 4: 42-54; November 1976.

21. GRADMAN, HARRY L. "Reduced Redundancy Testing: A Reconsideration." In: Maureen Concannon O'Brien, editor. *Testing in Second Language Teaching.* Dublin, Ireland: Dublin University Press, 1973. pp. 41-48.

22. GRADMAN, HARRY L. "What Methodologists Ignore in 'Contrastive Teaching.'" *Working Papers in Linguistics* 3: 73-77; 1971.

23. GRADMAN, HARRY L., and STEPHEN J. GAIES. "Reduced Redundancy Testing and Error Analysis." In: *Language Testing* (papers selected from the Fourth International Congress of Applied Linguistics), forthcoming.

24. GRADMAN, HARRY L., and BERNARD SPOLSKY. "Reduced Redundancy Testing: A Progress Report." In: Randall Jones and Bernard Spolsky, editors. *Language Testing Symposium.* Washington, D.C.: Center for Applied Linguistics, 1975. pp. 59-71.

25. HANANIA, EDITH A. S. "Acquisition of English Structures: A Case Study of an Adult Native Speaker of Arabic in an English-Speaking Environment." Unpublished doctoral dissertation, Indiana University, Bloomington, 1974.

26. HANANIA, EDITH A. S., and HARRY L. GRADMAN. "Acquisition of English Structures: A Case Study of an Adult Native Speaker of Arabic in an English-Speaking Environment." *Language Learning* 27: 75-91; June 1977.

27. *Lau* v. *Nichols,* 414 U.S. 560 (1974).

28. MCNEILL, DAVID. *The Acquisition of Language: The Study of Developmental Psycholinguistics.* New York: Harper & Row, Publishers, Inc., 1970.

29. MCNEILL, DAVID. "Developmental Psycholinguistics." In: Frank Smith and George A. Miller, editors. *Genesis of Language.* Cambridge, Massachusetts: The MIT Press, 1966. pp. 15-84.

30. OLLER, JOHN W., JR. "Contrastive Analysis, Difficulty, and Predictability." *Foreign Language Annals* 6: 95-106; October 1972.

31. OLLER, JOHN W., JR. "Dictation as a Device for Testing Foreign-Language Proficiency." *English Language Teaching* 25: 254-59; 1971.

32. OLLER, JOHN W., JR., and CHRISTINE A. CONRAD. "The Cloze Technique and ESL Proficiency." *Language Learning* 21: 183-95; December 1971.

33. PIMSLEUR, PAUL. "Predicting Success in High School Foreign Language Courses." *Educational and Psychological Measurement* 23: 349-57; 1963.

34. POLITZER, ROBERT L. "Assiduity and Achievement." *Modern Language Journal* 44: 14-16; 1960.

35. RAVEM, ROAR. "Language Acquisition in a Second Language Environment." *International Review of Applied Linguistics* 6: 175-85; 1968.

36. RICHARDS, JACK C. "Error Analysis and Second Language Strategies." *Language Sciences* 17: 12-22; 1971.

37. RICHARDS, JACK C. "A Non-Contrastive Approach to Error Analysis." *English Language Teaching* 25: 204-19; 1971.

38. SELINKER, LARRY. "A Brief Reappraisal of Contrastive Linguistics." *Working Papers in Linguistics* 3: 1-10; 1971.

39. SELINKER, LARRY. "Interlanguage." *International Review of Applied Linguistics* 10: 209-31; 1972.

40. SLOBIN, DAN I. "Universals of Grammatical Development in Children." In: G. B. Flores D'Arcais and W. J. M. Levelt, editors. *Advances in Psycholinguistics*. New York: Elsevier, 1971. pp. 174-86.

41. SPOLSKY, BERNARD. "Attitudinal Aspects of Second Language Learning." *Language Learning* 19: 271-83; 1969.

42. SPOLSKY, BERNARD, BENGT SIGURD, MASAHITO SAKO, EDWARD WALKER, and CATHERINE ATERBURN. "Preliminary Studies in the Development of Techniques for Testing Overall Second Language Proficiency." *Language Learning* 18: 79-101; 1968.

43. TARONE, ELAINE, MERRILL SWAIN, and ANN FATHMAN. "Some Limitations to the Classroom Applications of Current Second Language Acquisition Research." *TESOL Quarterly* 10: 19-32; March 1976.

44. *Vietnamese Refugee Education Series*. Arlington, Virginia: Center for Applied Linguistics, 1975-1976.

6. Listening in Review
Milton Marten

NOW *hear this! Now hear this!* No doubt everyone freezes a bit when this well-known shipboard call is aired—it is a signal that something of importance is about to be said. What of importance have we learned about listening?

It was as recently as 1926 that Paul Rankin began the systematic study of listening. Since that time research in this area of communication has increased steadily in quantity and quality as our "symbol-saturated society" began to become more efficient and to understand that the act of listening is more than a developmental facet of maturation which instruction presumably could not change. Although the quantity of research in this area does not begin to rival that in reading, more and more scholarly attention has been given to listening.

As Chapter One indicated, trends in listening research mirror the problems in education in general, as well as reflect the changing needs of society and school functions. Although certain aspects of the listening process continue to receive attention, newer studies have centered on conflicting theories and on hypotheses that are constantly being proved or disproved.

This review, while not exhaustive, seeks to deal with significant research which has been done in listening since 1969—research too recent to have been reported in the 1971 ASCD language arts review.

For the reader's convenience, the publications are grouped around topics such as the nature of listening, the effect of teaching on listening, and assessment of listening skills.

Just What Is Listening?

The nature of listening—its psychological and physical characteristics—has provided focal points for many studies. Newer inquiries deal with listening as a language function, in a linguistic and instructional setting. Riding (57) in a study of the nature of language and listening found extremely complex relationships between the linguistic characteristics, the semantic organization of the material, and the comprehension of the listeners. In his study the added variable of rate added significant complications. Adjacent details aided recall, for example, but hindered reception.

Wilkinson and Stratla (83) studied facets of listening which may account for poor listening performance; suggestions for teaching are implied. Stein and Glenn (66) studied the time lapse and its influence on recall. Although length of time and age of people made a difference, the meaningful information gained was quite stable in terms of organization and saliency. Arnold and Brooks (2) and Wetstone and Friedlander (81) pointed out that the absence or presence of clues or "organizers" given before listening experience considerably influences the higher level listening skills and responses. Fifth-grade children related more to these clues than did second-grade children.

Lundsteen (41), after reviewing research from 1966-1971, proposed 21 appropriate teacher behaviors or responses that could promote maximum listening learning.

Kinds of listening. Many articles indicate that listening and reading are parallel communication skills, while some also suggest there is a normal transfer from one to the other. Research into the range of listening skills is far from widespread, however, so that each researcher tends to isolate or to emphasize certain subskills. It is interesting to note that writers of instructional materials tend to be more precise in ordering the skills than do researchers.

Arnold and Brooks (2) measured and compared recall and inference responses, demonstrating that more complicated skills such as inferring are influenced by many more variables than is simple recall. Penfield and Marascuilo (51) centered their testing on 11 isolated listening skills. Their order was unique and emphasized higher-level thinking skills.

The Relationship of Listening to Other Language Skills

Whether or not reading and listening are parallel skills and whether or not there is a cause and effect relationship between listening and the other language functions have been sources of investigation since Rankin began his studies in the twenties. The degree of interdependence is still being probed, but added dimensions are included in research about learning to listen in science, mathematics, and social studies. By far the greatest attention is still given to comparing and contrasting reading and listening.

Walker's (77) search for the relationship between listening and reading showed that printed language is more precise than spontaneous speech, and could be the cause of the greater difficulty in learning to read. Swalm (68) found that reading and listening are of an equal level of difficulty for learning in the early grades if the material is at the learner's maturation level. As the material becomes more difficult in relation to the learner's maturity, listening becomes the better avenue.

Schneeburg (63) found that listening to the reading of a book while reading it *increased* the reading scores on standardized tests, while Schneyer (64) found that listening instruction did *not* result in reading improvement in the same skills. In Walker's (78) study, listening performance was inferior to reading performance when learning from reading a book and learning from a videotape were compared. Cunningham (14) described a technique that seemed feasible for transferring learned listening skills to reading.

Linguistics: a new element. With increased emphasis on linguistics as a base for reading and general language growth, it is natural that the linguistic principles be studied and applied in listening learning, too. Guthrie and Tyler (30) compared "psychological processing techniques" in reading and in listening for good and poor readers. For average pupils the demands were similar in reading and listening. For poor learners the psychological linguistic processing was adequate in dealing with the spoken word but not with the printed word.

School Programs in Teaching Listening

Programs that focused on teaching listening generally did not enjoy the stature of those in reading or courses related to a specific field such as the social studies. Often they were a small segment of the whole language concept—sharing the modules or other devices publishers provided. Loveland, Colorado, and Alameda County in California proved to be notable exceptions. Marascuilo and Penfield (42) reported extensive programs in listening at the second, fifth, eighth, and eleventh grade levels. Dramatic success, they said, was experienced at the second grade level, regardless of the socioeconomic status (SES) of the learner, although results were not as significant in the other grades. The report also suggested that training in listening might be terminated after the sixth grade.

Tutolo (74, 75), Giannangelo and Frazee (24), Rutherford and Weaner (62), and Vukelich (76) explored ways in which effective programs in listening could be organized. Bryant (6) examined the use of "listening centers" but noted that this approach should be reevaluated periodically to avoid observable faults and failures.

The Effect of Teaching Listening

Insofar as methodology and teaching techniques are concerned, descriptive material rather than research predominated in the literature. Research reports were largely special thrusts or studies from which teaching strategies presumably could be inferred. Wetstone and Friedlander (81) tested three methods of teaching listening to children in kindergarten and the first three grades. All enhanced listening skills, but videotape was more effective than either "live" presentation or audio cassette. They concluded that listening is affected very much by the style of presentation.

Bursuk (7) compared listening/reading and pure reading performances for comprehension of content. The combination of listening/reading appeared to be particularly effective for auditory learners or for students with no modality choice. In her study involving Title I children from grades one to three, Blackburn (4) found that pupils who experienced daily lessons in listening skills were superior to those who did not. Swalm (68, 69), however, concluded that no one method to improve listening should be used in a given classroom of heterogeneously grouped children; while Goolsby and Lasco (29) found that immediate feedback of performance success enhanced listening learning, and the lack of it lowered achievement.

Childers (11, 12) concluded that listening can be learned—that it is a teachable skill—as a child passes through the grades. Groups who had lower intelligence test ratings scored higher in listening after instruction. Penfield and Marascuilo (51) tested pupils in grades two and five in 11 isolated comprehension listening skills. They found training effective at both levels, with no sex differences observable. In this study the fifth-grade students recorded the greatest gains.

Affective considerations. An examination of the general literature suggests a growing interest in the affective or emotional tone of the listening. This apparently has implications for teacher behavior and its modification. For instance, Trubowitz (73) isolated 10 teacher behaviors likely to increase pupils' listening because of emphasis placed on humanistic interactions. Pedrini and others (50) have experimented with testing programs for teachers to increase teacher effectiveness. Their study proposed an in-service program for developing skill in improving children's ability to listen.

Assessing Listening Performance

A search of the literature as of 1977 failed to unearth a comprehensive diagnostic listening test. Only a few standard tests that provide a standard score are available. Yet many researchers probably have found themselves in need of an appropriate testing instrument to replace those now in print.

In an effort to serve this need, Wallner (79) developed two forms of a listening comprehension test for kindergarten and grade one; subtests were devised to some diagnostic data at this grade level. In seeking new ways to determine listening comprehension, Carver (9) found the "chunk" test or "chunked concepts" [6] to be reliable in measuring listening as well as reading comprehension. Schneyer (64), in studying listening and reading comprehension, found great discrepancies in scores of standardized tests and performance tests designed for specific learnings. Rudegeair (61) concluded from his studies that traditional auditory discrimination tests are ill-conceived from a practical point of view. Linguistic studies, he concluded, indicate that there are speech sound variables that extant auditory tests do not include.

The cloze technique. The use of cloze test [7] procedures has moved into the area of listening assessment from the field of reading, where it was pioneered by Bormuth. The procedures—both in diagnosing and in teaching—are experiencing gradually widening use. Kennedy and Weener (35) showed in an experiment that the cloze procedure is effective in improving both listening and reading skills if used in an individual treatment approach. Neville and Pugh (48) used parallel tests with matched groups in cloze tests of reading and listening. Significantly fewer responses were made in listening than in reading. Analysis of errors in both modes showed syntactically appropriate responses had been given. Both Ammon (1) and Carver (9) used cloze tests; the latter tried the "chunked test" technique. Swalm (69) used the cloze test technique with apparent success for measuring comprehension in listening and reading and not merely skill achievement.

Learner Characteristics

Early studies and research in listening usually were based on the assumption that most learners were "normal." With the passing of time, and especially since the mid-sixties, investigations have begun to show greater awareness of ethnicity and socioeconomic differences, and of slow learners, language-deficient children, and other non-typical learners. Studies and descriptive papers related to the atypical child are increasing both in number and in specificity.

Marquardt and Saxman (43), in studying kindergarten children with articulatory problems, found that these children demonstrate "syntax performance" deficits, a finding which suggests an interdependence of language elements. Swalm (68) studied comprehension of listening, oral reading, and silent reading in grades two, three, and four. Above average readers fared better in both forms of reading than in listening. Below average readers found listening to be a more effective means of gaining comprehension. Swalm (69), repeating the study with a different population of grades two to four, and comparing only listening and

---

[6] A "chunk" is a small group of meaningfully related words within a sentence.
[7] A "cloze test" is one in which words are deleted from sentences for purposes of determining vocabulary or syntactic skills.

silent reading found similar results. He concluded that varied approaches for different learning modalities be offered at all the grade levels studied.

Marquardt and Saxman (43) examined auditory discrimination disorders in kindergarten children and found that their deficiencies in discriminating among sounds contribute to poor syntax utilization and to poor listening skills. Rudegeair (60) concluded that traditional tests underestimate normal children's perception of certain phonological elements.

Listening and dialect. Ramsey (55) concluded that children's use of black dialect or standard English made no significant difference in their ability to answer questions about stories that had been heard. In his study of dialect and its possible influences on listening, Frentz (19) found dialect users had no trouble with standard or black nonstandard English; while in her doctoral study, Harber (32) obtained similar results with individual black students in grades three and five. Johnson (34), however, found evidence that black-dialect-speaking children sometimes failed to hear certain final consonants, with consequent listening comprehension loss.

Miscellaneous learner status findings. McCroskey and Thompson (44) concluded that children with disorders in auditory discriminatory skills need a slower rate of oral presentation. Quay and others (54) found that socioeconomic status in itself did not make a difference in encoding and decoding language functions of children; and Doyle (18)—in a review of compensatory education programs—concluded that oral/listening language experiences increase the general language facility of kindergarten children. Penfield and Marascuilo (51) found that training in listening narrowed the listening ability gap between learners who were separated by socioeconomic stratification—a conclusion with significant implications for classroom activities. Conversely, Goolsby and Lasco (29) found that cultural status had no effect on levels of listening performance. Undoubtedly, "the jury is still out" with respect to many studies, either because they conflict or because more data are needed!

As in every area, there is a group of miscellaneous studies of learner characteristics that continues to hold the interest of some scholars as they contemplate new research. Since most listening studies almost invariably involve subjects of both sexes, for instance, it is always easy to explore sex as a variable. A few articles and studies concerned themselves with television viewing and visual media as influences on boys and girls. A new emphasis, more apparent in literature than in research, is the concern over listener accountability.

In the battle of the sexes, Neville (47) reported that boys were consistently better in listening *performance* than girls. Marascuilo and Penfield (42), however, found that girls *improved* more than boys did in their study.

Friedlander and others (21) concluded after studying preschool children's responses to national television programs for children that the content of the programs was—as of 1974—quite inappropriate for them, even though many were designed expressly for them.

Williams (84), dealing with the "accountability of the listener," developed a rationale and experiences intended to increase the listener's response and responsibility in listening situations. Williams' schema is much more elaborate than an earlier one by Nichols and seems more closely related to kinds of listening that learners do in typical situations.

Listening Rate—Compressed Speech

Although its application has been demonstrated for no more than a decade, a great interest recently has been displayed in "speeded-up" listening—sometimes spoken of as "compressed speech." Playback equipment has been produced to increase the speed of recordings without changing the voice pitch or quality. Several "listening-teaching" programs have employed compressed speech without becoming a controversial issue in the teaching experiences. With growing attention to different kinds of learners, as has been noted, the interest in listening rate has not been confined to *acceleration* but also has been expressed in the *reduction* of word rate.

McCroskey and Thompson (44) found that a slower rate of presentation is beneficial for young children and for auditorially or verbally disadvantaged children. In a similar vein, Berry and Erickson (3) concluded that a slow rate of presentation is necessary if listeners have not attained linguistic maturity. Carver (10), on the other hand, challenged the "double speed" type of presentations to improve listening skills because, in the process, the threshold of many listeners probably would be exceeded. Increased speed should be under the control and at the discretion of the listener, Carver felt.

Numerous studies of compressed speech or accelerated presentations have been reported with varying degrees of agreement by such writers as Fulmer (22) and Musial and Maple (46). Klavon (37), in a 1975 dissertation, found students at the college level were able to accept successfully accelerated rates of oral presentation. Neville (47), while testing middle school children, found that when they were simply listening at various rates, the speed did not affect their comprehension significantly. However, during visual/aural presentations, slower word rates produced better learning. This was especially true of those in the sample who were classified as remedial readers. Riding (57) likewise found that reduced rates can be an asset—especially when the syntactic material or the organization of thoughts is complex.

References

1. AMMON, R. "Listening as a Means of Developing Language." *Elementary English* 51: 515-18; April 1974.

2. ARNOLD, D. J., and P. H. BROOKS. "Influence of Contextual Organizing Material on Children's Listening Comprehension." *Journal of Educational Psychology* 68: 711-16; December 1976.

3. BERRY, M. D., and R. L. ERICKSON. "Speaking Rate: Effects on Children's Comprehension of Normal Speech." *Journal of Speech and Hearing Research* 16: 367-74; September 1973.

4. BLACKBURN, SUSAN FLEMING. "The Construction, the Implementation, and the Evaluation of a Title I Primary Grade Listening Program." Doctoral dissertation, University of Mississippi, University, 1976. ERIC ED 127 626

5. BRACKEN, D. K. "Teacher's Function in Developing Listening Skills." In: Howard A. Klein, editor. *Quest for Competency in Teaching Reading* (International Reading Association Conference Papers) 16: 254-61; 1971.

6. BRYANT, J. E. "Listening Centers: A Sound Investment in Education." *Journal of Learning Disabilities* 3: 156-59; 1970.

7. BURSUK, L. Z. "Evaluation of Correlated Listening—Reading Comprehension Lessons." In: Howard A. Klein, editor. *Quest for Competency in Teaching Reading* (International Reading Association Conference Papers) 16: 262-68; 1971. ERIC ED 056 840

8. BUTLER, JOSEPH. "Comparison of Listening Abilities Categorized as Good and Poor, of Inner-City Children in the Sixth Grade." Doctoral dissertation, Indiana University, Bloomington, September 1970.

9. CARVER, R. P. "Analysis of Chunked Test Items in Measures of Reading and Listening Comprehension." *Journal of Educational Measurement* 7: 141-50; July 1970.

10. CARVER, R. P. "Effect of Increasing the Rate of Speech Presentation Upon Comprehension." *Journal of Educational Psychology* 65: 118-26; August 1973.

11. CHILDERS, P. R. "Black Students Can Be Taught To Listen." *Journal of Experimental Education* 39: 245; Summer 1971.

12. CHILDERS, P. R. "Listening Ability Is a Modifiable Skill." *Journal of Experimental Education* 38: 1-3; September 1970.

13. CULLEN, VICKY. "Factors Affecting Student Performance in Listening Comprehension and Their Development in the Classroom." *Babel: Journal of the Australian Federation of Modern Language Teacher's Association* 7 (3): 29-35; October 1975. ERIC EJ 132 693

14. CUNNINGHAM, P. M. "Transferring Comprehension from Listening to Reading." *Reading Teacher* 29: 169-72; November 1975. ERIC EJ 125 755

15. CZEKANSKI, D. E. "Neglected Scientific Skill: Listening." *Science and Children* 12: 23-25; September 1974.

16. DALLAS, L. A. "What Did You Say? Activity To Develop the Skills of Listening and Following Instructions." *Science and Children* 10: 25; October 1972.

17. DOYLE, A. B. "Listening to Distraction: A Developmental Study of Selective Attention." *Journal of Experimental Child Psychology* 15: 100-15; February 1973.

18. DOYLE, M. "Review of Three Significant Compensatory Education Language Programs for the Culturally Disadvantaged." *Elementary English* 48: 193-97; February 1976.

19. FRENTZ, T. S. "Children's Comprehension of Standard and Negro Non-Standard English Sentences." *Speech Monographs* 38: 10-16; March 1971.

20. FRIEDLANDER, B. Z., and H. C. DELARA. "Receptive Language Anomaly and Language/Reading Disfunction in Normal Primary Grade School Children." *Psychology in the Schools* 10: 12-18; January 1973.

21. FRIEDLANDER, B. Z., et al. "Suburban Preschool Children's Comprehension of an Age-Appropriate Informational T.V. Program." *Child Development* 46: 561-65; June 1974.

22. FULMER, ROBERT. "Rate of Reading and Auding." Qualifying Paper, Harvard University, Cambridge, Massachusetts, May 1976. ERIC ED 124 920

23. GAGNEY, M. A. "Children's Ability To Understand Standard English and Black Dialect." *Reading Teacher* 30: 607-10; March 1977.

24. GIANNANGELO, DUANE M., and BRUCE M. FRAZEE. "Listening: A Critical Skill That Must Be Taught." *Kappa Delta Pi Record* 12 (2): 42-43; December 1975.

25. GILSON, J., and R. PAST. "Listening and Response Theory: Implications for Linguistically Different Learners." *Elementary English* 47: 1060-66; December 1970.

26. GOLD, Y. "Improvements of Teaching Listening Skills." *Reading Improvement* 10: 14-16; Winter 1973.

27. GOLDHABER, G. M. "Listeners' Comprehension of Compressed Speech as a Function of the Academic Grade Level of Subjects." *Journal of Communication* 20: 167-73; June 1970.

28. GOLDMAN, S. R. "Reading Skill and the Minimum Distance Principle: A Comparison of Listening and Reading Comprehension." *Journal of Experimental Child Psychology* 22: 123-42; August 1976.

29. GOOLSBY, T. M., and R. A. LASCO. "Training Non-Readers in Listening Achievement." *Journal of Learning Disabilities* 3: 467-70; September 1970.

30. GUTHRIE, JOHN T., and S. JANE TYLER. "Psycholinguistic Processing in Reading and Listening Among Good and Poor Readers." Paper presented at the Annual Meeting of American Educational Research Association, San Francisco, California, April 19-23, 1976.

31. HALLEY, R. D. "Some Suggestions for the Teaching of Listening." *Speech Teacher* 24: 386-89; November 1976. ERIC EJ 127 604

32. HARBER, JEAN ROSNER. "The Effect of Abstract Reasoning Ability, Degree of Bidialectism, and Grade Level on the Performance of Black, Inner-City Children on Equivalent Reading Tasks, Presented in Standard English, Black English, Standard Orthography, and Black English, Nonstandard Orthography." Doctoral dissertation, Temple University, 1976. ERIC ED 126 433

33. HOSEY, J. G. "Oral Reading, Misused?" *Elementary School Journal* 77: 218-20; January 1977.

34. JOHNSON, K. R. "A Comparison of Black-Dialect-Speaking Children and Standard-English-Speaking Children and Their Ability To Hear Final Consonant Stops." Paper presented at the Annual Convention of The International Reading Association, Denver, Colorado, May 1973.

35. KENNEDY, D. K., and P. WEENER. "Visual and Auditory Training with Cloze Procedure To Improve Reading and Listening Comprehension." *Reading Research Quarterly* 8: 524-41; Summer 1973. Also: J. L. Wardrop and D. L. Essex. "Reply with Rejoinder." Same issue, pp. 542-92.

36. KIBLER, R. S., et al. "Effects of Sex Upon Comprehension and Retention." *Speech Monographs* 37: 287-92; November 1970.

37. KLAVON, ALBERT JAMES. "The Time-Compressed Lecture: An Alternative for Increased Teacher-Learner Instruction." Doctoral dissertation, University of Maryland, College Park, 1975. ERIC ED 126 535

38. KURILOFF, ARTHUR, and DALE YODER. "Communications in Task Analysis Training Manual IV Technical Report No. 8." Los Angeles: California State University Foundation, 1975. ERIC ED 123 643

39. LEWIS, M. S. "Teaching Children To Listen." *Education* 80: 455-59; April 1960.

40. LUNDSTEEN, S. W. *Listening: Its Impact on Reading and Other Language Arts.* Urbana, Illinois: National Council of Teachers of English and ERIC Clearinghouse on the Teaching of English, 1971.

41. LUNDSTEEN, S. W. "Research Review and Suggested Directions: Teaching Listening Skills to Children in the Elementary School." *Language Arts* 53: 348-51; March 1976.

42. MARASCUILO, L. A., and D. A. PENFIELD. "Learning To Listen: A Study on Auditory Perception." *California Journal of Educational Research* 23: 4-16; January 1972.

43. MARQUARDT, T. P., and J. H. SAXMAN. "Language Comprehension and Auditory Discrimination in Articulation Deficient Kindergarten Children." *Journal of Speech and Hearing Research* 15: 382-89; June 1972.

44. MCCROSKEY, R. L., and H. W. THOMPSON. "Comprehension of Rate Controlled Speech by Children with Special Learning Disabilities." *Journal of Learning Disabilities* 6: 621-27; December 1973.

45. MURPHY, J. F. "Learning by Listening: A Public School Approach to Learning Disabilities." *Academic Therapy* 8: 167-89; Winter 1972-73.

46. MUSIAL, DIANNE, and ROBERT MAPLE. "The Influence of Compressed Speech Upon Reading, Listening, and Verbal Comprehension." *Illinois School Research* 12 (1): 43-50; February 1974. ERIC EJ 130 538

47. NEVILLE, M. H. "Effectiveness of Rate of Aural Message on Reading and Listening." *Educational Research* 18: 37-43; November 1975.

48. NEVILLE, M. H., and A. K. PUGH. "Context in Reading and Listening—A Comparison of Children's Errors in Cloze Tests." *British Journal of Educational Psychology* 44: 224-32; November 1974.

49. PALMATIER, R. H., and G. MCHINCH. "Source of Gains in Listening Skill: Experimental or Pretest Experience." *Journal of Communication* 22: 70-76; March 1972.

50. PEDRINI, D. T., et al. "Pre-, Post-, and Follow-up Testing of Teacher Effectiveness Training." *Education* 96: 240-44; Spring 1976.

51. PENFIELD, D. A., and L. A. MARASCUILO. "Learning To Listen: An Experimental Study." *Educational Research* 14: 220-24; June 1972.

52. PETRIE, C. R., JR., and S. D. CARNEL. "Relationship of Motivation, Listening Capability, Initial Information, and Verbal Organization and Ability to Lecture Comprehension and Retention." *Communication Monographs* 43: 187-94; August 1976.

53. PLAISTER, TED. "The Eyes May Have It, But What About the Ears? Some Considerations in Teaching Listening Comprehension." Paper presented at the Conference for the Teachers of English to Speakers of Other Languages, Los Angeles, California, March 1975. ERIC ED 123 881

54. QUAY, LORENE C., et al. "Encoding and Decoding in Children from Different Socioeconomic and Racial Groups." Paper presented at the Annual Meeting of the American Educational Research Association, San Francisco, California, April 19-23, 1976.

55. RAMSEY, IMOGENE. "Comparison of First Grade Negro Dialect Speakers' Comprehension of Standard English and Negro Dialect." *Elementary English* 49: 688-96; May 1972.

56. REDDIN, E. "Factors Related to Listening." *The Reading Teacher* 24: 461, 463; January 1971.

57. RIDING, R. J. "Effects of Semantic Organization and Presentation Rate on Prose Recall by Children." *Education Review* 28: 42-50; November 1975.

58. ROHWER, W. D., JR., and R. D. MATZ. "Improving Aural Comprehension in White and Black Children; Pictures vs. Print." *Journal of Experimental Child Psychology* 19: 23-36; February 1975.

59. ROSSITER, C. M., JR. "Sex of the Speaker, Sex of the Listener, and Listening Comprehension." *Journal of Communication* 22: 64-69; March 1972.

60. RUDEGEAIR, ROBERT E. "Linguistic Factors in the Assessment of Speech Sound Discrimination." Report No. 52. Los Alamitos, California: Southwest Regional Laboratory for Educational Research and Development, April 25, 1975. ERIC ED 125 004

61. RUDEGEAIR, ROBERT E. "A New Approach to Assessing Speech Sound Perception in Children." Professional Paper No. 31. Los Alamitos, California: Southwest Regional Laboratory for Educational Research and Development, May 9, 1975. ERIC ED 125 005

62. RUTHERFORD, W. L., and T. W. WEANER. "Hierarchy of Listening Skills." *Elementary English* 51: 1146-50; November 1974.

63. SCHNEEBURG, H. "Listening While Reading: A Four Year Study." *The Reading Teacher* 30: 629-35; March 1977.

64. SCHNEYER, J. WESLEY. "Research in Listening." *The Reading Teacher* 24: 369; January 1971.

65. SCHUBACH, DEANE FORD. "Listening Bibliography." St. Thomas: College of the Virgin Islands, 1975. ERIC ED 119 188

66. STEIN, NANCY L., and CHRISTINE G. GLENN. "An Analysis of Story Comprehension in Elementary School Children: A Test of a Schema." St. Louis, Missouri: Washington University, 1975. ERIC ED 121 474

67. SUND, R. B. "Growing Through Sensitive Listening and Questioning." *Childhood Education* 51: 68-71; November 1974.

68. SWALM, J. E. "Comparison of Oral Reading, Silent Reading, and Listening Comprehension." *Education* 92: 111-15; April 1972.

69. SWALM, J. E. "Is Listening Really More Effective for Learning in Early Grades?" *Elementary English* 51: 1110-13; November 1974.

70. THAMES, KENNETH H., and C. M. ROSSITER. "Effects of Reading Practice with Compressed Speech on Reading Rate and Listening Comprehension." *AV Communication Review* 20(1): 35-42; Spring 1972.

71. THOMPSON, R. A. "Developing Listening Skills To Improve Reading." *Education* 91: 261-65; February 1971.

72. TREBILCOCK, E. L. "Can Auding by Kindergarten Children Be Improved in a Normal Classroom Situation Through Direct Teaching of This Skill?" *Dissertation Asbtracts* 3: 687A; 1970.

73. TRUBOWITZ, S. "Listening Teacher." *Childhood Education* 51: 319-22; April 1975.

74. TUTOLO, DANIEL. "Cognitive Approach to Teaching Listening." *Language Arts* 54: 262-65; March 1977.

75. TUTOLO, DANIEL. "Teaching Critical Listening." *Language Arts* 52: 1108-12; November 1975. ERIC EJ 136 019

76. VUKELICH, C. "Development of Listening Comprehension Through Storytime." *Language Arts* 53: 889-91; November 1976.

77. WALKER, L. "Comparative Study of Selected Reading and Listening Processes." *Reading Research Quarterly* 10: 255-57; 1974-1975.

78. WALKER, L. "Comprehending Writing and Spontaneous Speech." *Reading Research Quarterly* 11: 144-67; 1975-1976. ERIC EJ 132 409

79. WALLNER, NANCY K. "Development of a Listening Comprehension Test for Kindergarten and Beginning First Grade." *Educational and Psychological Measurement* 34: 391-96; Summer 1974.

80. WAY, J. G. "Teaching Listening Skills." *The Reading Teacher* 26: 472-76; February 1973.

81. WETSTONE, H. S., and B. Z. FRIEDLANDER. "Effects of Live, T.V., and Audio Story Narration on Primary Grade Children's Listening Comprehension." *Journal of Educational Research* 68: 32-35; September 1974.

82. WILKINSON, A., and L. STRATTA. "Listening and the Study of Spoken Language." *Education Review* 25: 3-20; November 1972.

83. WILKINSON, A., and L. STRATTA. "Listening Comprehension at 13 Plus." *Educational Research* 22: 228-42; June 1970.

84. WILLIAMS, S. S. "Building Listener Accountability." *The Speech Teacher* 23: 53-56; January 1974.

85. WILLS, J. H., and H. BANAS. "Learning To Listen." *Academic Therapy* 6: 317-20; Spring 1971.

86. WITKIN, B. R. "Auditory Perception—Implications for Language Development." *Journal of Research and Development in Education* 3: 53-68; 1969.

87. WITKIN, B. R. "Reading Improvement Through Auditory Perceptual Training." Hayward, California: Alameda County School Department, 1972.

7. What Research Says About Beginning Reading
Linda S. Lotto

RESEARCH and related writing in beginning reading from 1970 to 1976 remains as popular, and as controversial, as in the past. Two developments in particular characterize this period. First, the government funds which sponsored so many major studies during the 1960's have dried up. A great number of research studies reported herein are doctoral dissertations. Second, it has become even more evident that research has neither shown conclusively how children learn to read—what approach to beginning reading is most efficient and under what conditions—nor lent support to any one model of the reading process. In general, the seventies have been marked by a strong interest in the synthesis of experimental findings on the models and theories they are beginning to support.

Two areas have received greater attention during this period than in the past: (a) studies in cognitive style and (b) inquiries into the affective domain. Both reflect current trends in educational research in all areas and promise to broaden our understanding of beginning reading.

Three Views on Reading

In *Reading and Instructional Approaches: What Research Says to the Teacher,* Goldbecker (17) set the stage for a discussion of beginning reading. She presented three views on the reading process and described the approaches to beginning reading advocated by each. According to Goldbecker, the theoretical basis for reading generally accepted by proponents of basal readers is best exemplified by the late William Gray (18). He classified reading into four components: (a) word perception or recognition; (b) comprehension and interpretation; (c) reaction on the part of the reader; and (d) assimilation of the concepts presented. This long-established view holds that beginning readers are qualitatively the same as mature readers, differing only in complexity and purpose of materials read.

Goldbecker pointed out that a different view was espoused by Henry (22).

61

He contended that reading occurs within a series of logical processes, and he emphasized the importance of concept development. In Henry's model of the reading process, the beginning reader differs from the mature reader only in the refinement of strategies the reader employs during analysis and synthesis—the two basic modes of thinking employed in reading.

A third view construed beginning reading to be a decoding process, and thus radically different from mature reading. Leonard Bloomfield and Charles Fries are among the linguists who proposed this viewpoint. Such a model divides reading into three stages: (a) the *transfer* stage in which the beginning reader moves from auditory signs for language symbols to new visual signs for the same symbols; (b) the *productive* stage in which the student responds unconsciously to the visual signs; and (c) the *imaginative* stage in which the reading process becomes so automatic that it is equal to or greater than language in providing experiential input.

In reporting what research has to say about these views, Goldbecker centered on the issue of where meaning becomes important in reading. Proponents of the "meaning-emphasis" approach claim that beginning readers must have the benefit of all available clues—phonic, syntax, semantics, concepts—in order to understand fully the material being read. The "code-emphasis" group claims that meaning can only come after the child has learned to "crack the code."

The Reading Process

Learning to read by reading. Hoskisson's (25) theory of learning to read through "successive approximation" relates the process of learning to read to that of learning language. Since children learn language in stages, each more closely approximating adult language, he contended that children learn to read the same way. According to Hoskisson each child has a mind set for *diversity* and a mind set for *pattern search* which enable him or her to process the diversity of the language in which he or she is immersed, and to seek out patterns which more and more closely approximate adult language.

The parallel process in reading is to immerse children in reading, exposing them to the diversity of syntax, semantics, and orthography in our written language. From this exposure, presumably they will be able to form their own generalizations and, gradually, to discover the systematic nature of our orthographic system. "Perhaps one of education's greatest delusions is that we teach children to read," Hoskisson said. "All that may really occur is that materials are presented to a child in one form or another and he uses them to solve the reading problem" (25: 446).

Discovering processes involved in learning to read. Many researchers believe that word-learning is essentially associational in nature. However, according to Barr, ". . . recent studies of word-learning suggest that learning to read demands an active structuring and integration of new task materials into pre-existing structures rather than the passive building of associations through drill, repetition, and reinforcement" (3: 258). Following this assumption, Barr has attempted to infer children's reading strategies through an analysis of their oral reading errors. The results show that the teacher's instructional method has a significant effect on the child's response to printed words. Children taught with a phonics approach substituted words that were phonetically acceptable yet not necessarily semantically correct. The reverse was true for children instructed with a "whole word" approach. The fact that the method of instruction does play a role in determining a child's response to printed words challenges the assumption that the reading process is merely associational.

Cohen (6) has followed Barr's lead in analyzing oral reading errors or miscues. Through an analysis of the errors of both good and poor readers who had been instructed with a code-emphasis approach or 'Open Court' approach instead of a basal reader approach, she stated that she was able to gain insight into the underlying processes involved in beginning reading:

This study suggests that it may be the skill of scanning words for salient features that is acquired by good but not poor readers during the first year of instruction. Poor readers tend to use fewer letter cues. This appears to be a behavior which is different from what is generally thought of as blending of each letter-sound, but which may include it (6: 650).

In other words, we cannot assume that the phonic skills we teach will transfer to the reading process. We must teach some students to scan words for letter cues, and to blend letter-sounds into meanings.

Reading subskills. Although many reading teachers seem to assume that reading skills must be taught in a sequence leading from simple to more complex, until recently this assumption has not been supported experimentally. Filp (15) conducted a study to test the hypothesis that a hierarchy from simple to complex exists among a given set of grapheme-morpheme correspondence skills. The results pointed to the existence of such a hierarchy and therefore also lent credence to the proposition that there exists a sequence from simple to complex in learning to read. It must be noted that there was greater evidence of a hierarchy in slow than in normal readers.

The Method

Phonics. Most approaches to beginning reading instruction teach phonics, or letter-sound relationships, as a means of decoding unfamiliar words. Meaning-emphasis approaches usually use what is called *analytic* phonics: the child analyzes and compares known words and thus discovers letter-sound relationships. Code-emphasis approaches employ *synthetic* phonics, in which the child is taught the letter-sound relationship in isolation and then is asked to blend the sounds to form new words.

In a study conducted by Monaghan (32), a 40-item nonsense word list was administered to 27 first graders who had been taught letter-sound correspondences in isolation. The results showed four distinct stages of development in sounding out nonsense words. During the *first* stage the child does not know the correspondences between sounds and letters, and therefore cannot sound out any words. At the *second* stage the child knows the isolated letter-sound correspondences but cannot blend them into a word. The *third* stage occurs when the child is able to do some blending. At the *fourth* and final stage, the child is able to pronounce most words at sight.

An interesting finding was that the child's overall speed on reading the list was a significant predictor of his or her subsequent rank when administered the Metropolitan Achievement Test in second and third grade. While good pronunciation does not mean good reading, the reverse is probably true. In conclusion Monaghan stated:

This view would hold that the only obstacle to the child's understanding the written language is his failure to grasp the graphemic system. Once he has grasped this, he can use the ability he already has to monitor and refine any ambiguities that arise from the graphemic system (32: 16).

In other work in the area of phonics, Muller (33) has shown that the transfer phenomena observed in adults do not generalize to the pre-reader. Therefore, training in phonic blending is necessary in order for phonic letter training skills to transfer to a word reading task.

Sight word learning. Sight word learning originated in the old "look-say" method of reading instruction. Today most basal reading programs utilize a basic sight word vocabulary. These sight words are likely to be those frequently occurring words that are irregular in spelling and pronunciation. They are taught as sight words because they do not fit the letter-sound correspondences taught the children. Recent research (10, 11, 12) has criticized the sight word approach to beginning reading instruction. The debate turns on how much sight word learning is beneficial.

Since many teachers teach sight words to some extent, reports on three studies that describe methods of facilitating sight word learning are identified. John Koehler and others (27) demonstrated that grammatical context has more value than letter pattern tracing in teaching sight words. In her doctoral dissertation, Page (34) demonstrated that pupils who are tutored make greater gains on sight words than those who are not, while Robert Hillerich (23) selected a new list of 240 sight words published in *The Reading Teacher*.

Language experience. The language experience approach capitalizes on the child's ability with language. The child dictates stories to the teacher in his or her own words, and the stories are then read by the child and by his or her classmates. A detailed discussion of this approach can be found in Moe's (31) article in *Reading Horizons*.

The language experience approach has been especially useful with disadvantaged children, who often speak non-standard English. Siegel (38) conducted a doctoral study which tentatively indicated that trained teachers and community workers can use children's recorded natural conversations as a basis for language experience stories. Although it frequently has been stated that Black English has its own syntax, Siegel's study showed no evidence of such a vernacular syntax; in fact it indicated the existence of a black-white linguistic overlap.

In the opinion of Ammon (1) the overemphasis of phonics has led to the inhibition of children's natural generative capacities with language. He recommended the use of cloze procedures. "Cloze" involves deleting a certain word or words from a sentence; the child must then supply the missing items. The technique requires that the child use his or her knowledge of syntax and semantics as cues in reading, rather than phonics.

Comparative studies. As of 1978, the debate in beginning reading rages on. However, it is no longer between specific instructional programs, but between the two more generalized approaches—"meaning-emphasis" and "code-emphasis." In a study conducted by Britton (5) comparing these two approaches, he concluded that, although it is important to teach specific reading skills, the mechanics of the reading process are but a means to an end in the communication between author and reader. His doctoral research indicated that the child brings certain abilities to reading—abilities that are determined by a combination of social, genetic, and environmental factors. Britton concluded that a code-emphasis approach produces greater achievement in reading.

Factors related to success in beginning reading. Success in reading can be attributed to many factors. The studies reported in this section refer to factors over which teachers have control and which they may use both in predicting and in facilitating reading achievement in the classroom.

Larrivee (29) studied the interaction among individualization, teacher directiveness, and learner support in first-grade reading achievement. She indicated that a combination of low teacher directiveness and high learner support produced grade equivalency scores a full year higher than any other combined patterns. The results of Barr's (2) study suggest that both strategy and prior experience with certain word patterns influence the frequency of response to printed words. Besides the instructional method, the actual material read also influences a child's reading achievement.

The effects of grouping on reading achievement were explored by MacDonald and Wurster (30). They compared the results on the Gates-MacGinite Achievement Tests at the beginning of second grade for two randomly selected groups. One was grouped in first grade in a multiple-grade primary situation, the other in an isolated first grade room. The results showed no significant difference in achievement between the groups.

A study by Treiman (41) explored the effect of task familiarity on experiments that related cognitive synthesis and beginning reading achievement. The subjects, 56 kindergartners, were divided into four groups: the control group, a "familiarity alone" group, and two groups taught to respond to two or three symbols as a unit. The post-test results showed significant gains for all but the control group, thus demonstrating the importance of task familiarity. According to Treiman, these results could invalidate all previous experiments linking reading achievement and cognitive synthesis.

The Child

Language and beginning reading. The relationship between oral language facility and reading achievement was demonstrated in a 1971 study by Compton (7). In that study, 140 first-grade students were placed in either a verbal or a nonverbal group by teacher selection and tests in intelligence and verbal fluency. There was a significant difference in reading achievement between the groups in vocabulary and comprehension. This evidence gives support to the theory that oral language facility is an asset in reading achievement.

Attitudes. The attitude a child brings to reading will influence his or her success as surely as will his or her IQ score. Yet attitude is a difficult area to quantify despite the fact that data have been obtained through the use of a variety of instruments. It is in this realm that proponents of the language experience approach claim to have an advantage over a phonics approach. Attitudes and the whole affective domain are only now beginning to receive the attention of educational research. Both studies reported here discuss the effects on attitude of differing approaches to beginning reading instruction.

Riendeau (35) analyzed the effects of beginning reading instruction on 13 concepts related to a child's self-concept. The experimental group received instruction via a language experience approach; the control group used basal readers. The results showed that boys in the language experience group had developed greater self-esteem, social interests, individuation, realism, and preference for father than the reader-based group. Girls in the language experience group developed greater self-esteem, social interest, and identification with friends than did the girls in the basal reader group. Girls in the reader-based group developed greater identification with the teacher than did the language experience group girls. Thus some of the claims of the language experience proponents seem justified—although controversy is likely to continue!

DuBois (12) used a formal method, the Inventory of Reading Attitudes,[8] to compare the reading attitudes through grade six of children instructed in ITA (Initial Teaching Alphabet) and TO (Traditional Orthography). The results showed no significant difference in attitude regardless of first grade method of instruction. It is important to keep in mind that Riendeau was analyzing *self-concept,* while DuBois was concerned with *attitudes toward reading.*

Cognitive style. Cognitive style has been an object of interest lately, as a means of achieving more efficient learning. Research has shown that children do learn differently. If this is so, then it would appear to follow that matching instructional approach with different learning styles would facilitate learning. Wepman and Morency (42) tested the idea that matching a child's learning style (as determined by his or her perceptual ability) to a compatible teaching method would increase his or her progress in learning to read. An earlier study by Robinson (36) confirmed that high perceptual ability is linked to success in reading.

The theoretical model behind the work of Wepman and Morency was that children develop perceptually in stages, using neurological potential for increasingly complex behavior—from simple reflex activity, to perceptual, and eventually to conceptual behavior. At the perceptual level the child develops the capacity to discriminate a wide range of stimuli. For children with a balanced perceptual development, teaching method makes no difference; but for children whose development is imbalanced—for example, with greater discriminatory ability in one sense modality than another—learning could be enhanced by using a method for the preferred modality. Not doing this could slow learning. The results confirmed their hypothesis for grade one. Due to attrition of their sample, they were unable to test the hypothesis in grades two and three.

Another aspect of perceptual modality (the natural dominance of the mode of perception in learning, for example, visual, auditory, tactile, or kinesthetic preferences) was explored by Robinson (36). First, she grouped entering first-grade children as high visual–high auditory, high visual–low auditory, low visual–high auditory, or low visual–low auditory. Then she compared each group's progress in reading through third grade. The results showed that high visual–high auditory children scored the highest, while low visual–low auditory children scored the lowest. The method of reading instruction made no difference.

---

[8] This inventory was developed by Roger Farr, James Laffy, and Carl Smith, and described in *Taxonomy of Evaluation Techniques for Reading Programs.* Bloomington: Indiana University, August 1960.

Regardless of method, auditory discrimination made a significant contribution to reading, while visual perception did not.

Sunshine and DiVesta (40) analyzed two other ranges of cognitive style: "reflective-impulsive" and "field dependent-independent," as relating to processing requirements in letter discrimination. The children were asked to match 12 letter-like symbols with their transformations in horizontal-vertical and high-low density formats. The results showed that reflective, field-independent children made the fewest errors.

The "impulsives" made errors because they failed to take the time to identify the distinctive features necessary to characterize a letter. They were certain of their response. The "reflectives," on the other hand, were uncertain of their response and took the time to study the letters. The "field-dependents" màde errors because of contextual factors surrounding the letter to be discriminated. They were uncertain of the stimulus.[9]

Systematic scanning, shown by Cohen (6) to be a characteristic of good readers, may be only partially developed in impulsives and field-dependents. However, the difference can be offset by the use of nontraditional formats—vertical and/or low density arrangements.

Reading Programs

SWRL. The Southwest Regional Laboratory for Educational Research and Development (SWRL) in Los Alamitos, California, has produced a phonics-based reading program for grades K-3. "A basic premise undergirding this program is that in order to read words not previously introduced in reading instruction, children must have an understanding of the spelling-to-sound correspondences of English orthography and must know how to apply those correspondences appropriately" (8: 27).

A great deal of highly detailed technical work went into the production of the SWRL program (4, 9, 16, 28, 37, 39). First a lexicon of 9,000 words was compiled; then, with the aid of a computer, the spelling-to-sound correspondences for these words were established. These correspondences were then sequenced and stories using these words were composed.

The effects of the implementation of this program are detailed in a report by Hanson and Schutz (21). The conclusions reached are highly complimentary to the SWRL program. In effect Hanson and Schutz determined that even disadvantaged children can learn to read if this program is correctly implemented. Specifically, they ascertained that high overall levels of proficiency can be reliably

---

[9] In simple language, this means that children whose cognitive style can be characterized as reflective and field-independent will be more successful at discriminating letters because they will study the symbols (reflect) and be able to discriminate them from their context or field (field-independent).

attained in a kindergarten reading instruction, that pupils from a full range of racial ethnic characteristics can achieve high levels of proficiency under ordinary school conditions, and that individual variations in program outcome are relative to program use and instructional emphasis rather than the personal deficiencies of pupils or their family situations.

ITA. Initial Teaching Alphabet (ITA) long has attracted both fervent admirers and bitter antagonists. The admirers claim that the one-to-one sound-symbol relationships in ITA overcome the spelling irregularities of Traditional Orthography (TO) that cause many beginning readers so much difficulty. They point with pride to skills in composition and favorable attitudes toward reading and writing. Conversely, the critics claim that ITA is fine, but eventually a transition to TO must take place. They point to pupils who have difficulty making the change, and to others who spell poorly. Other disadvantages include the high cost of ITA materials and the problem of incoming students who have attended a school which teaches in TO.

In Great Britain *The Bullock Commission's Judgement of ITA* was published by the Government Department of Education and Science in February 1975. Downing reported their conclusions:

> There is no one method, medium, approach, device, or philosophy that holds the key to the process of learning to read (p. 371). The Commission treats ITA not as a method, but as an alternative medium for printing children's books. In other words, the Bullock Commission's conclusion is that reading teachers should think again about ITA (11: 382).

In another study of ITA by Henry (22), this time in Cleveland, 700 students from nine school districts were divided into three groups. One group started TO in grade one; one started ITA in grade one; and one started ITA in kindergarten. The ITA groups transferred to TO during the second semester of second grade. Tests in grade one showed the ITA groups were superior to the TO groups in skills requiring letter-sound association. After the transition few significant differences were found on spelling or other reading subtests. Of particular interest is the fact that the group which started ITA in kindergarten maintained their advantage through grade three.

Children who read early. As a follow-up to her book on children who read early, Durkin (14) made a six-year study of a language arts program for four-year-olds. Part I was the language arts program itself (13). Part II was a four-year effort to trace the progress made in reading by children who took part in Part I and compare it with the progress of their classmates who did not. Durkin's previous findings showed that children who learned to read early maintained their advantage. These children learned to read in interesting and enjoyable ways—ways Durkin tried to incorporate into a school situation. The children in the experimental group obtained higher mean scores than those in the control group at the end of grades one and two. At the end of grades three and four this was *not* true, however.

Durkin drew the conclusion that schools are not willing to abandon their old ways. Children who were reading when they entered first grade were still given preprimers. The school failed to take advantage of the early starts in reading. In her opinion the teaching of reading in kindergarten has more to do with parental support and the availability of materials than with any research findings.

References

1. AMMON, RICHARD. "Generating Expectancies To Enhance Comprehension." *The Reading Teacher* 29: 245-49; December 1975.

2. BARR, REBECCA. "Influence of Reading Materials on Response to Printed Words." *Journal of Reading Behavior* 7: 125-35; Summer 1975.

3. BARR, REBECCA. "Processes Underlying the Learning of Printed Words." *Elementary School Journal* 75: 258-68; January 1975.

4. BERDIANSKY, BETTY, et al. "Design for Sequencing Spelling-to-Sound Correspondences in Mod 2 Reading Program, Vol. I and II." Los Alamitos, California: Southwest Regional Laboratory for Educational Research and Development, June 1971.

5. BRITTON, EARL WILLIAM. "A Comparison of Two Methods of Teaching Beginning Reading." Doctoral dissertation, Montana State University, Missoula, 1974.

6. COHEN, ALICE SHEFF. "Oral Reading Errors of First Grade Children Taught by a Code-Emphasis Approach." *Reading Research Quarterly* 10: 615-50; 1974-75.

7. COMPTON, MARY ELIZABETH. "A Study of the Relationship Between Oral Language Facility and Reading Achievement of Selected First Grade Children." Doctoral thesis, University of North Carolina at Chapel Hill, 1971.

8. CRONNELL, BRUCE. "Designing a Reading Program Based on Research Findings in Orthography." *Elementary English* 50: 27-34; January 1973. Copyright © 1973 by the National Council of Teachers of English. Reprinted by permission of the publisher.

9. CRONNELL, BRUCE. "Sequenced Contractions and Abbreviations for Model 2 Reading." Los Alamitos, California: Southwest Regional Laboratory for Educational Research and Development, December 1970.

10. CULLINGFORD, CEDRIS. "The Crisis in Reading." *London Educational Review* 3: 70-72; Autumn 1974.

11. DOWNING, JOHN. "The Bullock Commission's Judgement of I.T.A." *The Reading Teacher* 29: 379-82; January 1976.

12. DUBOIS, JESSIE. "A Comparison of Reading Attitudes Between First Grade Reading Instruction in I/T/A and T/O." *Contemporary Education* 42:169-72; February 1971.

13. DURKIN, DOLORES. "A Language Arts Program for Pre-First Grade Children: Two Year Achievement Report." *Reading Research Quarterly* 5: 534-65; Summer 1970.

14. DURKIN, DOLORES. "A Six Year Study of Children Who Learned To Read in School at the Age of Four." Paper presented at the Annual Meeting of the American Educational Research Association, Chicago, Illinois, April 15-19, 1974.

15. FILP, JOHANNA. "Relationship Among Reading Skills: A Hierarchical Hypothesis." *Journal of Reading Behavior* 7: 229-40; Fall 1975.

16. FOLLETTIE, JOSEPH F. "Some Patterns for Initially-Stressed Two Syllable Words." Los Alamitos, California: Southwest Regional Laboratory for Educational Research and Development, 1971.

17. GOLDBECKER, SHERALYN S. *Reading and Instructional Approaches: What Research Says to the Teacher.* Washington, D.C.: National Education Association, 1975.

18. GRAY, WILLIAM. *On Their Own in Reading.* Second edition. Chicago, Illinois: Scott-Foresman and Company, 1970.

19. GROFF, PATRICK. "The Mythology of Reading: I—Sight Words." *Reading Horizons* 15: 208-11; Summer 1975.

20. GROFF, PATRICK. "Sight Words: The Humpty Dumpty of Reading Instruction." *Reading* 8: 11-16; December 1974.

21. HANSON, RALK A., and RICHARD E. SCHUTZ. "Instructional Product Implementation and Schooling Effects: Lessons from the Second-Year Installation of the SWRL/Ginn Kindergarten Program." Los Alamitos, California: Southwest Regional Laboratory for Educational Research and Development, 1976.

22. HENRY, GEORGE. *Teaching Reading as Concept Development: Emphasis on Affective Thinking.* Newark, Delaware: International Reading Association, 1974.

23. HILLERICH, ROBERT. "Word Lists—Getting It All Together." *The Reading Teacher* 27: 353-60; January 1974.

24. WAI-CHING HO and others. "Longitudinal Effects of I.T.A. on Pupils' Reading Achievement Through Grade Three." Cleveland, Ohio: Education Research Council of America, March 1970.

25. HOSKISSON, KENNETH. "Successive Approximation and Beginning Reading." *Elementary School Journal* 175: 442-51; April 1975. Copyright © 1975 by the University of Chicago Press.

26. INGEBO, GEORGE. "A Six-Year Experiment in the Use of the Initial Teaching Alphabet (I.T.A.) in the Teaching of Reading." Portland, Oregon: Portland Public Schools, June 1973.

27. KOEHLER, JOHN, et al. "The Effects of Letter Pattern Training and Grammatical Context on Sight Word Learning in Kindergartners." Los Alamitos, California: Southwest Regional Laboratory for Educational Research and Development, August 1971.

28. KUCHENBECKER, SHARI YOUNG. "Component Skills in the Word Decoding Task for Beginning Readers: An Annotated Cross-Referenced Bibliography. Technical Note No. 2-72-03." Los Alamitos, California: Southwest Regional Laboratory for Educational Research and Development, January 1972.

29. LARRIVEE, BARBARA ANN. "The Effects of Individualization, Teacher-Directiveness, and Learner Support on First-Grade Reading Achievement." Doctoral thesis, University of Massachusetts, Amherst, 1976.

30. MACDONALD, PHYLLIS A., and STANLEY R. WURSTER. "Multiple Grade Primary vs. Segregated First Grade: Effects on Reading Achievement." Unpublished research conducted at Arizona State University, Tempe, June 1974.

31. MOE, ALDEN J. "Using the Child's Oral Language in Beginning Reading Instruction." *Reading Horizons* 16: 32-35; Fall 1975.

32. MONAGHAN, JENNIFER. "Sounding, Blending, and Psycholinguistics." Paper presented at the 20th Annual Meeting of the International Reading Association, New York City, May 13-16, 1975.

33. MULLER, DOUGLAS. "Phonic Blending and Transfer of Letter Training to Word Reading in Children." *Journal of Reading Behavior* 5: 212-17; Summer 1973.

34. PAGE, IRE ADAMS. "The Effects of Tutoring on Sight Word Gains of Primary Pupils." Doctoral dissertation, University of Illinois at Champaign-Urbana, 1975.

35. RIENDEAU, BETTY A. "An Exploratory Investigation of the Effect of Two Differing Approaches of Reading Instruction on the Self-Social Concepts of First Grade Children." Doctoral thesis, American University, Washington, D.C., 1973.

36. ROBINSON, HELEN M. "Visual and Auditory Modalities Related to Methods for Beginning Reading." *Reading Research Quarterly* 8: 7-39; Fall 1972.

37. RUDEGEAIR, ROBERT E. "An Analysis of Tasks Reflecting Subskills of Novel Word Decoding." Los Alamitos, California: Southwest Regional Laboratory for Educational Research and Development, January 1972.

38. SIEGEL, FLORENCE FINKEL. "Conditions Which Promote Urban Child Language as a Base for Beginning Reading." Doctoral dissertation, Rensselaer Polytechnic Institute, Troy, New York, 1975.

39. SULLIVAN, HOWARD J. "Story Specifications for Mod 2 Third-Year and Fouth-Year Reading." Los Alamitos, California: Southwest Regional Laboratory for Educational Research and Development, April 1971.

40. SUNSHINE, PHYLLIS M., and FRANCIS J. M. DiVESTA. "Effects of Density and Format on Letter Discrimination by Beginning Readers with Different Learning Styles." *Journal of Educational Psychology* 68: 15-18; February 1976.

41. TREIMAN, JOAN LITTLE. "Cognitive Synthesis, Task Familiarity and Achievement in Beginning Reading." Doctoral dissertation, Rutgers, The State University of New Jersey, 1974.

42. WEPMAN, JOSEPH M., and ANNE S. MORENCY. "Perceptual Development and Learning: An Experimental Study on Modality Reading Instruction. Section II, Final Report." Chicago: University of Chicago, November 1975.

8. Reading in the Elementary School
Peter F. Connallon, Jr.

THE task of reviewing research related to reading instruction in the 1970's is complicated by both the volume and the scope of such research. Therefore, instead of trying to cover all aspects of reading, this chapter focuses on elementary school research that promises to be of most value to the classroom teacher.

Diagnosis

Many experts such as Farr (24), Gove (38), Hillerich (43), London and Sigmond (59), and Zaeske (81) agree that the key to reading instruction is early and accurate diagnosis of any problems or potential problems. The most skillful and creative presentation of a concept is likely to fail if the child is not yet ready to assimilate that concept. Diagnosis is the determination of the specific needs of the individual at a given time and includes decisions with respect to the pacing of instruction. Particularly since chapters by Lotto and Bjurstrom in this review also treat research in reading, this chapter concentrates on various aspects of the diagnosis of reading difficulties in the elementary school.

Diagnostic studies. Diagnosis may be broken into two main categories, formal and informal. Formal diagnosis, as the term is used here, refers to those commercially prepared instruments that are normed. Informal diagnosis is defined as those measures, techniques, observations, and devices, not commercially prepared, that the teacher may choose to use.

Formal diagnosis is not considered in this chapter except for passing mention of the reasons for its exclusion. One reason these instruments are not discussed is that they have been the object of criticism for failing to diagnose reading needs fully. Among the critics are Aaron (2), Askov (5), Farr (24), Livingston (58), Pederson (68), and Salter (75). The second and probably more significant reason for excluding formal instruments is based on the fact that they are not always available for classroom use. Formal or standardized instruments cost money, and those teachers who lack funds for such tools would find little value in a review of them. At the same time, this exclusion should not be construed to be a blanket indictment of commercial materials.

Informal Diagnostic Strategies

Informal diagnosis is examined in this section under five topics: (a) informal reading inventories, (b) miscue analysis, (c) cloze technique, (d) word lists, and (e) observation as an informal diagnostic approach.

Informal reading inventories. The amount of information on informal reading inventories (IRI's) is so extensive as almost to create a state of confusion. Powell (70), Walter (78), Johns (48), Barbe (8), and Belden (10) are among those who have presented historical overviews of IRI's that also dealt with the development of the instrument. Powell (70: 2) stated that an IRI:

. . . can be an instrument for use in the classroom placement, diagnostic assessment, clinical analysis, and for instant and continuous processing of oral behavior.

He went on to say that he considered IRI's significant diagnostic instruments. Walter (78) is another writer who reviewed IRI's, but with not quite as much enthusiasm as Powell. Walter concluded that, although IRI's have been useful in placing students and in diagnosing other aspects of the reading process, the training prerequisite to their use may sometimes preclude their use in the classroom.

Most reviewers and researchers recognize the worth of the IRI as a diagnostic instrument, but that is usually the extent of their agreement. O'Brien (61) contended that the short passages used are too random when it comes to presenting new words. She suggested that new words in the text should be extracted and that, from those words, a reading passage should be developed. That passage presumably would have a higher density of new words, hence would more accurately represent the difficulty of the passage.

Livingston (58) criticized the make-up of the questions used to measure comprehension. Questions should be developed with the hierarchical comprehension skills as the criteria for development; he contended that only then will the IRI assess literal comprehension, interpretation, and critical reading which make up general comprehension. Kelly (53) pointed to the lack of competency in teaching personnel as a sometimes significant problem and outlined an in-service program designed to upgrade competencies. Johns (48) surveyed teachers involved with the use of IRI at various levels. He concluded that IRI's are most effective when used in a clinical situation; outside clinical situations, variance in scoring techniques is so great as to give them little value. He further stated that there is disagreement about what should be coded as an error, what topics to use, how to construct questions related to comprehension, and the difference between oral and silent reading.

IRI levels. The determination of independent, instructional, and frustrational levels is a classic question with respect to the IRI, according to Walter (78), Powell (70), Ekwall (21), Packman (64), and Pikulski (69). Ekwall (21) approached the question of frustration in a manner that is both unique and interesting. He administered IRI's to third, fourth, and fifth grade children while recording their galvanic skin responses on a polygraph. Frustrational level was affected by difficulty of material, intelligence, cognitive style, and perceptual acuity. However, age, sex, and ethnic background did not affect frustrational level in this study.

Amidst all the criticism and disagreement over informal reading inventories, considerable support for the IRI persists. Livingston (58) contended that IRI's are better than existing standardized instruments, with their greatest strength residing in examiner judgment. Levin (56) characterized the IRI as the most valid means of assessing reading levels and went on to credit the group IRI as the most efficient. Hollander (45) defended the time expended in their use with the argument that IRI's provide more valid information than do standardized instruments.

Valmont (77) agreed that questions used in connection with the IRI are of critical importance, but chose to look upon this as an asset. He presented 20 points that he deemed useful in question development. Kelly (53) addressed the problem of examiner competency with a study aimed at the improvement of in-service program development, while Windell (80) made an extensive inquiry into training programs for the use of the IRI in diagnosing reading needs in the field of special education.

From the foregoing discussion of IRI's, some conclusions can be drawn. First, IRI's can be used to measure certain aspects of reading. Second, success and depth of measurement are dependent on the skill and training of the person serving as the administrator. Specially trained persons must be employed to make decisions about standardization of scoring and about cutoff points for levels of instruction. This hardly seems the fault of the instrument, but does complicate its use.

Miscue analysis. The concept of miscue analysis has not been around long. It began to surface in the middle and later sixties with the work of Kenneth Goodman (29, 30, 31, 32, 33, 34, and 35). Goodman's work represents an attempt to apply the psycholinguistic theory of grammar that emerged in the fifties to reading. Allen and Watson (4) prepared a brief, understandable history of the philosophical and historical development of miscue analysis. Burke and Goodman (15) also gave a comprehensive and readable explanation with examples of miscue analysis. To their credit, they did so in a limited number of pages—pages which provide the uninitiated with an explanation of miscue analysis.

An examination of the philosophical basis of miscue analysis is necessary at this point. Reading, as Goodman conceived it, is more than an oral reproduction of the printed word. The reader brings more to the reading process than just the ability to reproduce words. The word "error" is not used in the analysis, "miscue" being used in its stead. A miscue may be caused by many factors. For instance, the reader may subconsciously be trying to translate what is written into his or her own speech patterns. Again, some other word in the sentence may have helped trigger a response that is not exactly what is on the printed page. Factors in the reader's past also may trigger the miscue; hence even the most fluent readers experience miscues. A professional sports announcer given a page on neurosurgery, for example, could produce many miscues caused by the unfamiliar nature of the material, by increased dependence on graphic decoding, or by the effort to apply elements from his or her background to the reading process. Some of the causes of miscues may reflect serious gaps in reading skills, while others may be inconsequential.

Goodman and Burke (37), working from this philosophical base, developed a system for coding miscues intended for classroom use. The coding system is based on research into the production of miscues or errors, and attempts to categorize them with regard to their effect on an intended meaning. The *Manual* they have prepared gives instructions on how to code, how to interpret, and how to select strategies suggested by the interpretation. Their procedure is time-consuming, but it does yield considerable insight into the needs of the student. There are also several sections of the *Manual* that impressed this writer as difficult to interpret.

Dempsey (16) suggested miscue analysis coupled with consideration of reader style and reader attitude as inferred from individual conferences. She also recommended sight word testing. This, it would seem, is contrary to the miscue philosophy because it removes words from their contextual framework.

Several authors such as Windell (80), Rogers (73), and Pikulski (69), in articles related directly to informal reading inventories, have used terminology and philosophical principles closely associated with miscue analysis. This is a shift from the purely quantity-oriented IRI to the qualitative/quantitative approach used in miscue analysis. It seems, in biological terms, as suggested by Williamson and Young (79), that a hybrid has emerged.

The cloze technique. The cloze technique, explained in footnote 7, has been subject to much of the same criticism leveled at informal reading inventories. There are many forms of cloze but no specific uniform grading procedures to be used with it. Breneman (14) suggested fifth word deletion for fiction and tenth word deletion for nonfiction. Boyce (13) suggested seventh word deletion but cautioned against using more than just the cloze technique to make placement decisions—a caution which appeared to suggest limited reliability. Lisman (57) investigated the value of a vowel deletion form of the cloze based on the premise that such deletions would be easier to grade and administer than word omissions. She concluded that some aspects of reading comprehension can be measured as well or slightly better with vowel deletion.

Cloze is based on the assumption of predictability in the English language. A reader confronted with a blank space in the middle of a sentence bases his or her response on contextual cues, on grammatical acceptability, and, finally, on his or her experiential background. The ability to provide the correct response is accepted as a demonstration of the sophistication of the reader's language. If the reader is successful in enough instances, his or her sophistication presumably is at or above the level of the material being read. This sort of conclusion is similar to the one sought through miscue analysis.

As with IRI's, it is claimed that the cloze technique is more effective than standardized tests intended to diagnose specific aspects of reading. Norman and Balyeat (60) used the cloze technique with "Language Experience Passages" in an effort to develop an unbiased diagnostic instrument for rural Appalachian children. They determined that multiple choice cloze was effective for placement purposes when compared to the component subtests of the Stanford Achievement Test. The multiple choice cloze tests were derived from material written by the children and local norms were developed. Olson (63) constructed Paragraph Reading Tests using short passages with no more than 10 deletions—mostly of content words. These passages were then normed locally, a procedure which the author contended gives a clearer picture of the local population.

It appears that the main strength of the cloze technique with respect to placement is the teacher's opportunity to construct these tests with the actual material the children will be using in their reading. Bowermaster (12) measured the effect of choice on reading level. Under three conditions of choice ranging from "no choice" to "reading whatever you want," reading levels were determined. Boys given choice scored significantly higher, while there was no significant difference for girls regardless of the condition. Beagle (9), in a study designed to measure the difference between oral and written responses to cloze tests, found no significant difference between the two. This finding may be of value to teachers working with younger children or children who have physical disabilities.

It is not yet clear, however, at what developmental level it first becomes feasible to use cloze with younger children. Bortnick and Lopardo (11) cautioned about the premature use of cloze due to younger children's lack of word recognition skills. Conversely, Gove (38) contended that cloze is an excellent means to develop reading skills with first graders. Apparently further inquiry into this matter is needed.

In addition to diagnosis it is claimed that cloze can be used successfully in various other forms of instruction. To illustrate: Horton (46), in his study of its construct validity, suggested cloze for use in the development of communication skills. Paradis and Bayne (67) suggested that children discuss acceptable substitutions of deleted words to include the effect on whole passage meaning.

Word lists. The use of word lists, for purposes of informal diagnosis of reading problems, should be undertaken only after the teacher has pondered several questions. For instance: (a) Do word lists fit into the teacher's conception of reading? and (b) Can word lists give him or her the diagnostic information that is needed or can he or she get it elsewhere with a smaller investment of time and energy?

If miscue analysis is used as a major informal diagnostic technique, then the answer to the first question is probably "no." Word lists remove the written word from the complex context of reading, and it is therefore difficult to imagine a reading task with a word in isolation and out of context. The word "fire" when written alone, for instance, may pertain to a fire extinguisher, a fireplace, a rifle, or some analogous cue. If isolated words exist in some sort of contextual way, why then present them devoid of any context clues as in word lists?

The answer to this query may be found in research which sometimes has led to conclusions favoring word lists. Among the advocates of lists are Dolch (17), Froese (26), LaPray and Ross (54), and Duzat (20). These persons contend that isolation is what provides the strength of word lists. A reader weak in graphic skills might mask this weakness through the effective use of other stronger skills. Isolation of words, however, forces the reader to demonstrate his or her sophistication. Examination of the nature of errors, therefore, can be used effectively for diagnosis. Miscue advocates would argue that miscue analysis does this, too. It is not yet clear as to whether this is true with regard to the miscue approach; the need for further research is apparent.

Observation as an informal diagnostic approach. At the beginning of this article, early and accurate diagnosis was identified as one important component of reading programs. One nebulous area of informal diagnosis remains to be discussed: the realm of personal observation. Success with this diagnostic approach is dependent on the sensitivity of the classroom teacher coupled with a knowledge of the physical manifestations of reading difficulty. Zaeske (81) suggested a screening program, based on observation, for all new students. His proposal included informal inventories and checking on motor activities. London and Sigmond (59) developed a handbook that includes informal instruments, observational forms, record keeping forms, and suggestions for strategies. Hillerich (43) agreed that early and accurate diagnosis of reading difficulties is vital, but he also felt that the information gained, if not properly used, can serve as a predictor of failure.

One other aspect of observational diagnosis resides in the nature of the information gained. Some of the information may merely be a clue to the need for a more definitive diagnosis and treatment by specialists such as eye doctors or hearing specialists. Again, gathering this information requires sensitivity, alertness, and the ability to synthesize the data in useful form.

Conclusion. Judging from the research and literature of the seventies, it appears that integration of IRI's, miscue analysis, and cloze technique provides a distinct trend, although it is still too early to determine how strong the trend will become. At the moment diagnostic techniques seem to be undergoing an evolutionary process. Unfortunately, in education this process often is slow.

Since the direction in which practice is heading appears to be a desirable one, a more rapid and orderly integration of concepts of diagnosis should be sought. Jongsma (51, 52) made this point in a criticism of recent research. It seems to lack direction and definition, he wrote, and commented that design is often weakened by uncontrolled variables and by statistical treatments that are inadequate. Well defined, well conducted, and carefully analyzed research would make evaluation and comparison of studies easier, he concluded, but this is not now the case.

It appears that informal diagnosis of reading difficulties in the elementary school is a potentially powerful classroom tool; but it is a tool in need of sharpening by inquiries that determine more fully the form diagnosis should take.

References

1. AARON, IRA E. "An Informal Reading Inventory." *Elementary English* 37: 457-60; November 1960.

2. AARON, ROBERT L. "Using the Cloze Sight Vocabulary To Develop a Group Informal Reading Inventory." Paper presented at the Annual Meeting of the International Reading Association, New York City, May 13-16, 1975.

3. ALLEN, P. DAVID. "Cue Systems Available During the Reading Process: A Psycholinguistic Viewpoint." *Elementary School Journal* 72: 258-64; 1972.

4. ALLEN, P. DAVID, and DOROTHY J. WATSON, editors. *Findings of Research in Miscue Analysis: Classroom Implications.* Urbana, Illinois: ERIC Clearinghouse on Reading and Communication Skills, National Council of Teachers of English, 1976.

5. ASKOV, EUNICE N. "Criterion Referenced Strategies for Diagnosis." Paper presented at the Annual Meeting of the International Reading Association, Anaheim, California, May 1976.

6. AULLS, M. W. "Towards a Systematic Approach to How the Reader Uses Context To Determine Meaning." National Reading Conference, St. Petersburg, Florida, December 3-5, 1970.

7. AUSTIN, MARY C., and MILDRED H. HEUBNER. "Evaluating Progress in Reading Through Informal Procedures." *The Reading Teacher* 15: 338-43; March 1962.

8. BARBE, WALTER B. *Educator's Guide to Personalized Reading Instruction.* Englewood Cliffs, New Jersey: Prentice-Hall, Inc., 1961.

9. BEAGLE, BARBARA A. "A Comparison of Oral and Written Responses on Cloze Tests." Unpublished master's thesis, Rutgers, The State University of New Jersey, January 1974.

10. BELDEN, H. O. "Informal Reading Testing: Historical Review and Review of Research." In: William K. Durr, editor. *Reading Difficulties: Diagnosis, Correction, and Remediation.* Newark, Delaware: International Reading Association, 1970. pp. 67-84.

11. BORTNICK, ROBERT, and GENEVIEVE S. LOPARDO. "The Case for Cloze in the Classroom." Paper presented at the International Reading Association Convention, New Orleans, May 1-4, 1974.

12. BOWERMASTER, JANET MARIE. "The Effects of Choice on Children's Reading Comprehension and Attitudes." Unpublished master's thesis, University of Illinois at Urbana-Champaign, 1976.

13. BOYCE, MAX WILLIAM. "Some Difficulties in Using the Cloze Procedure To Assess Readability." Unpublished master's thesis, University of Melbourne, Australia, April 1974.

14. BRENEMAN, BETH. "Reaction: The Cloze and the Composition Process." Paper presented at the Annual Meeting of the National Council of Teachers of English, San Diego, California, November 26-29, 1975.

15. BURKE, CAROLYN L., and KENNETH S. GOODMAN. "When a Child Reads: A Psycholinguistic Analysis." *Elementary English* 47: 121-29; January 1970.

16. DEMPSEY, JANE. "Diagnostic and Prescriptive Strategies Designed To Bring Back the Joy." Paper presented at the Annual Meeting of the California Reading Association, Fresno, California, November 1975.

17. DOLCH, EDWARD W. "How To Diagnose Children's Reading Difficulties by Informal Classroom Techniques." *The Reading Teacher* 6: 10-14; January 1953.

18. DULIN, KENNETH L. "Measuring the Difficulty of Reading Materials." *Reading Improvement* 8: 3-6; Spring 1971.

19. DURR, WILLIAM K., editor. *Reading Difficulties: Diagnosis, Correction, and Remediation.* Newark, Delaware: International Reading Association, 1970.

20. DUZAT, SAM V. "Informal Diagnosis: The Nucleus of Individualized Reading Instruction." Paper presented to the Annual Meeting of the International Reading Association, New York City, May 13-16, 1975.

21. EKWALL, ELDON E. "Informal Reading Inventories: The Instructional Level." *The Reading Teacher* 29: 662-65; April 1976.

22. EKWALL, ELDON E. "Should Repetitions Be Counted as Errors?" *The Reading Teacher* 27: 365-67; January 1974.

23. EKWALL, ELDON E., and JUDY K. ENGLISH. "The Use of the Polygraph To Determine Elementary Students' Frustration Reading Level." El Paso: Texas University—El Paso, May 29, 1971.

24. FARR, ROGER. *Reading: What Can Be Measured?* Newark, Delaware: International Reading Association, 1969.

25. FROESE, VICTOR. "Cloze Reliability Versus the Dale-Chall Formula." Paper presented to the meeting of the International Reading Association, Atlantic City, New Jersey, April 1971.

26. FROESE, VICTOR. "Functional Reading Levels: From Graded Word Lists." Paper presented to the Annual Meeting of the International Reading Association, New York City, May 13-16, 1975.

27. FROESE, VICTOR. "Word Recognition Tests: Are They Useful Beyond Grade Three?" *The Reading Teacher* 24: 432-38; February 1971.

28. GEESLIN, ROBERT H. "The Placement Inventory Alternative." *The Reading Teacher* 25: 332-35; January 1972.

29. GOODMAN, KENNETH S. "Dialect Barriers to Reading Comprehension." *Elementary English* 42: 853, 860; December 1965.

30. GOODMAN, KENNETH S. "A Linguistic Study of Cues and Miscues in Reading." *Elementary English* 42: 639-43; October 1965.

31. GOODMAN, KENNETH S. "The Linguistics of Reading." *Elementary School Journal* 64: 355-61; April 1964.

32. GOODMAN, KENNETH S. *The Psycholinguistic Nature of the Reading Process.* Detroit, Michigan: Wayne State University Press, 1968.

33. GOODMAN, KENNETH S. "Reading: A Psycholinguistic Guessing Game." *Journal of the Reading Specialist* 4: 126-35; May 1967.

34. GOODMAN, KENNETH S., and D. MENOSKY. "Unlocking the Program . . . Two Viewpoints." *Instructor* 80: 44-46; March 1971.

35. GOODMAN, KENNETH S., editor. *Miscue Analysis: Application to Reading Instruction.* Urbana, Illinois: ERIC Clearinghouse on Reading and Communication Skills, National Council of Teachers of English, October 1975.

36. GOODMAN, YETTA. "Using Children's Reading Miscues for New Teaching Strategies." *The Reading Teacher* 23: 455-59; February 1970.

37. GOODMAN, YETTA, and CAROLYN L. BURKE. *Reading Miscue Inventory Manual Procedure for Diagnosis and Evaluation.* New York: The Macmillan Company, 1972.

38. GOVE, MARY KAY. "Using the Cloze Procedure in a First Grade Classroom." *The Reading Teacher* 29: 36-38; October 1975.

39. GUSZAK, FRANK J. "Dilemmas in Informal Reading Assessment." *Elementary English* 47: 666-70; May 1970.

40. HANSEN, LEE H., and KARL D. HESSE. "A Criterion-Referenced Assessment of Reading Literacy Using the Cloze Procedure." Paper presented at the Annual Meeting of the American Educational Research Association, Chicago, Illinois, April 1974.

41. HARDIN, VERALEE B., and WILBUR S. AMES. "A Comparison of the Results of Two Oral Reading Tests." *The Reading Teacher* 22: 329-34; January 1969.

42. HAYES, WARREN S. "Criteria for the Instructional Level of Reading." Phoenix: University of Arizona, 1975.

43. HILLERICH, ROBERT L. "Kindergarten Screening Procedures: Early Identification or Merely Early Labeling?" Paper presented to the Annual Meeting of the International Reading Association, New York City, May 13-16, 1975.

44. HODGES, R., and E. H. RUDORF, editors. *Language and Learning To Read: What Teachers Should Know About Reading.* Boston: Houghton Mifflin Company, 1972.

45. HOLLANDER, SHEILA K. "Why's a Busy Teacher Like You Giving an IRI?" *Elementary English* 51: 905-907; September 1974.

46. HORTON, RAYMOND JOSEPH. "The Construct Validity of Cloze Procedure and an Exploratory Factor Analysis of Cloze, Paragraph Reading, and Structure-of-Intellect Tests." *Reading Research Quarterly* 10: 248-51; 1974-75.

47. HUNT, LYMAN C., JR. "The Effects of Self-Selection, Interest, and Motivation Upon Independent, Instructional, and Frustrational Levels." *The Reading Teacher* 24: 146-51, 158; November 1970.

48. JOHNS, JERRY L. "Informal Reading Inventories: A Survey Among Professionals." Paper presented at the Annual Meeting of the International Reading Association, Anaheim, California, May 1967.

49. JOHNS, JERRY L., SHARON GARTON, PAULA SCHOENFELDER, and PATRICIA SKRIBA. *Assessing Reading Behavior: Informal Reading Inventories—An Annotated Bibliography.* Newark, Delaware: International Reading Association, 1977.

50. JOHNSON, MARJORIE SEDDON. "Reading Inventories for Classroom Use." *The Reading Teacher* 14: 9-13; September 1960.

51. JONGSMA, EUGENE R. "The Cloze Procedure: A Survey of the Research." In: *Occasional Papers in Reading.* Bloomington: Indiana University, 1971.

52. JONGSMA, EUGENE R. "The Cloze Procedure as a Teaching Technique." *Reading Information Series: Where Do We Go?* Newark, Delaware: International Reading Association, 1971.

53. KELLY, DEAN. "Using an Informal Reading Inventory To Place Children in Instructional Material." In: William K. Durr, editor. *Reading Difficulties: Diagnosis, Correction, and Remediation.* Newark, Delaware: International Reading Association, 1970. pp. 111-19.

54. LAPRAY, MARGARET, and RAMON ROSS. "The Graded Word List: Quick Gauge of Reading Ability." *Journal of Reading* 12: 305-307; January 1969.

55. LAYTON, JAMES R. "Diagnostic Reading Evaluations: Which Scores To Report?" Paper presented to the Annual Meeting of the Plains Regional Conference of the International Reading Association, St. Louis, Missouri, February 20-22, 1975.

56. LEVIN, BEATRICE J. "The Informal Reading Inventory." *Reading Improvement* 8: 18-20; Spring 1971.

57. LISMAN, LINDA C. "Vowel Deletion and Cloze Tests Compared with a Reading Ability Test." Unpublished master's thesis, Rutgers, The State University of New Jersey, October 1971.

58. LIVINGSTON, HOWARD F. "Measuring and Teaching Reading with an Informal Reading Inventory." *Elementary English* 51: 878-79; September 1974.

59. LONDON, MARGERY, and MARY V. SIGMOND. "Diagnostic Strategies in Reading for Primary Children with Special Needs." Arlington, Virginia: Arlington County Public Schools, January 1975.

60. NORMAN, DOUGLAS, and RALPH BALYEAT. "A Longitudinal Study of the Effectiveness of the Language Experience Approach Combined with a Form of the Cloze Procedure as a Means of Predicting Reading Performance Among Rural Appalachian Pupils." Baxter, Tennessee: Upper Cumberland Reading Project, July 1974.

61. O'BRIEN, PATTI. "An Informal Reading Inventory—A New Approach." Paper presented at the Annual Meeting of the International Reading Association, Anaheim, California, May 1970.

62. OLIVER, MARVIN C. "Reading Performance and Rectangles." *Education* 92: 68-69; November/December 1971.

63. OLSON, MARGOT A. "Criterion-Referenced Reading Assessment in a Large City School District." Paper presented at the Annual Meeting of the American Educational Research Association, Washington, D.C., March 30-April 3, 1975.

64. PACKMAN, LINDA. "Selected Oral Reading Errors and Levels of Reading Comprehension." In: Howard A. Klein, editor. *The Quest for Competency in Teaching Reading.* Newark, Delaware: International Reading Association, 1972. pp. 203-208.

65. PAGE, W. D. "The Post-Oral Reading Cloze Test: New Link Between Oral Reading and Comprehension." *Journal of Reading Behavior* 7: 383-89; Winter 1975.

66. PAGE, W. D., editor. *Help for the Reading Teacher: New Directions in Research.* Urbana, Illinois: National Conference on Research in English, ERIC Clearinghouse for Reading and Communication Skills, 1975.

67. PARADIS, EDWARD, and MINA BAYNE. "An Examination of the Use of Cloze Tasks During Primary Grade Reading Instruction." Paper presented at the Annual Meeting of the International Reading Association, New York City, May 13-16, 1975.

68. PEDERSON, CLARA A., DEBORAH MEIER, and ROBERT MCCRACKEN. "All About Reading." *Insights into Open Education* 7: 1-12; October 1974. (Grand Forks: North Dakota University, Center for Teaching and Learning.)

69. PIKULSKI, JOHN. "A Critical Review: Informal Reading Inventories." *The Reading Teacher* 28: 141-51; November 1974.

70. POWELL, WILLIAM R. "Monitoring Reading Behavior: Criteria for Performance." Paper presented at the Annual Meeting of the International Reading Association, Anaheim, California, May 1976.

71. RAYBURN, ELAINE. "An Exploration of the Cloze Procedure in Arithmetic Reading." Paper presented at the Annual Meeting of the Texas State Council of the International Reading Association, Houston, Texas, March 21-23, 1974.

72. ROBINSON, R. D. *An Introduction to the Cloze Procedure: An Annotated Bibliography.* Newark, Delaware: International Reading Association, 1972.

73. ROGERS, C. D. "Diagnosing Reading Needs Through the Telltale Error." *Reading Improvement* 11: 48-49; Winter 1974.

74. RUPLEY, WILLIAM H. "Informal Reading Diagnosis." *The Reading Teacher* 29: 106-107; October 1975.

75. SALTER, RUTH. "Resources for the Implementation of a Productivity Study in Education." Albany: New York State Education Department, Bureau of School and Cultural Research, April 1975.

76. SCHELL, L. M. "Promising Possibilities for Improving Comprehension." *Journal of Reading* 15: 415-24; March 1972.

77. VALMONT, WILLIAM J. "Creating Questions for Informal Reading Inventories." *The Reading Teacher* 25: 509-12; March 1972.

78. WALTER, RICHARD B. "History and the Development of the Informal Reading Inventory." Unpublished study prepared at Kean College of New Jersey, 1974.

79. WILLIAMSON, LEON E., and FREDA YOUNG. "The IRI and RMI Diagnostic Concepts Should be Synthesized." *Journal of Reading Behavior* 6: 183-94; July 1974.

80. WINDELL, IDAJEAN. "Development and Evaluation of a Module To Train Special Education Teacher Trainees To Determine a Pupil's Instructional Reading Level." Bloomington: Indiana University, Center for Innovation in Teaching the Handicapped, December 1975.

81. ZAESKE, ARNOLD. "Motor, Auditory, and Visual Development—A Taxonomy for Diagnosis and Training." Paper presented to the Annual Meeting of the Plains Regional Conference of the International Reading Association, St. Louis, Missouri, February 20-22, 1975.

82. ZINTZ, MILES V. *The Reading Process: The Teacher and the Learner.* Dubuque, Iowa: William C. Brown Company, 1975.

9. Reading as a Secondary School Subject
Dixie Potter Bjurstrom

WHAT do you mean you can't read the assignment? Of course you can read! You're in high school, aren't you!" and an annoyed high school teacher grumbles about the ineptness of elementary teachers. At the same time yet another student feels a surge of hopelessness and failure.

Content-Area Reading

Many such situations need not arise since the literature abounds with suggestions for aiding the content teacher to help those students whose reading skills are either minimal or below grade level.

Content reading—a review of the literature. Blossom (17) reported on an effective Arizona high school reading project in which the participating teachers wrote a glossary of terms specifically for their content areas, thus providing each class member with a mini-dictionary for mathematics, science, and the like. As a result, the dropout rate was reduced and reading levels were increased. In the same vein, Burmeister (24) found that learning was facilitated if content teachers taught reading skills prerequisite to an understanding of their content field. Estes and Staiger (53), for their part, reported on a 1973 consortium which sought to establish that concern with reading in subject areas was effectively met when reading instruction was made an integral part of each discipline.

Earle and Sanders (45) advised that teachers should give more direction than merely saying, "Read so-and-so pages for tomorrow"; while Cunningham and Shablak (38) reported on an actual process whereby teachers guided the reading of the assignment with specific directions, such as "Skip this page, read the third paragraph carefully, skim part four," and so on. Palmer (118) felt it necessary that every subject teacher of every level be prepared to help students meet new demands in reading and to develop the special strategies those demands require. Smith (140) called this approach "bookthinking," and added that students need to be shown how to take an active attitude about using books. Putnam (124) was among those advocating a program which helped students express the main idea(s) of a textbook assignment in concise statements.

Herber (77) and Robinson (127) published books that emphasized the teaching of reading in the content areas. Herber's book suggested ways to teach students how to read their content materials and increase their understanding of the content at the same time. Robinson emphasized helping classroom teachers improve their reading and study programs by guiding students in the acquisition of independent strategies for working with ideas in print.

Russell (132) sounded a note of controversy, however, by questioning whether reading can be taught in the content area by those teachers unwilling and untrained to do so. McDonald (106), on the other hand, contended that effective fusing of reading and content is possible in secondary level curricula but that it involves total faculty commitment. Axelrod (9) agreed that reading instruction must be the concern of all teachers in a school.

The importance of faculty commitment was supported by several writers. Bullerman and Franco (22) described an effective in-service program for teachers in Hillsborough County, Florida. Schleich (136) made the point that secondary schools must provide basic teacher training for secondary reading development as well as for ongoing in-service education. Criscuolo (35) believed that teachers are already demonstrating a healthy commitment to comprehensive reading programs and described the program in progress during 1975-76 at the New Haven Public Schools in Connecticut as an example.

Ahrendt and Haselton (3) cautioned that while teachers might have little interest in learning about reading per se, they are enthusiastic about learning how to make better use of materials written for their own content fields. Roe (128) advocated in-service workshops where content teachers are taught how to rewrite material for low achievers in reading. Duke and Powers (43) maintained that the key to reading success lies in recognizing just what the textual material being used demands, and devising ways to assure that the students are better able to cope with those demands. Bundy (23) reminded his readers that the most effective reading instruction occurs when the teacher adapts materials and instructional techniques to fit the unique needs of individual students. In a mild rebuff to teachers, Cassidy (27) said the difficulty with content area reading is not in developing workable and valid methods of reading instruction but in getting area teachers to implement those methods. He suggested that a reading specialist periodically visit the classrooms to demonstrate teaching strategies.

Weiss (156) agreed that if the reading teachers helped others realize the specificity of reading skills in various content areas they could then suggest useful methods and materials that would help teachers teach reading in their own classrooms. Although Rosewell (130) stated that few teachers believe "Every teacher is a teacher of reading," he firmly endorsed school-wide in-service programs to improve faulty reading instruction.

Because of the long-standing problem of providing basic reading skill instruction in the content areas, Landis, Jones, and Kennedy (95) suggested curricular modifications that would include secondary school reading. Adams and Shuman (1) agreed, adding that the main and most important ingredient in initiating a secondary school reading program is imaginative leadership within the secondary school. Sanders (133) concluded that common sense suggested that skills instruction be accompanied by a deliberate and concerted effort to "take the child where he or she is" and reverse the student's negative self-image.

"I'm a content specialist! I don't know anything about reading—and besides, that's the reading teacher's job!" Such phrases as these often reflect the frustrations of content teachers who do not know specifically how to incorporate reading techniques into their daily plans. Figure 1 provides a quick overview of numerous articles in specific subject areas which deal with reading in content areas.

Figure 1. Summary of Articles Treating Content-Area Reading

Driver Education
(135)	"Content Reading—They'll Like It"
(19)	"They Learn To Read in Auto I—Honest!"

English

(general)
(98)	"Conpass English: A Demonstration Project"
(141)	"English Teacher as Reading Teacher"

(movie)
(99)	"A Modern Modest Proposal: Read the Movie First"

(newspaper)
(146)	"Impressions of the Penny Press"
(51)	"What Happened on the Day You Were Born?"
(114)	*Newspaper in the Classroom Project*
(82)	"The Newspaper: A New Textbook Every Day—Part I"
(83)	"The Newspaper: A New Textbook Every Day—Part II"
(163)	"Using Your Daily Newspaper To Teach Remedial Reading"
(152)	"Using Your Daily Newspaper To Turn on the Resistant Reader"
(144)	"The Newspaper as a Tool for Teaching Kids To Read"
(16)	"The Athens Model and Results of a High Saturation Program in Newspaper Reading Skill"

Specific School Reading Programs

Program data from ERIC. The teaching of high school reading has been complicated by several issues. The most troublesome of these is that educators are not agreed on what exactly the reading process is. Giordano (71) said that individual teachers must establish what *they* wish to accomplish (objectives or goals) and then proceed to obtain fruition of them (methods or procedures), although many school systems specify goals *for* the teachers if one judges by their curriculum guides.

In recent years a substantial number of writers have delineated the work being done in their respective schools. In this context *Effective Reading Programs* (49), a publication of the ERIC Clearinghouse on Reading and Communication Skills, might be of particular interest to reading teachers and curriculum directors. This book describes 222 reading programs presumed to be of merit throughout the United States. Approximately 40 junior high and secondary programs are described under six headings: (a) program size and target population; (b) year started; (c) staff; (d) major features; (e) facilities, material, equipment; and (f) cost.[10]

Thirty-seven additional programs described in the elementary section also serve secondary students. In this reviewer's opinion, this is an especially good source of information on current, viable reading programs.

Bilingual and minority reading problems. The topic of minority and bilingual reading did not receive as much emphasis in the literature of the 1970's as might have been expected from widespread discussion of the topic. The teaching of reading to Spanish-speaking students, to American Indians, and to blacks was discussed in only a few articles.

Justin (86) studied the reading habits of Mexican-Americans and found a cultural bias against obtaining an education. It appeared that these youngsters live for the present, bow to authority, and have fatalistic attitudes about life—qualities not conducive to motivation in school. Garcia (68) studied Spanish-speaking youth in Chicago to determine whether knowing a second language helped or hurt mastery of English. He concluded that bilingualism, per se, was not detrimental to English language development.

Kimble and Davison (91) identified areas of specific needs in the reading levels of American Indians and developed a program based on rewards (for example, radios, watches, cameras) to improve performance. Martin (100) stated that blacks often have a negative self-image based on a white, middle-class oriented curriculum. She felt teachers often fallaciously believe that minority groups are economically disadvantaged and that they mistake "reading com-

[10] The publication also provides information on where and to whom to write for more extensive data.

petence" and "reading style" for dialectal interference. She was convinced that language experience reading is good for black high school students as well as elementary children. Rist (126) reported on a study in East St. Louis, Illinois, where black college students were employed to test the Rosenthal theory of the self-fulfilling prophecy. With high expectancy from these college students, gains were dramatic in the experimental group. Rist felt that the combination of black study material and the use of paraprofessionals provides the necessary ingredients for the formulation of a successful reading program in black urban schools. Knapp (93) stressed the need for college courses which would provide teachers with the necessary training and knowledge to understand and aid the linguistically different child.

SSR—sustained silent reading. A program which received several favorable reviews in the literature was SSR—Sustained Silent Reading. Initiated by Lyman C. Hunt, Jr., of the University of Vermont, this approach requires scheduled blocks of time (10 minutes or more) daily or weekly where everyone in the entire school can read. Principals, janitors, secretaries, and even the teachers read. Only the person designated to answer the phone and greet visitors is exempted from this planned activity.

McCracken (104) and Ganz and Theofield (67) reported on the proper methods for beginning SSR in a school. Petre (122) reported on the success of this program in 50 schools in Maryland where everyone read 35 minutes daily. He reminded those interested in implementing such a program that (a) there has to be a daily time for all to read, (b) everyone is allowed to select his or her own material, and (c) administrators and teachers have to read, too. In addition, a committee helped to select paperbacks that would create greater diversity among materials read and help facilitate the program.

Remedial reading. "Students shouldn't enter high school until they can read" is a sentiment that probably is expressed by a substantial cohort of high school teachers. The fact remains that many young people who read poorly are enrolled. The problem thus becomes one of providing suitable experiences for the disabled reader.

Bachner (11) believed that a successful remedial reading program should be based on a balanced investment of able teachers and good materials. Kelly (89) agreed but expressed caution since teachers often use other criteria (for example, deviant behavior) rather than ability to read in selecting nominees for remedial reading. Williamson (160) stressed that the special reading teacher is in a unique position to improve students' self-concepts—an area which presumably correlates highly with reading achievement. Chapman (28) insisted that teachers should weave together (a) specific reading comprehension skills,

(b) materials in the content area, and (c) methods using all modalities—hearing, seeing, and body movement.

Additional specific remedial suggestions and programs were published by several writers. Cohn (31) suggested the pairing of remedial students as an aid in the fulfillment of certain emotional needs related to reading. Wulffson (165) recommended using a recorded Bob Dylan lyric to help provide correct identification of words. Ivarie (80) described a matrix for use with disabled readers, while Gates (69) told of the successful role of a "read-mobile" in which she traveled from school to school in order to provide "the right book for the right child at the right time" (69: 90).

On the less positive side, Bogart and Houk (18) worried about the future of remedial reading because of the lack of what they deemed a national commitment to reading and the necessary funds for curriculum reform. Harker (74) felt that too much emphasis is placed on increasing "motivation" and not enough on teaching the reading skills necessary for successful reading. Evans (54) doubted if remedial programs are a solution for the disabled reader. He added that benefits, as indicated by longitudinal studies, are often lost and suggested that preventive measures be sought. Steinacher (145) contended that instruction in "reading flexibility" is so little supported by available research that educators could not justify its being taught.

Additional categories of interest. A number of articles considered such topics as individualized reading and reading resource centers. Figure 2 gives an overview of some of these articles.

Specific research. In 1969, Early (47) reported that secondary reading programs were limited, and that the effectiveness of total reading programs in high school had not been evaluated properly. Scattered research in developmental and remedial or corrective reading, however, suggested that such programs had positive effects and that in-service programs proved helpful. In a companion report the following month, Moore (112) indicated that teachers' success in motivating students to read needs to be researched. Two years later Wunderlich and Bradtmueller (166) reported that most secondary teachers cannot predict accurately the reading levels of their students.

Fiedler (59) attempted to analyze reading behaviors of remedial readers after an interval of four years during which they received no additional help. Her analysis suggested that students change their attitudes toward reading as their skills increase but that this is not likely to be reflected in improved grades. Fiedler also emphasized that reading teachers' efforts have a more positive effect than is generally realized. In 1973, the Willermans (158) reported on a study designed to discover whether individual student-teacher "motivational conferences" could increase both reading achievement and the extent of independent

Figure 2. Summary of Articles in Other Categories

Individualized Reading
>Fleitz and Harmon (60): "Free Reading Is a Simple Idea, But It Works!"
>Allan and MacDonald (5): "Recreational Reading and the Reluctant Reader"
>Elza and Owatt (50): "Turning to Individualized Instruction: Reading in the Round"
>Means (108): "Nine Years of Individualized Reading"
>Meints (109): "The Task System in an Individualized Reading Class"

Reading—An Elective
>Kettlewell and Gore (90): "Readings for Teens: An Elective Unit"
>Hodges (79): "Reading as an Elective in the English Program"
>Kummer (94): "Reading as an Elective"

Reading Resource Center
>Schottenfeld and Lang (137): "Reading Resource Center: Programs and Personnel in Modular Scheduling"
>Bennie (15): "Pupil Attitudes Toward Individually Prescribed Lab Programs"
>Pendrak (119): "Performance Contracting and the Secondary Reading Lab"
>Angello et al. (8): "So You Want To Start a Reading Skills Center for Secondary Students"
>Urbana, Illinois, School District 116 (151): "Urbana Junior High School Reading Laboratory"
>Frankel (61): "Learning Centers for Reading in Junior High"

Miscellany
>Donze (41): "Open-End Reading Program"
>Dramer (42): "Self-Contained Reading-Oriented Classes in Secondary Schools"
>Wiggins (157): "The Reading Teacher: Heart of the Curriculum"
>Niensted (115): "Pupil Self-Help in Whole Class Setting"
>Reidelberger (125): "Serendipity—A Reading Program"
>Baer and Fisher (12): "Let Me Read!: Five Techniques That Worked for Us"
>Edwards (48): "Panorama: A Study Technique"
>Kline (92): "Five Sites in Search of the Word"
>Criscuolo (36): "Quality Reading Programs at Bargain Basement Prices"
>Criscuolo (37): "Seven Creative Reading Programs for the Secondary Schools"
>Gillespie (70): "A Classroom Experiment in 'Last Chance' Reading"
>Coleman (32): "The Optimum List and Reading for Meaning"
>Janek (81): "Reading the Media: Unit Plans"
>Breda (21): "Confronting Reading Problems in Senior High"
>Clayton (30): "Success Story of an Inner-City School"
>Shuman (138): "Of Course He Can Read—He's in High School!"
>Niensted (116): "Read + Write + Talk = Progress"
>Rossman (131): "How One High School Set Up a Reading Program for 500 Students"

reading by ninth grade students. They inferred that teacher-student motivational conferences are generally ineffective. Mavrogenes (101) attempted to explore the use of psycholinguistic knowledge to improve secondary reading.

In 1975 Thompson (149) scanned four decades of research in individualized reading. His findings revealed that individualized reading programs apparently facilitate reading achievement to the same extent as does a basal reading program, and that individualized reading programs often increase reading achievement. He added that individualized reading has been used successfully at practically all grade levels. In the same year, Wirt (162) reported the results of field work in six diagnostic/prescriptive reading projects in and around Santa Monica, California. The adaptations and implementation problems observed in these projects strongly suggested that such an approach to organizing reading instruction requires behavioral changes in teachers and also demands substantial extra resources.

The *Reading Research Quarterly* annually summarizes studies in the category "Teaching Reading—High School." Authors and titles of these articles are given in Figure 3 for those interested in specific research reports.

Surveys. Early's (46) survey of reading in the 1970's indicated that little change had occurred in the past three decades. "In 1972 as in 1942," she wrote, "we are still debating the merits of special reading services and urging the whole school faculty to teach reading in the content fields" (46: 364). A few of her disconcerting changes: (a) students today read less, (b) teachers use textbooks less since students can't read them anyway, (c) reading teachers are reluctant to try the open classroom approach, and (d) middle schools seem more anxious to teach reading in new and better ways than do secondary schools.

In 1973 Freed (64) reported that secondary schools are not providing individual reading programs for all pupils needing them, and that most states do not require reading courses for certification of teachers. In 1974 the Roeders (129) did a nationwide survey to determine the extent to which teachers were prepared to cope with reading problems. At the secondary level 79.1 percent of the teacher institutions did not require a reading methods course. The Roeders recommended that: (a) all junior high and secondary teachers be required to take one reading methods course, (b) in-service workshops are needed, (c) reading consultants should work with classroom teachers, and (d) policy should require that every teacher be a teacher of reading.

Boyle (20) selected a small sample of Florida high schools to illustrate the effect of federal aid on initiating and developing programs. The two major obstacles for reading programs most often cited in her study were a lack of funds and a need for a high quality of teaching.

In 1975 Hill (78) surveyed reading activity in Western New York. He found the greatest increase in active reading programs to be in corrective and

Figure 3. Teaching Reading—High School
(Reported in *Reading Research Quarterly*)

1971

Andrews (7): "Directed Reading Question and Cognitive Organizer: Comparative Effect on Reading Comprehension"

Estes, Mills, and Barron (52): "Three Methods of Introducing Students to a Reading-Learning Task in Two Content Subjects"

Earle (44): "Use of the Structured Overview in Mathematics Classes"

1972

Harris and Ream (76): "A Program To Improve Study Habits of High-School Students"

Gwaltney (73): "An Evaluation of a Summer Reading Improvement Course for Disadvantaged High School Students"

1973

Williams and Stevens (159): "Understanding Paragraph Structure"

Sinatra (139): "Summer Reading Program on a Point Reinforcer System"

1974

Galloway (66): "How Secondary Students and Teachers Read Textbooks"

Alley, Davison, Kelley, and Kimble (6): "A Reading Improvement Strategy"

1975

Kaplan and Rothkopf (87): "Instructional Objectives as Directions to Learners: Effect of Passage Length and Amount of Objective-Relevant Content"

McCormick and Williams (103): "Effects of a Compensatory Program on Self-Report, Achievement, and Aspiration Level of 'Disadvantaged' High School Students"

Murphy (113): "Academic Implications of a High School Entrance Examination for Economically Disadvantaged and Other Students"

Snider (142): "Cognitive and Affective Learning Outcomes Resulting from the Use of Behavioral Objectives in Teaching Poetry"

---

remedial reading classes. In addition, he learned, developmental classes were offered most frequently at the seventh and eighth grade levels.

Petre (123) stated that the actual illiteracy rate reported by the 1970 U.S. Census was 1 percent, and it continues to decline. He stated that the reading priorities of the seventies should be: (a) to eliminate illiteracy, (b) to improve all reading instruction in order to raise achievement, and (c) to refine the existing reading curriculum to meet the needs of society.

Miscellaneous Reading Inquiries and Opinions

General information for teachers. The Right To Read program in 1974 claimed that almost 19 million adults and seven million children could not read.

Shuman (138) countered that this situation exists because educators are trying to make secondary schooling available to everyone. He proposed six steps for helping the disabled reader:

1. Encourage
2. Decrease assignments
3. Utilize group activities
4. Tape important factual records
5. Get students to want to read and put pressure on themselves
6. Analyze words in papers, ads, magazines, and the like for *good* vocabulary building.

"I read it but I don't understand it" is a complaint frequently voiced by students. Harker (75) presented a task analysis approach involving tasks in literal, inferential, and/or critical understanding. Peters (121) saw the need for a comprehensive approach and utilized a model portraying the content teacher as the focus, with reading teachers available on call.

Axelrod (10) questioned whether students don't have a right *not* to read, and conjectured whether teachers shouldn't examine themselves before dealing with students and reaching decisions on their reading experiences.

Goodman (72) maintained that children learn to pay attention to the written language in their environment which has meaning for them. Ferguson (58) believed a student who is given more freedom—as in an independent reading program—is naturally more motivated toward reading what he or she wants to read. Mertz (110) further agreed that teaching can best help students by recognizing their special needs and interests.

Carlsen (25), in 1975, reported a substantial change in adolescent reading habits. It appeared that the interest had changed from books about "doing your own thing" to books about "getting it all together." In addition, Algra and Fillbrandt (4) cautioned that what the teacher does in the classroom affects students' interest in reading. In 1976 Fader (55) emphasized that, despite the time and money invested, many students still don't read, or read poorly. He also felt that parents no longer provide reading models in the home since many prefer to watch television.

Frederick (63) explicitly warned that teachers should constantly ask themselves, "What can my students do after they've been in my class that they couldn't do before?" A student whom he cited commented, "The poor readers should have the same opportunities of wide choices as anyone else. Once they find the right book, they'll read. After all, they're human, too" (63: 47).

Evaluation of tests, texts, and reading programs. Farr and Roser (56) commented on the pros and cons of testing in the field of reading. They suggested that committees study: (a) the administration of such tests, (b) the use made of tests, (c) policies regarding the release of test information, and (d) interpretation of normed scores. Mavrogenes, Winkley, Hanson, and Vacca (102) published a "Concise Guide to Standardized Secondary and College Reading Tests" in the *Journal of Reading* in 1974. The breakdown they used included: (a) Survey Tests—11, (b) Analytical Tests—11, (c) Diagnostic Tests—13, and (d) Special Tests—23. The following categories provided comprehensive information on each of the 58 tests: test and publisher, what it measures (usually subtests), levels (grades), date of publication or latest revision, time (minutes), and a brief résumé of evaluation.

McDonald and Moorman (107) reported on the significance of criterion-referenced testing as a fast-growing technique for evaluating school achievement today, while Vaughan (154) emphasized that readability has to be ". . . one of today's hottest topics in reading, if not in education" (154: 635). His article reported on the discrepancies between the Dale-Chall and Fry scores and SMOG scores for readability levels of texts. McCuaig and Hutchings (105) argued for the use of Fry's graph in determining the reading difficulties of books, and Barry and Stevenson (13) designated a Fortran computer program as the most accurate measure of readability of textbooks using the Dale-Chall formula.

Strong (147) maintained that assessing skills in reading is not a particularly mysterious process; but he did acknowledge that it requires the exercise of common sense and some organization of diagnostic materials and procedures. Winkeljohann (161) presented and explained criteria developed by NCTE Committee on Curriculum bulletins for the evaluation of reading programs:

1. Does the program provide ways for the teacher to determine readiness?

2. Does the reading program suggest procedures to help teachers develop students' reading skills?

3. Does the program recognize that a total reading program reaches beyond the development of basic reading skills?

4. Does the reading program relate the skills of reading to the total or regional program?

The Pennsylvania State Department of Education (120) designed an evaluation instrument with questions for the learner, staff, community, instruction, materials, environment, time, evaluation, and budget.

Wood (164) listed guidelines to help expose the inherent priorities and values of the operation. Her suggestions were:

1. Talk with the teachers who spend the money and run the program. Find out what kind of people they are.

2. Come into the classroom and look around.

3. Look at and listen to the students.

4. Talk to the parents.

5. Talk to the counselors and the other teachers.

Closing on a positive note. In March 1976 Tuinman, Rowls, and Farr (150) attempted to ascertain the reading achievement of youth in the United States. They concluded: (a) there was steady improvement in reading achievement from 1940 to 1965; (b) after 1965 the picture was less clear, though the children of the past decade read significantly better than the children of 20 years ago; (c) it is extremely difficult for anyone interested in evaluating trends in literacy to obtain adequate data (therefore, one wonders where the information that illustrated declining literacy rates was obtained); and (d) there may have been a slight decline in reading achievement from 1965 to 1975.

In short, there is no reason for en masse pessimism, the authors said. They were convinced that ". . . anyone who says that he *knows* that literacy is decreasing is ignoring the data. Such a person is at best unscholarly and at worst dishonest" (150: 463).

References

1. ADAMS, ANNE H., and R. BAIRD SHUMAN. "Singing To Build an Atmosphere for Secondary School Reading." *Journal of Reading* 16: 20-24; October 1972.

2. AHRENDT, KENNETH M., and SHIRLEY S. HASELTON. "Essential Reading Skills in Bookkeeping." *Journal of Reading* 16: 314-17; January 1973.

3. AHRENDT, KENNETH M., and SHIRLEY S. HASELTON. "Informal Skills Assessment for Individualized Instruction." *Journal of Reading* 17: 52-57; 1973.

4. ALGRA, CECELIA, and JAMES FILLBRANDT. "A Study of Student Reading Interests." *Reading Improvement* 8: 39-42; Fall 1971.

5. ALLAN, T. L., and CATHERINE MACDONALD. "Recreational Reading and the Reluctant Reader." *Teaching English* 4: 3-5; May 1971.

6. ALLEY, ROBERT D., RONALD G. DAVISON, WALTER T. KELLEY, and RAYMOND L. KIMBLE. "A Reading Improvement Strategy." *Journal of American Indian Education* 8: 14-20; January 1974.

7. ANDREWS, L. "Directed Reading Question and Cognitive Organizer: Comparative Effect on Reading Comprehension." *Research in the Teaching of English* 5: 79-83; 1971.

8. ANGELLO, NANCY, et al. "So You Want To Start a Reading Skills Center for Secondary Students." Olympia: Washington Office of the State Superintendent of Public Instruction, August 1975.

9. AXELROD, JEROME. "A Few Recommendations on How To Conduct In-Service Reading Instruction for Content-Area Teachers." *English Journal* 64: 81-82; February 1975.

10. AXELROD, JEROME. "Open Door or Closed Admissions?" *Journal of Reading* 15: 593-96; May 1972.

11. BACHNER, SAUL. "Teaching Reading and Literature to the Disadvantaged." *Journal of Reading* 18: 292-97; January 1975.

12. BAER, CONSTANCE JOAN, and LINDA RUTH FISHER. "Let Me Read!: Five Techniques That Worked for Us." *Journal of Reading* 16: 227-35; December 1972.

13. BARRY, JEANNE GARDNER, and TIMOTHY E. STEVENSON. "Using a Computer To Calculate the Dale-Chall Formula." *Journal of Reading* 19: 218-22; December 1975.

14. BECKER, GEORGE J., and JOAN F. CURRY. "What Do You Do When the Machines Break Down?" *Journal of Reading* 19: 451-54; March 1976.

15. BENNIE, FRANCES. "Pupil Attitudes Toward Individually Prescribed Lab Programs." *Journal of Reading* 17: 108-12; November 1973.

16. BERRYMAN, CHARLES. "The Athens Model and Results of a High Saturation Program in Newspaper Reading Skill." Paper presented at the Annual Meeting of the International Reading Association, New York City, May 13-16, 1975.

17. BLOSSOM, GRACE A. "The Tolleson School Reading Project." *Reading Improvement* 10: 30-31; Winter 1973.

18. BOGART, CARLOTTA, and ANNELLE S. HOUK. "What Is the Next Step?" *Journal of Reading* 14: 531-36, 582; May 1971.

19. BOSANKO, ROBERT G. "They Learn To Read in Auto I—Honest!" *Journal of Reading* 19: 33-35; October 1975.

20. BOYLE, SUSAN. "Trends in Florida High School Reading Programs." *Journal of Reading* 14: 299-301; February 1971.

21. BREDA, W. B. "Confronting Reading Problems in Senior High." *NASSP Bulletin* 60: 114-15; January 1976.

22. BULLERMAN, MARY, and E. J. FRANCO. "Teach Content Material But Teach Reading, Too!" *Journal of Reading* 19: 21-23; October 1975.

23. BUNDY, LESTER L. "Our Current Reading Instruction Is Inadequate." *The Reading Teacher* 27: 774-77; May 1974.

24. BURMEISTER, LOU E. *Reading Strategies for Secondary School Teachers.* Reading, Massachusetts: Addison-Wesley Publishing Co., 1974.

25. CARLSEN, G. R. "Big Change in Adolescent Reading." *Intellect* 104: 8; July/August 1975.

26. CARNEY, JOHN J., and WILLIAM LOSINGER. "Reading and Content in Technical-Vocational Education." *Journal of Reading* 20: 14-17; October 1976.

27. CASSIDY, JACK. "Project C.A.R.E. (Content Area Reading Enrichment)." *Journal of Reading* 17: 192-94; December 1973.

28. CHAPMAN, CARITA A. "Teaching Comprehension to the Disabled Reader." *Journal of Reading* 20: 37-42; October 1976.

29. CIANI, ALFRED J., and DONALD E. HOGUE. "How To Help Industrial Arts Students with Reading." *Industrial Education* 65: 32-33; October 1976.

30. CLAYTON, M. S. "Success Story of an Inner-City School." *Today's Education* 60: 43-44, 46; September-October 1976.

31. COHN, MAXINE D. "Pairing of Remedial Students." *Journal of Reading* 14: 109-12; November 1970.

32. COLEMAN, E. B. "The Optimum List and Reading for Meaning." *Theory into Practice* 14: 195-207; June 1975.

33. CONROY, MICHAEL T. "Project Bookmark: Reading and Graphic Arts." *Journal of Reading* 15: 60-61; October 1971.

34. CORNETT, CHARLES F. "Reading for Fun . . . in Science Class?" *Science Teacher* 42: 58-59; May 1975.

35. CRISCUOLO, NICHOLAS P. "An Interdisciplinary Approach to Reading." *Journal of Reading* 19: 488-93; March 1976.

36. CRISCUOLO, NICHOLAS P. "Quality Reading Programs at Bargain Basement Prices." *Journal of Reading* 18: 127-30; November 1974.

37. CRISCUOLO, NICHOLAS P. "Seven Creative Reading Programs for the Secondary Schools." *English Journal* 64: 76-80; February 1975.

38. CUNNINGHAM, DICK, and SCOTT L. SHABLAK. "Selective Reading Guide-O-Rama: The Content Teacher's Best Friend." *Journal of Reading* 18: 380-82; February 1975.

39. DERBY, THOMAS L. "Informal Testing in Vo-Ed Reading." *Journal of Reading* 18: 541-43; April 1975.

40. DEVAN, STEVEN, ROZALYN KLEIN, and TERRENCE V. MURPHY. "Priming—A Method To Equalize Differences Between High and Low Achievement Students." *Journal of Reading* 19: 143-46; November 1975.

41. DONZE, SISTER MARY TERESE. "Open-End Reading Program." *Journal of Reading* 14: 293-98; February 1971.

42. DRAMER, DAN. "Self-Contained Reading-Oriented Classes in Secondary Schools." *Journal of Reading* 14: 365-68, 425; March 1971.

43. DUKE, CHARLES, and ANNE POWERS. "Reading in the Content Area." *The Clearing House* 47: 221-26; December 1973.

44. EARLE, R. A. "Use of the Structured Overview in Mathematics Classes." In: H. L. Herber and P. L. Sanders, editors. *Research in Reading in the Content Area: First Year Report.* Englewood Cliffs, New Jersey: Prentice-Hall, Inc., 1969. pp. 49-58.

45. EARLE, RICHARD A., and PETER L. SANDERS. "Individualized Reading Assignments." *Journal of Reading* 16: 550-55; April 1973.

46. EARLY, MARGARET J. "Taking Stock: Secondary School Reading in the 70's." *Journal of Reading* 16: 364-73; February 1973.

47. EARLY, MARGARET J. "What Does Research in Reading Reveal—About Successful Reading Programs?" *English Journal* 48: 534-47; April 1969.

48. EDWARDS, PETER. "Panorama: A Study Technique." *Journal of Reading* 17: 132-35; November 1973.

49. *Effective Reading Programs: Summaries of 222 Selected Programs.* Urbana, Illinois: ERIC Clearinghouse on Reading and Communication Skills, National Council of Teachers of English, October 1975.

50. ELZA, BETTY, and DIANA OWATT. "Turning to Individualized Instruction: Reading in the Round." *Journal of Reading* 19: 125-27; November 1975.

51. EPSTEIN, IRA D. "What Happened on the Day You Were Born?" *Journal of Reading* 20: 400-402; February 1977.

52. ESTES, T. H., D. C. MILLS, and R. F. BARRON. "Three Methods of Introducing Students to a Reading-Learning Task in Two Content Subjects." In: H. L. Herber and P. L. Sanders, editors. *Research in Reading in the Content Area: First Year Report.* Englewood Cliffs, New Jersey: Prentice-Hall, Inc., 1969. pp. 40-48.

53. ESTES, THOMAS H., and RALPH C. STAIGER. "IRA Project Conpass: An Overview." *Journal of Reading* 16: 520-24; April 1973.

54. EVANS, HOWARD M. "Remedial Reading in Secondary Schools—Still a Matter of Faith." *Journal of Reading* 16: 111-14; November 1972.

55. FADER, DANIEL. "Why Students Still Don't Read." *Media and Methods* 12: 26-27; March 1976.

56. FARR, ROGER, and NANCY L. ROSER. "Reading Assessment: A Look at Problems and Issues." *Journal of Reading* 17: 592-99; May 1974.

57. FEIRER, JOHN L. "Teaching Reading Is Everybody's Business." *Industrial Education* 65: 4; October 1976.

58. FERGUSON, SHELA. "Revolution in the Classroom: Underground English." *The Clearing House* 47: 47-51; September 1972.

59. FIEDLER, MARGARET. "Did the Clinic Help?" *Journal of Reading* 16: 25-29; October 1972.

60. FLEITZ, JEANETTE, and RONALD HARMON. "Free Reading Is a Simple Idea, But It Works!" *Arizona English Bulletin* 11: 6-8; April 1969.

61. FRANKEL, JILL CATHERINE. "Learning Centers for Reading in Junior High." *Journal of Reading* 19: 243-46; December 1975.

62. FRANKEL, JILL CATHERINE. "Reading Skills Through Social Studies Content and Student Involvement." *Journal of Reading* 18: 23-26; October 1974.

63. FREDERICK, E. COSTON. "Will the Real Reading Teacher Please Stand Up?" *English Journal* 63: 45-47; November 1974.

64. FREED, BARBARA F. "Secondary Reading—State of the Art." *Journal of Reading* 17: 195-201; December 1973.

65. FUHR, MORTON L. "The Typewriter and Retarded Readers." *Journal of Reading* 16: 30-32; October 1972.

66. GALLOWAY, PRISCILLA. "How Secondary Students and Teachers Read Textbooks." *Journal of Reading* 17: 216-19; December 1973.

67. GANZ, PAUL, and MARY B. THEOFIELD. "Suggestions for Starting SSR." *Journal of Reading* 17: 614-16; May 1974.

68. GARCIA, RICARDO L. "Mexican American Bilingualism and English Language Development." *Journal of Reading* 18: 467-73; March 1974.

69. GATES, KAREN M. "A Readmobile Takes to the Road." *Journal of Reading* 14: 89-93; November 1970.

70. GILLESPIE, BONITA M. "A Classroom Experiment in 'Last Chance' Reading." *Journal of Reading* 18: 391-94; February 1975.

71. GIORDANO, GERARD. "The Teaching of Reading—Art or Science?" *Theory into Practice* 14: 208-12; June 1975.

72. GOODMAN, YETTA. "Everyone Learns To Read." *English Journal* 64: 8-9; November 1975.

73. GWALTNEY, WAYNE K. "An Evaluation of a Summer Reading Improvement Course for Disadvantaged High School Students." *Journal of Reading Behavior* 3: 14-21; Fall 1970-71.

74. HARKER, W. JOHN. "Materials for Problem Readers: Why Aren't They Working?" *Journal of Reading* 18: 451-54; March 1975.

75. HARKER, W. JOHN. "Teaching Comprehension: A Task Analysis Approach." *Journal of Reading* 16: 379-82; February 1973.

76. HARRIS, MARY B., and FRED REAM. "A Program To Improve Study Habits of High-School Students." *Psychology in the Schools* 9: 325-30; July 1972.

77. HERBER, HAROLD L. *Teaching Reading in Content Areas.* Englewood Cliffs, New Jersey: Prentice-Hall, Inc., 1970.

78. HILL, WALTER. "Secondary Reading Active in Western New York: A Survey." *Journal of Reading* 19: 13-19; October 1975.

79. HODGES, PAULINE. "Reading as an Elective in the English Program." *Journal of Reading* 18: 30-33; October 1974.

80. IVARIE, JUDITH J. "Programming for Individualization in the Junior High School." *Journal of Reading* 20: 295-300; January 1977.

81. JANEK, NANCY. "Reading the Media: Unit Plans." *Theory into Practice* 14: 213-19; June 1975.

82. JOHNSON, LAURA S. "The Newspaper: A New Textbook Every Day—Part I." *Journal of Reading* 13: 107-12, 164; November 1969.

83. JOHNSON, LAURA S. "The Newspaper: A New Textbook Every Day—Part II." *Journal of Reading* 13: 203-206, 240-45; December 1969.

84. JOHNSTON, JOYCE D. "The Reading Teacher in the Vocational Classroom." *Journal of Reading* 18: 27-29; October 1974.

85. JONES, LINDA. "Games, Games, Games—and Reading Class." *Journal of Reading* 15: 41-46; October 1971.

86. JUSTIN, NEAL. "Mexican-American Reading Habits and Their Cultural Basis." *Journal of Reading* 16: 467-73; March 1973.

87. KAPLAN, ROBERT, and ERNST Z. ROTHKOPF. "Instructional Objectives as Directions to Learners: Effect of Passage Length and Amount of Objective-Relevant Content." *Journal of Educational Psychology* 64: 448-56; June 1974.

88. KELLEY, DANIEL J. "Program Design for a Vo-Ed Reading Center." *Journal of Reading* 19: 121-24; November 1975.

89. KELLY, DELOS H. "The Role of Teachers' Nominations in the Perpetuation of Deviant Adolescent Careers." *Education* 96: 209-17; Spring 1976.

90. KETTLEWELL, GAIL B., and ROBENA S. GORE. "Readings for Teens: An Elective Unit." *Journal of Reading* 14: 309-15; February 1971.

91. KIMBLE, RAYMOND L., and RONALD G. DAVISON. "Reading Improvement for Disadvantaged American Indian Youth." *Journal of Reading* 15: 342-46; February 1972.

92. KLINE, LLOYD W. "Five Sites in Search of the Word." *Journal of Reading* 17: 444-48; March 1974.

93. KNAPP, MARGARET O. "Black Dialect and Reading: What Teachers Need To Know." *Journal of Reading* 19: 231-35; December 1975.

94. KUMMER, ROBERT. "Reading as an Elective." *Journal of Reading* 19: 640-43; May 1976.

95. LANDIS, JOHN, ROBERT W. JONES, and LARRY D. KENNEDY. "Curricular Modification for Secondary School Reading." *Journal of Reading* 16: 374-78; February 1973.

96. LEES, FRED. "Mathematics and Reading." *Journal of Reading* 19: 621-26; May 1976.

97. MAFFEI, ANTHONY C. "Reading Analysis in Mathematics." *Journal of Reading* 16: 546-49; April 1973.

98. MANZO, ANTHONY V. "Conpass English: A Demonstration Project." *Journal of Reading* 16: 539-45; April 1973.

99. MARCUS, FRED W. "A Modern Modest Proposal: Read the Movie First." *English Journal* 63: 94-97; November 1974.

100. MARTIN, RUBY W. "Realities and Fallacies of Teaching Reading to Black High School Students." *Journal of Reading* 18: 445-50; March 1975.

101. MAVROGENES, NANCY A. "Using Psycholinguistic Knowledge To Improve Secondary Reading." *Journal of Reading* 18: 280-86; January 1975.

102. MAVROGENES, NANCY A., CAROL K. WINKLEY, EARL HANSON, and RICHARD T. VACCA. "Concise Guide to Standardized Secondary and College Reading Tests." *Journal of Reading* 18: 12-22; October 1974.

103. MCCORMICK, MARIJO R., and JUANITA H. WILLIAMS. "Effects of a Compensatory Program on Self-Report, Achievement, and Aspiration Level of 'Disadvantaged' High School Students." *Journal of Negro Education* 43: 47-52; Winter 1974.

104. MCCRACKEN, ROBERT A. "Initiating Sustained Silent Reading." *Journal of Reading* 14: 521-24, 582-83; May 1971.

105. MCCUAIG, SUSANNAH M., and BARTON HUTCHINGS. "Using Fry's Graph To Describe the Variation of Readability." *Journal of Reading* 18: 298-300; January 1975.

106. McDONALD, THOMAS F. "An All School Secondary Reading Program." *Journal of Reading* 14: 553-58; May 1971.

107. McDONALD, THOMAS F., and GARY B. MOORMAN. "Criterion Referenced Testing for Functional Literacy." *Journal of Reading* 17: 363-66; February 1974.

108. MEANS, HARRISON J. "Nine Years of Individualized Reading." *Journal of Reading* 20: 144-49; November 1976.

109. MEINTS, DONALD W. "The Task System in an Individualized Reading Class." *Journal of Reading* 20: 301-304; January 1977.

110. MERTZ, MAIA PANK. "Understanding the Adolescent Reader." *Theory into Practice* 14: 179-85; June 1975.

111. MITCHELL, GERTRUDE E. "Welcome Back, Writing." *American Education* 12: 15-20; October 1976.

112. MOORE, WALTER J. "What Does Research in Reading Reveal—About Reading in the Content Fields?" *English Journal* 58: 707-18; May 1969.

113. MURPHY, MAUREEN CARTWRIGHT. "Academic Implications of a High School Entrance Examination for Economically Disadvantaged and Other Students." *Journal of Educational Research* 67: 303-306; March 1974.

114. *Newspaper in the Classroom Project, Teacher's Guide.* 1972. Available from *The Tennessean,* 1100 Broadway, Nashville, Tennessee 37203.

115. NIENSTED, SERENA. "Pupil Self-Help in Whole Class Setting." *Journal of Reading* 15: 222-26; December 1971.

116. NIENSTED, SERENA. "Read + Write + Talk = Progress." *Journal of Reading* 20: 305-309; January 1977.

117. PALMER, WILLIAM S. "Conpass Social Studies: Suggestions for Improvement." *Journal of Reading* 16: 529-38; April 1973.

118. PALMER, WILLIAM S. "Teaching Reading in Content Areas." *Journal of Reading* 19: 43-51; October 1975.

119. PENDRAK, MICHAEL. "Performance Contracting and the Secondary Reading Lab." *Journal of Reading* 17: 453-56; March 1974.

120. Pennsylvania State Department of Education. "Criteria for Excellence in Reading: An Evaluation Scale." Harrisburg, Pennsylvania: Bureau of Curriculum Services, 1975.

121. PETERS, CHARLES W. "How To Get More Comprehensive Reading Programs at the Secondary Level." *Journal of Reading* 20: 513-19; January 1977.

122. PETRE, RICHARD M. "Reading Breaks Make It in Maryland." *Journal of Reading* 15: 191-94; December 1971.

123. PETRE, RICHARD M. "The 70's: Decade of Achievement?" *Journal of Reading* 16: 200-206; December 1972.

124. PUTNAM, LILLIAN R. "Don't Tell Them To Do It . . . Show Them How." *Journal of Reading* 18: 41-43; October 1974.

125. REIDELBERGER, HELEN. "Serendipity—A Reading Program." *Journal of Reading* 15: 584-89; May 1972.

126. RIST, RAY C. "Black Studies and Paraprofessionals—A Prescription for Ailing Reading Programs in Urban Black Schools." *Journal of Reading* 14: 525-30, 583; May 1971.

127. ROBINSON, H. ALAN. *Teaching Reading and Study Strategies: The Content Areas.* Boston, Massachusetts: Allyn and Bacon, Inc., 1975.

128. ROE, BETTY DANIEL. "Teacher Prepared Material for Slow Readers." *Journal of Reading* 15: 277-79; January 1972.

129. ROEDER, HAROLD H., and MARCIA A. ROEDER. "1,000,000 Reasons for Improving Preparation of Secondary Teachers." *Journal of Reading* 17: 604-607; May 1974.

130. ROSEWELL, PAUL T. "We All Teach Reading." *The Clearing House* 48: 213-17; December 1973.

131. ROSSMAN, JEAN F. "How One High School Set Up a Reading Program for 500 Students." *Journal of Reading* 20: 393-97; February 1977.

132. RUSSELL, SHELDON N. "A Crucial Problem Facing Secondary Education." *Journal of Reading* 17: 600-603; May 1974.

133. SANDERS, PETER. "Reading and the English Teacher." *English Journal* 63: 59-60; September 1974.

134. SARACENO, JOSEPH A., and ANGELINA C. PISCITELLO. "A Play! A Homemade Play!" *Journal of Reading* 17: 44-46; October 1973.

135. SARTAIN, HARRY W. "Content Reading—They'll Like It." *Journal of Reading* 17: 47-51; October 1973.

136. SCHLEICH, MIRIAM. "Groundwork for Better Reading in Content Areas." *Journal of Reading* 15: 119-26; November 1971.

137. SCHOTTENFELD, LORRAINE, and FLORENCE MAGGIE LANG. "Reading Resource Center: Programs and Personnel in Modular Scheduling." *Journal of Reading* 17: 104-107; November 1973.

138. SHUMAN, R. BAIRD. "Of Course He Can Read—He's in High School!" *Journal of Reading* 19: 36-42; October 1975.

139. SINATRA, RICHARD C. "Summer Reading Program on a Point Reinforcer System." *Journal of Reading* 16: 395-400; February 1973.

140. SMITH, CARL BERNARD. "Teaching Reading in the Secondary School." *Educational Leadership* 33: 509-12; April 1976.

141. SMITH, RICHARD J. "English Teacher as Reading Teacher." *Journal of Reading* 16: 245-50; December 1972.

142. SNIDER, SARAH J. "Cognitive and Affective Learning Outcomes Resulting from the Use of Behavioral Objectives in Teaching Poetry." *Journal of Educational Research* 48: 333-38; May-June 1975.

143. SOLOMON, BERNARD. "The Television Reading Program." *Language Arts* 53: 135; February 1976.

144. SOVERLY, RON, et al. "The Newspaper as a Tool for Teaching Kids To Read." *Phi Delta Kappan* 57: 260-61; December 1975.

145. STEINACHER, RICHARD. "Reading Flexibility: Dilemma and Solution." *Journal of Reading* 15: 143-50; November 1972.

146. STOCKS, PATRICIA. "Impressions of the Penny Press." *Journal of Reading* 18: 388-91; February 1975.

147. STRONG, WILLIAM. "Assessing Student Reading Skills." *Media and Methods* 12: 28-30+; March 1976.

148. THELEN, JUDITH N. "Conpass Science: Learning in Several Directions." *Journal of Reading* 16: 525-28; April 1973.

149. THOMPSON, RICHARD. "Individualized Reading: A Summary of Research." *Educational Leadership* 33: 56-61+; October 1975.

150. TUINMAN, JAAP, MICHAEL ROWLS, and ROGER FARR. "Reading Achievement in the United States: Then and Now." *Journal of Reading* 19: 455-63; March 1976.

151. "Urbana Junior High School Reading Laboratory." Urbana, Illinois: School District 116, November 1975.

152. "Using Your Daily Newspaper To Turn On the Resistant Reader." 1973. Available from Hawaii Newspaper Agency, 605 Kapiolani Boulevard, P.O. Box 3350, Honolulu, Hawaii 96801.

153. VACCA, RICHARD T. "Reading Reinforcement Through Magic Squares." *Journal of Reading* 18: 587-90; May 1975.

154. VAUGHAN, JOSEPH L., JR. "Interpreting Readability Assessments." *Journal of Reading* 19: 635-39; May 1976.

155. WAGNER, ELAINE H. "Recipe for Reading Comprehension." *Journal of Reading* 20: 498-502; January 1977.

156. WEISS, M. JERRY. "Understanding the Role of the Teacher of Readers." *Theory into Practice* 14: 173-78; June 1975.

157. WIGGINS, PHYLLIS WYNN. "The Reading Teacher: Heart of the Curriculum." *Journal of Reading* 15: 482-84; April 1972.

158. WILLERMAN, MARVIN, and BARBARA WILLERMAN. "Effects of Motivational Conferences." *Journal of Reading* 17: 224-27; December 1973.

159. WILLIAMS, MAURICE, and VIRGINIA M. R. STEVENS. "Understanding Paragraph Structure." *Journal of Reading* 15: 513-16; April 1972.

160. WILLAMSON, ANN POLLARD. "Affective Strategies of the Special Reading Teacher." *Journal of Reading* 17: 228-33; December 1973.

161. WINKELJOHANN, SR. ROSEMARY. "Improving the Secondary School Reading Curriculum: An ERIC/RCS Report." *English Journal* 63: 113-15; November 1974. Copyright © 1974 by the National Council of Teachers of English. Reprinted by permission of the publisher.

162. WIRT, JOHN G. "Implementing Diagnostic/Prescriptive Reading Innovations." Santa Monica, California: Rand Corporation, April 1975.

163. WONG, FLORENCE, and BARBARA BOWLING. "Using Your Daily News-paper To Teach Remedial Reading." 1970. Available from Hawaii Newspaper Agency, Inc., 605 Kapiolani Boulevard, P.O. Box 3350, Honolulu, Hawaii 96801.

164. WOOD, PHYLLIS ANDERSON. "Judging the Value of a Reading Program." *Journal of Reading* 19: 618-20; May 1976.

165. WULFFSON, DON L. "Music To Teach Reading." *Journal of Reading* 14: 179-82; December 1970.

166. WUNDERLICH, ELAINE, and MARY BRADTMUELLER. "Teacher Estimates of Reading Levels Compared with IRPI Instructional Level Scores." *Journal of Reading* 14: 303-38; February 1971.

10. The Second "R" Is Alive and Well
Joanne Gentry

THE second "R" may not have been murdered as George Riemer suggests in his book, *How They Murdered the Second "R"* (40), but when one scans the amount of research reported concerning the topic of reading and the amount reported concerning written communication from the years 1970-74, it is obvious that *written* communication suffers painfully by comparison.

The Research Dearth

In a summary of research studies in the November/December 1974 issue of *Elementary English* (46), 27 percent of the studies were concerned with reading, while only 2 percent examined written communication. In the January 1976 issue of *Language Arts* (45) (formerly *Elementary English*), 40 percent of the research studies reported in a similar survey investigated reading, while no reports of studies of written communication appeared.

While the research efforts aimed at improving the instruction of reading are unquestionably of the utmost importance, the contrast between the attention paid to reading and that paid to written communication gives rise to speculation as to the reason. Perhaps it is a lack of emphasis accorded written communication by that particular publication. As suggested hereafter, the lack of research studies apparently does *not* indicate that elementary school children are producing superior written communication; and the craft does require research to improve it!

Is writing ability in decline? Porter (38) noted that on February 2, 1972, the National Assessment of Educational Progress report *Writing Mechanics* was made public at an open press conference in Washington, D.C. The report showed that no group of nine-year-olds had mastered the basic conventions of writing; that only the best 13-year-olds had; and that, by age 17, only 50 percent of the teenagers could put together simple sentences, use commas, and express simple ideas. Mellon (31) reported that the writing of both 13- and 17-year-olds in

1974 was judged poorer in overall quality than that of their 1969 counterparts. "Although we cannot establish . . . whether the decrease is part of a trend, . . . a composite picture is created that provides ample grounds for believing that the writing skills of school children are currently in a state of decline" (31: 71). While apparently the decline is not a crisis, the National Assessment generated concern, and a greater number of research studies related to written communication were produced in 1974-76; this could indicate that authorities in the field do agree that the second "R" is indeed of prime importance.

The Case for the Craft

The value of written communication. Though explicit research supporting the value of written communication appears to be in relatively short supply, the statements which follow are supportive ones:

Riemer (40: 702): The student's organized (written) expression must be the goal of his education, for truly his expression is his knowledge. A nation makes its mark in history not through its readers but through its writers.

Cramer (6: 507): The purpose of fostering . . . writing in the classroom is to make a contribution to each child's academic and personal growth.

Cooper et al. (4: 57): We write to find out what we think and feel. Writing is in part a process of finding out—of discovering.

Mellon (30: 115): Despite the rise of visual studies and broadsides announcing the post-literate society, writing . . . continues to be viewed by teachers and non-teachers alike as one of the most important subjects taught in school.

Corbin (5: 16): Writing is, indeed, the capstone of the communication process.

Hogan (19: 29): One of the most important forms of communication in our modern world is the kind of communication that goes on between a writer and his readers. One of the most important communication systems for any literate human being is the system of the written form of his own . . . language. It is only through the systems of written language that writers of a hundred or more years ago continue to communicate with us today. Much of our education and much of our culture is communicated to us by means of one or another system of written language. . . .

Cramer (6: 507): No higher gift of literacy can be passed on to our children than the desire and the ability to write.

Daly and Miller (7: 244): Our age demands competence in writing. Naming an occupation where writing is not a requirement is difficult. Although it may not be a composition or essay that is required, most individuals must daily face the demand for writing competency.

National Council of Teachers of English (34: 194): Writing is an important medium for self-expression, for communication, and for the discovery of meaning—its need is increased rather than decreased by the development of new media for mass communication.

Guffin (18): Our need to reach decisions in an orderly way and convey them sensibly to those around us is contingent on the act of (written) composition. In this sense, composing and writing are among the surest acts of affirmation in a democratic, economically affluent, culturally explosive age.

Practice makes perfect. Assuming that teachers almost invariably believe written communication is important, why then do we have what appears to be a consistent decline in performance? Is it that less time is spent in the classroom in developing the skill of written communication? We cannot be sure, since no studies could be located that measured the number of minutes or hours in a day, week, month, or semester—past and present—which have been devoted to the teaching and learning of written composition. Informal observation of elementary classrooms reinforces the notion that much more time, especially during the primary school years, is spent in teaching children to read than is invested in teaching children to excel in written communication.

The need to allocate more time to writing is reinforced by statements from:

Blake (1: 609): Children learn to write by writing. . . . They spend much of their time writing . . . and this extensive practice of writing on nearly every subject imaginable eventually helps most children to become capable writers.

Fillmer (12: 736): . . . one learns to write by writing.

Fox (14: 38): Johnny can't write because he doesn't. Jane writes less because she has more alternatives and fewer opportunities.

Leonard (23: 59): Skill in writing is something like skill at playing the piano.... Talent always is involved, but so is practice, for only through practice is talent honed, refined, finished.

National Council of Teachers of English (34: 194): Learning to write requires writing; writing practice should be a major emphasis of the course.

In the interpretive section of the NAEP report, Lloyd-Jones and Winterowd recognized that the 1969-74 changes are real and offered the following explanation:

Students write less well because they now read less; motivation to write is on the wane due to the increase in telephone use and visual communication and less reliance on writing in business; teachers are assigning less writing because their class size has increased and with it their theme marking time . . . (31: 71).

Studies done during the 1960's and reported by Braddock (2) in the *Encyclopedia of Educational Research* emphasize, however, that mere frequency of writing, without the motivation to write well or careful instruction in how to write well, produces no measurable improvement over a period as short as a semester. Braddock, quoting a study by McColly and Remstad, concluded that ". . . the act of writing in and of itself is fruitless," and that English teachers ". . . should not assign or elicit any writing for the purpose of developing composition ability unless this writing becomes the vehicle for functional instruction" (2: 454).

An uncomfortable feeling begins to manifest itself as one reads the literature. Perhaps students are showing a decline in writing ability for a very simple reason: they are not being taught how to write. Hunt's study (20) showed that novice writers gain control over the ability to use different sentence-building pathways through a glacially slow process, currently without much direct help from teachers. As Strickland (50) pointed out 15 years ago, ". . . in writing, one must come to terms with his thoughts in advance of writing. Some of children's poor writing results from lack of help in doing just this."

A Scrutiny of Structure

The necessity for structure. Defending the position that the teaching of written communication is a process which demands a certain amount of structure, Evans said:

Misled by an understandable desire to arouse interest and provide motivation, teachers have unduly encouraged a random and unstructured kind of writing assumed, on no clear grounds, to be "creative"; and they have minimized or wholly neglected guided exercises in precisely those forms of writing most closely related to the rest of the child's present and future needs, both in school and out. . . . The elementary student's writing would improve rapidly—even dramatically—if his training in composition were to stress language as a means of dealing with the external world— of objectively reporting events, explaining processes, and describing objects.

The first and just possibly the most important lesson the child must learn is that language is an instrument of many uses, and that all of these uses demand of him attention and control. . . . One of the best ways of teaching such a lesson is to require the pupil to write clearly about what is clearly and permanently there for all to see, rather than vaguely about his private, everchanging, and usually irrelevant feelings (9: 527).

At the opposite end of the opinion spectrum, Personke (36) protested that emphasis on subject matter and the development of a disciplined writer may have a dehumanizing effect and that classroom policies should take into consideration the growth and development of the child. He cited Loban's study (25) which indicated that if a child's oral language and cognitive development were restricted, the young learner would be unable to produce disciplined, well organized, and logical compositions.

Other researchers have attempted to gauge the habits and procedures utilized by students who displayed superior writing ability and to determine from these measures what might be done to enable the student with less ability to become more successful in communicating through writing.

Stallard (49) in 1974 identified the following behaviors of good writers: (a) planning; (b) revision; (c) rate of writing; (d) audience awareness; (e) purpose; (f) stylistic concerns; (g) attitude; and (h) the practice of stopping to read at intervals during the process of writing. Even though this study analyzed the writing behavior of secondary students, the inquiry probably has implications for developing a sequence or structure at the elementary level —at least with older students.

Judging by Stallard's earlier doctoral study (48), good writers during their senior year took an average of 4.18 minutes for planning. The amount of time devoted to pre-writing activities for an elementary student presumably would be longer under some circumstances, but nonetheless should be included. Perron (35) said demanding that children plunge into writing via experience, without giving them help in translating their inner potential to the surface in writing, may well be frustrating and impair their future interest in writing.

Pre-writing activities. A number of authors suggested that there be a pre-writing stage which includes systematic *oral* language exercises as a means of improving *written* communication. Miller and Ney (32) reported a decade ago that:

1. Students who participated in the systematic oral language exercises wrote with greater freedom and facility.

2. Experimental subjects who practiced certain structures in their oral and written forms used these structures significantly more often than did control subjects.

3. Students who practiced putting together sentences in oral and written forms so that simple sentences were changed to complex structures used a greater number of complex sentences.

A sampling of other advocates of the development of oral language skills as a prerequisite for written communication includes:

Waldschmidt (54) found that student performance in writing and attitude improved significantly with a talk-write approach.

Yesulaitis (56) reinforced the theory that oral language should be an integral part of all school subjects.

Willardson (55) measured the effects of practice in oral expression on the subsequent writing ability of second grade students.

Maxwell and Hook (reported by Porter, 38) agreed that student-to-student oral exchanges encourage personal and imaginative writing.

Martin (also referred to by Porter, 38) had as the purpose of his investigation the exploration of several aspects of a sentence-writing model for classroom instruction.

Using the Strickland (51), Loban (25), and Chomsky (3) studies as points of departure, Martin (28) attempted to establish a useful set of relationships between speaking and writing competencies, while Blake (1) reported that better writing is achieved when children first have an opportunity to talk about the subject. Kirkton (22) asserted that much current theory about the writing process suggests writing grows out of speaking and is akin to present-tense speech. Cramer (6), reasoning along the same lines, also concluded that children develop ideas for writing through interaction with the world of words and experience.

Petroskey (37) cited Lim's dissertation (24), which reported that 85 percent of the teachers in her sample encouraged their students to talk as a preliminary activity before writing. Rupley (42), who drew on an earlier article by Hunter (21), reported that:

. . . helping students develop their writing skills is important throughout the writing activities and may consist, in the beginning stages, of working on ideas as a total class with the teacher taking over the responsibility of the mechanics of writing while the students talk out plot variations . . . (42: 589).

Moss (33) suggested that talking and listening form the groundwork for the development of reading and writing; and Lundsteen (27) agreed that written composition is tied to oral language in many ways. Teaching strategies, the literature suggests, should emphasize and exploit the links between written and oral communication.

The effect of structure on written communication skills. Opinion and research clearly support the importance of structure and sequence in the development of improved written communication skills. Stallard (49) investigated the behavior of good student writers and found that it included structure, organization, style, and the like. Sink (47) discussed the "teach-write" as well as the "write-teach" structure; while Meighan and Wilson (29) presented a summary of research which indicated that writing is more effective during the second year of instruction—that is, after more structure and teacher-direction have been provided.

Shapiro and Shapiro (44), who focused on the work of fourth graders, found in regard to the students' ability to write poetry that "semi-structured" lessons appeared to have been more effective than a "free" or unstructured approach. Martin (28) concentrated on sentence writing skills. He reported that a sequential, structured, and linguistically-oriented program which emphasized the relationships between written and oral sentences produced significantly greater achievement in sentence construction. Other writings supporting structure included those of:

Sweet (52), who recommended that since figurative language is a component of a high-quality written product, instruction in the use and understanding of figurative language should be built into composition programs for grades four through six

Fisher (13), who concluded that including sentence-combining exercises in instruction did enable students in the fifth, seventh, and ninth grades to write more maturely than they did before the experiment

Hunt (20), who recommended an approach he called "sentence combining" to enable a novice writer to gain control over the ability to use different sentence-building pathways

National Council of Teachers of English (34), which in 1975 issued an official statement indicating that instruction in writing techniques and rhetorical strategies should be part of the writing course adjusted to the age and need of the students

Fillmer (12), who contended that through the statement of specific objectives, the careful examination of literary models, and the study of specific structural elements, pupils learn about the mechanical aspects of composition

Robards (41), whose doctoral study pointed out that pre- and in-service programs should focus on developing teacher competencies in structuring the teaching of composition to elementary pupils.

The role of literature in composition. The use of literature as a stimulus during the pre-writing activities is widely advocated and reported. Evertts (10), Sebasta (43), and Thompson (53) are among those who called attention to the interrelationship of composition and literature in the elementary grades. Each of the three directed a segment of the *Nebraska Curriculum for English*. This document presents a comprehensive program based on the use and study of literature from grades one through six—a venture in which children's composition is an important element of each unit where literary selections are used as a stimulus. The Nebraska material is based on the reasonable assumption that competence in composition develops from a continuing exposure to literature of superior quality.

Ruth Strickland, distinguished authority in the language arts field, in many of her writings has advised that contact with literature through both listening and reading gives children a feeling for the style and flow of English speech that is essential to good writing.

Finally, Blake argued convincingly that:

. . . reading to children not only stimulates thought . . . but it also helps improve writing style through hearing the vocabulary, sentence construction, grammatical and syntactal arrangements, organization, and approach used by other writers (1: 610).

Evaluating the "Second R"

The impact of evaluation. The processes of evaluation also have an effect on the quantity and quality of the written communication produced by elementary students. Emig (8) identified developmental stages and suggested types and times of teacher "interventions" that are both helpful and necessary for children involved in learning the process of writing.

Graves (16) suggested that the focal point for developing self-evaluative and self-critical powers in the young writer is in individual writing conferences. Fillmer (12) also commented on the topic. If clearly defined goals are lacking, he said, it is impossible either to evaluate one's written product effectively or to implement those measures needed for improvement. He went on to say that the teacher's responsibility includes providing such awareness in young learners by helping them develop specific objectives.

Most research indicates that students respond favorably and with more enthusiasm for continued writing when rewarded with praise instead of criticism. Groff (17), however, reviewed studies on the effect of teachers' criticism on students' writing and concluded that, as a whole, the research does not support the contention that ". . . negative criticism will result in a reduction in the quality and originality of students' writing" (17: 1034).

Objective instruments for measuring the elementary students' writing are included in an NCTE publication compiled by Fagan, Cooper, and Jensen (11). Braddock (2), quoting Lyman in the *Encyclopedia of Educational Research*, questioned the use of such scales and indicated they are not very helpful. The positive term *editing* was used by Lundsteen (26) instead of *evaluation*. "The purpose of editing is to help young authors say what they want to say," she wrote in *Children Learn To Communicate*. "Respect for children's own words is thus maintained," Lundsteen continued, "and planning or accepting of a better approach is less likely to damage self-esteem" (26: 51).

Concluding Comment

In summary, it seems clear there is widespread concern over the national decline of students' written communication since the mid-sixties and support for regarding it as an important and necessary skill. Here, however, agreement in the literature ends once writers have identified the "second R" as a science instead of an art. The question of how teachers can best instruct simply has not yet been definitively answered.

Perhaps the Bay Area Writing Project, a program aimed at reducing the number of high school graduates who are prepared to write little more than one-word orders in a tavern, offers a partial solution. The project, supported by the University of California, is implemented through a five-week summer institute where 25 Bay Area teachers with experience in the elementary school–college level spectrum share experiences and theories of how to teach writing. James Gray, project director, was quoted by Ganz (15) as saying in 1977, "We are tapping the experiences of successful teachers. Instruction is passed around."

In this enterprise, teachers themselves are expected to write during the summer. Lavin, an associate with the project, explained this requirement: "The more you know about language and writing yourself, the better you are able to teach it."

Graduates of the institute are expected to become teacher consultants to their colleagues and go back to their schools to lead the project's in-service workshops. Already there are signs that the project is working. The average verbal achievement scores of students at Las Lomas High School in Walnut Creek jumped 85 points on College Entrance Examination Board (CEEB) tests after their teachers took part in the program. The number of University of California —Berkeley freshmen required to take the school's remedial writing course dropped last fall from 45 percent to just over one-third.

High schools in the San Francisco Bay area apparently are eager to send their teachers to the project's summer institute and to begin to work on in-service classes during the school year. In addition, the National Endowment for the Humanities is considering a $200,000 program to spread the idea to 14 centers around the nation. Such support is critically important. When money is appropriated, interest will grow! But the real lesson of the project may be that we need, as teachers of writing skills, to find ways of organizing to *help ourselves.*

References

1. BLAKE, HOWARD E. "Written Composition in English Primary Schools." *Elementary English* 48: 605-15; October 1971.

2. BRADDOCK, ROBERT. "English Composition." *Encyclopedia of Educational Research.* New York: The Macmillan Company, 1969.

3. CHOMSKY, NOAM. *Aspects of the Theory of Syntax.* Cambridge, Massachusetts: The MIT Press, 1965.

4. COOPER, CHARLES R., NANCIE M. ATWELL, DENISE L. DAVID, RITA C. GIGLIA, WILLIAM J. GROBE, and CAROL P. LOCKE. "Tonawanda Middle School's New Writing Program." *English Journal* 65: 56-61; November 1976.

5. CORBIN, RICHARD. *The Teaching of Writing in Our Schools.* New York: The Macmillan Company, 1966.

6. CRAMER, RONALD L. "The Nature and Nurture of Creative Writing." *Elementary School Journal* 75: 507-12; May 1975.

7. DALY, JOHN A., and MICHAEL D. MILLER. "The Empirical Development of an Instrument To Measure Writing Apprehension." *Research in the Teaching of English* 9: 242-49; Winter 1975.

8. EMIG, JANET. "On Teaching Composition: Some Hypotheses as Definitions." *Research in the Teaching of English* 1: 127-35; Fall 1967.

9. EVANS, ROBERT. "A Glove Thrown Down." *Elementary English* 44: 523-27; May 1967. Copyright © 1967 by the National Council of Teachers of English. Reprinted by permission of the publisher.

10. EVERTTS, ELDONNA, et al. "Nebraska Study of the Syntax of Children's Writing, 1964-65: I." Lincoln: University of Nebraska Press, 1967.

11. FAGAN, WILLIAM T., CHARLES R. COOPER, and JULIE M. JENSEN. *Measures for Research and Evaluation in the English Language.* Urbana, Illinois: National Council of Teachers of English, 1975.

12. FILLMER, HENRY T. "Teaching Composition Through Literature." *Elementary English* 45: 736-39; October 1968.

13. FISHER, KENNETH DAVID. "An Investigation To Determine If Selected Exercises in Sentence-Combining Can Improve Reading and Writing." Unpublished doctoral dissertation, Indiana University, Bloomington, 1973. *Dissertation Abstracts* 34: 4556-57; February 1974.

14. FOX, PATRICIA. "Why Johnny Can't and the Cat in the Hat." *English Journal* 65: 38-39; November 1976.

15. GANZ, MARY. "Why Can't Students Write: Teachers at Fault, Study Says." *Indianapolis Star,* March 27, 1977. Section 4, p. 17. See also: Shirley Boes Neill. "How To Improve Student Writing." *American Education* 12: 6-12; October 1976.

16. GRAVES, DONALD H. "Let's Get Rid of the Welfare Mess in the Teaching of Writing." *Language Arts* 53: 645-51; September 1976.

17. GROFF, PATRICK. "Does Negative Criticism Discourage Children's Composition?" *Language Arts* 52: 1032-34; October 1975.

18. GUFFIN, JAN A. "Writing." In: R. Baird Shuman, editor. *Creative Approaches to the Teaching of English: Secondary.* Itasca, Illinois: F. E. Peacock, Inc., 1974.

19. HOGAN, ROBERT F., editor. *The English Language in the School Program.* Champaign, Illinois: National Council of Teachers of English, 1966.

20. HUNT, KELLOGG. *Grammatical Structures Written at Three Grade Levels.* Research Report No. 3. Urbana, Illinois: National Council of Teachers of English, 1965.

21. HUNTER, ELIZABETH. "Fostering Creative Expression." *Childhood Education* 44: 369-73; February 1966.

22. KIRKTON, CAROLE M. "Learning To Write: Steps in the Process." NCTE Report. *Elementary English* 48: 303-11; April 1971.

23. LEONARD, MICHAEL H. "Practice Makes Better: Notes on a Writing Program." *English Journal* 65: 59-63; September 1976.

24. LIM, CONSTANCE CHUNGCHAIE CHUN. "The Analyses of Teachers' Attitudes Toward Students' Writing." Unpublished doctoral dissertation, Rutgers, The State University of New Jersey, 1974. *Dissertation Abstracts* 35: 3301; December 1974.

25. LOBAN, WALTER. *The Language of Elementary School Children.* NCTE Research Report No. 1. Champaign, Illinois: National Council of Teachers of English, 1963.

26. LUNDSTEEN, SARA W. *Children Learn To Communicate.* Englewood Cliffs, New Jersey: Prentice-Hall, Inc., 1976.

27. LUNDSTEEN, SARA W., editor. *Help for the Teacher of Written Composition (K-9): New Directions in Research.* Urbana, Illinois: ERIC Clearinghouse on Reading and Communication Skills, 1976.

28. MARTIN, JAMES J. "The Development of Sentence Writing Skills at Grades Three, Four, and Five." *Elementary English* 49: 867-79; October 1972.

29. MEIGHAN, SHIRLEY FINK, and ROBERT M. WILSON. "Research Reports: A Reading/Language Arts Program Supplies Input for Decision Making." *Educational Leadership* 34: 311-15; January 1977.

30. MELLON, JOHN C. *National Assessment and the Teaching of English.* Urbana, Illinois: National Council of Teachers of English, 1975.

31. MELLON, JOHN C. "Round Two of the National Writing Assessment— Interpreting the Apparent Decline of Writing Ability: A Review." *Research in the Teaching of English* 10: 67-74; Spring 1976. Copyright © 1976 by the National Council of Teachers of English. Reprinted by permission of the publisher.

32. MILLER, BARBARA D., and JAMES W. NEY. "The Effect of Systematic Oral Exercises on the Writing of Fourth-Grade Students." *Research in the Teaching of English* 2: 44-61; Spring 1968. Reprinted by permission.

33. MOSS, JOY. "A General Language Arts Program in an Informal Classroom." *Elementary School Journal* 76: 245-50; January 1976.

34. NATIONAL COUNCIL OF TEACHERS OF ENGLISH. "Composition: A Position Statement." *Elementary English* 52: 194-96; February 1975.

35. PERRON, JACK. "Beginning Writing: It's All in the Mind." *Language Arts* 53: 652-57; September 1976.

36. PERSONKE, CARL. "A Gauntlet Retrieved." *Elementary English* 45: 464-67; April 1968.

37. PETROSKEY, ANTHONY. "Research Roundup: Apprehension, Attitudes, and Writing." *English Journal* 65: 74-77; December 1976.

38. PORTER, JANE. "Research Report." *Elementary English* 49: 863-70; October 1972.

39. PORTER, JANE. "Research Report." *Elementary English* 49: 1028-1037; November 1972.

40. RIEMER, GEORGE. *How They Murdered the Second "R."* New York: W. W. Norton and Co., Inc., 1969.

41. ROBARDS, SHIRLEY JEAN NEEDS. "An Analysis of Selected Textbooks To Identify Scope and Sequence in Elementary School Composition." Unpublished doctoral dissertation, Indiana University, Bloomington, 1972. *Dissertation Abstracts* 33: 6599; May 1973.

42. RUPLEY, WILLIAM H. "Teaching and Evaluating Creative Writing in the Elementary Grades." *Language Arts* 53: 586-90; May 1976.

43. SEBASTA, SAM, et al. "Nebraska Study of the Syntax of Children's Writing 1965-1966: II." Lincoln: University of Nebraska Press, 1967.

44. SHAPIRO, PHYLLIS P., and BERNARD J. SHAPIRO. "Two Methods of Teaching Poetry Writing in the Fourth Grade." *Elementary English* 48: 225-28; April 1971.

45. SHELDON, WILLIAM, DONALD R. LASHINGER, DOROTHY R. TROIKE, and LYNN E. MERCER. "A Summary of Research Studies Relating to Language Arts in Elementary Education: 1974." *Language Arts* 53: 85-110; January 1976.

46. SHELDON, WILLIAM D., DONALD R. LASHINGER, DOROTHY R. TROIKE, and JON E. SHAPIRO. "A Summary of Research Studies Related to Language Arts in Elementary Education: 1973." *Elementary English* 51: 1177-99; November-December 1974.

47. SINK, D. MICHAEL. "Teach-Write/Write-Teach." *Elementary English* 52: 175-77, 186; February 1975.

48. STALLARD, CHARLES KELSON, JR. "An Analysis of the Writing Behavior of Good Student Writers." Unpublished doctoral dissertation, University of Virginia, Charlottesville, 1972. *Dissertation Abstracts* 33: 3408; January 1973.

49. STALLARD, CHARLES K. "An Analysis of the Writing Behavior of Good Student Writers." *Research in the Teaching of English* 8: 206-18; Fall 1974.

50. STRICKLAND, RUTH. "Implications of Research in Linguistics for Elementary Teaching." *Elementary English* 50: 168-71; February 1963.

51. STRICKLAND, RUTH G. "The Language of Elementary School Children: Its Relationship to the Language of Reading Textbooks and the Quality of Reading of Selected Children." *Bulletin of the School of Education* (Indiana University, Bloomington) 38 (4): whole issue; July 1962.

52. SWEET, JAMES A. "An Analysis of the Writing of Elementary Children, Grades Four Through Six, To Determine the Relationship Between Specified Genre and the Development and Use of Figurative Language." Unpublished doctoral dissertation, Indiana University, Bloomington, 1974. *Dissertation Abstracts* 35: 5697-98; March 1975.

53. THOMPSON, NELL C., et al. "Nebraska Study of the Syntax of Children's Writing, 1966-67: III." Lincoln: University of Nebraska Press, 1967.

54. WALDSCHMIDT, ELMER CLEMENT. "Pilot Studies in Composition: Their Effects Upon Students and Participating English Teachers." Unpublished doctoral dissertation, University of Illinois, Urbana-Champaign, 1973. *Dissertation Abstracts* 34: 7634; June 1974.

55. WILLARDSON, MARLYN LARRY. "A Study of the Writing Ability of Second Grade Students in a Communication Skills Through Authorship Program." Unpublished doctoral dissertation, University of Idaho, Moscow, 1971. *Dissertation Abstracts* 32: 3585; January 1972.

56. YESULAITIS, MARY PATRICIA CRONIN. "Procedures for Developing Oral Language Facility in Children Pre-K Through Grade Three: A National Survey." Unpublished doctoral dissertation, University of North Carolina, Chapel Hill, 1972. *Dissertation Abstracts* 34: 79; July 1973.

11. Spelling and Handwriting
Nelly Ceres Ferreira

BOTH spelling and handwriting have been the objects of research for several generations. As was noted in the first chapter, one of the earliest bona fide research studies—a study of spelling—was done by Joseph M. Rice in 1897! Despite the time and energy invested in inquiries, however, the literature of the 1970's indicates that further study is in order. Teachers of every age group continue to seek better methods and better programs to improve instruction in both fields.

The following pages recapitulate the work of those who have continued the path opened by Dr. Rice 81 years ago. Despite the stress given here to research, the writer urges readers to keep in mind that teachers are the best instruments we have to test the ideas scholars study; they are an invaluable source of feedback. Furthermore, we must remember that the ideas presented in these pages are not invariably new. They have been with us for decades, but they are subject to constant review in the quest for self-renewal and for better methods.

The Realm of Spelling

Research related to spelling in the seventies. Benowitz and Busse (5), investigating the effectiveness of offering a material reward in a typical classroom situation, concluded—as might be anticipated—that significantly higher scores were achieved by both boys and girls when material rewards were offered. Cramer's (10) study investigated the facility with which two groups of first graders spelled phonologically regular and irregular words, and also probed the possible influence of their reading instruction on spelling achievement. The findings showed that:

1. There was no significant difference in the facility with which the Language Experience Approach (LEA) group spelled regular and irregular words, whereas the Basal Reader Approach (BRA) group spelled regular words better than irregular words near the end of the school year.

119

2. The LEA group spelled both regular and irregular words better than the BRA group.

3. The LEA group achieved a significantly higher spelling score in written composition than did the Basal Reader classes.

Nikas (41) reported that children's subsequent spelling performance is unaffected by earlier use of the Initial Teaching Alphabet (ITA), while Graham's (18) finding supported the hypothesis that spelling error would be similarly patterned throughout all dialects.

After eight years of research and testing, Lightbody and Day (36) concluded that what they identified as the linguistic approach tends to free a child from reliance on rote learning. Cohen and others (8) summarized spelling research from the beginning of the "demon list," through the computerized study of spelling errors, to recent work which indicates that "phoneme-grapheme correspondences of some consistency do exist in English and that the difficulty of an individual word should be related to the magnitude of the correspondence with the word" (8: 297).

Kuhn and Schroeder (32) engaged in a study of a multi-sensory approach for use in testing spelling performance and recommended the implementation of a combined oral-visual test correction procedure which, they felt, served to increase student attention spans as well as concentration during spelling instruction. Personke (42) based his study on nonsense words invented and used earlier by Spaulding. The results obtained, he said, indicated that ". . . nonsense words used in a recall-dictation test will indicate the ability of children to use phonetic generalizations in spelling." He also commented that such use ". . . may supply better information than the use of real words since the nonsense words assure the unfamiliarity of the stimulus" (42:1236).

Reviewing in depth the literature on the teaching of spelling prior to 1973, Groff (19: 94) concluded that "speech therapy, dialect, 'correction,' or saying words as they are spelled are not likely to have much effect on children's spelling." Later he added that the effects of dialect on spelling suggest the need for a change in materials used to teach children to spell. Finally, he stated that there is a need to focus attention on the task of writing and spelling materials that vary with regional, local, racial, and socioeconomic class dialects.

The major purpose of a study done by Petty and others (43) was to determine whether children who have been taught principles or generalizations about sound-to-symbol correspondences make spelling errors and represent sounds more rationally than do children instructed in other ways. "The evidence obtained from the spelling attempts of the children who were taught the Initial Teaching Alphabet (ITA) tends to show that little would be gained from teaching patterns of sound-to-symbol generalization" (43: 313). An investigation by Mason and others (38) was to determine:

1. Whether teaching spelling to first graders promoted growth in spelling, reading, or composition

2. Whether methods coordinated with reading were more effective or less effective than methods not coordinated with reading

3. Whether direct teaching of spelling was preferable to incidental teaching of spelling through composition.

The conclusion reached was that the coordination or the correlation of instruction in the language arts stimulates growth, not only in reading but also in the other arts of written language. Failure to coordinate the variables appears detrimental to achievement.

Rieth and others (48) devised a four-part study in order to compare different means of presenting spelling words to students. They inferred from experiments I, II, and III that students did better on weekly review tests when they were exposed to a portion of the words each day and also were tested daily. They did less well when they received all words at the beginning of the week and did not have daily tests. Experiment IV indicated that, insofar as retention was concerned, receiving a portion of the word list each day without daily testing was inferior to receiving a portion of the words each day with daily testing, but better than receiving all words at the beginning of the week without daily testing.

Anthony (1) reported on the results of a study intended to determine relationships between spelling and other school subjects as well as between spelling and other variables which might generally be presumed to have a bearing on spelling achievement. Anthony found that:

. . . neither teacher nor non-teacher classroom variables influence class median spelling achievement. Likewise, the level of class intellectual functioning in terms of class median IQ appears not to influence such achievement. It may be that classroom time spent studying spelling is, on the average, wasted (1: 132-33).

It was claimed in an article (55) for which no author was identified that a child's correcting his or her own test is the single most important factor in his or her learning to spell. This is analogous to down-to-earth advice from Robert Fitzsimmons and Bradley Loomer (55), who pointed out that:

• One should give a child the spelling test first, then allow him to study words missed since this is more effective than having the child study first and take the test later.

• To have a child look at "hard spots" in words is not helpful and might be harmful.

• Writing words several times does not ensure retention.

• Learning words by the whole word method is preferable to learning them by syllables.

- Presenting spelling words in list form is preferable to presenting them in sentences or paragraphs.

- Relating interest in spelling to material rewards for achievement is ineffective; rewards come from intrinsic incentives like positive attitudes.[11]

To improve efficiency in instruction, Fitzsimmons and Loomer urged, on the basis of their study, that educators reassess spelling procedures, practices, and methods. They also advocated the use of self-corrected tests, pretests, and student-kept records of words most likely to be misspelled. Geedy (17), reviewing the literature in the teaching of spelling, concluded that "no one channel or approach is an effective answer to the question of how best to teach children to spell. Each discipline can suggest means to make the process more successful or meaningful to children" (17: 236).

In view of so much diverse opinion expressed in the literature, an additional scrutiny of the teaching of spelling seems in order.

Suggestions for improving the teaching of spelling. Langer (34) asked why young children cannot be permitted to use their own phonetic alphabets, then suggested the teacher gradually should provide standard alternatives as the child shows readiness to accept them. Considerable time and study, one would infer, are demanded by such a proposal.

Jackson and Guber (28) claimed that spelling should be taught through three approaches engineered to meet the needs of students: (a) phonetics (the sounds and their spellings), (b) linguistics, and (c) mnemonics (memory devices). These areas, they asserted, should be taught simultaneously through oral reading and expression, discussion, prearranged discoveries, and various forms of practice or drill. Shah (50), in a similar vein, said that by examining the English language in order to understand what the patterns are, students could be trained to relate the spelling of particular sounds to their patterns.

Lefcourt (35) observed that teaching spelling through a linguistic approach encouraged many children to use the dictionary and, with increased ease, to spell more new words correctly. Poteet (45), on the other hand, came up with the idea that when students are not sure how to spell a word, they need only to look for a synonym of that word in the thesaurus—or, if they cannot find the word they want to use, another synonym can be utilized.

Simon and Simon (53), as an outcome of their study on the use of phonemic information, suggested two main alternatives for improving spelling—

---

[11] The reader will quickly note that opinions in the literature, after many decades, continue to be in conflict! Benowitz and Busse (see p. XI-1) came to the opposite conclusion with respect to material rewards for spelling achievement.

spelling processes[12] and computer programs. Jackson and Guber (28) revived a vintage idea when they suggested that a "Language Experience Approach" to spelling teaching be based on the simple device of having children develop and maintain "spelling dictionaries," with each child's writing activities providing the entries for his or her own personalized spelling lists. Wheeler and Wheeler (59) also reiterated an old point in commenting that a major difficulty in the teaching of spelling is the lack of correspondence between our written and spoken language. They pointed out two helpful procedures. The first is to seek to help young learners recognize relationships between the letters (graphemes) and sounds (phonemes) of language. The second stresses internal relationships among the graphemes when words are written.

Conely (9) reminded teachers of four long-recognized causes of spelling problems: the eccentricities of the English language itself, mispronunciation, confusion of similar words, and confusion with respect to root words. He also mentioned certain long-accepted procedures: the use of rules, listing trouble-some words, and memorization through association, rhymes, and mnemonic devices. Shell (51), after making the obvious point that the ultimate reason for teaching spelling is so the knowledge and skill gained during the spelling period can and will be used in all writing situations, said that unless the improvement of spelling in other writing situations occurs, spelling instruction has been meaningless and futile. There were no surprises in his conclusion that one way to improve spelling in any written activity is to require the speller to proofread and correct misspelled words.

Manolakes (37) reported a pilot study of considerable interest that was undertaken with children in a suburban school district. His findings showed that:

1. Children in the sample knew how to spell a number of words for one grade above their present placement.

2. The performance of the girls and boys on word lists was significant at .01 level both for their grade and for the grade above.

3. The specific kind of errors made by a given child varied with his or her level of achievement.

4. There were difficulties encountered by children in copying certain elements within a word.

5. Analysis of error patterns suggested the need for a reassessment of the prominent role of phonics in many of the available spelling programs.

6. The data suggested the possibility that some difficulties in spelling are related to factors other than structural or configurational characteristics.

---

[12] "Spelling processes" are defined by Simon and Simon as ". . . a number of alternative routes along which the spelling of a particular word can be recalled. Each route requires different forms of information storage in long-term memory and different processes for using the information" (53: 118).

Homes (22) discussed the point that parents in particular and adults in general are hung up on spelling, and argued that their expectations are neither clearly nor realistically defined, but understandable. His article included a sample of children's misspellings which nonetheless communicated meaning. Horn (23) advocated that instead of having pupils study before testing they should encounter testing before study, thus releasing them from the rite of studying words they already know. Ediger (13) indicated that the following are specific spelling strategies students can learn to use:

1. Spelling unfamiliar words on the assumption of consistency between symbols and sound even though no consistent spelling pattern may exist

2. Pronouncing selected words correctly and thus increasing the likelihood of correct spelling

3. Developing a personal methodology in learning to spell words

4. Developing a sense of purpose in learning to spell selected words

5. Working to achieve legible handwriting.

Although times have changed greatly since the first ASCD language arts monograph appeared in the mid-1950's, one cannot miss noting that similar ideas surface in each decade. This seems to happen more often in writings concerned with spelling than with, say, reading. The recycling of viewpoints on spelling continues to be conspicuous in the following section.

Miscellaneous comments on spelling. Blake (7) contended (somewhat wishfully in terms of 1977 academic score decline data) that teachers of spelling should know thoroughly the intricacies of the various approaches to spelling instruction, including the terminology of each and related theory-research concepts. Benthul's (6) assertion that spelling has remained important and that children should study it sounded a shade wistful to this reviewer despite his claim that in the 1970's we can expect revolutionary developments in communication which will bring increased importance to writing, and hence to spelling. He felt the media and society as a whole will prove the pertinence of spelling and therefore the need for adequate spelling instruction.

Umbach's (57) article had a déjà vu quality when he suggested that room be made for individual differences in spelling as in other subject areas. His advice that schools introduce variety into their programs in order to get them out of their usual rut was first proffered at least 50 years ago. This comment also applies to Rowell's (49) suggestion that an individualized spelling program can be developed when the following strategies are made operable:

1. Arranging skills and concepts to be taught on a simple-to-complex continuum

2. Finding the point on the spelling continuum to which each individual has progressed

3. Diagnosing problems that obstruct the learning of any of the skills and concepts

4. Providing activities appropriate for teaching the skills and concepts to one student or to a group of students

5. Streamlining procedures for keeping records of each student as he or she progresses through the continuum.

Shores and Yee (52) advocated that a major step in the development of a modern spelling program is the formation of appropriate standardized measures of spelling skills for experimental and evaluative purposes.

Hinrichs (20) advised that a good spelling program should include three components. The first is a word list appropriate to the grade level, age level, or developmental level of the children in a given group; he also suggested that the program concentrate on teaching children to spell 4,000 high frequency words. The second component is the use of an efficient procedure by which the list of words is to be taught; for example, a pretest, self-correction, and a testing phase. The third component is a method for students to learn how to spell words they do not know, such as: (a) look at the word; (b) say it; (c) close eyes and say it, (d) write the word without looking; (e) check to see if it is correct— if not, start again.

Handwriting

General information regarding handwriting in the elementary school. Niemann (40) conducted a useful survey on three topics: handwriting, spelling, and creative writing during the early years of schooling. On the topic of handwriting, she traced the emerging changes that have occurred through the years— including, of course, the introduction of manuscript writing and the long struggle between its proponents and those who favored cursive writing. Niemann also discussed eye-hand movements as well as the transition from manuscript writing to cursive. On the topic of spelling, her review covered the introduction and use of the dictionary, how children are grouped according to their abilities in spelling, and the help the teacher should provide them.

Horton (24) concerned himself with the teaching of handwriting. Among his suggestions were: (a) encourage children to find creative and purposeful uses for their writing efforts; (b) impress upon them the appropriateness of different writing styles for different purposes; (c) use a variety of materials including pencils, ball points, and fountain pens. In addition, Horton suggested writing experiences with crayons, paint brushes, and charcoal. Evaluate each child's handwriting according to his or her personal stage of growth and record of improvement, he said, and help each child to analyze and diagnose his or her own handwriting to see where and why errors that impair legibility are being made. He concluded by reminding readers that handwriting is a tool for all subject areas and that new approaches should be tried to enliven practice.

Tenaglia (56) asserted that interest in penmanship and handwriting practice has been low. He then suggested that what he called "graphotherapy" and "graphodiagnostics" may provide new means of improving the instructional system. He concluded with a graphodiagnostic analysis of children's handwriting.

Bauer (4) suggested it may be a good idea to have the young child become proficient in only one letter at a time, while Ediger (14) advocated careful consideration of the psychology of learning when teaching handwriting in the elementary school. This involves—according to Ediger—the choice of varied activities which are interesting and the practice of handwriting in functional writing situations. Kuipers and Riccio (33) observed that handwriting had been assigned a low priority by the mid-seventies, and the result of this neglect clearly shows in the handwriting of many children and adults.

Handwriting instruction. Furner (16) set out to develop a program of instruction that emphasized the perception of letters and their formation through a guided examination of the formation process. Practice sessions were based on verbalizations by children, including their self-analysis of errors, plus efforts at improvement based on their descriptions. Her findings showed that these methods were effective as a means of instruction.

Westbrooks (58) designed a program of her own that focused on 12 cleverly labeled common mistakes, or "handwriting diseases": (a) Giantwritytis; (b) Tinywritytis; (c) Frillyosis (unnecessary decoration); (d) Slumps (words written above or below the line); (e) "T"sless (uncrossed t's); (f) Unmeasles (undotted i's); (g) Broken letter (gaps left in such letters as a, o, and s); (h) Looptheria; (i) Squeezles (squeezed too close together); (j) Disjointed; and (k) Sloppox (sloppy writing).

Tracing versus copying. Hirsch and Niedermeyer (21), working at the kindergarten level, in 1973 investigated the effect of two kinds of letter formation practice—copying and tracing—on the handwriting performance of 50 kindergarten children. After ten weeks of instruction, they concluded that the letter formation of the participating groups had improved significantly. However, those five-year-olds who had received copying exercises performed significantly better than those who had engaged in tracing exercises. Letter discrimination training had no effect on letter formation performance in this inquiry.

Askov and Greff (2) also engaged in research on copying versus tracing as the most effective type of practice for younger children. Their 1975 report confirmed the findings of the earlier study by Hirsch and Niedermeyer (21).

Karstadt (30) expressed the opinion that the young child or older disabled readers can be helped in their reading through a variety of tracing and writing activities when those activities are interesting enough for the child to enjoy the practice and to learn the word being studied. Sovik (54) studied the effect of different kinds of copying in relation to psychomotor skills. The copying performances of students rated as having good handwriting at school, he learned, did not exceed the copying quality of those rated as poor handwriters. Foerster (15) argued that tracing activities in handwriting are on their way out in our schools and that teachers should drop this practice. A main reason, she said, is that this activity tends to be failure-oriented rather than success-oriented for the child.

Cursive versus manuscript writing: new opinions in an old argument. Plattor and Woestehoff (44) conducted a survey on handwriting and reached an oft-reiterated conclusion, namely that the data seem to support the introduction of manuscript as the writing style in the primary grades and its maintenance throughout children's educational careers after cursive writing has been introduced. Also, they pointed out that the transition to cursive writing is complicated by factors that create problems for many children and therefore they were led to question whether a dual program of manuscript and cursive handwriting instruction is desirable. Cursive style, they observed, should be considered for what it really is—a complex skill that is difficult to acquire. Horton (25) also explained the success of manuscript handwriting as an enduring practice in the classroom.

It was Early's (11) contention that major advantages of cursive writing are: (a) each word is one continuous line where all elements flow together, and (b) it distracts children's attention less than manuscript writing from the ideas the young child wants to express. He also claimed there is a rhythm to cursive writing which cannot be duplicated in manuscript writing. Barham (3) took a similar position when she argued that children become frustrated in learning cursive writing stroke by stroke. She also said there is a need to emphasize the similarity between manuscript and cursive and that the first phase in learning cursive writing is reading it well.

Minkoff (39) indicated that instead of being presented as a new skill, cursive script can be introduced as the inevitable result of the pressure for speed in print. In other words, cursive writing changes the shapes of the manuscript letters in certain predictable ways, results in connected letters, and requires that the pencil be lifted less often. Investigating the effect of the initial teaching of cursive writing to first graders, Early et al. (12) observed, first, that the use of cursive writing will not adversely affect the child's reading or spelling performance, and second, that the use of cursive writing apparently results in significantly fewer reversal and transposition errors.

Miscellaneous comments on teaching handwriting. Krzesni's (31) study led him to conclude that third graders' performance increased appreciably when they used ballpoint or felt pens. Riesen (46, 47) noted that children responded well to mixing instruction in spelling and handwriting. She also described a three-step approach to writing. The first phase is writing letters without stems or loops; next is writing the six letters formed by loops or stems; third, writing the other six letters that have lower loops and the one with loops above and below. Horton (26) suggested it is helpful to develop a scale from each child's work as a means of helping the teacher determine progress in handwriting.

After reading current material on manuscript versus cursive writing, Huitt (27) polished his crystal ball and presented the following forecasts:

1. Most schools will continue to teach manuscript writing to children in kindergarten and first grade.

2. Increased emphasis will be given to the need for teaching the skills of handwriting during regularly scheduled periods of time.

3. College teachers will place renewed emphasis on teaching handwriting to undergraduates in preservice methods classes.

4. Handwriting will remain a most useful tool—one that helps to convey information, retain thoughts, organize thinking, and record events.

5. Legibility will remain a prime objective.

As was the case with spelling, the literature dealing with handwriting has tended to recapitulate many long-time issues and a cluster of persistent problems. There is one major difference, however. While issues and problems may be the same, the answers to them are different in the sense that our clientele in elementary and secondary schools is a new one. The challenge of poverty, the intricacies of ethnicity, and the greater holding power of secondary education keep old topics ever young.

References

1. ANTHONY, BOBBIE M. "Why Keep Spelling in the Curriculum?" *Education* 92: 130-33; September 1971.

2. ASKOV, EUNICE N., and KASPER N. GREFF. "Handwriting: Copying Versus Tracing as the Most Effective Type of Practice." *Journal of Educational Research* 69: 96-98; November 1975.

3. BARHAM, GENEVIEVE. "Cursive—It's the Real Thing!" *Instructor* 84: 71-73; October 1974.

4. BAUER, SISTER SUSANNE. "Each Child an Expert." *Teacher* 92: 78; November 1974.

5. BENOWITZ, MARTIN L., and THOMAS V. BUSSE. "Material Incentives and the Learning of Spelling Words in a Typical School Situation." *Journal of Educational Psychology* 61: 24-26; February 1970.

6. BENTHUL, HERMAN F. "Is Spelling Still Important?" *Instructor* 74: 61; April 1970.

7. BLAKE, HOWARD E. "Some Spelling Facts." *Elementary English* 46: 241-49; February 1970.

8. COHEN, LEONARD S., et al. "Spelling Difficulty—A Survey of the Research." *Review of Educational Research* 41: 281-301; October 1971.

9. CONELY, JAMES. "Spelling." *College Composition and Communication* 25: 243; October 1974.

10. CRAMER, RONALD L. "An Investigation of First-Grade Spelling Achievement." *Elementary English* 47: 230-37; February 1970.

11. EARLY, GEORGE H. "The Case for Cursive Writing." *Academic Therapy* 9: 105-108; Fall 1973.

12. EARLY, GEORGE H., et al. "Cursive Handwriting, Reading, and Spelling Achievement." *Academic Therapy* 12: 67; Fall 1976.

13. EDIGER, MARLOW. "Diagnosing S-p-e-l-l-i-n-g Deficiencies." *School and Community* 63: 10; December 1976.

14. EDIGER, MARLOW. "The Pupil, the Teacher, and Handwriting." *Reading Improvement* 11: 62-64; Spring 1974.

15. FOERSTER, LEONA M. "Teacher—Don't Let Your First Graders Trace!" *Elementary English* 49: 31-33; March 1972.

16. FURNER, BEATRICE A. "An Analysis of the Effectiveness of a Program of Instruction Emphasizing the Perceptual-Motor Nature of Learning in Handwriting." *Elementary English* 47: 61-69; January 1970.

17. GEEDY, PATRICIA S. "What Research Tells Us About Spelling." *Elementary English* 52: 233-36; February 1975.

18. GRAHAM, RICHARD T. "Dialect and Spelling." *Elementary English* 47: 363-76; March 1970.

19. GROFF, PATRICK. "Children's Speech Errors and Their Spelling." *Elementary School Journal* 74: 88-94; November 1973.

20. HINRICHS, RONALD W. "An Old but Valid Procedure." *Elementary English* 52: 249-52; February 1975.

21. HIRSCH, EDWARD, and FRED C. NIEDERMEYER. "The Effects of Tracing Prompts and Discrimination Training on Kindergarten Handwriting Performance." *Journal of Educational Research* 67: 8-86; October 1973.

22. HOMES, MIKE. "A Spelling Lessen (sic)." *English Journal* 64: 8-9; December 1975.

23. HORN, THOMAS D. "Test, Then Study in Spelling." *Instructor* 86: 81; December 1976.

24. HORTON, LOWELL. "Is Teaching Handwriting Really Important?" *Instructor* 82: 68-69; January 1973.

25. HORTON, LOWELL. "Print Script Handwriting: The Innovation That Endured." *Contemporary Education* 43: 287-88; April 1972.

26. HORTON, LOWELL. "Self-Check Chart." *Teacher* 91: 87; October 1973.

27. HUITT, RAY. "Handwriting: The State of the Craft." *Childhood Education* 48(3): 219-20, 222; January 1972. By permission of the Association for Childhood Education International, 3615 Wisconsin Ave., N.W., Washington, D.C. 20016. Copyright © 1972 by the Association.

28. JACKSON, GLADYS L., and ANNA MARIE GUBER. "The Way Out of the Spelling Labyrinth." *Elementary Teacher* 49: 40-100; January 1972.

29. JACKSON, MAE L. "Individualized Spelling Lists." *Teacher* 91: 86-88; January 1974.

30. KARSTADT, ROBERT. "Tracing and Writing Activities for Teaching Reading." *The Reading Teacher* 30: 297-98; December 1976.

31. KRZESNI, JOSEPH S. "Effect of Different Writing Tools and Paper on Performance of the Third Grader." *Elementary English* 48: 821-24; November 1971.

32. KUHN, JERRY N., and HOWARD H. SCHROEDER. "A Multi-Sensory Approach for Teaching Spelling." *Elementary English* 48: 865-69; November 1971.

33. KUIPERS, JOAN, and MARY LOU RICCIO. "From Graphomania to Graphophobia and Halfway Back." *Elementary English* 62: 216-20; February 1975.

34. LANGER, JOHN H. "Non-Standard Spelling and Language Experience in Beginning Reading." *Elementary English* 48: 951-52; December 1971.

35. LEFCOURT, ANN. "Spelling and the Dictionary." *Elementary English* 49: 1228-32, 1239; December 1972.

36. LIGHTBODY, PATRICIA C., and KATHERINE M. DAY. "Order Out of Spelling Chaos." *Instructor* 79: 60; April 1970.

37. MANOLAKES, GEORGE. "The Teaching of Spelling: A Pilot Study." *Elementary English* 52: 243-47; February 1975. Copyright © 1975 by the National Council of Teachers of English. Reprinted by permission of the publisher.

38. MASON, GEORGE, et al. "Relating Reading and Spelling: A Comparison of Methods." *Elementary School Journal* 74: 381-86; March 1974.

39. MINKOFF, HARVEY. "Teaching the Transition from Print to Script Analytically." *Elementary English* 52: 203-204; February 1975.

40. NIEMANN, ANN SMITH. "Handwriting, Spelling, and Creative Writing in the Primary Grades." *Elementary English* 48: 963-69; December 1971.

41. NIKAS, GEORGE. "Initial Teaching Alphabet and Traditional Orthography: Their Impact on Spelling and Writing." *Elementary School Journal* 70: 321-30; March 1970.

42. PERSONKE, CARL R. "The Use of Nonsense Words To Test Generalization Ability in Spelling." *Elementary English* 49: 1233-37; December 1972.

43. PETTY, WALTER T., et al. "Spelling Achievement and the Initial Teaching Alphabet." *Elementary School Journal* 74: 309-13; February 1974.

44. PLATTOR, EMMA E., and ELLSWORTH S. WOESTEHOFF. "Toward a Singular Style of Instruction in Handwriting." *Elementary English* 48: 1009-11; December 1971.

45. POTEET, HOWARD. "A Brief Note on Spelling." *English Journal* 62: 1029-30; October 1973.

46. RIESEN, JANET. "Script for Improvement." *Grade Teacher* 89: 38; December 1971.

47. RIESEN, JANET. "Spelling List Stories." *Grade Teacher* 89: 12; November 1971.

48. RIETH, HERBERT, et al. "Influence of Distributed Practice and Daily Testing on Weekly Spelling Tests." *Journal of Educational Research* 68: 73-77; October 1974.

49. ROWELL, GLENNON. "A Prototype for an Individualized Spelling Program." *Elementary English* 49: 335-40; March 1972.

50. SHAH, IRIS. "Spelling the Sound Way." *Elementary English* 49: 85-89; January 1972.

51. SHELL, LEO M. "Spelling: Encoding English." *Elementary English* 52: 221; February 1975.

52. SHORES, JAY H., and ALBERT H. YEE. "Spelling Achievement Tests: What Is Available and Needed?" *Journal of Special Education* 7: 301-309; Fall 1973.

53. SIMON, DOROTHEA P., and HERBERT A. SIMON. "Alternative Uses of Phonemic Information in Spelling." *Review of Educational Research* 43: 115-37; Winter 1973.

54. SOVIK, N. "Effects of Different Principles of Instruction in Children's Copying Performance." *Journal of Experimental Education* 45: 38-45; Fall 1976.

55. "Spelling Made Difficult." *Nation's Schools and Colleges* 2: 20-21; February 1975.

56. TENAGLIA, RICHARD. "Graphotherapy; Aiding Children's Personality Development." *Elementary English* 50: 775-79, 788; May 1973.

57. UMBACH, WALTER O. "Get Your Spelling Program Out of Its Rut." *School and Community* 57: 18-19; December 1970.

58. WESTBROOKS, LINDA K. "Prescription for Ailing Penmanship." *Teacher* 94: 100+; September 1976.

59. WHEELER, KIRK, and MARY WHEELER. "On the Regularity of Spelling." *Instructor* 83: 24; March 1974.

12. The Literature Experience
Kevin Sue Bailey

IDENTITY, interest, innovation—these catchwords resound in every methods course, and virtually every school, in every part of the nation. This chapter will attempt to provide an overview of the quest for relevancy and insight through literature classes and to present ways in which the literature suggests they can be achieved. Attention also will focus on the crucial factor of reader interest and curriculum trends related to content as well as genre. The chapter closes with a look at censorship and evaluation in the context of their effects on the teaching of English.

An Overview of Classroom Theory

Now what I want is Facts. Teach these boys and girls nothing but Facts. Facts alone are wanted in life. Plant nothing else, and root out everything else. You can only form the minds of reasoning animals upon Facts; nothing else will ever be of any service to them. This is the principle on which I bring up my own children, and this is the principle on which I bring up these children. Stick to Facts, sir!

Thus Mr. McChoakumchild decreed the type of education that was to be thrust upon the children in his school district in Dickens' novel appropriately entitled *Hard Times* (12).

Now, however, the literature suggests the once-strong emphasis on factual knowledge and authoritarian rule as a means of education has come to an end. As Cooper (9: 1064) phrased it:

A restless new generation of students is demanding of "all" of its teachers in the humanities and fine arts as well that they teach responsively, that they try honestly to find out who the student is and what he is like, and what he thinks he must know to live in this age.

Burton (4) has also stated that students will no longer accept literature without relevancy, while Pollan (40: 573) made the point that "English Chairmen and teachers seem to be floundering attempting to impress upon their students the relevancy of the subject matter they are attempting to teach but not sure themselves of what that relevancy could be."

Many English teachers also appear to be attempting to justify a literature course that is not intimately associated with classics. Current writings suggest these teachers are on the right track since many classics traditionally selected for reading in the English classroom are now deemed not only irrelevant to students but also incomprehensible to them. Golub (18) suggested the experiences to which students are exposed should be within their stage of cognitive development. Flanigan (17) gave three criteria for selection of novels that may facilitate student comprehension: (a) readability and availability, (b) high interest level, and (c) a recognizable standard of literary quality.

Why the emphasis on novel selection and student interest? After all is said and done in the English classroom, it is hoped students will retain a self-directed reading habit (36). If our true goal is lifelong reading enjoyment, as Milstead (31:5-6) phrased it, ". . . teachers must remove the main barriers to reading, which are the academic tradition in literature as represented by textbooks on the one hand and analytical systems devised in college literature courses on the other."

Approaches to literature instruction. More and more researchers and writers in the field of English education appear to recognize that most of today's students will not be tomorrow's literary scholars. For this reason they are encouraging English teachers to emphasize with students a method for deciphering complex literature and for fostering analytical and perceptive reading (50). The specific approaches suggested are as varied as the novels available; however, there seems to be some general agreement that teachers should attempt to build on the reader's affective response (52, 44, 2). Turner (50) also felt teachers should make students aware of the different methods one can use to analyze a work; for example, literal, historical, or cultural.

One approach to literature that holds a great deal of promise for the English classroom is bibliotherapy (33). Possibly the greatest value in bibliotherapy is that it strives effectively to stimulate both the affective and cognitive growth of the student. The objective is to use literature and the reader's identification with literature to promote mental health, to provide entertainment, to encourage self-analysis, and to clarify values. In short, bibliotherapy is a way of helping a student to find himself or herself and to become acquainted with great literature at the same time (33).

Regardless of the approach used, there is strong support in literature research for thoughtful discussion of the literature read. Inglis (24) said effective teaching of literature requires a "tripartite dialogue" among the teacher, the student, and the writer whose work is examined. He felt this type of discussion cuts down on chaos and allows its participants ". . . to emerge from it, not only with an extension of experience, but with improved equipment for approaching all the experience that is to come" (24: 11-12). In addition to these benefits, Penna (38) in his doctoral study found that the discussion techniques used in teaching literature caused participants to make significant gains in self-identity and self-acceptance.

Reader Interest

"Bookmanship"; mirror of life. "Bookmanship is the art of adjusting literature to life. . . . Bookmanship thus becomes the faculty of uniting a book with the life of the reader" (52: 313). The idea of "bookmanship" or the concept it represents is one that has the largest number of supporters among writers who have concerned themselves with the literature experience of young people today (34, 39, 29, 1, 6, 18). Nestor (34: 66) asserted:

When a course in literature provides students with the opportunity to examine the realities of human existence as well as to analyze and appreciate good literary style and technique, it can be an exceptionally valuable learning experience. Discussing the life situations through which fictional characters struggle involves a kind of objectivity that allows students to air their own questions and problems indirectly, in terms of a fictional character, rather than through deeply personal references to themselves.

The novel is a form which seems to achieve this objective without sacrificing artistry. Good examples include Hermann Hesse's *Narcissus and Goldmund*, D. H. Lawrence's *Sons and Lovers*, J. D. Salinger's *Franny and Zooey*, John Steinbeck's *East of Eden*, and James Dickey's *Deliverance*, according to Perry (39), who went on to note that literature transcends self-understanding in fostering understanding of the reader's personal history, family, peers, and others.

Such an experience with literature, as Haley pointed out, can prove vitally important to students who are members of a "fractured family."

Kids who are trying to "make it" in a broken home need to read books about other kids who face similar situations. They need to know that they are not alone in their experiences—that others feel pain and anger, loneliness and frustration. . . . They can learn the possible alternatives that exist by seeing what others (even fictional "others") do. In this way they may realize that they do have lives of their own independent of their parents (19: 70).

Haley (19) also suggested some novels that have proved to be of interest to adolescents trying to survive broken homes: *Deathman, Do Not Follow Me* by Jay Bennett, *The Pigman* and *My Darling, My Hamburger* by Paul Zindel, and S. E. Hinton's *That Was Then, This Is Now*.

Seiger (45) interpreted the role of literature as including means of (a) dealing with human values, (b) guiding students to read and grasp interpersonal conflicts, (c) making value decisions, and (d) adding needed structure to students' lives. He stated that the able teacher is one who looks ". . . to the study of literature as one vehicle which may help the student see beyond his circumscribed existence and come to grips with the social and moral dilemmas of our time" (45: 139-40).

Additional viewpoints concerning reader interest. In addition to "bookmanship" as a motivation or stimulant in capturing reader interest, other factors have been found which have significant impact on the interest of the reader. In one study by Hanzelka (20), short stories were rated by a panel of students and a panel of English specialists. He found that both groups preferred stories with clear plots and believed that readability and clarity were closely related.

Colbert (8) applied a criteria checklist for purposes of assessing "content components" of 107 selections for adolescents chosen from 12 leading anthologies. Her study led her to conclude that no more than half of the 107 excerpts satisfied 20 out of 32 criteria.

Pollan (40) administered a questionnaire to high school students. She found the most widely read books to include Kurt Vonnegut, Jr.'s *Cat's Cradle*; Hermann Hesse's *Demian* and *Siddhartha*; J. D. Salinger's *Catcher in the Rye*; Richard Brautigan's *The Abortion;* and Ken Kesey's *One Flew over the Cuckoo's Nest*. In the category of classical literature *Wuthering Heights, Jane Eyre*, and F. Scott Fitzgerald's books were mentioned most frequently.

Curriculum Trends

Minority literature. The effects of the women's liberation movement, of integration, and of affirmative action have left an indelible mark on society, so it comes as a surprise to find that they are not widely reflected in literature of the early seventies. Nelson (32), for instance, noted that a double standard continued to be found in a number of adolescent novels. She analyzed the role of women characters portrayed in five novels commonly read by eleventh and twelfth grade students and found little "model diversity." The women continued to be stereotyped as wives and mothers. Sex experiences yielded automatic pregnancy, and "girltalk" centered on boys and dates.

Similar problems of stereotyping also exist when the male role is depicted in the adolescent novel. Kelty (26: 57) expressed concern over the "stereotyped initiation of the male character who persistently becomes a man when he performs an act of violence against an animal and/or the natural world." For instance, such violent actions are portrayed in well-known novels such as *The Yearling* by Marjorie Kinnan Rawlings, *Old Yeller* by Fred Gipson, and Ernest

Hemingway's *The Old Man and the Sea*—although they antedate the "lib" movements of recent years.

Moving from sexuality to race relations, the writer found that Carr (5) had reviewed secondary school anthologies and reported that as of 1972 they gave a misleading view of the black experience—if they presented blacks at all. An analogous 1974 study by Duff (15) led her to conclude that 72.2 percent of the 18 anthologies she examined were inadequate in their selection of writings by black writers. Hipple (22: 9) suggested that we do away with the idea of developing separate courses for "Black Literature." He felt that "appropriate black literature should be included in all literature classes."

Trout (49) proposed in 1974 that we take the Indians off the reservations and strive for a more realistic portrayal of them in literature. It was admitted, however, that the suggestion may encounter opposition from those who prefer to view Indians as always romantic and stoic! Trout went on to recommend novels that serve to expose students to authentic Indian experiences, among them: *Hatter Fox* by Marilyn Harriss, *House Made of Dawn* by N. Scott Momaday, *When the Legends Die* by Hal Borland, and *Journey to Ixtlan* by Carlos Castaneda.

Elective English. One of the more notable trends in English education during the late sixties and early seventies is the adoption of elective English programs. This appears to be the departmental answer to students' pleas for relevancy. Jagust (25: 1325) reported success in using relevant literature and in letting students suggest additions or deletions in the reading lists. He noted the need for changes made in his course since the sixties, saying, "I have changed in these years; students have changed even more; schools have had to change. Any course that did not change would be a dead course."

However, most of what has been written on elective English programs centers around curriculum guides providing course descriptions and objectives. The majority of the schools using elective programs do not administer standardized tests. One study cited by Suhor (46: 48) ascertained that only seven of 48 schools with elective English programs used standardized tests. This is a troublesome development in at least one sense; very little data are provided on the effectiveness of such programs.

Developments in poetry. "Poetry cannot really be taught. It can, however, be caught," according to Lesser (28: 24). The idea of "poetic contagion" is stressed by a number of researchers and critics concerned with making poetry an enjoyable experience for students (28, 21, 7). Lesser (28) and Curtis (11) agreed that poem selection is vital to a successful experience. Curtis (11: 1326) warned, "Too often when children play with giants permanent injury results. Sometimes it is fatal."

Trout (48: 104) suggested that exposing students to many poetry paper-backs is ". . . one way to motivate and support the student's writing and reading poetry." She argued the teacher's role is that of a resource person, guiding students in the appreciation of poets who correspond to the students' style or interest. Womack (51) also supported the idea of allowing students to browse until they find poems they like. Norris (35) and Roeming (43) reported success in poetry programs that involved bringing poets into the classroom.

Though some writers such as Harcourt (21) and Womack (51) stressed the importance of teaching the "technical elements" in poetry, others such as Clare (7) or Evans (16) advised caution lest a given poem be torn apart until there is nothing left, destroying the aesthetic and emotional experience that should have accompanied it. Stress on the value of experiencing an emotional reaction to poetry is supported in a 1973 survey which identified 3,500 drug addicts, alcoholics, and mentally retarded persons around the country and over 400 therapists who make use of poetry for psychotherapeutic value. Evidently there are reasons to preserve this therapeutic effect of poetry among our students.

Science fiction. With the advent of *Star Trek* in the visual media, there appears to have been a heightening of interest in science fiction in the print media. Some teachers report greater success with this type of fiction than with any other kind. Lawler (27) termed science fiction the "new mythology," with implications for stimulating reader imagination. Hollister and Thompson (23) also praised science fiction, not only for its help in stimulating creative thinking but also as a means of exploring social issues such as overpopulation, love-hate relationships, nuclear destruction, and non-conformity. Reynolds (42) proposed that science fiction be used as a means instead of an end in teaching reading and writing.

Various materials have become available to help teachers develop science fiction courses and to organize materials for use therein, according to Millies (30) and Paine and Martinez (37).

Censorship

"The Grim Reaper." The censor is seen by many writers as the "Grim Reaper" of the English classroom because his or her edicts diminish the chances a child might have to participate in a guided experience that involves reading and discussing controversial materials. Donelson (14: 1197-98) wrote with considerable eloquence on the topic:

English teachers and their students must have freedom to read and see and think and discuss and learn if there is any hope of reality entering the classroom. Where censors grant teachers "limited" freedom as long as students read only "wholesome" books and "uplifting" magazines about "good" Americans and "happy" things, view only "suitable" and "clean" and "Christian" films, create only "optimistic" and "positive" and "inspirational" media materials, and discuss only "noncontroversial" and "safe" topics, there is no possibility of education and the search for truth, only the indoctrination into the community's contemporary mores.

Eight categories of traditionally "suspect" books have been singled out by Donelson (13: 48) as the targets of censors: (a) sex, (b) politics, (c) war and peace, (d) religion, (e) sociology and race, (f) language, (g) drugs, and (h) inappropriate adolescent behavior.

Since as long as there are issues and conflicts, there is likely to be censorship, Symula (47) suggested that teachers be prepared to defend what they choose to teach. He recommended strategic measures such as (a) sending newsletters to parents stating the teacher's objectives or giving critics' reviews, (b) forming PTA discussion groups, (c) encouraging a book evaluation committee to investigate censorship problems, and (d) alerting mature students to the views and tensions involved in censorship.

Donelson (13) suggested the English department use problem-preventive measures by establishing department policy and guides for the selection of literature, and by having teachers prepare clear-cut statements of objectives and strive to improve school-community communication. He warned (13: 51), "If we do not prepare in advance or if we do not care to prepare, we . . . will wind up losing everything—our books, our students, and our freedom."

Evaluation

In drawing toward the end of any scholarly pursuit, whether it be the close of a well-presented unit or the conclusion to a chapter on literature in the secondary schools, the well-prepared teacher knows he or she is faced with the ultimate task—evaluation. Unfortunately the realm of testing in literature has become especially controversial territory. Literature tests sometimes overlook the more important aspects of literature such as experiencing culture, creating a literate populace, or cultivating critical and aesthetic taste. According to Purves (41), tests usually evaluate only a student's cognitive level on normative tests.

Suhor (46) enumerated some of the subtle problems encountered in testing students' ability in literature. He pointed out that reading is a major requirement or prerequisite for success on most literature tests, while "poor readers can understand ideas well beyond their ability to decode" (46: 46). Second, Suhor noted that tests which ask students to interpret, to distinguish main ideas, to infer, or to draw conclusions are actually tests of broader context thinking—of complex mental operations. Even though teachers and professional organizations may denounce dwelling on the factual aspects of a literary work, he concluded that "much of mass testing continues to focus on recall of facts" (46:

46-47), and that some scholars such as Buros have found that sometimes ". . . the student whose thinking is subtle and precise is actually penalized by ambiguous multiple choice tests" (46: 47).

The carefully written essay question can include comprehension and a knowledge of literary forms, lead to emotional response, sharpen aesthetic judgment, and reveal the value of the literary experience to the student (41). However, the grading of essay tests has often been riddled with problems. The College Entrance Examination Board (CEEB) and Educational Testing Service (ETS) apparently have found ways of obtaining reliable results, Suhor reported, through ". . . holistic readings of short essays by trained readers" (46: 48). This does not always help the classroom teacher, however, because of the time and expense of CEEB and ETS tests. Also, they usually are administered only to seniors and a limited number of juniors.

At this point one may be asking the question, as did Suhor, "Is mass testing necessary?" Suhor's answer was: "If mass testing does not measure things that are worth measuring, and if the measurement that takes place results in distortions, mass testing presents a false report to the community" (46: 48).

A Parting Word

After reading, reviewing, and writing about the demands on classroom literature today, the writer feels a strong urge to share with her fellow teachers the simple and venerable maxim, "We must never let the teaching of *literature*— or any other subject—interfere with our main job: that of teaching *children* and *youth*!"

As teachers we have a responsibility to share literature with them at *their* cognitive level and allow *them* the privilege of affective response. The children, along with teachers, have been subjected to a "Future Shock" world; and censors, teachers, and parents alike owe them an opportunity to learn about that world as it is reflected in literature, with the guidance and cooperation of an insightful classroom teacher. The challenge for the English teacher in the years ahead is to justify the ranking of Literature as part of the "*human*-ities."

References

1. BACON, WALLACE A. "Oral Interpretation and the Teaching of Literature in Secondary Schools." Paper presented at the meeting of the Speech Communication Association, New York, November 1974.

2. BARTH, RODNEY J. "ERIC/RCS Report and Teaching Adolescent Literature." *English Journal* 63: 103-105; February 1974.

3. BAYLESS, CHARLES EUGENE. "An Analysis of the Alienation Motif in Secondary School Literature." Unpublished doctoral dissertation, Duke University, Durham, North Carolina, 1975.

4. BURTON, DWIGHT L. "Well, Where Are We in Teaching Literature?" *English Journal* 63: 28-33; February 1974.

5. CARR, JOHN C. *My Brother's Keeper and a View of Blacks in Secondary School Literature Anthologies.* Dubuque, Iowa: William C. Brown Company, Publishers, 1972.

6. CHRISTENSEN, J. A. "Fiction of Loneliness." *Media and Methods—Exploration in Education* 8: 24-28; February 1972.

7. CLARE, SISTER FRANCIS. "Poetry Teach-ins an 'In' Thing." *Elementary English* 49: 625-28; April 1972.

8. COLBERT, JOY EDITH. "Nonfiction and Adolescent Reading Interests." Unpublished doctoral dissertation, Virginia Polytechnic Institute and State University, Blacksburg, 1974.

9. COOPER, CHARLES R. "The New Climate for Personal Responses to Literature in the Classroom." *English Journal* 60: 1063-71; November 1971.

10. CORUM, SHIRLEY. "The Independent Reading of Young Adults." In: Donald Nemanick, editor. "Literature." *Illinois English Bulletin* 61: 17-20; January 1974.

11. CURTIS, BRIAN J. "The Necessity of the Rod McKuens." *English Journal* 61: 1326-27, 1381; December 1972.

12. DICKENS, CHARLES. *Hard Times.* New York: W. W. Norton and Company, Inc., 1966.

13. DONELSON, KENNETH. "Censorship in the 1970's and Some Ways To Handle It When It Comes (and It Will)." *English Journal* 63: 47-51; February 1974.

14. DONELSON, KENNETH L. "White Walls and High Windows and Some Contemporary Censorship Problems." *English Journal* 61: 1191-98; November 1972. Copyright © 1972 by the National Council of Teachers of English. Reprinted by permission of the publisher.

15. DUFF, OGLE ELOISE BURKS. "The Treatment of Blacks in Selected Literature Anthologies for Grades Nine Through Twelve Published Since 1968." Unpublished doctoral dissertation, University of Pittsburgh, Pennsylvania, 1974.

16. EVANS, RONALD V. "Poetry Therapy." Paper presented at the Anniversary Meeting of Florida Council of Teachers of English State Conference, Daytona Beach, Florida, October 17-19, 1974.

17. FLANIGAN, JEAN CULP. "Novels for Class Study in Junior High School and Some Recommendations." Unpublished master's thesis, Auburn University, Auburn, Alabama, 1973.

18. GOLUB, LESTER S. "National Approaches to Teaching Literature and Moral Development." ERIC ED 105 522

19. HALEY, BEVERLY. "The Fractured Family in Adolescent Literature." *English Journal* 63: 70-72; February 1974. Copyright © by the National Council of Teachers of English. Reprinted by permission of the publisher.

20. HANZELKA, RICHARD LOUIS. "Characteristics of Short Stories Associated with Preferences of Ninth Grade Students." Unpublished doctoral dissertation, University of Iowa, 1974.

21. HARCOURT, ROGER. "Sharing Poems." *Use of English* 25: 325-37; Summer 1974.

22. HIPPLE, THEODORE. "Let's Take the 'Black' Out of Black Literature." *English Journal* 63: 8-9; February 1974.

23. HOLLISTER, BERNARD C., and DEANE C. THOMPSON. *Grokking the Future And Science Fiction in the Classroom.* Dayton, Ohio: Pflaum/Standard, 1963.

24. INGLIS, JAMES, et al. "The Teaching of Literature." *Teaching English* 7: 10-22; October 1973.

25. JAGUST, EARL. "A Senior Elective Course 1960-1972." *English Journal* 61: 1322-25; December 1972.

26. KELTY, JEAN MCCLURE. "The Cult of Kill in Adolescent Fiction." *English Journal* 64: 56-61; February 1975.

27. LAWLER, DONALD L. "Certain Assistances and the Utilities of Science Fiction and Fantasy in Shaping the Future." ERIC ED 112 424

28. LESSER, PETER A. "Teaching Poetry in the Secondary Schools." *Use of English* 26: 24-34; Autumn 1974.

29. MILLER, JEAN SAWYER. "The Search for Identity in Selected Novels of Hermann Hesse and a Thematic Study for the Secondary Schools." Unpublished doctoral dissertation, University of Georgia, Athens, 1972.

30. MILLIES, SUZANNE. *Science Fiction Primer for Teachers.* Dayton, Ohio: Pflaum/Standard, 1974.

31. MILSTEAD, JOHN. "Form Is Not Enough: Thinking the Unthinkable About Teaching Literature." In: Donald Nemanick, editor. "Teacher Literature." *Illinois English Bulletin* 62: 4-11; October 1974.

32. NELSON, GAYLE. "The Double Standard in Adolescent Novels." *English Journal* 64: 53-55; February 1975.

33. NEMANICK, DONALD, editor. "Teacher Literature." *Illinois English Bulletin* 62; October 1974. Also cf. "Bibliotherapy," chapter by Lina M. Brewer, p. 11-15.

34. NESTOR, MAURA. "Human Relations in Literature." *English Journal* 63: 66-68; February 1974. Copyright © 1974 by the National Council of Teachers of English. Reprinted by permission of the publisher.

35. NORRIS, RUBY LEE, editor. *The Turtle and the Teacher and a Dialogue Between Poets.* Richmond, Virginia: Richmond Intercultural Center for the Humanities, 1973.

36. ODLAND, NORINE. "Teaching Children's Literature—From the Point of View of the Reader." Paper presented at the Annual Meeting of the National Council of Teachers of English, Las Vegas, Nevada, November 25-27, 1971.

37. PAINE, DORIS M., and DIANA MARTINEZ. *Guide to Science Fiction and Exploring Possibilities and Alternatives.* New York: Bantam Books, Inc., 1974.

38. PENNA, ROBERT FRANK. "The Relative Effectiveness of the Classroom Discussion Approach and the Tutorial Approach to Literature for the Development of Adolescent Ego Identity." Unpublished doctoral dissertation, Fordham University, New York City, 1975.

39. PERRY, JESSE. "Literature, a Mirror to Understanding Oneself and Others Today, Tomorrow, and Yesterday." Paper presented to the California Association of Teachers of English, Los Angeles, California, February 1974.

40. POLLAN, CORRINE. "What High School Students Are Really Reading." *English Journal* 62: 573-76; April 1973.

41. PURVES, ALAN C. "Testing 'Testing' in Literature." Paper presented at the meeting of the California Association of Teachers of English, Los Angeles, California, 1974.

42. REYNOLDS, WILLIAM D. "The Status of Science Fiction Anthologies and Their Applicability to Teaching." Paper presented at the Annual Meeting of the Midwest Modern Language Association, St. Louis, Missouri, October 31-November 2, 1974.

43. ROEMING, ROBERT F. *Developing Awareness Through Poetry.* Milwaukee: University of Wisconsin—Milwaukee, 1972.

44. SCHARFF, CHARLES E. "On Teaching the Process of Literature and Levels of Understanding." Paper presented at the meeting of the National Council of Teachers of English, New Orleans, Louisiana, November 1974.

45. SEIGER, FREDERICK J. "Literature and the Concern for Human Values." *Journal of Reading* 15: 139-42; November 1971.

46. SUHOR, CHARLES. "This Is an Article on . . . Mass Testing in Literature." *English Journal* 64: 46-49; March 1975.

47. SYMULA, JAMES F. "Censorship and Teacher Responsibility." *English Journal* 60: 128-31; January 1971.

48. TROUT, LAWANA. "I'm Reading Paperbacks and Writing Poetry." *English Journal* 63: 104-107; October 1974.

49. TROUT, LAWANA. "Paperbacks in the Classroom." *English Journal* 63: 93-94; December 1974.

50. TURNER, DARWIN T. "Literary Criticism and the Teacher as Servant to the Student." Paper presented to the National Council of Teachers of English, Philadelphia, Pennsylvania, November 1973.

51. WOMACK, NANCY. "A Student Oriented Approach to Teaching Poetry." 1974. ERIC ED 097 690

52. YODER, ALBERT C. "Reading Literature and Two Schools of Thought." *Journal of Reading* 18: 312-15; January 1975.

13. Epilog: Speculations About Research in the Coming Decade

James D. Walden and
Kathryn R. Akural

It is, of course, impossible to predict the precise direction of research in the various fields of education in the next several years. Few of us have investigated in any depth more than one or two areas of the language arts; hence it is not easy to write with confidence about the years ahead. In general terms, however, it seems safe to say that research affords the soundest basis for improving the educational enterprise.

Three Questions

This belief motivates us to discuss three major facets of research in the years ahead: (a) who will be doing research, (b) where the research will be done, and (c) what the nature of such research activities may be.

Who will do research? The October 1960 issue of *Harper's Magazine* carried an article entitled "The Cults of Research and Creativity." The author, Jacques Barzun, expressed great concern about the then current practice of luring scholars from one university to another with an offer of a larger salary and with the lure of superior facilities for research. During the 1960's, furthermore, faculty members at colleges and universities were criticized by Barzun for neglecting teaching responsibilities while they "did research."

By the early 1970's, conditions had changed. Student enrollments began to decline, faculty positions and mobility were reduced, and "soft" money support through grants became severely limited. Reduced "hard" money budgets also led to increased teaching loads, and as a concomitant, to less time to engage in research activities.

The attrition of persons prepared for careers in educational research has always been heavy. Some have left education to enter other fields. Some remain in education but move into administrative positions, while others find the press of the promotion-and-tenure system too demanding and become dropouts. For whatever reasons, the ranks have been and continue to be depleted.

The problem is further complicated by the decline in college and university enrollments. While it is true that the greatest drop-off has been at the undergraduate and master's degree levels, there is reason to believe that graduate enrollments will face sharper declines during the next few years as declines at the undergraduate level begin to affect graduate enrollments. Perhaps even more significant was the termination, in 1976, of the Education Professions Development Act (EPDA) which helped to support graduate level students. Furthermore, during the mid-seventies the tight job market in education fields left less incentive for young students who wish to pursue advanced degrees. We hope, of course, that during the next five to seven years the unfavorable conditions which currently hinder educational research may be somewhat ameliorated.

Where will research be done? Factors, usually beyond the control of institutions of higher education, have reduced the number of sources available for gathering data required for research activities. These factors not only influence the amount of research being conducted, but they also have an effect on the nature of this research.

The pressure to mount field-based instructional programs for preservice and in-service teachers—pressure sometimes mandated by law—has increased the traffic in elementary and secondary classrooms. That increase has forced schools of education to do less with proposals for language arts research studies using public school students as subjects.

School policies for granting permission to use school settings for research purposes also are less flexible as a result of the passage of the Family Educational Rights and Privacy Act in 1974. One obvious result of the changes has been an increase in the amount of time required to obtain permission to gather data, a development which probably is discouraging some doctoral students from considering studies that require an elementary or secondary school population. Parents, through misunderstanding, also seem more reluctant to give permission for their children to serve as research subjects. As a result, designs requiring the matching of students or random selection of subjects have become more difficult to execute.

These factors, reinforced by evidence from the past few years, suggest that what support is available for research activities is likely to go to private research agencies or to a small number of universities for highly specified research targets.

What will be the nature of such research activities? The best indicators of future research in a given field are the past and current trends in the area. We shall, therefore, begin our examination of this question with a brief review of current trends in the language arts. The emphasis on reading that will be evident in this discussion reflects the fact that reading has developed the broadest research base of all of the language arts. In their recent summary of reading research, Weintraub et al. (11) reviewed 599 studies on reading published in 1975-1976.

One major trend evident in the language arts today is the influence of psycholinguistics. The relatively young field of psycholinguistics represents an interdisciplinary effort by psychologists and linguists to probe questions concerning language use, language comprehension, and language acquisition. Psycholinguistics is considered by Tiedt and Tiedt (10) to be one of the two major "new directions" in reading instruction in the 1970's.

The other is the trend toward including formal reading instruction in the junior and senior high school English curricula. By emphasizing the relationship among the processes involved in oral language acquisition, reading, and writing, psycholinguistic theory and research have provided an impressive rationale for the teaching of the language arts as an integrated unit rather than as separate subjects. The current emphasis on comprehension, both in reading research and in classroom practice, is a direct reflection of psycholinguistic influence. So, too, is the recent interest in the reading process itself, as evidenced by the proliferation of reading theories now flooding the literature. A cursory review of professional journals such as *Language Arts* and *The Reading Teacher* for the past seven or eight years will reveal, appearing almost monthly, numerous articles concerning theories of reading. A basic reference work in this new and exciting area is by Harry Singer and Robert R. Ruddell (8).

Psycholinguistic insights also have had an impact on the teaching of composition (5). There is every reason to believe that the influence of psycholinguistics on the language arts is likely to continue for some time in the coming years.

Another major trend characterizing the current state of the language arts is reflected in the related emphases on providing students with basic competencies and actively involving them in the learning process. This concern for process as well as content, affect as well as cognition, skills as well as knowledge, is clearly evident in both the NCTE *Statement on the Preparation of Teachers of English and the Language Arts* (9) and the 1976 Yearbook of the National Society for the Study of Education (7). Considering the past swings of the educational pendulum, however, it is difficult to predict the longevity of this trend.

In light of this brief review of current trends in the language arts, it may now be possible to provide some tentative answers to the question of what the nature of future research activities may be. First of all, although the coming years may see a considerable decline in the quantity of educational research in general, it seems safe to predict that the area of reading will continue to receive more than its share of attention and available funds. Moreover, although the ranks of educational researchers may dwindle, the "influx of 'outsiders'" from other disciplines noted by Chall (2: 6) in 1976 seems likely to continue. If this holds true, these specialists from the fields of cognitive psychology, sociolinguistics, and psycholinguistics may both invigorate language arts research and compensate for the declining number of educational researchers.

The need for improved communication between researchers and practitioners in the language arts is currently widely recognized (1, 2, 3); it will become even more essential as specialists from other fields contribute to research in the language arts. This communication must proceed in both directions, however. Although few dispute the fact that research can be of genuine benefit to classroom teachers, it is also agreed that teachers must be able to borrow from and implement these findings critically and with discrimination. To attain the objective of improved communication between researchers and teachers, Calfee recommended that future research be carried out "in real schools," as a mutual commitment between researchers and the school community (1: 43). It may be hoped that those factors mitigating against the realization of this recommendation will ameliorate in the next few years as the advantages of on-site research become more widely recognized.

In regard to recommendations for future research in reading, Chall cautioned against the present trend toward great specificity in the testing and teaching of reading. Noting the elaborate reading systems developed by a number of basal publishers in the past several years, she asked, "Will there be a time in such a system for the children who work slowly to perhaps read a book and write a story?" (2: 11). Chall is not against the use of a management system per se; she is concerned, however, that the human element not be sacrificed to the massive record-keeping required in these basal reading systems.

Another recommendation for further study in the language arts, which is perhaps the broadest and most far-reaching, is this: that the language arts in general, and reading in particular, develop a judicious working relationship with linguistics, psychology, psycholinguistics, and most especially epistemology. For most of this century, reading and other educational researchers have attempted to achieve credibility and respectability by emulating the scientific paradigm; that is, by applying the inductive methods and techniques of the natural sciences —particularly physics—to problems of teaching and learning. This uncritical acceptance of what Medawar calls "the whole discredited farrago of inductivism" (6: 12) long prevented educational researchers in general, and reading experts in particular, from observing the great changes that were taking place in theoretical physics. With these new developments, in Levy's words, physics ". . . stepped beyond the world of absolutes into the speculative, integrating, subjective, holistic mode of knowing" (4: 47).

Levy's statement may be taken as a caution that scientific empiricism may not after all be well-suited to research in reading. It is hoped that this "speculative" mode of knowing, with its roots deep in the rationalism of Plato, Descartes, and the Logical Positivists of the early 20th century (Whitehead, Russell, and Wittgenstein), may begin to exert a beneficial influence on future research in all of the language arts.

A Final Note

We have several concerns for educational research in the next several years. On the whole, the short-term outlook is not as good as it was in the early seventies when the most recent ASCD language arts research monograph appeared. However, what actually happens in the next decade will depend on those who believe in the value of research. Each of us needs to strive to make certain that the next years will be productive in the field of the language arts. At the local school level, for example, we must attempt to convince policy makers of the need for and value of our research efforts. Prospective researchers, including those in classrooms as well as in graduate schools, need to be encouraged to conduct their studies. Responsible involvement in the process is a necessary ingredient if our profession is to retain its vitality.

Active participation in national organizations such as the Association for Supervision and Curriculum Development (ASCD) may be one way to convince thoughtful colleagues, including policy makers, of the need for continued research support. Action programs designed to strengthen our working relationships with agencies that have the potential to support research will be critical, too. Finally, we must take advantage of each personal research opportunity—large or small, funded or not—if the next several years are to be rewarding ones.

References

1. CALFEE, ROBERT C. "A Proposal for Practical (but Good) Research on Reading." *Research in the Teaching of English* 10: 41-50; Spring 1976.

2. CHALL, JEANNE S. *Reading and Development.* Keynote Address, Twentieth Annual Convention, International Reading Association. Newark, Delaware: International Reading Association, 1976.

3. HARRIS, ALBERT J. "Practical Applications of Reading Research." *The Reading Teacher* 29: 559-65; March 1976.

4. LEVY, JACK J. "Zen and the Art of Reading." In: Malcolm P. Douglass, editor. *Claremont Reading Conference.* Forty-First Yearbook. Claremont, California: Claremont Graduate School, 1977. pp. 41-47.

5. LUNDSTEEN, SARA W., editor. *Help for the Teacher of Written Composition: New Directions in Research.* Urbana, Illinois: National Council of Teachers of English, 1976.

6. MEDAWAR, P. B. "Unnatural Science." *New York Review,* February 3, 1977. pp. 12-18.

7. PETTY, WALTER H., DOROTHY C. PETTY, ANABEL P. NEWMAN, and ELOISE M. SKEEN. "Language Competencies for Coping in Our Society." Chapter III in: *The Teaching of English.* Seventy-Sixth Yearbook of the National Society for the Study of Education. Chicago, Illinois: NSSE, 1977. pp. 66-95.

8. SINGER, HARRY S., and ROBERT R. RUDDELL, editors. *Theoretical Models and Processes of Reading.* Newark, Delaware: International Reading Association, 1976.

9. *Statement on the Preparation of Teachers of English and the Language Arts.* Urbana, Illinois: National Council of Teachers of English, 1976.

10. TIEDT, IRIS M., and SIDNEY W. TIEDT. *Contemporary English in the Elementary School.* Englewood Cliffs, New Jersey: Prentice-Hall, Inc., 1975.

11. WEINTRAUB, SAMUEL, et al. "Summary of Investigations Relating to Reading: July 1, 1975-June 30, 1976." *Reading Research Quarterly* 12: 231-565; Summer 1977.

Contributors

KATHRYN R. AKURAL is Supervisor of the Reading Practicum Center, Indiana University, Bloomington.

KEVIN SUE BAILEY is a teacher at Floyd Central High School, New Albany, Indiana, and is an associate faculty member at Indiana State University, Bloomington.

DIXIE POTTER BJURSTROM is in the English Department at Ladue High School, St. Louis, Missouri.

PETER F. CONNALLON, JR., is an Associate Instructor in Elementary Education at Indiana University, Bloomington.

NELLY CERES FERREIRA is working toward her doctorate at Indiana University, Bloomington.

DONALD R. FROST, President of ASCD, 1978-79, is Curriculum Director, Leyden High Schools, Franklin Park and Northlake, Illinois.

JOANNE GENTRY is Coordinator of the Suburban Cluster Student Teaching Project, Indiana University, Bloomington.

HARRY L. GRADMAN is Associate Professor of Education, Indiana University, Bloomington.

ROBERT C. LAFAYETTE is Associate Professor of Education, Indiana University, Bloomington.

LINDA S. LOTTO is a Research Assistant at Indiana University, Bloomington.

DOLORES MACNAUGHTON is Research Associate, Canadian Institute for Research in the Behavioral and Social Sciences, Calgary, Alberta.

MILTON MARTEN is Associate Professor of Education, Indiana University, Bloomington.

DENNIS W. PETT is Professor of Education and Director of Instructional Services, Indiana University, Bloomington.

HAROLD G. SHANE is University Professor of Education, Indiana University, Bloomington.

JAMES D. WALDEN is Professor of Education, Indiana University, Bloomington.

ASCD Publications, Autumn 1978

Yearbooks

Education for an Open Society
(610-74012) $8.00
Education for Peace: Focus on Mankind
(610-17946) $7.50
Evaluation as Feedback and Guide
(610-17700) $6.50
Feeling, Valuing, and the Art of Growing:
Insights into the Affective
(610-77104) $9.75
Freedom, Bureaucracy, & Schooling
(610-17508) $6.50
Improving the Human Condition: A Curricular
Response to Critical Realities
(610-78132) $9.75
Learning and Mental Health in the School
(610-17674) $5.00
Life Skills in School and Society
(610-17786) $5.50
A New Look at Progressive Education
(610-17812) $8.00
Perspectives on Curriculum Development
1776-1976 (610-76078) $9.50
Schools in Search of Meaning
(610-75044) $8.50
Perceiving, Behaving, Becoming: A New Focus
for Education (610-17278) $5.00
To Nurture Humaneness: Commitment for
the '70's (610-17810) $6.00

Books and Booklets

About Learning Materials (611-78134) $4.50
Action Learning: Student Community Service
Projects (611-74018) $2.50
Adventuring, Mastering, Associating: New
Strategies for Teaching Children
(611-76080) $5.00
Beyond Jencks: The Myth of Equal Schooling
(611-17928) $2.00
The Changing Curriculum: Mathematics
(611-17724) $2.00
Classroom-Relevant Research in the Language
Arts (611-78140) $7.50
Criteria for Theories of Instruction
(611-17756) $2.00
Curricular Concerns in a Revolutionary Era
(611-17852) $6.00
Curriculum Leaders: Improving Their Influence
(611-76084) $4.00
Curriculum Theory (611-77112) $7.00
Degrading the Grading Myths: A Primer of
Alternatives to Grades and Marks
(611-76082) $6.00
Differentiated Staffing (611-17924) $3.50
Discipline for Today's Children and Youth
(611-17314) $1.50
Educational Accountability: Beyond Behavioral
Objectives (611-17856) $2.50
Elementary School Mathematics: A Guide to
Current Research (611-75056) $5.00
Elementary School Science: A Guide to
Current Research (611-17726) $2.25
Eliminating Ethnic Bias in Instructional
Materials: Comment and Bibliography
(611-74020) $3.25
Emerging Moral Dimensions in Society:
Implications for Schooling
(611-75052) $3.75
Ethnic Modification of the Curriculum
(611-17832) $1.00
Global Studies: Problems and Promises for
Elementary Teachers (611-76086) $4.50
Humanistic Education: Objectives and
Assessment (611-78136) $4.75
The Humanities and the Curriculum
(611-17708) $2.00

Impact of Decentralization on Curriculum:
Selected Viewpoints (611-75050) $3.75
Improving Educational Assessment & An
Inventory of Measures of Affective
Behavior (611-17804) $4.50
International Dimension of Education
(611-17816) $2.25
Interpreting Language Arts Research for the
Teacher (611-17846) $4.00
Learning More About Learning
(611-17310) $2.00
Linguistics and the Classroom Teacher
(611-17720) $2.75
A Man for Tomorrow's World
(611-17838) $2.25
Middle School in the Making
(611-74024) $5.00
The Middle School We Need
(611-75060) $2.50
Multicultural Education: Commitments, Issues,
and Applications (611-77108) $7.00
Needs Assessment: A Focus for Curriculum
Development (611-75048) $4.00
Observational Methods in the Classroom
(611-17948) $3.50
Open Education: Critique and Assessment
(611-75054) $4.75
Professional Supervision for Professional
Teachers (611-75046) $4.50
Removing Barriers to Humaneness in the High
School (611-17848) $2.50
Reschooling Society: A Conceptual Model
(611-17950) $2.00
The School of the Future—NOW
(611-17920) $3.75
Schools Become Accountable: A PACT
Approach (611-74016) $3.50
The School's Role as Moral Authority
(611-77110) $4.50
Selecting Learning Experiences: Linking
Theory and Practice (611-78138) $4.75
Social Studies for the Evolving Individual
(611-17952) $3.00
Staff Development: Staff Liberation
(611-77106) $6.50
Supervision: Emerging Profession
(611-17796) $5.00
Supervision in a New Key (611-17926) $2.50
Supervision: Perspectives and Propositions
(611-17732) $2.00
What Are the Sources of the Curriculum?
(611-17522) $1.50
Vitalizing the High School (611-74026) $3.50
Developmental Characteristics of Children and
Youth (wall chart) (611-75058) $2.00

Books by Janet Dailey

Calder Born, Calder Bred
Stands a Calder Man
This Calder Range
This Calder Sky
The Best Way to Lose
Touch the Wind
The Glory Game
The Pride of Hannah Wade
Silver Wings, Santiago Blue
For the Love of God
Foxfire Light
The Hostage Bride
The Lancaster Men
Leftover Love
Mistletoe and Holly
The Second Time
Separate Cabins
Terms of Surrender
Western Man
Nightway
Ride the Thunder
The Rogue

"I Thought You Were a Calder," Jessy Said. "I Thought You Had Some Feeling for the Land.

Are you willing to destroy the Calder land for the coal underneath it?"

"Dammit, Jessy! I don't have any choice. I need the money to keep the ranch going."

"What ranch? There won't be anything left—it'll be scrub desert in thirty years."

"You don't understand." Ty tried to control his temper.

"No, you don't understand," Jessy retorted. "You are doing it for money—for profit. It's business, you say. It's progress. You've been given a legacy, Ty. A tradition that has prided itself on caring for the land and people. You're going to lose both because you think money is more important. People built this ranch. The only way it could ever be destroyed is from the inside. And you're the core of it. If the heart is no good, the rest of it will slowly die."

It was a long moment before Ty offered any response.

"You've made your point," he said.

JANET DAILEY

CALDER BORN, CALDER BRED

POCKET BOOKS
New York   London   Toronto   Sydney   Singapore

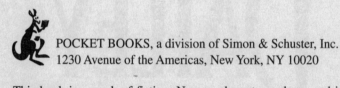 POCKET BOOKS, a division of Simon & Schuster, Inc.
1230 Avenue of the Americas, New York, NY 10020

ISBN: 0-7434-8290-5

This Pocket Books trade paperback edition July 2003

10 9 8 7 6 5 4 3 2 1

POCKET and colophon are registered trademarks of
Simon & Schuster, Inc.

Manufactured in the United States of America

For information regarding special discounts for bulk purchases,
please contact Simon & Schuster Special Sales at 1-800-456-6798
or business@simonandschuster.com.

I

Wanting to belong isn't easy
When they're making it rough instead.
And the hardest of all is knowing
They're all Calder born—and Calder bred.

1

The windswept Montana plains rolled with empty monotony beneath a freeze-dried sky. Along a fence line that stretched into the far-flung horizon, old snow formed low drifts. A brooming wind had brushed clean the brown carpet of frozen grass that covered the rough-and-tumble roll of the plains and held the thin layer of soil in place.

There was no room in this bleak, rough country for anyone not wise to its ways. To those who understood it, its wealth was given. But those who tried to take it eventually paid a brutal price.

Its primitive beauty lay in the starkness of its landscape. The vast reaches of nothingness seemed to go on forever. Winter came early and stayed late in this lonely land where cattle outnumbered people. The cattle on this particular million-acre stretch of empty range carried the brand of the Triple C, marking them as the property of the Calder Cattle Company.

A lone pickup truck was bouncing over the frozen ruts of the ranch road, just one of some two hundred miles of private roads that interlaced the Triple C Ranch. A vaporous cloud from the engine's exhaust trailed behind the pickup in a gray-white plume. Like the road, the truck seemed to be going nowhere. There was no destination in sight until the truck crested a low rise in the plains and came upon a hollow that nature had scooped into the deceptively flat-appearing terrain.

The camp known as South Branch was located in this large pocket of ground, one of a half-dozen such camps that formed an outlying circle around the nucleus of the ranch, breaking its vastness into manageable districts. The term "camp" was a

3

holdover from the early days when line camps were established to offer crude shelters to cowboys working the range far from the ranch's home buildings.

There was a weathered solidness and permanence to the buildings at South Branch, structures built to last by caring hands. Stumpy Niles, who managed this district of the ranch, lived in the big log home with his wife and three children. A log bunkhouse, a long squatty building set into the hillside, was not far from the barn and calving sheds in the hollow.

The truck stopped by the ranch buildings. Chase Calder stepped from the driver's side and unhurriedly turned up the sheepskin collar of his coat against the keening wind. Like his father and his father's father, the reins of the Triple C Ranch were in his hands. His grip had to be firm enough to curb the unruly, sure enough to direct the operations, and steady enough to ride out the rough patches.

Authority had rested long on his shoulders, and he had learned to carry it well. This land that bore his family's name had left its mark on him, weathering his face to a leather tan, creasing his strong features with hard experience, and narrowing his brown eyes which had to see the potential trouble lurking beyond the far horizon. Chase was on the wrong side of thirty, pushing hard at forty, and all those years had been spent on Calder land. It was ingrained in his soul, the same way his wife, Maggie, was ingrained in his heart.

The slam of the pickup's passenger door sounded loudly. Chase's glance swung idly to the tall, lanky boy coming around the truck to join him, but there was nothing idle about the inspection behind that look. This sixteen-year-old was his son. Ty had been born a Calder, but he hadn't been raised one, something Chase regretted more than the trouble that had driven Maggie and himself apart nearly sixteen years ago.

Those had been long years, a time forever lost to them. Her father's death had aroused too much bitterness and hatred toward anyone carrying the Calder name. He hadn't tried to stop her when she left; and he had made no attempt to find out where she went. There had been no reason to try—or so he had thought at the time. But he hadn't known of the existence of his son until the fifteen-year-old boy had arrived, claiming him as his father. As much as he loved Maggie, at odd moments he resented that she had never told him about Ty. During their years of separation, Ty had grown to near manhood in a soft environment of southern California.

All this land would be Ty's someday, but precious years of training had been lost. Chase was nagged by the feeling that he had to cram fifteen years of experience into Ty in the shortest period of time possible. The kid had potential. He had try, but he was only greenbroke, like a young horse that wasn't sure about the rider on its back or the bit in its mouth—or what was expected from it.

With school out of session for spring break, Chase was taking advantage of the time to expose Ty to another facet of the ranch's operation—the ordeal of spring calving. For the regular cowboys, it was a seven-day-a-week job until the last cow had calved in all the districts of the Triple C Ranch. Since Stumpy Niles was shorthanded, Chase had brought Ty to help out and, at the same time, learn something more about the business.

As he stopped beside him, Ty hunched his shoulders against the bitter March wind rolling off the unbroken plains. In a comradely gesture, Chase threw a hand on his son's shoulder, heavily padded by the thick winter coat.

"You met most of the boys here when you worked the roundup last fall." Chase eyed his son with a hint of pride, not really noticing the strong family resemblance of dark hair and eyes and roughly planed features. It was the glint of determination he saw, and the slightly challenging thrust of Ty's chin.

Ty's memory of the roundup wasn't a pleasant one, so he just nodded at the information and held silent on his opinion of "the boys." They had made his life miserable. The worst horses on the ranch had been put in his string to ride. When "the boys" weren't throwing their hats under his horse, they were hoorahing him for grabbing leather when the horse started bucking or they were slapping his hands with a rope. If he forgot to recheck the saddle cinch before mounting, it was a sure bet one of them had loosened it. They had told him so many wild tales about the tricks to catch a steer that Ty felt if they had told him to shake salt on its tail, he would have been gullible enough to believe them.

They had pulled more practical jokes on him than he cared

to remember. The worst had been waking up one morning and finding a rattlesnake coiled on top of his chest. It had been hibernating and the cold made it too sluggish to do anything, but Ty hadn't known that. He had damned near crapped his pants, and all "the boys" had stood around and laughed their sides out.

It was like being the new kid on the block. Of course, Ty never used that phrase around his father. His father had the opinion that city life made a man weak. More than anything else, Ty wanted to prove to his father that he wasn't weak, but he didn't know how much more of this endless hazing he could take. A couple of the old-timers, Nate Moore for one, had told him that all new men went through this, but it seemed to Ty that they were doing an extra job on him.

The hand on his shoulder tightened as his father spoke again. "Stumpy's probably in the calving sheds. Let's go find him and get you settled in."

"Okay." Stirring, Ty reluctantly lifted his gaze to the sheds where there was a suggestion of activity.

A pigtailed girl about ten years old crawled between the railings of a board fence and ambled toward them. A heavy winter coat with patches and mismatched buttons gave bulk to her skinny frame, as did the double layer of jeans tucked inside a pair of run-down and patched boots. A wool scarf tied her cowboy hat on her head, a pair of honey-brown braids poking out the front.

"H'lo, Mr. Calder." She greeted Chase with the proper respect, but it was that of a youngster toward an elder rather than any degree of servility.

"Hello, Jess." A faint smile eased the tautness around his mouth as Chase recognized Stumpy's oldest child.

From the start, Jessy Niles had been a tomboy. Stumpy always claimed it was because, when she was teething, they'd let her chew on a strip of braided rawhide rein. She played with ropes and bridle bits when other girls were playing with dolls. She preferred tagging after her father to helping her mother in the kitchen or looking after her two brothers who followed her in succession.

There was never any little-girl cuteness about her. She'd been like a gangly filly, all arms and legs, and skinny to boot.

She wasn't homely, but her features were too strong—the cheekbones prominent and the jawline sharply angling. Her coloring was bland, her hair a washed-out brown, and her eyes an ordinary hazel—except they gleamed with intelligence, always direct, and sometimes piercing.

"I saw you drive up," she announced as she turned to size up Ty. "I told my dad you were here, so he'll probably be out shortly."

Ty bristled faintly under her penetrating stare. Even though he had become used to adults measuring him against his father, it was irritating to have this child slide him under her microscope. He gritted his teeth. He was sick of having to prove himself to everyone he met.

"You haven't met Stumpy's daughter, have you?" Chase realized and made the introductions. "This is Jessy Niles. My son, Ty."

She pushed a gloved hand at him, and Ty grudgingly shook it. "I heard about ya," she stated, and Ty bitterly wondered what that meant. It didn't sit well to think of some pigtailed kid laughing about some of the dumb things he'd done. "We've got a lot of first-calf heifers this year, so we sure could use the help." Jess spoke as if she were in charge. "Do you know anything about calving?"

A response seemed to be expected of him, from both his father and the young girl. Ty knew better than to claim knowledge he didn't possess. "No, but I've helped with a lot of foaling," he answered tersely.

The youngster wasn't impressed. "It's not quite the same. A mare's contractions are a lot more powerful than a cow's, so the birthing doesn't take as long." The information was absently tossed out, as if it were something everyone should know.

"How's it going?" inquired Chase.

"So far, we've only lost one calf," she said with a lift of her shoulders that seemed to indicate it was too soon to make a prognosis. Then a flash of humor brought a sparkle to her eyes. "Three of the boys already told Dad they were quitting at the end of the month and drawing their pay to head south. That's one ahead of this time last year."

Chase chuckled in his throat, fully aware more cowboys

threatened to quit during calving season than any other time, although few actually did. His gaze lifted past the girl to watch Stumpy's approach from the calving sheds, his footsteps crunching on the frozen ground.

"Here comes my dad," Jessy said, turning her head.

Stumpy Niles was a squatly built man, needing the nearly two-inch riding heels on his boots to reach the five-foot-seven-inch mark. But what he lacked in size he made up for in skill and stamina. He was always ready to laugh, but at the same time he was serious about his work and responsibility. Like Chase, Stumpy had been born and raised on the ranch; his grandfather had worked for Chase's grandfather, and the tradition was being carried on by succeeding generations. There were several families on the ranch that had never known any other home. No one retired when they grew old; they were simply given easier jobs.

At ten years, Jessy Niles already came to her father's shoulder. There was no resemblance to mark them as father and daughter. She was long-legged and skinny, while he was short and compact. His hair was dark, nearly black; so were his eyes. Energy seemed to be coiled inside him, always just below the surface, while she appeared quiet and contained.

After an exchange of greetings, Stumpy inserted, "We sure can use the help. They couldn't have picked a better time to let kids out of school for spring vacation."

"Nearly everyone's son on the Triple C is being put to work in the calving sheds," Chase remarked. "There's no reason for Ty to be an exception. You just tell him where you want him to go and what you want him to do."

Stumpy looked at Ty. "You might as well take your gear over to the bunkhouse and catch some rest if you can. We work the sheds in two shifts. You'll be on the night crew, so you'll be goin' on duty at five and workin' till six in the morning."

Figures, Ty thought, but he kept the rancor to himself. If there was a rotten job or lousy hours to be had, he always got them. His father had warned him it would be like this until he had proved himself, but Ty had never dreamed this testing would last so long. He was expected to endure the razzing and hazing without complaint, but the frustration was mounting

inside him and the pressure from outside was only adding to
the strain. More than anything else in this world, he wanted
to make his father proud of him, but that day seemed farther
away all the time.

"I'll take him to the bunkhouse for you, Dad," Jessy
volunteered, "and show him where everything is."

"You do that." Her father smiled and nodded his approval.

"Where's your outfit?" Jessy turned to Ty and gave him
another one of her level looks. Although it didn't show, she
liked this strong-faced and lanky-muscled boy, even if he
thought a rope honda was some kind of motorbike. That was
a real shame, him being a Calder and all.

"In the back of the truck." The cold seemed to make him
talk through his teeth, or so Jessy thought, not recognizing
the irritation that hardened his jaw. "I'll get it."

After Ty had hauled his war bag and bulky bedroll out of
the rear bed of the pickup, Jessy started for the chinked-log
bunkhouse and glanced around to make sure he was following.

"I'll be back Sunday afternoon to pick you up, Ty," Chase
called after his son and saw the bob of the cowboy hat in
acknowledgment. He watched the pair walk silently toward
the bunkhouse but directed his words to Stumpy. "A lot of
people think ranchers leave cows to their own devices to drop
their calves out on the range at the mercy of the elements,
predators, and birthing complications."

It was an indirect way of saying that was what Ty had
thought until Chase had explained differently. That's the way
it had been done a hundred years ago, but certainly not now.

"That cow and her calf are too valuable to leave it all up to
nature. Eight times out of ten, a cow won't have any trouble,
but those two times, it pays to have a two-legged critter
around to help out," Stumpy declared, then snorted out a
laugh, his breath coming out in a billowing vapor cloud.
"Hell, most city folks think all a rancher or a cowboy does is
turn a cow loose with a bull, let her calve, and round 'em up
in the spring to brand 'em and again in the fall to take them to
market. They don't think about the castrating, dehorning,
vaccinating, doctoring, and feeding—not to mention all the
grief they give ya in between."

"Yeah, we got an easy life, Stumpy, and don't know it."
His mouth was pulled into a wry line as he continued to watch
the pair of youngsters approaching the bunkhouse. "That's
quite a girl you've got there. She has her mother's looks,
doesn't she?"

It wasn't really a question, since Chase had known Judy
Niles almost as long as Stumpy had. She was a genial,
sandy-haired woman, a couple inches taller than her husband,
and attractive in an average sort of way.

"You should see her in those calving sheds, pulling calves in
subzero temperatures." Stumpy puffed up a bit with pride.
"The two boys, Ben and Mike, spend more time horsing
around than helping. 'Course, they're young yet. But Jessy,
she pitches right in there without being asked. As long as she
wants to do it, I'm not going to stop her. It's a pity she isn't a
boy. She's got the makings of a top hand."

"She'll outgrow this tomboy stage when she discovers
boys." Chase winked in amusement.

"Probably," Stumpy agreed and showed a reluctance for
that coming day. "I know her mother would like it if she
helped more around the house. Speaking of mothers—" He
paused, lifting his head to cast an interested look at Chase.
"How's Maggie?"

"The doctor says she's doing fine. Nothing to worry
about." A glowing warmth seemed to radiate from the brown
depths of his eyes, an inner pride bursting forth.

"It's getting close to her time, isn't it?" Stumpy asked,
frowning slightly as he tried to recall.

"The first of May, so she's got a little over two months
before the baby is due." But he wasn't as calm or casual about
the coming event as he tried to appear. "The senator is flying
in with some people he wants me to meet, so I'd better be
getting back to The Homestead."

As Ty followed the girl across the threshold into the
bunkhouse, he heard the truck starting up and looked over
his shoulder to see the pickup reverse to turn onto the single
road leading away from the camp. He knew he was completely on his own again. A wary tension strung his senses to a high
pitch of alertness as he swung the door shut and turned to
face the room.

He was standing in a small common room. A table and a collection of chairs stood in one corner, and a sofa and a couple of armchairs, all showing the scars of cowboys' indifference, occupied the other corner. A converted barrel heater split the room in the middle, its sides glowing almost a cherry-red as it waged a continual combat to keep the cold outside temperatures from invading the bunkhouse. Propped against the back wall, there was a broken chair to to used for kindling in the wood stove. A variety of cartoons, western pictures, and pinup girls were tacked to the walls in a crazy quilt of decoration.

"The bathroom's through that door." Jessy pointed to the right and walked to the barrel heater to warm her hands. "The beds are in there." She indicated the opposite direction with a nod of her hatted head. "You can take your pick of the empty ones."

Ty hefted his duffel bag a little higher to change his grip on it and headed for the open doorway on his left. The sleeping area of the bunkhouse was thinly partitioned into small rooms, furnished with plain wire-and-steel frame beds with a cowboy's bedroll serving as mattress and blanket. The first few beds, the ones closest to the common room and able to benefit from the wood stove's heat, were all occupied, either by possessions or by quilted shapes actually sleeping in the beds. Ty stopped at the first empty bunk he found and tossed his duffel bag and thick bedroll onto the wire frame. Coat hooks were screwed into the wall to hold his hat and coat and the odd piece of clothing or two.

"Did ya find one?" The girl's querying voice searched him out.

"Yeah." He half turned away from the doorway and began shrugging out of his heavy jacket. His thermal underwear and wool shirt were more than adequate in the relative warmth of the bunkhouse.

Her footsteps stopped at the doorway. "If you don't feel like layin' down right away, there's coffee in the pot on the hot plate."

"No, thanks." Ty left his hat on but hung up his coat and turned to untie his bedroll and spread it open on the bed.

He caught her out of the corner of his eye, leaning against

the doorway, her coat unbuttoned and the scarf loose around her neck. He wished she'd quit watching him with those measuring eyes. It made him uncomfortable. He noticed the cup of steaming coffee in her now-ungloved hand. She lifted it to her wide mouth, blowing to cool it even as she sipped at the hot, thickly black coffee. He still couldn't stomach the strong coffee everyone on the ranch drank with such regularity unless he drowned it in milk.

"You shouldn't be drinking that stuff." He jerked the string tying his bedroll and unrolled the mattresslike quilt pad with its sheets, quilt, and canvas tarp bound inside. "It'll stunt your growth."

"I been drinking coffee since I was six." Scoffing amusement riddled her voice. "I'd hate to think how tall I'd be now if I hadn't." She paused, then added for good measure, "And it hasn't made my hair curly or grown hair on my chest."

After he had the pad and blankets straightened out, Ty set the duffel bag with his clothes and shaving kit at the head of the bed for a pillow. When the girl showed no signs of leaving, he stretched himself out the full length of the bed and set his hat forward on the front of his face.

"I'm going to get some rest," Ty said, in case she hadn't got the message. The hat partially muffled his voice.

"See you tonight," Jessy Niles replied, not finding his behavior in the least rude, and straightened from the doorway to saunter down the hall to the common room.

As the sound of her footsteps retreated, Ty pushed his hat back. Raising his arms, he cupped the back of his head in his hands and stared at the ceiling. There was a rawness in him that was close to pain. He had no one to turn to, no one to whom he could talk out his frustrations. He was too old to go crying to his mother, and since it was his father's respect he so desperately wanted to earn, he couldn't very well go running to him with his troubles. He wanted to work them out on his own, but so far no one was giving him a chance. There were so many things to learn that just when he felt he was grasping the rudiments of one thing, something new was thrown at him, and always the hazing and the handing out of misinformation until he felt like some gullible dimwit.

*   *   *

The return trip to The Homestead, the name given to the house occupied by the head of the Triple C, took the best part of two hours. The sleek twin-engine plane parked by the private airstrip near the buildings of the ranch's headquarters advised Chase that Senator Bulfert had arrived in his absence.

Leaving the truck parked in front of the imposing two-story house, Chase mounted the steps to the wide porch running the length of the south front and crossed to the solid wood double doors. The house had been built decades ago with a craftsman's care and possessed that rare quality of character. Two hundred years from now it would still be standing and, if Chase had his way, a Calder would still be living in it.

When he entered the large open foyer, Chase heard voices coming from the study on his left. Doug Trumbo, one of the ranch hands, was carrying an armload of luggage up the staircase leading from the living room to the second floor and its guest bedrooms.

With a shift in direction, Chase headed for the open doors of the den, where his guests had obviously gathered. Upon entering, his glance first sought out Maggie. She was sitting in a chair near the window, her black hair gleaming in the sunlight and an arm resting on the protruding roundness of her stomach. The sight of her always had the power to stir a hungry response in him while at the same time evoking feelings that were profoundly tender.

Her smile greeted him as Chase walked to her chair, pulling off his gloves and stuffing them in his coat pocket. Even as his attention was divided by the guests in the room, he was reaching to take her small hand in his large one.

"I'm sorry I wasn't on hand when you arrived," Chase apologized and let his gaze travel over his four guests. The ruddy-faced senator and his aide, Wes Govern, he already knew.

"No problem. Made better time than we thought. Had a good tail wind," the quick-talking senator replied. Age was beginning to sag his round cheeks, leaving jowls and pockets under his eyes. "Just arrived a few minutes ago. Wes hasn't had time to pour a round of drinks yet." With a slight turn of his head, he issued a booming directive to his assistant. "Chase drinks whiskey, Wes."

"I remember." The man nodded and added another glass to the liquor tray.

"How have things been? Well, I hope," the senator declared and continued without giving Chase an opportunity to respond. "No more land purchases you need my help with, are there?" he inquired with a conspiratorial wink.

"None." There was a dryness about Chase's eyes at the reference to the purchase of ten thousand acres of land from the government that Bulfert had arranged some years ago. It was the last parcel of previously leased land to come under the Calder title. He now owned all the land that constituted the Triple C Ranch.

"Chase, I want you to meet Eddy Joe Dyson." The politician curved an arm around the shoulders of a slightly built man, the gesture and body language suggesting to Chase that the two were united in their cause, whatever it was. "Been looking forward to getting the two of you together for quite a while. E.J., meet Chase Calder."

Chase stepped away from Maggie's side to shake hands with the older man, dressed in an expensive navy pinstripe suit, styled in western lines with a yoked front and boot-cut pants. Chase put the man's age somewhere in the middle forties. The man's hand was smooth of any calluses, and his skin didn't have the leathery tan of a cattleman despite the white felt Stetson on his head.

"Welcome to the Triple C, Mr. Dyson." The western clothes were just a facade, but Chase didn't detect any shallowness in the level gaze that returned his silent inspection. If anything, he noted a hint of shrewdness.

"It's my pleasure," the man drawled. "And my friends call me E.J. I'd be pleased if you and your wife did the same." He half turned to invite the second man forward. "This is my business partner, George Stricklin."

Ten years younger, tall, with yellow hair, the man wore gold wire glasses which he removed and slipped precisely into the breast pocket of his suit jacket. Despite his athletic build, there was a studious and silent quality about him. His fingers were long and finely shaped, and Stricklin did no more than nod when he shook hands with Chase.

Dyson spoke again. Angling his head toward Maggie, he inclined it in a courtly gesture. "I must say that I thought our Texas ladies couldn't be matched for beauty, but I've been forced to revise my opinion since meeting your lovely wife."

"I believe I'm much more prejudiced," Chase murmured and glanced backward into Maggie's vibrantly green eyes. Now that the phase of morning sickness had passed, she looked positively radiant. He'd heard it said that women were more beautiful when they were pregnant and had dismissed it. But he was now willing to concede that it might be in the eye of the beholder, because Maggie had never looked more beautiful to him than she did this minute.

"You're from Texas?" Maggie inserted, skillfully directing the conversation away from flattering comments about her. No matter how healthy and happy she felt, there was still that feeling of gaucheness and awkwardness which insisted compliments be turned aside.

"Yes." The slow, twanging drawl in his voice was both smooth and attractive, like oiled leather. "That set of horns above the mantel makes me feel right at home, too," he said, indicating the mounted pair of longhorns on the massive stone fireplace that dominated the room with its size and cheery log fire.

"They belonged to a Texas steer. I guess you could say this ranch was founded on Texas longhorns," Chase admitted and accepted the short glass of whiskey and ice from the senator's aide.

"I remember your father telling me your family came from the Fort Worth area." The senator took a fat cigar from his pocket, then glanced inquiringly at Maggie, who silently nodded her permission. "That's E.J.'s home turf." He felt his pockets for a light, but his assistant produced a lighter before the senator found one. "Something of an entrepreneur, eh, E.J.?"

The relationship between Dyson and his partner had always struck the senator as an unusual one. Once he had described Stricklin as the brains of the company and Dyson as the guts of it. Every act, every move, of the silent Stricklin was deliberately thought out beforehand by that computer-like mind. Logic and reason dictated his decisions. But Dyson acted on instinct and had the guts to gamble on his hunches. It was a curious blend in a partnership, one balancing the other, with Dyson naturally appearing to be the dominant member of the team.

"I do have several business interests," Dyson admitted while eyeing Chase as if he were the source of his next.

"If you're thinking of venturing into the cattle-ranching business, it means investing a lot of money in nondepreciable assets," Chase warned dryly.

There was a quick glance exchanged between the politician and the Texan. "I guess you could say I'm more interested in what's under the ground than what's on top of it. Which is why I asked the senator to introduce me to you. I dabble in oil and natural-gas exploration."

An eyebrow quirked in mild curiosity as Chase let the statement sink in. Taking his time, he set his glass down on the table by Maggie's chair and shed his coat. The flames crackled in the fireplace, filling the brief silence.

"I think you're in the wrong part of Montana," Chase stated finally. "You want to be over in the Badlands, or in the Powder River country."

"Drilling companies are already working those fields," E.J. disagreed. "Now, I don't pretend to be an expert, but I try to hire them. I like to gamble my money on finding new fields, not striking it in old ones and having to fight the big companies."

"Am I to surmise that you're here because you think there is oil to be found on the Triple C?" Chase was vaguely bemused by the idea.

"If you know about the Powder River and the Badlands, then you must know they've made some finds near the base of the Rockies. They're near the western edge of your boundaries," he reminded Chase in a calm and knowing tone. "I could have brought my geologist with me and let him tell you all about rock strata—and how promising a section of your land looks. It wouldn't mean any more to you than it does to me, and I don't know one from the other. Now, Stricklin, he's gone over all the figures and calculations and says there is more than a good chance of finding oil. So I'm here to see about acquiring those rights."

There was no change in expression to indicate Chase's inner feelings. He looked at Maggie and took a sip of his drink. When his gaze finally returned to the man, it was sharply measuring.

"The subject is certainly open to discussion." He'd hear the man out, but it wasn't a decision he was going to make quickly.

2

Sleeping lightly, Maggie stirred and awakened at the faint noise of someone moving about the room in the dark. Rising on an elbow, she reached for the switch of the bedside lamp.

"Chase, is that you?" she asked as the light went on and revealed him seated in an armchair, pulling off his boots.

"I didn't mean to wake you." He set a boot on the floor next to its mate and began tugging his shirttail out of his pants to unbutton it. Tiredness gave a drawn and weary look to his ruggedly masculine features. There was an air of preoccupation about him despite the warm look he gave her.

"Have you been sitting up all this time talking?" The hands of the clock were approaching the midnight hour. Maggie had retired much earlier in the evening, her pregnant body demanding rest.

"Yes."

She felt a flash of irritation at his closemouthed answer. Although Chase didn't attempt to exclude her from business discussions, he still had that western tendency never to seek a woman's counsel.

"Well?" The sharpness of challenge was in her voice, prodding him to tell her what he was thinking because it was impossible to know how he felt about something when he was wearing that poker mask. "What's your reaction to Dyson's proposal?"

His mouth twisted into a hard, dry smile. "I'll let you know after I've had a chance to run a private check on the man. There's something in this for the senator, so I'm not about to take his recommendations of the man." He paused, knowing he hadn't really told her anything. "As to leasing part of the ranch for drilling purposes, I'm open to it. The days of cattlemen objecting to the presence of drilling rigs on their property have long since passed."

"So you've decided to decide later." Her arm grew tired of supporting her weight, so she positioned both pillows behind her and reclined against them.

"There's no reason to rush. If there is gas or oil under that grass, it'll still be there two months from now—or two years." Chase stood up and began emptying his pants pockets. When he went to lay the contents on the occasional table by the chair, he noticed the small stack of mail sitting there. "What's this?"

"A report came from the psychiatrist handling my brother's case, and a short note from Culley, too." Although she smiled, there was a troubled light in her green eyes. She knew the mental institution was the best place for her brother, but Culley was the only family she had. "The doctor said there's been some improvement. It's possible they might even let him have visitors soon."

"Not until after the baby is born, Maggie." His look hardened. "I don't care if the doctor says you can see him tomorrow."

"I'll wait." But not because he was ordering it. "The doctor feels it would be unwise in this stage of Culley's treatment for him to learn that I'm going to have your baby. And it's a fact I can't easily hide." The last was a weak attempt at a joke, but the hand she placed on her stomach was protective rather than a gesture designed to draw attention to her condition. It was Culley's sick, unreasoning hatred of anything associated with a Calder that had driven him over the edge.

Chase fingered the envelope bearing the return address of the institution, but he didn't remove the letter. "What did Culley have to say in his note?"

"He was concerned about his ranch and how the livestock had fared through the winter." Her brother believed Maggie was managing the small O'Rourke family ranch that bordered a part of the Triple C Ranch on the north. It hadn't been deemed wise to inform him it was being worked by Triple C riders.

A noncommittal sound came from his throat, acknowledging her reply, as Chase replaced the envelope on the table and finished undressing. Maggie shifted so he could use half the pillows when he slipped naked into the bed. But Chase wasn't satisfied with that. He curved an arm beneath her and gathered her close to his side. The heat from his body flooded down her length, making her feel all toasty and warm.

"How are you feeling?" His head moved closer to hers as Chase nuzzled the silky black curls near her temple.

"Pregnant." Maggie turned her head on the pillow to gaze at him, her lip corners curved inward with a hint of a smile.

His hand moved familiarly over her swollen stomach, thinly covered by her ivory silk nightgown. A marveling light darkened his eyes with pleasure when Chase felt a slight movement. "Our child is going to be an active character."

Maggie's expression grew serious. "If it's a girl, I'd like to name her Cathleen, after my aunt."

"Cathleen Calder." He tested it out, then faintly nodded his approval. "I like it."

"Good." She sighed contentedly, a smile widening her mouth.

"Poor Ty pulled the night shift at the calving sheds," Chase murmured while his gaze traveled over the heavy fullness of her breasts pushing against the lace-trimmed bodice of her gown.

"It must be freezing outside." She suppressed a shudder and snuggled closer to the solid warmth of his long, muscled body.

A little groan came from him. "I love you, Maggie," he

muttered thickly and leaned over to hungrily cover her mouth
with a needing kiss.

The lonely cry of a coyote drifted on the cold midnight air.
Outside the calving sheds, the sky was a mass of brittle ice
stars that seemed to touch the frozen Montana plains. A polar
wind prowled around the buildings tucked in a pocket of the
heaving land, driving the freezing temperature even lower.

Numbed by the brutal cold, Ty hunkered deeper into his
coat and buried his chin and mouth in the sheepskin collar,
using it to warm the air he breathed. There was hardly any
sensation in his legs, making it awkward to walk, but he had
to keep moving to keep the circulation going. The cold was
making his nose run. He kept sniffing to clear it, breathing
most of the time through his mouth. His arms were crossed in
front of him, his gloved hands tucked under his armpits for
extra protection.

The bare light bulbs, strung the length of the calving shed,
were coated with dust that muted the glare of their bald light.
Straw rustled under the hooves of the restless animals. The
odd lowing of the confined cows was interspersed with the
occasional muffled swearing of some cowboy.

Ty glanced again at the heifer in labor. Stumpy Niles had
left him to keep a vigil on the young cow while he went to
assist one of the other cowboys, whose cow was rejecting her
newborn calf. When Ty had come on duty at the outset of the
night shift, Stumpy had taken him under his wing and stayed
at his side through each calving, giving him instructions and
advice. All of the births had gone smoothly, the cows
requiring little assistance from Ty.

There hadn't been much razzing, mainly due to Stumpy's
presence. As the night crew had come on duty to take over
from the day shift, two of the cowboys Ty had met during the
fall roundup gave him a hard time, asking him whether he
knew which hole the calf came out of and warning him against
poking around the wrong one. Ty had done his best to ignore
them.

Ty ran a glance down the calving shed, but there was no
sign of Stumpy returning, and he looked back at the heifer.
Her labor was well advanced; she was fully dilated, but

nothing was happening. The large brown eyes were rolling, showing rings of white around them. Ty began to get the uneasy feeling that something was going wrong.

Jiggling his weight from one foot to the other, he tried to generate some warmth. It felt as if his ears were going to fall off despite the wool knit scarf that covered them. He'd never been so cold in all his life as he moved closer to the heifer and crouched down beside her tail.

"What's holding back your calf, little momma?" The words of concern were stiffly murmured, his facial muscles too numb with the cold to let his mouth properly form the words.

"Is she in trouble?"

Ty looked up to see a red-cheeked Jessy Niles, layered in warm clothing that gave a slight waddle to her walk. She didn't wait for an answer as she came over to stand beside Ty, bending in the middle to get a closer view of the situation.

Earlier in the evening, he'd noticed her around the calving shed, but he hadn't seen her for a while. Ty didn't like the idea of some ten-year-old kid looking over his shoulder, especially when he didn't know for sure what he was doing.

"What are you doing out here? It's past your bedtime, isn't it?" he muttered.

"I couldn't sleep, so I got up." The shrugging movement of her shoulders was barely noticeable under the heavy jacket she was wearing. "The calf should be coming any minute now."

That was what Ty had thought several minutes ago, but so far there wasn't a sign of it. The cow was in some kind of difficulty. The beginnings of a nervous sweat started to chill his skin. Then he saw something and relief shivered through him.

"Here it comes," he announced as a contraction expelled another inch of the dark, sac-enclosed object.

A second later, his hope sank to the pit of his stomach. Instead of a miniature pair of cloven hooves emerging, it was the calf's white-faced head. His hands curled into fists.

"You'd better get your dad," he told the girl. "Tell him to come quick. The calf's coming head first."

Jessy Niles needed no second urging as she sped away to locate her father and advise him of the situation. Ty spent agonizing minutes waiting for help to come, fully aware the opening wasn't large enough to permit passage of the calf's chest and front legs. The natural calving order was front feet first; then came the head of the fetus.

When Jessy came running back, out of breath from the cold, he looked up anxiously. She stopped beside him, shaking her head while trying to summon her voice. She sank to her knees on the straw floor.

"He can't come," she panted, and a shaft of fear went through him. "He said . . . you'll have to handle it."

"Me?" Ty looked back at the cow, feeling helpless.

It took Jessy only a second to realize he didn't know what to do. Instantly she took charge. She'd been told that she'd seen her first animal born when she was four years old. Since then, she'd spent a large part of every calving season in the sheds. She had observed nearly every calving situation imaginable and had recently taken part in her share of them.

"First you have to push the head back through the birthing channel between contractions. Better hurry up and get your coat and gloves off," she advised him.

Only for a minute did Ty hesitate. The calm authority in her voice was reminiscent of her father's. His numbed fingers worked hurriedly to unfasten the buttons while he shrugged out of the bulky coat. There was too much on his mind, the situation too urgent to pay any attention to the frigid air as he pushed the sleeve of his sweat shirt past his elbow and rolled the wool sleeve of his shirt just as high.

With Jessy hovering close by and giving him instructions, Ty managed to maneuver the calf fetus back inside the cow's womb, then groped around to find the front legs and shift it into the normal birthing position. All the while, he was scared to the marrow of his bones. His heart was hammering in his throat. He felt weak and shaky, his stomach churning with sickening intensity. A nervous sweat had broken out, chilling his skin.

At regular intervals, muscular contractions clamped down on his arm, squeezing it hard and sometimes forcing him to wait until the pressure eased. But the contractions grew steadily weaker. By the time he had the calf coming the right way out of the birthing channel, the young cow was too exhausted from her prolonged labor to help him.

His breath was coming in grunting gasps as Ty strained muscles already quivering from the high tension and alternately pulled and rested, pulled and rested. The front feet and head emerged, then the chest and shoulders.

"Hurry," Jessy urged with an anxiety in her voice that Ty didn't understand.

The next thing he knew, she was crowding beside him and grabbing at the calf to help him pull it the rest of the way. When it was lying on the straw, Ty sagged back on his heels, taking a second to gather his shattered nerves. But Jessy didn't pause. She began wiping the mucuslike membrane sac away from the calf's nostrils.

"Don't just sit there!" Impatience flashed in her hazel eyes. "The cord's wrapped around its neck."

After the ordeal he'd just been through, he just couldn't bear to lose the calf.

Ty shouldered her out of the way and lifted the calf's head to carefully unwrap the umbilical cord that had become twisted around its neck. Bending over the wet and curly white face, he blew into its nostrils the way he'd once seen a groom do with a newly born foal to clear its air passages.

"When you were trying to turn the calf inside the cow, was there any movement?" Jessy had grabbed a rag and was briskly rubbing the rest of the calf's body to stimulate circulation.

"I don't remember." Ty felt for a heartbeat, trying to recall if the calf had done any kicking.

"It's dead, isn't it?" she concluded matter-of-factly and ceased her efforts.

He ground his teeth together, not wanting to admit the calf was stillborn. He felt he was to blame. If he'd known more, maybe the calf could have been saved. Dejected, he lowered his head.

"Here." Jessy pushed a rag at him. "You'd better wipe that slime off your arm."

Her prompting made him aware of the clammy numbness of his bare arm, the cold congealing the wetness on his skin.

Soon it would freeze. Taking the rag, Ty scrubbed his arm until his nerve ends tingled in protest; then he pushed down his sleeves and reached for the heavy coat to combat the miserable cold that was finally making itself felt.

"At least the heifer is going to be all right," the young girl offered consolingly.

Ty's eyes were dark and troubled with guilt when he met her gaze. He looked at the rusty-red-coated calf with its spanking white face and legs, motionless in death. It was small comfort to know he could have lost its mother, too.

A bitter laugh welled in his throat as he realized he didn't even know what the hell to do with a dead calf. The ground was too frozen to bury it. Maybe he was supposed to throw it outside for the coyotes to feast on.

"You look cold." Jessy observed the whiteness where the skin was stretched tautly over the high bones of his cheeks and jawline, and the wildness in his eyes. "Maybe you'd better get some coffee from the thermos by the door. It'll probably be a while before the afterbirth is passed. If you want to go get a cup, I'll stay here."

"No." His teeth were starting to chatter, but Ty was determined not to leave until the job was finished. Stumpy had told him to handle it, and he wasn't going to earn a black mark against him by abandoning the job before it was done. But it sure as hell was obvious the girl could handle it better than he could.

"Hey, kid!" a voice called out in advance of the approaching tread of boots scuffling through the straw. Ty pushed to his feet, his shoulders and back stiffening when he recognized Sid Ramsey, one of the cowboys who were always giving him grief. "Stumpy said you needed some help."

"Not anymore," replied Ty.

The cowboy grinned, the breath coming out of his mouth like smoke into the frigid air, yet he seemed oblivious to the cold as he sauntered over. "Did you finally figure out which hole the calf comes out of?"

"The calf's dead," he replied tersely. "It was strangled."

"You aren't supposed to choke it to death when you're pulling it out, kid," the cowboy joked as he drew close enough to view the dead calf in the straw.

"The cord was wrapped around its neck," Ty informed him, defensive and angry.

"At least you furnished us with some more coyote bait, so I guess you're good for something." Turning aside, the cowboy spat tobacco juice into the straw and wiped his mouth with the back of a gloved hand, eyeing Ty with a taunting look.

"You got no call to say a thing like that, Sid Ramsey!" Jessy shot the stern reprimand at the cowboy. She'd been around enough of the men to know that their sense of humor sometimes ran on the cruel side. In her opinion, he was unfairly picking on Ty Calder, and it went against her nature to remain silent.

Being defended by a pigtailed girl who hadn't even reached puberty was the final straw for Ty. "Stay out of this, Jessy!" he snapped harshly.

"Well, well," the cowboy mocked. "The dude's got a temper."

Blood was running hotly through his veins. If he didn't get out of there, Ty felt, he'd explode. "Just shut up, Ramsey," he muttered through his teeth and took a long stride to leave the area.

"Hey, not so fast." The cowboy moved into his path to stop him. "Where are you going?"

"It's none of your business, so just get out of my way." Even though the cowboy had ten years on him, Ty had the advantage of size and weight, regardless of how much he lacked in experience.

Without any hesitation, he slammed both hands into the cowboy's shoulders and pushed him backwards into one of the center supporting posts of the shed's roof. His aggression took the cowboy by surprise. Ty let the forward momentum carry him past the cowboy toward the distant door, paying scant attention to the surprised and bewildered cowboy when he pushed off the post.

"What'd I ever do to you?" the cowboy demanded in confused anger. "Hell, I was just funnin'."

Ty stopped and swung around. "Your fun ain't funny to me, so just lay off."

"What am I supposed to do?" he challenged with a trace of offended belligerence.

"All I want you to do is quit hassling me and leave me alone." A rawness edged the rumbling of his voice. "Just leave me alone."

Ramsey studied him with narrowed eyes but made no response. Ty swung away, that brief flare of anger burning itself out by the time he reached the end of the shed. Cold, tired, miserable, and plagued by feelings of guilt and inadequacy, he walked blindly to the coffee thermos and filled one of the mugs sitting beside it. He didn't really want the potent black coffee, but it gave him an excuse for being there.

Straw bales were lined against a wall. Ty slumped onto one of them and leaned forward, resting his elbows on his thighs and spreading his knees to let the coffee mug dangle between them, both hands wrapped around it. There was a tightness in his throat, a threat of tears stinging his eyes. His teeth were bared with the effort of holding back all the anguish he was feeling.

Nothing had turned out the way he thought it would when he ran away from his California home almost a year ago and hitchhiked across half the country to find the man whose name was listed in the family Bible as his father. At first, everything had seemed so perfect. His parents had even gone back together again, marrying and making the three of them a whole family. He idolized his father and wanted to be just like him, but he couldn't seem to fit in. Living on a ranch the size of the Triple C, the son of the owner, how could he have wished for more than that? But he didn't belong. Nobody cared about the ribbons he'd won at horse shows in California; nothing he'd accomplished meant anything here. More than anything else, he wanted to be accepted.

Yet it didn't seem to matter what he did or how hard he tried, it always turned out wrong. He'd botched the calving and calf had died. On top of that, he'd alienated Ramsey. It all seemed so hopeless to him.

He heard footsteps coming his way and stole a look from under his hat brim. It was Stumpy. Ty tipped his head down again and braced himself for the quiet condemnation, the tactic used by the ranch veterans which was more devastating than being shouted at and berated for being a fool.

"There's nothing like a hot cup of coffee on a cold night like this," Stumpy declared above the sound of liquid being poured into a container.

After looking at his own cup, Ty straightened and took a sip of the strong brew. Its bitterness made him shudder.

"The taste grows on ya." There was a smile in Stumpy's voice.

"The calf's dead," Ty announced flatly.

"It happens. You always want all of them to live, but you always lose a couple." Stumpy continued to stand by the thermos.

"It came head first, and I didn't know what to do," Ty admitted and continued to stare at the coffee in his cup. "If it hadn't been for your daughter— Hell, a ten-year-old knows more than I do."

"She's been around it a lot longer than you have," Stumpy reminded him.

"It's no use." His shoulders slouched with defeat as he finally lifted his gaze to his new mentor. There was a brightness in his eyes that were so darkly brown. "I might as well give up. I'm never going to be able to cut it."

The gentle understanding went out of Stumpy's expression as it became hard and angry. "Don't ever say that!" he snapped in a low voice. "It's been rough on you. But if you quit now, you'll always be sorry. You've got to stick it out if it kills you."

"Why?" Ty demanded to know. "I'll never be the man my father is."

"You damn well won't," Stumpy agreed coldly. "And if that's what you're trying to do, that's your first mistake. You are Ty Calder and no one else."

"Being Ty Calder isn't a whole lot to brag about," he muttered. It had been foolish to think Stumpy would understand.

"You are a Calder, ain't ya?" he challenged. "I think that would be a whole helluva lot to brag about. What are you going to do? Sit there and feel sorry for yourself? Or get up off your butt and get back on the job?"

With his challenge finished, Stumpy downed the hot coffee in the asbestos-mouthed tradition of a veteran cowboy and set the empty cup by the thermos. He didn't so much as glance in

Ty's direction as he walked away with quick, short strides. He'd said his piece. Now the decision was up to Ty.

For a lonely minute longer, he sat on the bale with his head bowed. All that stuff was easy for Stumpy to say. He wasn't going through it. Ty wavered indecisively, searching for some other alternative.

"Hell," he muttered and tipped back his head to throw the coffee down his throat. It had cooled considerably, but that didn't make it any more palatable.

Rising to his feet, he left his cup by Stumpy's and headed down the calving shed in a scuffling walk. His attitude hadn't changed. He still felt rotten and miserable. If there was any conscious decision, it was simply to get it over with, but Ty wasn't entirely sure what "it" was.

"Hey, kid!" somebody called to him before he was halfway back to where he'd left Jessy. "Give me a hand."

Tiny Yates, one of the married cowboys, had his arms around a wobbly newborn calf. Its mother was eyeing the man and the calf with wary alarm, anxious and uneasy. Ty hesitated, wondering what the prank was this time, then altered his course to join them.

"The damned calf doesn't know what the tits are for and keeps buttin' her bag," the cowboy muttered with disgust. "And she's got so much milk in there she's in agony. I'll get the calf over there and you reach under there and squeeze some milk out of a tit. That oughta give him the idea."

The plan didn't appeal to any of the four participants, but after much cursing, calf bleating and cow lowing, and maneuvering in the straw, the desired result was achieved. Ty rubbed his leg where the cow had kicked it and watched the bull calf nurse aggressively while the cow washed its brick-red coat with her tongue.

"Helluva sight, isn't it?" Tiny declared, then slapped Ty on the back and moved away.

There was no "Thanks for the help." That wasn't the custom. A man did the job that was expected of him, because it was what he should do. There wasn't any reason to thank someone for doing his job. A long sigh spilled from Ty as he turned away and started down the line again.

II

It's not that I'm wanting to hurt you,
I just can't walk the path that you tread.
Don't stand between me and what I can be
'Cause you're Calder born—and Calder bred.

3

The house seemed unnaturally quiet when Maggie entered it. She paused in the foyer, listening to the midafternoon silence. A smile touched her mouth as she started forward, her high heels clicking on the hardwood floors.

There was a stack of mail on the cherrywood table waiting to be sorted, ranch correspondence separated from the personal mail. She stopped beside it and slipped out of her springweight suede coat, laying it over the back of a living-room chair for the time being. Beneath it, she wore a classically simple dress in a wine-colored watered silk. Its style gave the impression of height to her petite build and discreetly flattered the mature curves of her slender figure.

One of the envelopes was addressed to Ty. Her glance flicked curiously to the return address and stayed. A quiver of anticipation darted through her when Maggie saw it was from the Admissions Department of the University of Texas in Austin. She nibbled anxiously at her lower lip, wanting to open it and find out if Ty was being accepted for the fall term. With all her attention focused on the envelope, she didn't hear Ruth Haskell come in from the kitchen.

"I thought I heard someone but I didn't know it was you, Maggie. I didn't think you'd be back till later in the afternoon." When Ruth's voice broke the silence, Maggie turned with almost a guilty start, the envelope in hand. Ruth noticed it and apologized with a nervous quickness that had become a part of her speech pattern. "I'm sorry. I meant to sort the mail earlier and leave it in the den, but I was doing something else and didn't get back to it."

"It doesn't matter." Maggie smiled an assurance at the woman, who had once been housekeeper and cook at The Homestead. Now she came only occasionally to sit with the newest addition to the Calder family when Maggie had to be away.

Like so many others, Ruth was descended from one of the original drovers who had trailed cattle north from Texas to Montana with the first Calder and had stayed on to help build the ranch. It gave the ranch a tradition and a continuity of bonds forged long ago and still remaining strong.

As Maggie studied the woman, she couldn't help noticing how Ruth was showing her age. Her blond hair had faded to gray, and a network of age lines had withered her face. Her gentle blue eyes had lost their sparkle. Once Ruth had been on the plump side, but nerves had eaten away until she was thin. There was a perpetual tremor in her hands now, agitation making it worse at some times than others.

To those who knew her, as Maggie did, the source of her decline could be traced directly to her son. After last summer's attempt to kill both Ty and herself as part of a wild plot to obtain control of the ranch, Buck Haskell had been tried, convicted, and sentenced to a long prison term. In the way of these hard-core western people, his name had been dropped from all conversation. Even though Ruth visited him regularly, no one asked about him or even referred to her absences from the ranch. It was part of the tradition of this land, the same as when a person died. No one mentioned the deceased because deep feelings, especially sorrow and grief, were to be kept inside. To do otherwise was to show weakness.

Sometimes Maggie thought it would help Ruth if she could talk about her son, to bring out in the open the sense of failure and guilt she probably felt, as well as the all-forgiving love of a mother for her child. But as much as she pitied Ruth, Maggie had no compassion at all for her son. Because she couldn't find it in her heart to forgive him, she didn't mention him.

Regretting that she'd let her thoughts take that unpleasant turn, Maggie swung her attention back to the mail and reluctantly set the envelope addressed to Ty apart from the other stacks.

"Is Cathleen upstairs taking her afternoon nap?" she asked Ruth, giving her a quick smile.

"Oh, no, she's with her daddy."

Maggie lifted her head, turning to the woman with mild curiosity. "She must not have taken a very long nap."

"She hasn't had her nap yet this afternoon," Ruth informed her anxiously. "Chase left shortly after lunch and took her with him. She cried so when he got ready to go that he just didn't have the heart to leave her. You know how he dotes on her."

"I know," she murmured dryly. Her strong, tough husband was little more than putty in the hands of their two-year-old daughter. "Where did they go?"

"Out to the drilling site in the Broken Butte range. He had some messages to deliver to the rig foreman." She glanced nervously at the watch hanging loosely around her wrist. "He said he wouldn't be gone long."

Maggie sighed and fell to sorting the rest of the mail again. "I'm sure he didn't intend to be gone this long."

The front door opened, bringing forth a high-pitched, bubbling giggle. "Duck your head, Cat," Chase's voice warned as Maggie turned to see father and daughter enter the house. Cathleen was riding on his shoulders, her little hands crushing the silver-belly felt hat on his head. His hands had a firm hold on her corduroy-covered thighs so she wouldn't fall. When he spied Maggie, his leathery tan features broke into a dazzling smile. "Didn't I tell you your mother was home?" he said to the raven-haired tot on his shoulders.

As he crossed the foyer to join her in the living room, Maggie's impatience at him for depriving Cathleen of her afternoon nap faded to a mild exasperation. His face radiated such strength, as if it had been sculpted from the raw elements of this Montana land he loved so much. With Ruth present, Chase didn't kiss her. Instead, he hooked an arm around the child and swung her off his shoulders and onto his hip as she shrieked with delight.

"Give Momma a kiss," Chase instructed and watched with satisfaction as the two leaned to each other, their hair equally black, and green eyes the emerald color.

"Look at you." Maggie surveyed the dark circles of dirt

ground into the knees of Cathleen's corduroy pants and the grime on her ruffled white blouse, not to mention the dirty face and hands. "She looks like she's been playing in a pigpen."

"A little dirt won't hurt her. Besides, it's good Calder soil," Chase insisted with a small grin. "It was kinda muddy around the drilling site. She got a kick out of playing in it. You should have seen her before I cleaned her up."

"I'm glad I didn't," she retorted.

"Want down," Cathleen demanded and gave her father one of those level green looks as she wiggled in his tight hold, determined to be set on the floor.

"Come to Nanna Ruth, Cathleen." She held out her palsied hands to the child. "We'll go upstairs and get you washed up."

"No." The offer was firmly rejected, a lower lip jutting out in defiance.

"Wouldn't you like to take a bath? I'll put lots of bubbles in the tub," Ruth coaxed.

The little girl considered the offer for a long minute before she finally held out her hands to the older woman. Chase surrendered her into the woman's care, pride transforming his usually hard features as he listened to his daughter jabbering to the woman carrying her up the stairs.

"She knows exactly what she wants, doesn't she?" he murmured to Maggie.

"And you see to it that she gets it," she murmured dryly in return.

"That's a father's prerogative," Chase insisted as he bent his head to roll his mouth across her lips. "How was your visit with Culley?"

"Fine." It was always a wrenching experience to see her brother in that institution, but she took comfort from the knowledge he was being helped. "They let me show him a picture of Cathleen today. Culley insisted she looked just like me when I was a toddler."

"He was bound to notice the resemblance," he replied. "She's you all over again in miniature."

"But I was never spoiled the way she is," Maggie retorted.

"Someday you're going to be sorry for letting her have whatever she wants. She'll grow up thinking the world is hers for the taking." Realizing she had allowed the mention of their daughter to sidetrack her, she returned to her original topic. "Getting back to Culley, the doctor was encouraged by his reaction to Cathleen's photograph. It didn't seem to faze him at all that she's a Calder."

"That's probably because she looks like you instead of me." His mouth slanted in its familiar hard smile.

"Maybe," she conceded. "But it's a beginning."

"For your sake, Maggie, I hope it is." Her brother had never given him anything but trouble, so he didn't pretend to have any personal interest in the prospects for Culley's recovery. He knew how twisted with hatred Culley had been toward the Calders, infecting Maggie with it for a long time. Ultimately Buck Haskell had used that malice her brother had felt and made him a pawn in his deadly plot. It was something he couldn't forget, although he kept his silence on it.

Maggie knew his feelings and smiled faintly at his response as she looked again at the remainder of the mail to be sorted. "Ruth said you went to Broken Butte. What's the status on the drilling?"

"They expect to reach the desired depth in two weeks." He peered over her shoulder as she separated the ranch-related correspondence from the personal letters. "Don't expect a gusher this time either," he advised her mockingly. "The results from the first well and the tests that have been completed indicate it's a shallow field, maybe capable of supporting a dozen wells, so there's little chance that we are going to become oil tycoons. Hopefully we'll earn enough off the barrels being pumped to make some improvements on the ranch. All the roads need work, and there's some sections that need new fencing. And we do need better housing for some of the married men."

"I was thinking more along the lines of a new car, or new drapes for the upstairs bedrooms." So few of the profits from the Triple C were used for their personal lives. All of it seemed to find its way back to the ranch. It always amazed

Maggie how greedy the ranch was—not that she lacked for anything, but personal items were certainly far down the list of priorities.

"And I was thinking if there was anything left over, I might buy a helicopter. It would certainly be an asset during roundup," he teased.

"You're kidding right now, but when the time comes, you'll probably be serious," Maggie retorted.

"Why is this letter by itself?" The idle inquiry was followed by his hand reaching to pick it up.

Maggie tensed at his action. "It's for Ty." Out of the corner of her eye, she watched him stiffen as he read the return address on the envelope.

"What's this?" A frown narrowed his eyes as he shot an accusing look at her. "Why is he getting a letter from a university in Texas?"

"E. J. Dyson happens to be an alumnus of the University of Texas. When he was here this last winter, he talked to Ty about it. Ty expressed some interest in possibly going to college there." It was impossible to explain casually when she was so conscious of the gathering thunder in Chase's expression. "E.J. pulled a few strings to see if he could get him accepted. I imagine that letter is the answer."

"Why wasn't I told?" he demanded, his voice dropping to a dangerously low pitch.

"You were there when the discussion took place," she reminded him tensely.

This clash of wills had been brewing for a long time. Maggie was determined to have Ty obtain a college education, and Chase was just as adamantly opposed to it. This was an issue to which she doubted they would ever find a mutually acceptable compromise. She had dreaded this moment for a long time, but she had no intention of backing down now.

"I was there," Chase admitted roughly. "But I wasn't aware that it had gone beyond a mere discussion." His hand tightened on the envelope, bending it in half. "Dammit, Maggie. There are experts on the Triple C who know more than a bunch of damned college professors. This is where he needs to be!"

"He is entitled to the best education we can give him," she

countered with equal force. "And that doesn't mean just the kind you get from the back of a horse. And he needs time just to have some fun—something you and I never had! It was always work—work and struggle and hardship of one kind or another. I don't want Ty to grow up as fast as we had to."

"You want to make him soft," he accused. "He can't be soft and run the Triple C! A man almost has to be born on this land to have an adequate knowledge of managing it. Ty didn't have that advantage. All he's had is three years, and it's only been within this last year that he's developed enough skill to be considered even an average ranch hand. He needs a lot of seasoning and training and experience in the operations of a ranch this size. How the hell do you expect him to get it out of a book!"

"There is a lot that can be learned from books." Maggie trembled, but she refused to give rein to her temper. "Some member of the Calder family believed that, too, or all those shelves in the den wouldn't be lined with books!"

"It's too soon, Maggie," Chase insisted grimly. "It's too soon for him to be leaving the ranch. Practically all that he's learned will be lost. Let me have him here year-round for at least three more years. Don't take him from me now."

"If I listened to you, in three years you'd come up with some other reason why he should wait. No. I won't do it." Her head shook firmly, her eyes glittering with defiance. "If he goes to college, I want him to start with this fall's term."

"Maggie—"

"Four years ago, you gave me your word that when the time came, you would abide by Ty's decision about college. I'm going to hold you to that," she stated.

Chase reared his head back, breathing in deeply and holding it. His grim visage was hard and impenetrable. There was a rawness in the air, a tension almost palpable.

"You know damned well I keep my promises," he roughly informed her. "And I'll keep that one, too. But if he goes to college"—Chase put the emphasis on the if—"it will be here in Montana, not fifteen hundred miles away."

"It will be his decision." Maggie refused to give ground even on that point and rescued the envelope from his crumpling grasp.

"Don't try to influence that decision, Maggie," Chase warned.

"And don't you try to influence him either," she flashed. "You know that he regards you as some sort of god. It would only take a word from you, Chase. Please, don't say it." It was her own form of warning.

The split was there. Either way the ax fell, it would be there. Chase swung away, his long, loping stride carrying him to the front door. Maggie winced as he slammed out of the house.

When Ty entered the dining room that evening, he knew something was wrong. The atmosphere seethed with tension and the silence was heavy. He paused a minute, studying the man and woman so steadfastly avoiding each other's gaze. He had a pretty good idea that this had something to do with the letter he'd found lying on top of his dresser when he'd gone to his room to clean up for dinner.

At Ty's approach, Maggie looked up and watched her son walk to his chair at the table. Broad-shouldered and firmly muscled, he had grown to a height well over six feet. The slow, swivel-hipped walk peculiar to cowboys had become natural to him. And his sun-browned face had acquired that leathery texture that came from long hours outdoors in the sun and the wind. His features, still showing the freshness of manhood, had the Calder look about them, raw strength in their hard-boned structure.

"Where is Chatty Cathie?" Ty pulled out his chair and sat down.

His baby sister had been born during troubled times for him. For a while, he had envied the absence of discipline given her, and had even been a little jealous of the affection his father had displayed so openly to this newest member of the family. But the jabbering tyke had a way of growing on a person. Affection had eventually replaced his resentment.

"Your father took her with him this afternoon, so she didn't have a nap," his mother replied and began ladling creamed asparagus soup from the tureen. "She was so cranky and tired I fixed her an early supper and put her to bed."

Even as the bowls of soup were passed, the oppressive

tension persisted. It clung to the edges of the idle conversation his parents exchanged. Both were trying to act normally in front of him, but the falseness was apparent to him.

This moment had been coming for a long time. Nothing was going to make it easier. If he had learned anything in his life, it was that postponing something unpleasant didn't make it go away. Ty let his spoon settle to the bottom of his soup bowl.

"I had a letter from the University of Texas today." His voice sounded level and calm, but a hush fell over the room, as if someone had walked in with a loaded gun. "I've been accepted there this fall."

"We . . . saw the letter and wondered what it said," his mother admitted as her glance ricocheted off his father's face.

Ty's glance moved over both of them, fully aware they were poles apart on this issue, which put him awkwardly in the middle.

"I know you've always wanted me to go to college, Mom," Ty admitted. "It's always been very important to you." There was little expression on his father's face, except for a twitch in the muscle running along his jaw when Ty addressed him. "You told me once that I had a helluva lot to learn if I expected to run this ranch someday. At the time I didn't realize how much. But even if I learned for a lifetime, there are men here on this ranch that would always know more than I do."

"I'm glad you realize that," his father murmured in satisfaction.

"I think some of them were born knowing it." There was a faintly wry twist of his mouth as he expelled a long breath. "I've thought about this a lot before I got that letter today. I'll never know as much about ranching and cattle and this land as most of the men on the Triple C. Since I can't, I've decided that I should learn things they don't know. I'm going to enroll at the University of Texas this September."

"That's your decision?" his father asked in an unbearably flat tone.

Ty wondered if his father realized how difficult it had been for him to reach that decision. He fought the feeling that he was letting his father down, because he felt his decision was the right one even if his father didn't. So it was with a grim determination that Ty met his father's hard look.

"Yes, that's my decision," he stated and managed not to let his gaze falter under the probing eyes of his father.

Then Chase looked away. "Pass me that basket of crackers, Maggie." With the terse request, he closed the subject to further discussion. Wisely, his mother had not voiced her approval of Ty's decision. It would have only increased the feeling of estrangement at the table.

After dinner was finished, his father didn't linger over coffee, as was his custom. Ty listened to the footsteps advancing toward the den and pushed his chair away from the table to follow him.

"Ty." His mother made a quick protest.

He paused short of the door and turned. "I've got to talk to him." Ty couldn't stand the silence that had come between them. His father's acceptance was too important to him.

His mother's expression told him she disagreed, but she only cautioned him, "Don't let him talk you out of going."

A silent and humorless laugh came from his throat in the form of a loud breath. "I'm half Calder and half O'Rourke, and I don't know which of you is more stubborn once you get your mind to something. Doesn't that make me twice as determined to carry out my decision?" Ty looked at her, saddened, yet unwavering in his stand. "You didn't talk me into it, Mom. And he isn't going to talk me out of it."

When Ty entered the den, his father was standing in front of the massive stone fireplace. One hand rested on the mantel while he stared into the cold and blackened hearth. There was a slumped curve to his shoulders that told Ty just how hard his father was taking his decision. He was glad, at this minute, that he couldn't see his face.

"Dad—" Ty began and watched the wide shoulders and muscled neck stiffen. "I know you're disappointed in me."

"Disappointed!" The man whose word was law on the Triple C dropped the supporting hand from the mantelpiece and swung half around to stand tall and erect, his body angled toward Ty. A struggle was going on inside him, a battle between his emotions and his control of them. When he spoke again, his voice was contained, yet taut. "I promised your mother I'd abide by your decision, and I will. But I can't agree with something I know is wrong."

"I know that." Ty nodded stiffly.

"There's some sense to the reasons you gave," his father grudgingly conceded. "But they won't stand up." His mouth came together, disappearing entirely into a compressed line, taut with anger. "Dammit, Ty! Do you think I was never eighteen? I was like you! I thought I knew more than my father! Most of the time I listened to the warnings he gave me with a smile on my face. I thought he was exaggerating. Hell, I didn't know the half of it. And you don't comprehend any of it!"

The sweeping condemnation stung Ty into defending himself. "I understand more than you give me credit for."

"Do you?" his father challenged harshly. "Look at the map." He thrust a pointing finger at the hand-drawn map mounted in a frame and hung on the wall behind the large desk. Years had yellowed the canvas on which the boundaries of the Triple C Ranch were crudely outlined. "It's old, Ty. It's old, but it's still accurate. Do you have any idea how many big ranches there were then? Today, there's less than a handful that can still boast they exist—and most of those are owned by some absentee corporate investors. Those other ranches had their glory days. But the Calders lasted because they made a commitment to the land and all that lived on it, livestock and people."

"I understand that," Ty insisted with a gathering frown of irritation and resentment. He didn't need a sermon. Over the last three years, he'd heard more preaching than anything else. "I am capable of thinking for myself."

"Then you'd better start thinking," his father advised. "A place this size is vulnerable to outside forces, and it will collapse like a house of cards if the man heading it doesn't know what he's doing. And you'd better damned well understand that! If the core of something is weak, it can't support what surrounds it."

"I'm standing up to you for something I believe is right," he declared through his clenched teeth. "Dammit, that has to mean something."

"I'll give you that," his father conceded without taking

back anything he'd said. "But I know this land will make you into the kind of man this ranch needs. And you'll never convince me that a bunch of goddamned professors are going to do that. I won't stand in your way, Ty," he breathed heavily, "but I'm not going to lift a hand to help you either. You aren't going to learn about life in a classroom. It's out there!" His finger jabbed in the direction of the window.

"In time, I'll prove to you I'm right." Ty was hurt by his father's lack of support, but he didn't let it show.

"By God, you'll have to."

Ty's chin dipped a fraction of an inch lower as he turned to leave the room. The firmness of his conviction was shaken, but he was still determined to go through with his decision. His stubborn pride insisted that he prove he was right.

4

At summer's end, upwards of two hundred people—ranch hands and their families—gathered at the Triple C headquarters to have a going-away party for Ty before he headed for college.

There weren't any speeches, but there was a lot of back-slapping and some good-natured ribbing about college girls. Cold beer flowed freely from kegs, youngsters stealing sips from paper cups left unattended. Outdoor buffet tables were covered with a variety of salads, casseroles, pies, and cakes supplied by the wives of the ranch hands.

Tucker, the bald-headed ranch cook, struggled to maintain his supremacy against the invasion of women and finally retreated to reign over the barbecue fires with a long-pronged fork and a carving knife. There was a constant ebb and flow of people to and from the tables of food set up beneath a large canvas tent with its sides rolled up to permit access from all directions. Makeshift picnic tables of board planks atop sawhorses were scattered around under what shade trees were available.

Those who weren't eating or drinking had gathered at the large corral by the barn. Part of the afternoon-long festivities included some friendly competition among the cowboys, matching their skills in ranch-related events such as team roping, cutting cattle, tug-of-war on horseback, and break-away roping, and in gymkhana events such as barrel racing and pole bending.

Ty had participated in many of the events with no hopes of winning, but as the guest of honor, his active involvement was expected. At least he had the satisfaction of making a respectable showing in the events he rode in.

One of the cowboys swung the gate open as Ty walked his speckle-faced sorrel out of the corral and finished coiling his rope after taking his turn in the breakaway roping competition. It differed from straight calf roping in that the cowboy was only required to rope the calf and let the loop snug up around its neck, then throw the rope away. The calf wasn't thrown and tied.

Outside the corral, he circled his horse around to the fence to watch the next contestant. After he tied the coiled rope in place on his saddle, Ty hooked a leg on the saddle horn and leaned on it. There was always an odd comment or two directed at him by the participants or spectators on the sidelines; most of the time, they didn't require more than a nod or a brief smile in response.

Sid Ramsey was in the corral, hazing loose livestock back to the catch pens. During a break in the action, he stopped his horse close to the corral fence where Ty sat on his horse.

"So you're pulling out for the big state of Texas, huh?" he said to Ty with the corners of his mouth pulled down.

"That's right." Ty nodded. "I'll be flying out with Dyson when he leaves the day after tomorrow."

Saddle leather creaked as the cowboy leaned to the side and spat at the ground near his horse's feet. "One thing about it, me and the rest of the boys won't have to be carrying your load of work anymore. You always was a sorry excuse for a cowboy."

"Hell, look what I had for teachers," he countered with a

mocking grin. He understood the derogatory comment was Ramsey's backhanded way of saying he'd be missed. It was part of that peculiar code of these men to speak with roughness when their feelings were deep. And the ones who gave him the hardest time were also the ones who seemed the sorriest that he was leaving, Ty had discovered.

Ramsey chortled, then touched a hand to his hat and spurred his horse toward the burst of action in the corral. A tightness gripped Ty's throat as he suddenly realized he was going to miss all this. He peered up from his hat brim at the endless expanse of open sky overhead. The sights and sounds became important—the slap of hooves on hard ground, the grunt of running animals, the clanking of spurs, the rank smell of manure and the sweat of bodies. There was a oneness here, a working partnership between man, animals, and the land. It seemed difficult to remember that he'd known any other kind of life.

There was a burst of applause and shouts of approval among the spectators around the corral arena. Ty swung his attention back to the action. A slim young rider was circling back to retrieve the rope presently being removed from the neck of a sturdy calf.

"Hot damn! Did you see that?" the cowboy on his left exclaimed. "I'll bet she did that in five seconds flat."

When the rider turned in the saddle and Ty saw the smiling face, he instantly recognized Jessy Niles. He'd only seen her a few times since he'd worked the calving sheds at South Branch two years ago. She hadn't changed much, except to grow taller. He realized she was even more of a tomboy now.

As she rode to the corral gate, he looked at the horse she was riding and his interest quickened. The rangy blue-gray buckskin had the unmistakable lines of Cougar breeding, the stallion that had sired some of the best cow horses on the place. Ty was almost certain the grulla was Mouse. He'd been one of the first riders on that horse's back. Vaguely he recalled it being mentioned that Mouse had been added to the remuda at South Branch.

"Jessy," Ty called to her as she rode through the gate. Unhooking his leg, he pushed the toe of his boot into the stirrup and waited while she swung the mouse-gray horse around and eased it in beside his horse. "Looks like that was the winning time."

"I got lucky." But she was wearing a proud look that seemed natural to her strong features and widely drawn mouth. She smoothed a hand over the horse's arched neck. "Mouse still doesn't have this roping business down pat. He's so quick out of the starting gate that most of the time he runs past the calf. I had to throw my loop in a hurry and hope the calf ran into it. It did."

"I helped break that horse," Ty said. "I wondered whose string he was in."

"He's in my dad's string, but he's been letting me work him this summer." When she looked at him, Jessy searched his expression to find something that might confirm or deny the rumors she'd been hearing.

In spite of the large size of the Triple C, news and gossip had a way of traversing the distances in a hurry. Everyone took special interest when the topic was a Calder. Most of the time Jessy didn't care much about listening to gossip about other people's problems. Even though she recognized the position of the Calders in the ranch hierarchy, she wasn't particularly interested in their comings and goings—until she had met Ty. Jessy never attempted to reason out why it was so. But Ty was closer to her own age and he was the only member of the Calder family she'd spent much time with. She would have vigorously denied having a crush on him, but all the makings for one were present, even if she did consider the crushes of her contemporaries silly and stupid.

"Why are you leaving here?" Boldly inquisitive and unconscious of it, Jessy questioned him.

"I'm going to college."

"I know that," she retorted with calm patience. "But why are you going?" Without taking a breath, Jessy went on. "I know some of the boys have been riding you hard since you came here. You aren't quitting, are you, Ty?" Her face looked earnest and a little worried.

His smile came slowly, breaking across his strongly cast features. "No, I'm not quitting, Jessy," he reassured her, amused by this concern from one so young.

Masking her relief, Jessy adjusted the length of rein in her grip. "Well, I just wanted to make sure you were coming back," she replied with a forced air of nonchalance. "I gotta be finding my dad so we can get these horses loaded in the trailer." She pulled steadily on the bit to back the mouse-gray horse away from the corral fence. "See ya."

"See ya," Ty returned and watched her deftly guide the horse out of the close quarters with a combination of rein and leg movements. It wasn't fair to call her homely, but Jessy certainly wasn't a pretty thing either.

"Hey, Ty!" somebody shouted to him. "Your ma's looking for you!"

Lifting an acknowledging hand in the general direction of the voice, he reined the speckle-faced sorrel away from the fence and walked it toward the open tent in the ranch yard.

The fast-moving airplane laid a shadow on the rolling humps of grassland below. To the west, there was a collection of small, dark squares. They looked like they might be the buildings of the South Branch camp. Ty strained his eyes to see them, but they were too far away and the plane was traveling too fast. He felt the pull of the land calling to him and smiled faintly when he recalled how Jessy had been worried about whether he was coming back.

There was little to recommend it. He had cursed the bitter cold of winter and bitched about the broiling heat of summer and sworn at the rainless sky and griped about the yellow gumbo that caked his boots when it did rain. But it was home. He had struggled so long and so hard to become a part of it that it was strange to discover that now it felt a part of him.

The plane rushed toward the rimrock country of the Yellowstone River, leaving the southern boundary of the Triple C. Ty turned away from the small window and settled back in his seat, glancing at the older man who was going over the latest drilling reports on the Broken Butte site.

E. J. Dyson was somewhat of a stranger to him. Ty knew very little about him, except that the man and his partner had business dealings with his father. Ty had sat in on a few meetings and had been impressed with the man's cool reasoning and intelligence, but his personal life was a mystery.

There was a degree of fascination in Ty's attitude toward Dyson. Undoubtedly he was a power-equal of his father, but Dyson lived in the fast-paced world of jets, corporate conglomerates, and high finance. Not by any stretch of the imagination would Ty describe him as soft or weak, despite his city living. Dyson lacked the physical presence of Chase Calder, but Ty wasn't fooled by the slightness of the man's unprepossessing build. Beneath that Texas flash of western clothes, there was a keenly astute businessman.

"That's finished," Dyson drawled and flipped the report shut. His mouth twitched a smile in Ty's direction as he slid the report into one of the pockets of his briefcase, fully aware the boy had been studying him. At his age, Dyson regarded any eighteen-year-old male as a boy.

His own curiosity was better concealed. This offspring of Chase Calder didn't seem to fit his father's mold. It had been obvious at the ranch airstrip before they'd taken off this morning that the relationship between father and son was strained. Disagreement between parent and child was somewhat normal, but this situation particularly interested Dyson.

"I'm glad we're having a smooth flight so far," he said to open the conversation. "It's easier to talk when you aren't bouncing all over the sky."

"That's true."

Words weren't wasted elaborating on the fact. Ty was closemouthed like his father, Dyson observed. "The day you leave for college is a milestone in any man's life. It seems there is always a mixture of anticipation and regret." He subtly attempted to encourage Ty to state his feelings.

"I suppose so." He almost smiled, acknowledging to Dyson that his guess about mixed feelings was accurate.

"Have you given a thought about what you want to major in?" Dyson tipped his head to one side in a show of interest.

A trace of dry amusement briefly glittered in the brown eyes as his smile deepened. "Nothing, if I can get away with it."

The answer intrigued him. "What do you mean?"

"I want to take classes in everything—veterinary science, animal husbandry, land management, natural resources, some mechanical and engineering courses, accounting, psychology . . ." Ty paused, indicating the list was endless. "I want to learn something about everything."

"A little knowledge can be dangerous," Dyson warned while he made a closer study of the boy.

"I don't look at it that way, Mr. Dyson," he replied calmly.

"Make it E.J.," he invited.

"E.J." Ty nodded. "I'm only interested in learning. I don't give a damn about getting a degree. If I have a grasp of the basics in a variety of areas, it's going to be difficult for anyone to pull the wool over my eyes."

"Or easier," Dyson murmured.

The response drew a shrug and a faintly reckless grin. "As one of the old cowboys, Nate Moore, told me, common sense can't be taught. You either have it or you don't. All the education in the world won't make any difference if you don't have the common sense to apply it wisely."

"Smart man."

"Nate Moore is the resident cowboy philosopher." Ty smiled wryly. "He doesn't talk much, but when he does say something, it's usually worth remembering."

"Most of the true cowboys I've met never thought too much of formal schooling."

"Nearly all the kids in my high school were ranch kids. A few of them dropped out of school and went to work riding for somebody or helped full time at home. As far as I know, none of the others who graduated with me have enrolled in any college, unless it was a couple of the girls." With all the chores he had to do at home, Ty had never gotten very close to any of his classmates who didn't live on the Triple C. And on top of being an outsider to those who did, he was a Calder, so he'd never been real chummy with any of them either.

"You seem to be breaking the tradition," Dyson observed.

The amusement that flashed in his eyes was almost sardonic. "Closer to shattering it." Ty was too bitterly aware that his father still hadn't become reconciled to his decision to attend college.

"I have great respect for your father." Dyson had sensed Chase's displeasure toward his son this weekend, but he hadn't known the cause of it. After Ty's remark, he knew the reason. "He's a fair-dealing, down-to-earth man who isn't above putting the screws to someone to get what he wants. He's sharp, very sharp," Dyson stated firmly, a glint of admiration appearing in his faded blue eyes. "But his attitude is sometimes archaic. The days of the cattle barons are over. A ranch has to be treated like any other big business. The operation must be streamlined and highly efficient and it has to make use of the most modern methods available if it's going to survive and compete. Every available resource must be used to its capacity. Your father knows that, but he isn't willing to admit it. I guess that's one of the problems of growing older. You like doing things the way you are used to, positive it's the best way because it's the most familiar." Dyson smiled crookedly, including himself in the comment. "But you have a head on your shoulders, Ty. What you're doing will ultimately breathe new life into that ranch."

This unexpected endorsement of his decision from someone of E. J. Dyson's caliber, untainted by any personal prejudices or desires, washed the niggling doubts from Ty's mind. He didn't claim that he had looked at the situation in that light of Dyson's reasoning. His motives were more selfish, centering on a desire to contribute something no one else could offer.

"I hope that happens." Too many veteran cowboys had knocked him down a few pegs for Ty to express overconfidence. "That's why I want to take any course that might benefit me in the long run."

"You can't study all the time. You be sure to leave some room in there for a little fun and some girls." Dyson winked.

"I'll make sure there's room for the girls." Ty grinned.

"Now you're talkin' like a Texan," the man jested. "By the way, I meant what I said to your mother. While you're going to college, you're welcome in my home any weekend. Now, I'm not just saying that to hear myself talk. I'm expecting you to come."

"I will," he promised.

"Once you meet my daughter, I know you will," Dyson declared.

That was a detail that had slipped Ty's mind. He frowned as he tried to recall the discussion that had included mention of his daughter. "I remember that you said something about her once."

"That was probably when I was telling you about the university. Tara Lee has enrolled as a freshman there, the same as you, although I doubt if she's as serious about her education. She's a bright girl; getting good grades comes too easy for her, I'm afraid."

"It must be nice." His school grades had always been above average, but he'd had to study to get them.

"A word of warning about my daughter—from one man to another," Dyson said. "Tara Lee attracts boys like flies to a honey jar. She'll be meeting the plane when we arrive, so keep in mind when you see her that she's a regular butterfly, flittin' from one boy to another."

"I'll try to remember that." His curiosity was piqued. Ty simply couldn't fit that image of a girl to this slight, bland man. She obviously didn't look like her father; either that, or he was exaggerating her beauty out of paternal blindness.

The plane taxied to a stop in front of a private hangar lettered with a sign identifying it as Dy-Corp Development Ltd. Ty unbuckled his seat belt and waited for the older man to leave the plane first. Hot air rolled up from the concrete apron to envelop him in its stifling midst, heat shimmers putting waves in the nearby buildings. Ty felt the perspiration breaking out between his shoulder blades and above his lip. He was accustomed to Montana's dry heat, not this humidity of a Texas summer.

He straightened to his full height, stretching muscles cramped from the long flight. A miniature tractor with a small trailer in tow came chugging out to meet the plane while the members of the ground crew that had put chocks behind the wheels hurried to open the baggage compartment. Ty took a step in that direction.

"Never mind the luggage," Dyson told him. "They'll unload it and stow it in the trunk of my car."

A horn honked as a silver Cadillac whipped into the

parking lot next to the hangar. Dyson raised his hand in greeting, then walked briskly toward the car, indifferent to the glaring heat. Ty's long, lazy strides had no difficulty keeping up with him. A young woman climbed out of the driver's side of the car and came forward to greet them.

Ty stared. He couldn't help it. Dark and vivacious, she was everything both wholesome and sexy in a female. Her dark sable hair was long and softly curled about her shoulders in a style that was purely fresh and feminine. Her complexion had a clean look to it, glowing golden with a light suntan and radiating a warmth that he seemed to feel in his blood. The cherry-pink color on her lips matched the spaghetti-strapped sundress she was wearing.

Graceful as a doe, she ran up to her father and put both hands on his shoulders to lean up and kiss his cheek. "I'm sorry I'm late, Daddy. I hope you haven't been on the ground too long."

"We just got off the plane." He returned the kiss, then directed her attention to Ty. "I want you to meet my daughter, Tara Lee. This is Ty Calder."

When those velvety dark eyes turned on him, Ty was dazzled. He had dated some attractive girls. He'd lost his virginity shortly after he'd turned seventeen during a wild, partying weekend in Miles City and had met up with the same experienced lady since. But this was beauty.

"How do you do, Tara Lee." His voice was husky and low, vibrating with the inner turmoil she was stirring.

"Ty Calder." She repeated his name, a provocative pair of dimples appearing near the corners of her mouth. "Of *the* Calder family?" She slid a sidelong look at her father for confirmation, a hint of mocking, but not unkind, humor in her voice.

"The same." He nodded.

"Welcome to Texas, Ty Calder." She offered him her slim hand. He took it and held it. His gaze skittered down to the bodice of her sundress and observed the shimmer of perspiration collecting in the little bit of cleavage that showed. Firm young breasts rose slightly with the rhythm of her breathing. "Will you be staying long?"

"Yes . . . I'm pleased to say." His glance came back to meet her steady and knowing gaze. The faint smile that lifted the corners of her lips didn't reject his interest.

"Ty has enrolled in college here. I believe I mentioned it to you," E. J. Dyson inserted dryly.

"I remember that you were busy twisting arms on the admissions board to get somebody's son accepted at the university." She shrugged diffidently, bare shoulders gleaming golden in the waning sunlight. With a small tug, she slipped her hand free of his grip, gently teasing him with a look because he'd held it too long. Ty simply smiled, because he wanted her to know that he was attracted to her—more than attracted, he was captivated. "Daddy does business with so many people that I can't begin to keep track of who is who."

"Except *the* Calders?" He taunted her lightly with the phrase she had used earlier, marking his family as something separate.

"The stories Daddy brings home about your ranch up there—I'll bet most of them aren't to be believed." Her voice had a genteel southern accent, bearing little resemblance to Dyson's hard, twanging drawl. Ty could have listened to her talk all night. "Does your daddy really own a ranch almost as big as Rhode Island?"

"Close enough."

"You'll have to tell me about it sometime," she declared and linked an arm with her father, laughing up at him. "So I can compare stories and discover whether you've been telling me some tall tales."

She seemed to forget about Ty as the trio walked to the silver Cadillac. She smiled at the men loading the luggage in the trunk of the car, and Ty noticed the way the men fell all over themselves in their haste to respond. It was vaguely irritating.

"I see Tara Lee persuaded you to let her drive your car," Dyson said to his partner, George Stricklin, who waited by the Cadillac.

"Yes, she did," he admitted. Tara was the one emotional weakness Stricklin permitted himself. From the first moment he'd seen her as a teenager, she had reminded

him of the China doll his mother had kept locked in a
glass case. It was an object to be looked at and admired,
but not touched. He regarded Tara with the same distant
adoration.

5

After listing his major in agriscience and animal
husbandry with a minor in business administration, Ty signed
up for more than a full load of classes. During rush week, he
waited until he found out what sorority Tara Lee Dyson was
joining before he pledged to a fraternity. When it came to the
hazing that accompanied his initiation into the fraternity, Ty
was a pro at handling it. His only other extracurricular
activity was the college rodeo team.

Once the initial period of adjustment had passed and Ty
settled into the routine of university life, it seemed the first
semester came to an end almost before it started. Despite the
two weekends he'd spent at the Dyson home and the inter-
mixing of their respective fraternity and sorority, he had
spent little time with Tara. With her looks and personality,
she had become one of the most popular girls on campus in
the first month. The competition for her attention was fierce.

His frat house had a Christmas party on the weekend
before the holiday vacation period began. For most of the
evening, Ty was forced to watch Tara laughing and dancing
with others. Twice he had managed to ask her to dance, and
both times someone had taken advantage of his pledge status
and cut in. His frustration was reaching an intolerable level
when he finally saw his opening. Tara had just emerged from
the powder room to rejoin the party. Ty intercepted her
before any of his fraternity buddies noticed and steered her
away from the common room into the small sitting alcove
under the stairwell.

"Ty Calder, why ever did you bring me here?" The look in her eyes overruled the mild protest of her words and told him that she knew.

"Where else can I spend five minutes alone with you without someone interrupting us?" he countered huskily, her loveliness stirring up all the rawness of his desire.

"Daddy was wondering if you are planning to come to the house this weekend before you leave for home," she murmured.

The bench settee was hardly satisfactory, but it was the only seating available. She sat at an angle, facing him, with her shoulders against the corner. Her position kept him at a distance, only their knees touching as Ty leaned toward her, a hand spread on the leather-covered bench cushion near her hip. The faint gold light brought out the ebony sheen of her hair and the creamy smoothness of her skin. Her lips were cherry-red and shining a silent invitation that knotted the ache in his loins.

"Are you going to be there?" His want was in his voice, and he took no trouble to conceal that his decision was hinged on her presence.

"I'll be there part of the time, of course, but I've received invitations to at least a dozen parties." Her social calendar always seemed to be booked solid. Ty was never sure whether he was pleased or irritated by the social whirl that took so much of her time and constantly changed her escort. There was consolation in knowing she had no steady boyfriend and frustration in not having the opportunity to change that.

"I have a term paper to finish, so you'd better not expect me." He searched for a glimmer of disappointment, anything to give him encouragement.

"I'll tell Daddy," Tara replied smoothly, not giving him the satisfaction he sought.

Whoops of laughter spilled into the alcove, destroying the intimate atmosphere Ty sought. "Let's get out of here." His hand moved onto her knee, caressing its roundness beneath the cherry wool skirt. "Let's go somewhere quiet so we can talk. I haven't had five minutes with you all evening."

She cast a dark glance in the direction of the noise, then let it slide back to Ty. "It's a wonderful idea, but I promised Ed

Bruce that I'd ride back to the sorority house with him." She smiled apologetically. "Maybe another time."

"That's what you keep saying." A grimness edged his jaw. "I'm beginning to wonder when that will be. Tell him you've changed your mind and you're going with me."

"No," she refused and lifted his hand off her knee. "It isn't my fault he asked me first, so don't become churlish because I accepted. No one tells me what to do, Ty Calder, not even my daddy."

In a fluid movement, so characteristically graceful, she rose to her feet. A second later, Ty was standing, finally close to her. The perfumed scent of her body stimulated his already aroused senses while her dark, natural beauty touched deeply into his soul. His hand formed to the curve of her waist to stay her from walking away. He towered before her petite frame, looking down with all the hunger of his young male needs.

Despite her words and action, she wasn't angry with him. Tara was simply laying the ground rules. No one was going to dictate to her or control her—or limit her number of male friends. It was not conquests she wanted, but the freedom to be with whom she pleased, when she pleased.

"Dammit, I just want to see you and I never get the chance." His voice vibrated in frustration. Before, he hadn't been willing to join the contingent of boyfriends. He had wanted her all to himself, but at the moment Ty was desperate enough to settle for anything that would allow him the pleasure of her company.

Her softening expression nearly made him groan aloud. "No one has asked me to the first basketball game after the New Year."

"Will you go with me?" Ty asked thickly, leaning an inch closer.

"Yes." Her dark eyes glowed with promise, and their look broke the last vestiges of his restraint.

His grip tightened on her waist, bringing her against him, while his other hand tunneled into her hair to cup the back of her head. He didn't mean to be rough with her, but the pressure of his mouth on her warmly pliant lips was hard and demanding.

There was a rush of triumph when he tasted the brief flare

of a response. He wanted more and tried to take it, only to be met by a determined resistance. Her hands pushed at his chest as she pulled away from him.

Ty hurried to apologize. "Tara, I—" She pressed her fingertips to his lips to silence him.

"My daddy should have warned me about you," she murmured and eyed him with an awareness she hadn't shown before. Ty would have pressed this new advantage and gathered her again into his arms, but she slipped free of his grasp with a casualness that negated her earlier admission. "I'm not ready to be rushed into something, Ty Calder, so let's go back to the party."

She extended her hand to lead him back to the crowded, noisy room. It wasn't the warmth of her small hand he wanted to feel. It was the heat of her body under his and the moistness of her lips beneath his mouth that he wanted. One kiss could not satisfy an appetite that had become ravenous. Just being with her aroused him, and no solace was offered for the hard, stony ache in his loins.

The front door to the fraternity house swung open wide, aided by a gusting, cold wind that rushed the strands of silver tinsel on the foyer Christmas tree and swayed the brightly colored ornaments. Two of his fraternity mates came puffing inside, each carrying a case of cold beer on his shoulders.

"Shut the door!" someone shouted, a protest endorsed by others.

"One of those damn blue norther's arrived," a beer-toting Jack Springer explained as he kicked the door shut with his foot. Jack, like Ty, was a new pledge. "Blue norther" was the term applied to cold fronts that entered the Texas plains with a rush of wind that dropped temperatures to a chilling degree.

"Yeah, and it's all Montana's fault," his partner, Willie Atkins, decried with a look at Ty, who had been dubbed Montana by his mostly southern roommates. "You must have left a gate open on your way down here last fall." His glance went past Ty and lighted on the raven-tressed girl with him. The case of beer came off his shoulder and was shoved into Ty's middle. "Just for that, you have to forfeit your partner for the rest of the evening."

Instinctively, Ty grabbed for the heavy case of canned

beer. In doing so, he released Tara's hand. Willie Atkins immediately whisked her away in an exaggerated waltz that made her laugh.

Ty watched them go, his jaw clamped rigidly shut. As a pledge, there was little objection he could raise against his senior frat brother. Yet he was enraged at Tara's willingness to go with Atkins with no more regret than a careless smile and a vague shrug in his direction.

It wasn't the first time she had treated him this way, and he liked it less and less every time. What galled him most was the knowledge that he had no rights to her. She wasn't his girl, and she had given him no cause to believe she would be. His ego was bruised and his body was one big physical ache.

"Are you plannin' on holdin' that case of beer all night, Montana?" Jack Springer chided him from the arched doorway opening to the party. "We got a thirsty group in here."

Prodded into action, Ty adjusted the case to a more comfortable carrying position and followed the slim son of a Texas hill country rancher into the crowded room. A second after he had shoved the case onto the refreshment table, someone was pushing a cold beer into his hand. He took a swallow of it, then drifted to an empty space along a side wall and leaned against it.

Although there was some pairing up as the hour grew later, there were plenty of singles of both sexes who hadn't settled on a partner for the evening. The number of men vying for Tara's exclusive attention was dwindling, but Ty was fully aware that she was still among the single group.

His elbow was jostled, sloshing the beer in his can. He managed to avoid spilling any of it on himself as it splashed harmlessly onto the already stained carpet.

"Ooops, I'm sorry." The quick apology came on the heels of the elbowing.

"No harm done." Ty shrugged off the incident with barely a glance at the buxom girl with blond hair skillfully bleached the platinum color of flax.

But she sidled closer, forcing his attention to her. "I've heard about you," she declared with a sidelong look. "You're Ty Calder, aren't you?"

"Yes." He absently studied her, noting the expensive look of her clothes and jewelry.

"Your father is supposed to own some big ranch up north." She pretended to recall the information.

"In Montana." The faint smile that touched his mouth was edged with irony. The elbowing had simply been a ploy to meet him, not an accident at all. She had likely checked him out thoroughly before coming over.

"Montana, that's right." She nodded and continued to smile at him like a purring Persian cat, all feline and sexy. "I suppose that makes you something of a cowboy. I always did go for cowboys. There's something earthy about them."

"Is that a fact?" His laconic reply merely deepened her smile.

"You shouldn't be standing here drinking all alone. My name's Dott." She leaned against the wall so her shoulder touched his and the plumpness of her full breast brushed the sleeve of his shirt.

At the same moment, Ty noticed Tara being guided to a darkened area of the large room where there were less than a handful of couples swaying to some slow music. A hard physical need crowded his insides as he watched her being enveloped in the muscular embrace of the bullnecked Schroeder.

"Let's dance." His arm hooked the blonde around the waist and drew her along with him to the dance area. They left their beer cans at the first table they passed.

It was to assuage the throbbing soreness of his want that he gathered the amply curved Dott tightly to his length—and maybe a little to show Tara there were other girls available to him. While their feet shuffled an indifferent rhythm to the music, the platinum blonde took the initiative and began nuzzling the corded muscles in his neck. With so much passion held in check and needing a release, it didn't take Ty long to forget Tara and follow the lead of his partner's long, starkly hungry kiss.

His hands moved over her firmly packed bottom and pressed her against his grinding hips. Her full breasts were mounds of ripe flesh pushing against his chest. Dragging in a breath, Ty pulled away from her lips a fraction of an inch.

"What did you say your name was? Pat?" At the moment, he didn't give a damn who she was. He only wanted the satisfaction her eager flesh promised.

"Dott." Her moist and shiny lips parted, waiting for him to reclaim them.

"Let's get the hell out of here, Dott." His tongue felt thick and hard in his throat.

"Whatever you say, cowboy."

When Tara observed Ty departing with the buxom blonde hanging on his arm, she seethed with anger. Dott MacElroy's reputation was well known to her, since she was both a sorority sister and a member of Tara's social sphere. It came as no surprise to see the two of them together. She remembered too well the look of longing that had been in Ty's gaze. It was half the reason she had kept her distance from him. He stirred her more than most men did.

In certain regards, her upbringing had been very strict. This was her first real taste of freedom, and she intended to savor every minute of her four years at college. Only in numbers was there safety from serious, possessive relationships. She could be just as ruthless and single-minded as her father when it was necessary, so Tara was determined that Ty would never be more than one of many boyfriends.

She knew she had aroused him sexually and driven him into Dott MacElroy's arms. Knowing this didn't upset her. However, she was affronted by Ty's crudeness in so blatantly letting his intentions be displayed to her. A gentleman would have arranged to meet Dott somewhere, rather than be seen leaving the party with her. Everyone knew it was only the MacElroy oil that spared Dott the label of tramp. Considering her father's comments on how primitive the Calder attitude was at times, she should have anticipated such crude behavior from Ty.

It was doubtful that she would see him until after the Christmas vacation was over, since he wouldn't be coming to the house this weekend. She'd straighten him out then. There were subtle ways a woman could make her displeasure known, and Tara knew them all.

* * *

While Ty was home for the holidays, nothing on the ranch seemed to have changed except his little sister. Her vocabulary had expanded, and with it her talkativeness. She'd grown a couple of inches and lost some of her chubby baby fat.

Other than that, he could have been coming home from school instead of college. Every day his father had a list of ranch chores for him to do. After the mildness of a Texas winter, it had taken him a couple of days to adjust to the brutal cold of Montana.

There had been no big welcome for him, no indication that he had been missed—except by his mother, and Ty expected that. But it was from his father that he wanted it. Four months of college hadn't changed anything.

Maybe that was the cause of his depression, Ty reasoned. He was sprawled in the big armchair in front of the stone fireplace, slowly turning a snifter of brandy in his hand. Or maybe it was the huge pile of Christmas presents under the tree in the living room, a long-needled pine cut and brought down from the mountains on the edge of Calder land. Little Cathleen was finally old enough to understand what Christmas and Santa Claus were all about. Virtually all the gifts under the tree were for her, thanks to a toy-shopping splurge his father had in Denver. His mother had laughed and told Ty all about it when he remarked on the number of presents under the tree.

He rubbed a hand across his forehead. All the holiday festivities seemed to be for Cathleen's benefit, and he resented it. He was the one who'd been away, but no fatted calf was being killed on his return. Damn, but she didn't realize how lucky she was to grow up in these surroundings—to be a part of it from the beginning. He'd never had that head start. Instead, he'd come to the ranch as a teenager, completely green to the ways of the western land and its people. He'd been struggling to catch up ever since, and it worried him that maybe he never would. Sometimes he couldn't help envying his sister. She'd have an easier time of it than he had.

When he lowered his hand, his glance ran to the telephone. Maybe his dejection was caused by neither of those things. Maybe it was Tara Lee. Lord knew, her image haunted him, his mind doing cruel things to him, recalling too vividly her loveliness, the pride and strong will she showed him. Ty didn't want to be in Texas with her, but he damned sure wanted her here with him.

The party at the fraternity house hadn't ended right. Although he'd found the sexual gratification his flesh had craved, it had left a bad taste in his mouth. It was Tara he'd wanted, and Ty was irritated with himself for settling for less. Somehow it seemed to have cheapened his feelings toward her. If he could just explain to her, maybe he could make it right. The memory of her soft, cultured drawl made the urge stronger.

Ty pushed out of the armchair and walked to the black telephone on the desk. With the receiver in one hand, he started to dial the operator, then hesitated. The approach of footsteps made his decision, and he grimly replaced the receiver.

"There you are, Ty. I thought you were still upstairs," his mother exclaimed as she entered the room. "We were waiting until you came down to open the presents." When he turned to face her, she noticed his hand come away from the telephone. "I'm sorry. Were you on the phone?"

"No." The quick negative response sounded false. "I was going to call someone, but I changed my mind." He picked up the brandy snifter and swirled its contents, studying the action with grim interest.

There were only a few things that could put that troubled look on a person's face, and Maggie took a mother's guess at the reason. "A girl?"

His head lifted, wary and aloof; then a sudden, slanting smile gave a wryness to his expression. "Yes, a girl."

"If you were considering calling her on Christmas Eve, she must be someone special." She felt a twinge of apprehension, mixed with a little bit of amusement.

"She is." His smile lost its wryness to become warm and soft. A determination was running through him. "As a matter of fact, I'm going to marry her."

"What?" Maggie stiffened in vague alarm.

"Not to worry, Mother." Ty laughed softly at her. "It won't be any time soon. We both have college to finish."

"What's her name?" There had been no mention of a

steady girlfriend in his letters home. Of course, his letters had been few and far between, and typically short epistles at that. "I suppose she's one of those Texas beauties E.J. is always bragging about."

"Yes, she is," he admitted without telling her the girl was E. J. Dyson's daughter. He downed the small amount of brandy that remained in his glass, then set it on the desk and crossed the room to put an arm around his mother's shoulders. "Do you know she's just about your size? Her hair is dark, too, the color of mink. But her eyes are brown, almost black—not green like yours. She's darn near as pretty as you are, too."

"That last part I don't believe." She laughed, finally put at ease by his flattering comments. They came so glibly from him anymore. Yet it remained difficult for her to regard him as a grown male. He would always be her son, so she would probably always see the child in him. With a mother's eye for detail—like dirt behind the ears—Maggie reached up and smoothed the shaggy ends of dark hair at the back of his neck where his shirt collar had pushed it up. "You need a haircut."

"It's right in style, Mom," he assured her with a teasing wink. "Some of the fellas on campus wear their hair shoulder-length."

"You'd better not come home with it that long, or your father will have a heart attack." It was meant as a joke, but neither of them could manage a smile. Both knew such an incident would only harden his bias against college.

"Speaking of Dad"—Ty tactfully changed the subject—"we'd better go into the living room before he and Cathleen start opening the presents without us."

The branding iron gleamed white-hot, with a red glow showing in the heart of the C-shaped iron. Even through her gloves, Jessy could feel the heat traveling up the rod and into her hands. But she was used to it—just as she was used to the choking dust, the bawling noise, and the milling confusion of riders and animals. There had been too many roundups in her young life for her to find anything unusual about this one.

The dusty red flank of the Hereford calf was exposed for

the iron. There was a trick to making a clean brand. Jessy had finally got the hang of it two years ago, and now she wielded the iron like an expert. Hair sizzled and stank up the air already ripe with the smell of manure, blood, and sweat. She didn't even wrinkle her nose.

She pressed the hot iron firmly onto the flank, not deep enough to injure the flesh but deep enough to burn a clear print into the hide. Anything less, and the hair could grow back and obscure the brand. The action was repeated twice more to make three C's on the calf's flank. Jessy stepped back and nodded to the man holding the bawling, frightened calf on the ground.

"You can let 'im up," she said.

At a trot, Jessy headed for the branding fire, dodging horses and riders and swinging ropes, as well as other members of the hustling ground crew. When she reached the fire, she jabbed the iron into the hot coals to reheat and took another that glowed white-hot tinged with red.

Individual members of the ground crew converged on a roped bawling and bucking calf, each with a task assigned. One man flanked the calf and put it on the ground while another man ear-tagged it and a third jabbed it with a vaccinating needle and castrated the bull calves. Lastly, the brand was burned onto its hip. They worked slickly and efficiently, putting a calf on its feet almost before it had recovered from the terror of being half strangled by the rope around its neck.

The number of calves seemed unending as Jessy trotted to the next. A hefty bull calf was giving the men trouble, kicking and refusing to lie out straight. In deference to Jessy's supposedly delicate ears, most of the cursing was muttered under the breath, although she had long since heard every swear word imaginable and used a few herself, but not in front of her father. It would have been the surest way to be banished to the house, and Jessy loved the ranch work no matter how physically demanding it was.

She stood back, waiting until the others had finished their tasks and were ready for her to wield the iron. She listened absently to the run of conversation between the men, interrupted by grunts of exertion and muffled curses.

"Heard Ty's due home next month," one offered and swore at the calf when it kicked him in the shin. At the mention of Ty, Jessy was all ears.

At thirteen, she was at the age to think about boys, and Ty was the ideal choice, since he was older and roughly handsome—and absent, which enabled her to weave little fantasies about him. Her ideas of what was romantic were naturally colored by her personality. She imagined Ty and herself riding the range and working cattle together. He would be impressed with how skilled she was. So far, her dreams hadn't taken her past the point of holding hands and a small, chaste kiss.

"Be home for the summer, won't he?" Les Brewster held a red ear and snapped the tag in place. Jessy caught the affirmative nod of the first.

At the other end of the calf, a castrating knife was being wielded. "Heard he let his hair grow." He didn't look up from his task as he made a slicing incision to remove the testes. "Probably come back here lookin' like Jesus."

"Ty wouldn't do that," Jessy was shocked into protesting.

"Hauled hay to some cattle with him over Christmas," Les inserted. "Didn't seem to me like college had given him any uppity notions."

"We'll see if he needs a haircuttin' party when he gets home." He rocked back from the calf, a bloodied knife in his hand, and glanced sharply at Jessy. "You just going to stand there or are you goin' to slap that iron on this calf?"

Usually no one told her what to do or when to do it. She reddened slightly under the implied criticism and made a quick job of applying the brand.

At home that night, Jessy penned a short letter to Ty, telling him about the spring branding at South Branch. As soon as the niceties were written, she bluntly asked him if he'd grown his hair long and warned him against such foolishness. She phoned The Homestead and got his address, put the letter in an envelope, and mailed it when she returned to school on Monday.

When Ty read the letter from Jessy, he smiled to himself. It was so typical of the kid to cut straight through the rumors and go to the source to find out the answers. He doubted it ever occurred to her that she was being nosy and butting into something that wasn't any of her affair.

After reading it through again, he folded the letter and pushed it into his hip pocket, reminding himself to look her up when he got back home. The contents of the letter had briefly transported him away from the heat of a May afternoon in Texas back to the cool spring of Montana and the excitement and hubbub of branding time. He forgot the perspiration collecting on his skin as he combed his fingers through his hair, absently checking its length.

A horn honked just to his left, jerking his thoughts to the present. A sports-model convertible had pulled close to the street curb. Tara was behind the wheel, dressed in a smart white tennis outfit with a white band sleeking the hair away from her oval face. His blood quickened as Ty swerved off the sidewalk and crossed the grass to the car, idling at the curb.

"Hop in." She gave him one of her provocative half-smiles.

Lithely, Ty vaulted over the door and slid his long frame into the bucket seat beside her. The car smoothly accelerated away from the curb and into the light traffic on the campus street. Ty studied her profile and the perfection of her features, something he never tired of doing.

"You were deep in thought when I drove up." Her remark almost chastised him for not noticing her before she honked.

"I was trying to decide whether I needed a haircut."

Her glance wandered over his dark hair, rumpled by the breeze blowing over the car's front windscreen. "It looks fine to me."

He was conscious of the brevity of her costume and the bareness of her shapely, tanned legs. "Got a tennis date?" Ty guessed, already noticing how cool and refreshed she looked.

"Roger Mathison and I are partners in a mixed-doubles game at four," she admitted with considerable aplomb. "Are you on your way to the library or the frat house?"

"The library." He adjusted the ringed notebook on his lap and stared straight ahead, showing no reaction to her admission she had a tennis date with another man.

Nothing had changed between them, not the way he had hoped it would. If he was lucky, he dated her once or twice a month. In the meantime, she dated others while he satisfied his baser urges with a string of nameless girls. As Tara became better known on the Austin campus, the competition for her favor had grown more intense. A date with her became a prize guys bragged about. Ty had lost count of the number of rivals he faced. Some came and went, especially the ones who attempted to dominate and demand more of her attention—a fact Ty had observed early on. So he ate his pride and became one of the regulars.

"Do you have any plans for the summer?" he asked.

"Nothing specific." She shrugged.

"Your father usually makes one or two trips to Montana in the summer. Why don't you come along with him?" It would be a chance to have her all to himself, with no competition.

"We'll see."

He didn't push for a more definite answer as she stopped the car in front of the university library. Instead of reaching for the door handle, Ty partially turned in the seat to face her, his arm bridging the backs of the two bucket seats.

His hand cupped the back of her neck and pulled her closer as he leaned to her. There was a certain passivity in the way she let him draw her near, a passivity that bordered on indifference. But she tipped her head for his kiss to show him she did want it. That stirred him, as it was meant to do.

Ty struggled to keep his impulses in check as he kissed her, but his passion crowded through. She responded, yet kept something in reserve, never letting him have all that he wanted from her. Impatient, he pulled back, catching sight of the pale blue vein throbbing in her neck even while she smiled so calmly.

"Come to Montana, at least for a weekend this summer," he insisted. "Otherwise, it's going to be a damned long time until September."

She ran a finger over his lips, the glow in her dark eyes almost laughing. "It's too soon to be making summer plans," she chided him playfully. "The semester isn't even over yet. Now scat, or I'll be late for my date with Roger." When Ty reluctantly climbed out of the car, she blew him a careless kiss and drove away.

Tara didn't visit the ranch that summer. On three separate

occasions, E. J. Dyson and his partner, Stricklin, flew to the Triple C, but she didn't accompany him as she so easily could have done. Twice, Ty called her to renew the invitation. If it hadn't been for the heavy work load that left him, most nights, too tired to think, he would have gone wild, wondering what she was doing and whom she was with.

Again Ty found himself being razzed by the ranch hands, wanting to know what he'd learned in college. Some of the older veterans were a bit standoffish with him at the beginning of the summer, again relegating some of the dirtier jobs to him to see if he thought college had made him too good for such work. Eventually he was accepted again.

It was the middle of summer before he was assigned to work in the southern end of the ranch and happened to cross paths with the tall and still gangly thirteen-going-on-fourteen-year-old Jessy Niles. By then, he'd forgotten about the letter she'd written him.

6

The cattle guard rattled under the wheels of the car as it rolled onto the eastern limit of the Triple C Ranch. The east gate was an unimposing structure consisting of two high poles supporting a sun-bleached sign that hung across the road between them. It read simply The Calder Cattle Company, with the Triple C brand burned into the wood. There was nothing in sight but the flat high plains, undulating in golden waves of tall grass. It was another thirty miles plus before the main buildings of the ranch headquarters could be seen.

The silence in the car was weighted with brooding. Maggie's thoughts had turned back to the leave-taking at the airport. When Ty had left to attend his first year of college, she'd been happy for him. But this second time, it was more difficult. She didn't like being separated from him, even if he did come home every chance he could.

"I wish Ty were attending a college closer to home." She murmured her wish aloud.

"If you had listened to me, he would be," Chase snapped. "But, no, you insisted that Ty make his own choice."

"I know." Her answer was stiff, not inviting further discussion of the subject. There had been too many arguments over this issue of college already.

"Then stop complaining." His attention never left the ranch road.

"I wasn't complaining," Maggie retorted. "I was merely wishing."

"Well, I wish to hell he'd never gone to college at all!" Chase ground out the angry words.

"You've made your opinion quite clear before."

"Dammit, it is a waste of time." His hand slapped the wheel. "If he wanted to be an engineer, a teacher, a doctor, then this schooling would be valuable to him. But, dammit, he wants to be a rancher. He told me so! And the way to learn the ranching business is through practical experience."

"Why? Because that's the way you learned it? Does that mean it's the only way?" she countered in a rush of temper. Knowing how futile it was to argue with him, Maggie squared around in her seat and stiffly crossed her arms in front of her. "There's no reasoning with you, Chase," she said tautly. "As far as you're concerned, there's a right way and a wrong way—and your way. And if it isn't yours, it's naturally wrong."

"I know one damned thing for sure. My way works." It was a flat, hard answer.

The last twenty miles of the journey passed in charged silence. Chase wished the first word on the matter had never been said. He was never able to explain to Maggie how much he wanted to be wrong about this. Talking about it increased the tension between them instead of dissolving it. She always pushed at him, never giving an inch, never conceding he might be right, never acknowledging any validity in his concerns. She couldn't see that he needed her understanding; she was too busy defending her son's action.

He stopped the car by the front steps of The Homestead and kept the engine running. Maggie had opened the passenger door before she realized he wasn't coming with her. A curtness was still in her expression as she gave him a questioning look.

"Aren't you coming?"

"No." Glancing beyond her, Chase saw his daughter come running out of the house to greet them. "If I'm late for dinner, go ahead and eat. I'll warm up something when I get back."

Although she was too angry with him to ask where he was going, Maggie was troubled by his action. He drove away the minute she shut her car door—without stopping long enough to greet his young daughter. She couldn't recall Chase ever being so rushed that he didn't have time for a word with little Cathleen.

"Daddy!" Cathleen wailed and began stomping her feet on the wooden floor of the porch in a tantrum when her tears didn't bring him back.

Driving back to the two-lane, Chase followed it to a small collection of buildings out in the middle of nowhere. It was a boom-and-bust town called Blue Moon, lying by the road in one of its bust cycles. Another house had been abandoned to its weed-choked yard, its back broken and sagging. The sunburned paint on the sign above the grocery store and service station was peeling and faded. A pair of cars sat abandoned behind the building, wheelless and rusted.

The building next door appeared to be in better repair, except for a broken sign that had been snapped in half by an accumulation of ice followed by a high wind. It identified the building simply as Sally's. Chase parked the car in front of it alongside two dusty ranch pickups and went inside.

Half the tables were covered with gingham cloth and the other half were bare. A lone pool table sat in a far corner of the long room, a cowboy crouched over it taking aim on the cue ball. The jukebox in the corner was playing a cheating song.

Chase walked to the counter where an auburn-haired woman sat on an end stool. She smiled at him, a glint of sad longing showing briefly in her blue eyes.

"Hello, Chase." She slid off the stool and walked around behind the counter. "What can I buy you? Beer? Whiskey? Coffee?"

He glanced at the half-finished cup of black coffee she'd been drinking. It didn't look nearly strong enough. "Whiskey with water back," he ordered and crawled onto the stool next to the one she'd vacated.

She refused the money he laid on the counter when she set his drink in front of him. "The first drink's on the house."

His mouth twitched in grim remorse. "I guess I haven't been in since you started serving liquor, have I?" He bolted down the drink. At first he felt nothing; then it began to burn his throat.

When he looked at her above the brim of his hat, she was calmly watching him. Chase wasn't sure whether it was the whiskey or the calming influence of her presence that seemed to soothe him. There was a time before Maggie came back to him when he had considered marrying Sally. There was a pleasing quietness about her that was always comfortable and settling.

"I don't particularly like the idea of you running a bar, Sally," he said, accustomed to his opinion carrying weight.

"It was a business decision," she reasoned, not taking offense the way Maggie would have. "My clientele consists mainly of cowboys, and they're a drinking crowd. As much as they liked my food, they started driving elsewhere. If I wanted to keep the doors open, I didn't have a choice."

"You'll let me know if anybody gives you trouble."

Again there was that quiet smile that seemed to soften the lines around her mouth and eyes and make them attractive. "The boys get rowdy sometimes, but no one's stepped out of line. The place has sorta become a second home to most of them. I usually have plenty of defenders on hand if I ever need one."

"I suppose you do." He lowered his head and pushed the empty shot glass to her. "Fill it again, then sit down and finish your coffee."

This time he sipped at the whiskey while she settled onto the stool beside him. "How have things been at the ranch?"

"Fine." Chase studied the golden-brown liquor, then lifted it to take another small swallow. "I just got back from putting Ty on the plane to Texas."

"I've heard he's doing well."

"He'd do better staying at home." His sun-browned hand tightened around the glass, the bones showing white through his skin. "I can't make Maggie understand that, Sally. Everything's gone so smoothly since she's been back. She wasn't here during the rough times. I'm not just talking about the drought we had. There was the time when the small ranches on the north cut the fences and drifted their cattle onto our graze . . . and the hassle I had getting title to those ten thousand acres of federal land sitting almost smack in the middle of the ranch. There's always something or someone." Chase sighed heavily.

"It will work out," Sally murmured.

"Will it?" His glance ran over her face, his lip corners lifting with grim amusement. "I want Ty home, and Maggie thinks I'm being selfish."

"No two people see eye to eye on everything. You are bound to have something you disagree about."

Chase released a heavy breath. "That disagreement is becoming hell." He gazed into her serene eyes. "You're a woman, Sally. Tell me how I can get through to her."

"Is that why you came here?" There was a glimmer of regret and a little hurt in her look. "I'm not any good at giving advice, Chase."

His mouth went thin. "I didn't mean to make you uncomfortable, Sally. I guess I just needed to talk to someone and"—a remembering was in the darkness of his eyes when he looked at her—"I thought of you."

There was a mute shake of her copper-red hair as her throat worked convulsively before she could finally get the words out. "I think you'd better go home, Chase."

"Yeah." He grimly concurred with her suggestion and reached for the change from his second drink.

Through the course of that fall and winter, he found several more reasons to make the drive to Blue Moon. Each time, he stopped in at Sally's—just to pass the time of day. No mention was made again of his problems at home. And Chase kept telling himself that Sally was just an old friend.

The ancient gravestones stood in silent order, tall blades of grass sprouting around their bases. There was a stillness in the old cemetery, with its big shade trees protectively spreading their branches over the chipped and weathered stones.

"When you asked me to come with you this afternoon, I didn't realize you were going to take me on a tour of an old cemetery." Tara looked around her with a mixture of wide-eyed curiosity and unease. "I feel as if I should be whispering."

Ty just smiled and increased the pressure of his grip on her hand. An old, gnarled oak tree stood to one side of the pathway ahead of them.

"This way." He led Tara toward it.

"It wouldn't be so bad if you would tell me what it is you're hoping to find," she protested.

Next to the spreading trunk of the oak tree, Ty spied the tilted headstone and lengthened his stride in anticipation. It was a plain marker, no designs carved on it. Years of exposure to rain and wind, heat and cold, had smoothed its surface, but the name etched into it could still be read: Seth Calder. It was undated, initialed with Rest in Peace.

"Here it is," he said to Tara and stepped aside so she could view it. "He was my great-great-grandfather."

"I didn't know you had any family buried here in Fort Worth." Covertly she let her eyes stray from the gravestone to study the tall man, in many ways so much more mature than others his age.

"Neither did I," Ty admitted. "I didn't find out about him"—he indicated the grave of his ancestor with a nod of his head—"until this past Christmas. Dad was telling Cathleen the story about the first Calder to settle in Montana. He started the ranch with a herd of cattle he'd driven north from Texas. It's her favorite story. I'll bet I've heard Dad tell it to her a hundred times at least. But this time Cathleen asked about Benteen Calder's mommy and daddy and why they didn't come to Montana with him. My father explained that

Seth Calder had died a couple months before they left for Montana and had been buried here in Texas."

"What about his wife?"

"Supposedly she ran away with some Englishman when Benteen Calder was still a small boy. As far as Dad knows, she was never heard from after that. Ever since I found out this old cemetery was still here in Fort Worth, I've been meaning to come and look for his grave."

It was difficult to explain this need to know more about his family, a kind of seeking of identity. As he stood at the foot of the grave, looking at the Calder name etched into the headstone, Ty felt a closeness to the past, a sense of belonging. The Calder name was both his heritage and his future.

Tara moved a little restlessly beside him. His attention had strayed, and she drew it back to her. As Ty looked down at her, he observed the hint of impatience in her eyes.

"I suppose this seems crazy to you," he murmured. He couldn't say why he'd brought her, except that this was important to him, and because it was important to him, he wanted her to be a part of it.

"No, I don't think it's crazy." She knew it was what he wanted her to say, but she had no insight into the significance of this for him. "It isn't odd to want to pay your respects to a member of your family."

"I don't know much about my family or their history, just bits and pieces," Ty confessed with a heavy sigh. "My parents were separated until I was fifteen. I lived with my mother in California all that time, so I never grew up knowing details about my father's side of the family the way my little sister will. It wasn't easy for me at the ranch in the beginning. I tried so hard to belong." He laughed shortly as he realized it. "I guess, in my own way, I still am."

"It really means a lot for you to belong, doesn't it?" She eyed him with a curious and probing look. "Maybe that's what makes you different from the others. You seem more serious about your studies . . . and everything else."

"You make me sound very boring." There was a dazzling effect to his slow smile that snatched at her breath. It was recklessly sexy and challenging.

"Not boring," Tara corrected, trying to match his smile with a provocative look. "Just dangerous."

An eyebrow lifted in response. "Dangerous how?"

"I don't know if I can explain it." She shrugged. "Most of the guys at college, they want an education, but they're more interested in a good time. The priority is reversed with you. You party and go on beer-drinking sprees with them, but you're basically not here to have fun. Yet it's more than that. I guess I have the feeling that you pursue something until you get it."

"Like you, for instance." His gaze darkened on her with disturbing intensity.

"I didn't say that," Tara demurred as he seemed to come closer even though he hadn't moved an inch.

"But you know I want you." It was a calmly issued statement as he inspected her face and form as if he were already taking possession of her.

"People don't always get what they want," she countered smoothly.

"What is it that you want, Tara?"

"To have fun and enjoy my life." It was a stock answer, the properly feminine kind. Deep in her heart, she knew what she truly desired. She was the daughter of E. J. Dyson, so she had grown up surrounded by power. It carried a sense of exhilaration that was addictive. With her beauty, she possessed her own kind of power, and she knew it. At college, she had begun to exercise it and test it on those who weren't under her father's influence so she could discover the potential force of it.

"What about a home and family?" he prompted.

"In time." At the moment, her plans for the future were nebulous. There was a vague dream in her mind to become the ruling matriarch of a powerful family. "But I'm going to finish college first. After that, Daddy has promised me a year in Europe."

"Are you going?"

"Of course I'm going." She laughed, a merry, musical sound. "The alternatives are certainly not appealing. I just can't see myself getting a job and working five days a week. It would get boring very quickly."

"You could always get married and honeymoon in Europe for a month," Ty suggested.

"I could." Her red lips came together in an inviting line. "I have the feeling my daddy is hoping that I'll make an advantageous marriage someday so there would ultimately be a merger of two important families."

"Your father doesn't strike me as being that calculating." E. J. Dyson had always seemed to be a very indulgent father, willing to give in to her every whim and never pushing her one way or another. Ty had never gotten the impression that E.J., unlike his own father, expected his daughter to fulfill a particular role.

"Every father wants his daughter to make a perfect marriage, and have a husband who is worthy of her. There isn't anything wrong—or even calculating—in that." But she knew her father well enough to know it wasn't that casual with him. He was simply wise enough not to dictate choices to her. She strongly suspected that her father knew her desires would ultimately mesh with his.

All this talk of marriage pushed at him. "You'd make a beautiful bride, Tara," Ty murmured and reached out with his hand to stroke the dark silk of her hair. "I can see you in a white satin gown, studded with pearls, and a lace veil."

He lifted her left hand. There was a large topaz birthstone on her ring finger, flanked by diamonds. He covered the ring so he could picture the diamond he would give her. When Ty looked at her, the thoughts of wedding bands immediately brought him images of the wedding night.

"You're going to be mine, Tara," he declared rawly. "Sooner or later, you're going to be mine."

She started to laugh away his assertion, but he had no intention of allowing her to make light of it. His arms hooked her slender shape to his body while his mouth covered her smile. The driving force of his kiss bent her backwards, arching her spine and molding her small hips to his rigid thighs.

The rawness of wanting and being prevented for so long from taking what he wanted made him indifferent to the resisting push of her hands. There was only the soft sensation of her breasts, their round outline being drawn on his chest.

Her warm body excited him, and the honeyed sweetness of her lips made up for the reluctance of the response he forced from her.

Ty knew he was taking her further than she wanted to go, but his confidence was such that he felt he would ultimately convince her she wanted what he did. He set about to do it with his hands coercing and urging a closer intimacy as they felt the roundness of her taut bottom and closed on the uplifting swell of her breasts. He lipped at the lobe of her ear and nibbled on the sensitive skin of her throat and neck. All the while he was conscious of the disturbed, shallow breaths she gasped and the little sounds of protest she made in her throat.

When her hand suddenly cupped his mouth, staying his kisses, Ty reached up impatiently to pull it away. As his fingers closed around her slender wrist and dragged it down, he looked at her aroused and flushed face tilted up to him. Her eyes glowed darkly with a hard light of determination.

"If you care for me at all, Ty, you'll stop this right now before it goes any further," she insisted, taking advantage of that crazy code of honor she had long ago discovered in him. She had no qualms about exploiting what she saw as a weakness.

"Care for you?" His low-pitched voice threw back the puny description of the passionate furies she unleashed in him. "My God, Tara. I love you," Ty avowed, almost angrily.

She didn't relent. "I didn't come with you this afternoon to be seduced in a cemetery." Her hands pushed at his chest, demanding distance between them.

The reference to the inappropriate surroundings made him feel inept and somehow backwardly uncouth. She always made him feel like a lusting animal soiling her with his baser needs. Immediately Ty was angry with himself for allowing such a thought to occur. He had tried to coerce a willing submission from her, so it was hardly fair to condemn her because she had the strength of will to resist him.

"I'm sorry." He let her go and turned away to rub the back of his neck. "I had no right."

"Ty." The light touch of her hand was on his arm. The softness of her voice and the fragrance of her hair nearly made him groan aloud. "I'm not angry with you. To tell you the truth"—the lightness of amused self-reproach was in her voice—"I'd probably be hurt if you didn't want to make love to me. I'd wonder what was wrong with me."

Turning his head to look at her, Ty was moved once again by her incredible beauty. A longing rushed through him that was pure pain.

"There is nothing wrong with you." His low voice was half strangled by emotion. "You are perfect in every way. Any man who doesn't see that has to be blind." He covered the slim hand that rested on his arm and gripped it tightly. His gaze was earnestly intent. "When I told you I loved you, I meant it, Tara. This summer, will you come to Montana? I want you to meet my parents. I want you to see my home."

"I'll try to come," she promised.

"Don't try. Just come," Ty insisted.

But she didn't.

Four riders closed on the last of the cows being herded through the opened gate. Tall grass waved in the golden-ripe light of late summer. A lagging cow eyed the gate with distrust and stubbornly ignored the riders' urgings to pass through it.

Ty reined his horse alongside the reluctant animal and reached out to slap it on the rump with his coiled rope. It spied the gap between the riders, created by Ty. With a swing of its head, it bolted for the opening, tail high in defiance. Ty hauled back on the reins and pivoted his horse on its hind legs to give chase.

Another horse and rider were streaking after the fleeing cow, the slim rider snaking low on the grulla's back. Ty glimpsed the accompanying pursuit out of the corner of his eye, but he had the angle on the animal. With the sound of hoofbeats hammering the grass-covered sod thundering in his ears, he shook out his loop and raced along a few more strides until his horse was in position for him to make the cast.

As the loop went out straight and true, he sat back in the saddle and checked his horse, preparing for the second when the full weight of the cow hit the end of the rope. A shadow or the hiss of the rope must have warned the cow of its imminent capture. At the last second, it swung its head aside and the loop harmlessly slapped its chunky jaw and neck and slid emptily off its shoulders.

Silently cursing the missed cast, Ty put his spurs into the horse's side and sent it bounding after the cow again while he gathered in the rope. By then, the mouse-gray horse and its rider had taken a dead aim on the cow and had maneuvered into position to make the throw. The loop shot out with unerring accuracy and settled over the cow's head in picture-perfect style.

Ty eased up on his horse and let it come down naturally to a snorting trot. There had been few opportunities to demonstrate the improvement in his roping skills during the course of the summer work on the ranch. It irritated him that he'd missed this chance. And it didn't make it easier that he'd been bested by a girl, no matter how good she was.

His smile was on the grim side when he met the broad grin on Jessy Niles's face as she led the balky cow to the gate. She was tall and slim as a rail. Wisps of hay-brown hair straggled loose from the rubber band that collected its thick length at the back of her neck. With the shapeless cowboy hat atop her head, she resembled a happy waif. Her sun-browned skin glowed with the healthiness of outdoor living and added to the sunny sparkle in her hazel eyes.

"We got 'er." Her cheery voice was magnanimous in triumph over the capture of the cow, happily giving credit to Ty.

"You got 'er, Jessy," he corrected. Her expression sobered slightly, some of the exhilaration fading from her smile.

"We make a good team just the same," she said with a vague shrug of her shoulders to indicate it was insignificant which of them had actually roped the animal.

Since she had followed as his backup, there was some truth in her reply, but Ty was sensitive to the point that he had gone after the cow and Jessy was the one bringing it back in tow. It grated just a little, and he tried not to let it show.

Dropping his horse back, he herded the roped cow after Jessy so it wouldn't fight being led. Buzz Taylor was afoot by the gate, waiting to close it as soon as the cow was turned loose beyond it and Jessy had ridden back through. Once the gate was shut, Ty secured his coiled rope to the saddle and stepped to the ground.

With the herd shifted to a range with good graze and plenty of water, their work was finished for the day, and the riders paused for a smoke break before heading back to the camp at South Branch. Ty bent his head to touch the end of his unfiltered cigarette to the match flame Bill Summers offered.

"That wily ole cow ducked right out of your loop," Bill observed, commiserating.

"Yeah." Even though there wasn't a wind, Ty cupped his hand protectively around the cigarette out of habit so no live embers would be blown into the tinder-dry August grass.

"Ole sure-eye Jessy got 'er, didn't ya?" Buzz Taylor declared with a hearty grin of teasing approval directed at the girl standing slank-hipped with them.

"Ty hazed him into position for me." She blew out a quick puff of smoke from her cigarette and turned her head aside to spit the bits of tobacco from her tongue.

"Hell, he just got out of your way, that's all," Buzz retorted. He cast a suspicious eye at Jessy. "Does your pa know you're smoking?"

"Sure. He don't like it much," Jessy admitted with an uncaring shrug.

"Stumpy didn't like her bummin' cigarettes off the rest of us," Bill Summers corrected her answer, coming to her defense. "Finally he told her that if she was doin' a man's work and drawin' a man's pay and smokin' a man's cigarettes, she could either start buyin' her own or stop smokin'."

Jessy managed a wry grin at the explanation. That's about the way it had turned out after her father had gotten over his initial prejudice against a young girl smoking at all. Before that, he'd done just about everything but tan her hide to keep her from smoking. Of course, she hadn't listened to his railing lectures. Everyone around her smoked, so she didn't see why it was so wrong for her to smoke, too.

"It's a good thing it's payday," Buzz declared and fingered the nearly empty packet of Camels in his pocket. "I'm damned near out of cigarettes myself. I got just about enough to get me into town."

"What are you going to spend your money on, Jessy?" Bill

reached over and pulled the brim of her hat lower on her forehead. "Are you finally gonna let loose of some of that money you been hoardin' all summer and buy yourself a decent hat?"

"Don't be insultin' my hat, Summers. It's got character," she insisted with a smile. "And I've been savin' my money to pay for the roping saddle Barnes is makin' for me."

"A saddle." Summers shook his head in mock dismay. "And I thought you'd be buyin' a party dress for your birthday."

"I'd rather have a good saddle than a party dress," Jessy retorted. She already had two good Sunday dresses, so she didn't see the need for spending her money to buy another, especially one that she'd probably only have occasion to wear once a year. A saddle was something practical, and it would last for years with proper care. It was an investment, something she could take pride in. "Just wait till you boys see it."

"Barnes is a damned good saddlemaker. I've seen some of his work," Buzz Taylor reinforced her choice. "He's gettin' himself quite a reputation. Some cowboys from as far away as Colorado have had him make saddles for them."

Ty carried the cigarette to his lips and studied the lanky girl, squinting through the curling smoke. Her tomboy mannerisms were vaguely amusing, but he also noticed the smooth coordination of her movements, each action flowing deliberately and easily into the next. There was a kind of natural grace in the relaxed posture of her body, long and slim, yet supple. His glance idled an instant on the flatness of her chest, her young breasts making little more than small bumps under the blouse material.

"When's your birthday, Jessy?" Ty asked when he lifted his gaze and found her looking directly at him. The steadiness of her eyes made him slightly uncomfortable about the notice he'd taken of her immaturity.

"Next week," she answered.

"We're going to throw a bang-up party for you, too," Buzz winked. "We're going to invite Sheriff Potter so he'll quit stoppin' you for driving without a license."

"How old will you be?" Ty attempted to do a mental

calculation of the intervening years, but she answered him before he had finished his subtraction.

"Sixteen."

A teasing light entered his eye. "Sweet sixteen and never been kissed?"

"Jessy?" Buzz Taylor hooted with laughter at the idea of the tomboy in their midst ever being kissed. "I'll bet the only one what ever kissed her was her horse!"

Her eyes went brilliant with anger. She swept off her hat and slapped his shoulder with it. "Buzz Taylor, you shut up!" she raged in a temper, the likes of which Ty had not seen. None of the three had seen her so outraged and defensive, and it struck them all as funny. When they started laughing at her, it just made her all the madder. "I don't go around kissing my horse!"

"The poor gal ain't even been kissed by her horse!" Buzz roared with laughter and jabbed a pointing finger at her, all the while ducking the hat being flayed at him as she unleashed her temper on him.

"We can't have her turn sixteen without being kissed, can we, boys?" Ty challenged with a laughing grin.

For once he was on the attacking side and someone else was the victim of a cowboy's prank. After being shown up by Jessy, he subconsciously liked the idea of taking her down a notch or two. He pinched the fire of his cigarette between his gloved thumb and forefinger before dropping the butt under the toe of his boot and grinding it into the hard-baked ground.

When Ty took a step toward her, Jessy whirled around to face him, suddenly realizing it hadn't been an idle remark he'd made. Dismay and shock flashed across her face, clouding the angry glitter in her eyes. He managed to get an arm around her before she recovered and tried to buck free of his hold.

"Look out, Ty," Buzz warned with a laugh. "She's a wild one."

Her struggling wasn't the futile, feminine kind. Ty found he had his hands full as her steel-slim arms wedged themselves against his chest, warding him off while she directed some well-aimed kicks at his shins.

"Watch where you're kicking, Jessy," Bill Summers advised. "There'd be some explaining if you injured him in the wrong place."

A sudden high color stained her cheeks as she ended her violent resistance and threw back her head to glare at Ty with daring defiance. Her lips were pressed together in a rigid line. It amused him to see her so helplessly out of her league. He cupped her chin in his hand and held it still while he bent his head to her motionless lips.

Instead of kissing them lightly and letting it go at that as he probably would have done with any other inexperienced girl, he made the pressure more definite and held it for several seconds longer. When he lifted his head, her eyes were tightly shut. There was a tension about her features that was somehow vulnerable.

"Now you can say you've been kissed," Ty declared, struggling against the twinges of regret he was feeling.

As he let her go, she immediately dropped her chin and turned away. A dark flush rose in her face even though she maintained her controlled, tight-lipped expression.

"I'll be damned," Buzz murmured under his breath. "Jessy's blushing."

She flashed him an angry look as she scooped up the trailing reins of her horse. "Shut up, Buzz."

Ty felt guilty for having embarrassed her with that kiss. He wasn't the only one subdued by Jessy's silence. There was an uneasy shuffling as the other two cowboys moved to their horses. Jessy swung into her saddle and made to rein her horse away from the others. Ty grabbed at the bridle, checking her.

She gave him an angry look of wounded betrayal. He'd forgotten how sensitive he'd been to thoughtless actions of others at that age. No matter how self-contained and confident Jessy appeared, she did have feelings that could be hurt.

"I'm sorry, kid," he offered.

Her angry look hardened. "I'm not a kid," she declared in a clipped voice and laid the reins alongside the grulla's neck to turn it. Vaguely irritated by her failure to accept his apology, Ty let go of the bridle. No one had ever apologized to him, so maybe he should have just kept his mouth shut.

Jessy walked the mouse-gray horse away from the fence gate while the others swung loosely in behind her. She wasn't hot all over anymore, and for that she was grateful, but she was shaking inside. The sensation of his warm mouth on her lips continued to linger, along with the feel of his arms around her.

She wanted to touch her mouth, but she didn't dare raise her hand. They might think she was crying, and she'd die before she'd have them think that. It was bad enough that all had seen how embarrassed she'd been—embarrassed and hotly disturbed.

It had been her first kiss, and she'd always dreamed that Ty would be the one to give it to her. That dream had come true, but bitterly so. He had kissed her, all right, but only as a joke. And it had hurt to think Ty did it only to make fun of her . . . and in front of Buzz Taylor and Bill Summers to boot. By tomorrow, it would be all over the ranch and everyone would be laughing about it.

Jessy held her head a little higher as the four riders traveled in a loose group toward the South Branch camp. The conversation was minimal, but gradually Jessy took part in it. On the surface, everything seemed to be back to normal by the time they arrived at the camp, but it wasn't.

7

With a heaving toss, Jessy threw the large suitcase in the back end of the pickup truck, then shut the tailgate. The smell of snow was in the air; solid cloud cover hung low in the sky. She shoved her bare hands into the lined pockets of her new parka and trotted around the truck to the front porch of the big log house. She had one foot on the first step when the front door opened.

"Hi, Mr. Grayson," she said to the forty-year-old geologist. He was bundled in a pile-lined coat with a wool scarf wrapped around his cap and neck and fur-lined gloves on his hands. By contrast, Jessy had no gloves or scarf, and the top buttons of her parka were unfastened. She was wearing her good black Stetson—she always wore a hat. "I was just coming in to see if you were ready to go."

"I'm ready." He paused at the top of the steps to rub his gloved hands together and study the gloomy gray late-October sky. "It's a cold one today." Anything below forty was cold to the Texas native, and the morning temperature was hovering around that mark. "I put my suitcase on the porch earlier." Leo Grayson swung his head in search of it, peering through his wire-rimmed glasses.

"I've already loaded it in the trunk," Jessy informed him. "Did you have anything else?"

"No." He glanced expectantly toward the barn. "Is your father ready to leave?"

"Dad got detained at the last minute. I've been deputized to drive you over to The Homestead so you can catch your plane." She pulled her foot off the step and turned around to walk to the driver's side of the pickup cab.

"Shouldn't you be in school today?" There was a faint smile on his face as he followed her to the truck. In the short time he had stayed at this southern outpost of the Triple C Ranch, he'd learned that Jessy Niles had her own opinion on the relative importance of certain things.

"Not really." She shrugged indifferently, hopped into the truck, and slid behind the wheel, all in one fluid, effortless movement. She waited until he had climbed into the passenger side and shut the door before she elaborated. "There wasn't anything special going on in school today, no tests or anything. I can call Betty Trumbo tonight and find out what the assignments are. But I didn't see any point in going and maybe getting snowbound in town."

The truck rumbled to life under the turn of the ignition key and the pumping of her foot on the gas pedal. Her last comment drew a curious look from Leo Grayson. "The weather forecast said there was only a chance of flurries today."

"According to Abe Garvey, we're in for the first snowstorm of the season. He was born and raised here on the ranch, nearly seventy years ago. I'd take his word before I'd listen to some meteorologist who doesn't understand the peculiarities of this climate. Abe's hardly ever wrong," she concluded.

"It looks like I'm getting out of here just in time." Once Leo Grayson would have scoffed at the less than scientific weather predictions of old-timers in this area who cared not a hoot for the patterns of fronts. But he'd found their predictions just about as accurate as any professional meteorologist's. If one said snow flurries and the other said snowfall, something was bound to happen.

Once the buildings of the south camp were lost from sight, there was nothing for miles in any direction but the monotonous sweep of rolling grassland, rising on swells of earth and dipping into shallow hollows. Trees were so few and far between they became landmarks, consisting mainly of cottonwoods along some vagrant stream. The raw, gray day made the lonely stretch of country seem bleak and empty. There were wide, open spaces in Texas, but nothing in Grayson's experience as desolate as this.

Hot air began blowing full force out of the vents as the truck's engine warmed up enough to release its excess heat. When his glasses steamed over, Leo took them off and wiped them on the inside lining of his coat. Absently he squinted to look out the window, but not even his blurred vision could make the muscular landscape appear more inviting.

"I don't know how you can stand it out here." He adjusted his glasses on his nose, then glanced at Jessy.

"Never been anywhere else." She drove with the relaxed competence of a man, one hand resting on the top arc of the steering wheel and the other gripping it. Leo supposed she had been driving since she was eight or nine. That was about the age most of the ranch kids started, usually rigging up some kind of device so they could reach the brake and still see where they were going.

"I'll bet you can hardly wait until you're eighteen so you can leave here and see something more of the world than grass and sky." The lonely rigors of this kind of life didn't appeal to him. It was bound to be worse for a girl.

"I'm satisfied with my life here," Jessy replied, aware she was in a minority, since most of the other girls her age were always complaining about the things they were missing. But those "things" didn't interest her. "I've never had any desire to leave. I know"—she drew her attention away from the road long enough to flash him a smile—"that makes me strange. But I don't care about movies and parties and all that glamorous stuff. I like riding and roping and being outdoors, even when the work is so hard you get tired to the bone. I'd like to be one of those trees, sink my roots deep into this ground and never leave."

"You'll change your mind when you get older." He had observed she was something of a tomboy during the time he'd spent at the Southern Branch camp.

"So everybody keeps telling me." But she didn't see that happening. Most of them claimed it was a phase she was going through, but she truly loved what she was doing, and she didn't see it changing just because she got older.

Leo Grayson just smiled, the way adults did when she showed resistance to their prediction. "Wait until you discover boys."

"Where is it written that boys and horses don't mix?" Jessy countered.

Her one and only crush had been on Ty Calder, now in his third year at college. But it had been too one-sided to survive, especially after that humiliating experience with that kiss this past summer. It still made her cheeks redden when she remembered what a joke it had been to him. All the other boys she chummed around with at school events were just that—boys. None of them worth getting excited about.

"I guess it isn't." He looked at her again, recognizing a maturity in her attitude that he hadn't suspected.

There was a classic purity to her profile: the strong chin, the clean jawline, and the prominent ridge of her cheekbone. Her hair, the color of spun-dark caramel, hung in loose, thick waves to her shoulders. Leo Grayson found himself admiring and respecting the girl he saw. Her features contained a strength that seemed a match for the land, and she came on with a confidence that could face its challenge. Pretty she wasn't, but pretty wouldn't last out here, he realized.

"You are a handsome girl, Jessy." No other adjective suited her strong looks, yet it didn't diminish her potential womanliness in Grayson's eyes.

"Me? I'm as plain as a potato." She dismissed the compliment.

"No, you're not."

"Look." She sounded very patient with him for being so blind to her faults. "I'm too tall—I'm taller than most of the guys in my class." But Leo noticed she didn't slouch to disguise her height. "I'm too thin, and it doesn't matter how much I eat, I can't get any curves. And in the bosom department, I laid an egg—a pair of them."

The few times he'd encountered her frankness, it had always amused him, but he had to struggle to keep from laughing aloud at this candid assessment of her female attributes.

"What are you going to do when you graduate from high school?" he asked to change the subject.

"Stay here and work. That's one of the benefits that go with being born and raised on Calder land. All you have to do is go to the boss and ask him for a job. On a ranch this size, there's always a lot of work," she said.

"What will you do?" He frowned.

"I don't know." She shrugged that it was too far in the future to decide. "I might stick with range work, or help at the day school, or maybe work in the commissary." There were any number of choices, although she preferred the first.

But she also knew that even though some of the wives, especially the younger ones, pitched in during the calving season or on a roundup when they were short of cowboys, no female on horseback was drawing regular cowhand wages. There was a silent prejudice against women holding that male-reserved job on the ranch. Nothing had ever been said about her getting paid for a cowboy's work in the summer.

Jessy switched the subject, transferring the focus from herself to his work. "What's the verdict on all the tests you've been doing? Are the drilling rigs going to be shifting to our part of the ranch?"

"No. It's going to be my recommendation that it's too iffy here." Since his decision was a negative one, Leo didn't regard it as secret information. "I think we've exhausted all the possibilities of future oil or gas discoveries on the Triple C."

His gaze went to the side window of the truck, the glass steamed over at the corners. The contours of the rough land resembled rigidly flexed muscles, bulging biceps covered with hairy grass. To his eye, it looked worthless, too damned arid and barren. It required a hundred acres to support one cow with a calf. It seemed so unproductive, such a waste of so much land.

"It's a crime," he murmured aloud.

"What?" Jessy didn't quite catch what he said.

Leo roused himself. "I was just looking out the window and thinking of such a valuable resource sitting idle."

"You mean the grass?" The parched and freeze-dried grass was all she could see, definitely a resource in her experience.

"I'm talking about all the coal that's underneath it, so close to the surface." A huge deposit of low-sulfur coal underlay this whole region of eastern Montana. "All a man would need to do is scrape away that worthless soil and there it would be."

"You don't even have to scrape the ground away." Jessy smiled as if knowing a secret and let up on the accelerator, looking around to get her bearings on how far they'd come. "Do you want me to show you?"

"Do you mean there's a place where the vein of coal has been exposed?" he asked with growing interest, and she gave him an affirmative nod. "Yes, I'd like to see it—if it won't take us too much out of our way."

"It won't," she assured him and turned the truck onto a trail that was little more than two rutted tracks running through the grass. "But you'll have to hold on. It'll be a bumpy ride."

The warning was an understatement. Leo Grayson ended up with one hand braced overhead and one jammed against the dashboard as the pickup bounced over the rough trail. Jessy gripped the steering wheel with both hands to keep it from being jerked out of her grasp. Conversation was impossible on the teeth-jolting ride. The trail crested a rise and fell steeply into a hollow. Jessy braked the truck to a stop at the bottom where it leveled out.

"There it is." She gestured with her hand to a cutbank.

Except for a thin layer of sod matted with dead grass atop it, the exposed section was solidly black. There were plenty of indications that its enlargement was man-made.

"Most of the older homes on the ranch are heated with coal furnaces," Jessy explained. "There's a couple–three areas like this scattered around. We just come and get our own fuel. It doesn't cost anything but the labor."

Giving in to his professional curiosity, Leo braved the cold temperature and climbed out of the pickup to take a closer look. It was one thing to know the coal was under the ground and another to see the large exposed seam. He wrapped the scarf more tightly around his head and neck and walked forward to investigate the high black bank.

Jessy watched him from the warmth of the truck's cab, faintly amused by his fascination over something so common. Getting the winter supply of coal was not a chore anyone on the ranch fancied. It was dusty, dirty, hard work, and constantly having to stoke the furnace was another inconvenience. Which was why most of the homes had converted to more modern sources, usually oil or propane. Coal wasn't practical anymore, even if it was cheap.

Grayson poked around at the exposed seam of black coal, picking up small chunks to study. Finally the cold temperature drove him back to the truck. He scrambled inside the cab, shivering and rubbing his hands together, then blowing on them.

"Ready?" Jessy rested her hand on the gearshift.

"Wait." He reached inside his coat pocket and brought out a shiny black chunk. "Do you know what this is?"

"Coal." She gave him a look which questioned his intelligence.

"It's buried sunshine." His voice was enthusiastic. "Coal is the sun's energy that was trapped in ancient forests eons ago—giant ferns and trees. In an endless cycle, plants died and rotted and more grew on top of them to die and rot. Then came floods of water forming inland seas. The pressure of the water compacted the buried layers of plant life, first making peat, then coal." He looked at her. "This piece of coal holds the energy from sunlight of four hundred million years ago."

"Let me see it." With a frown of curiosity, Jessy took a closer look at the ordinary lump of coal.

The next morning, Leo Grayson was in the cool, air-conditioned office of E. J. Dyson, going over his final report and recommendations. In contrast to his previous day's attire, he was dressed in a lightweight business suit and tie, his head bare and showing the thinning patch at the crown of his brown hair.

The executive office of Dy-Corp Development Ltd. was plushly luxurious, displaying Texas money from its cloud-white carpet of two-inch-thick pile to its walls paneled with genuine walnut. The furniture was thickly padded and covered in the finest-grained leather. The walnut desk was Texas-sized, and the big swivel chair behind it was designed especially for its occupant so the slightly built man wouldn't appear dwarfed by his own desk.

Mixed in with the room's rich appointments were the odd pieces of Texas flash—like the Meissen vase sitting atop a table supported by twisted cowhorns or the spotted horsehide blanket thrown over the back of the leather sofa. The office lived up to the image created by its occupant.

Stricklin sat tall and erect in the leather-covered side chair, the wire-rimmed glasses increasing his studious air. He completed his perusal of Grayson's report and passed it to Dyson with a short nod, silently communicating his opinion to his partner.

"I can't say I'm surprised by your findings, Grayson." E.J. leafed through the report they had already gone over in detail. "I had a hunch we had exhausted the potential on Calder's ranch. It's a good thing I started buying up leases in Wyoming. We'll go ahead and move the balance of the men and equipment down there."

"Whatever you decide." Leo shrugged. His only recommendation had been to abandon the Calder ranch site and not attempt any future drilling, but he hadn't suggested where to go from there. It wasn't his job to become involved in such decisions.

"Are you satisfied in your own mind there isn't anything worth going after under any of the land Calder owns?" Dyson pinned the geologist with a hard look to make doubly sure Grayson didn't have any reservations. It was a psychological trick that tested the man's confidence in his judgment. The ones who lacked faith in themselves were rarely able to meet the challenge.

"The only thing under that ground is a mother lode of low-sulfur coal," Leo stated with a sad shake of his head. "It's too bad oil is so cheap. It cuts into the market for coal."

"Coal?" Dyson lifted his head, showing mild interest and darting a short glance at Stricklin, who was meticulously cleaning his nails with a pocket knife. "What do you mean by mother lode? Is there very much of it?"

"Very much of it? I guess so." Grayson laughed shortly. "I'd hate to have to guess how many million tons of bituminous coal are lying a few inches under the surface."

"A few inches. You must be exaggerating," E.J. declared with a dismissing smile and lowered his gaze to study the report again.

"It's no exaggeration," the geologist insisted. "In places, it's anywhere from a couple of feet to a couple of inches from the surface. A couple of bites with a power shovel and you'd find it."

"Is that a fact?" Dyson mused, then shrugged it off. "As you say, Leo, there isn't much of a demand for coal these days."

"It's a shame when it's so plentiful," he replied, then asked, "Is there anything else you wanted to go over with me?"

"No. That's all." Dyson continued looking through the report, barely glancing up as he dismissed the geologist.

After Grayson had left his office, Dyson stared at the same page of the report. All his life he'd been a hunch player. When the rest of the country had been converging on Texas and the other Sun Belt states, he had looked north and saw the next future in the western states. For a while he'd thought his hunch was wrong when the drilling hadn't produced the big oil discovery he had expected.

He swiveled his chair around and aimed it at Stricklin. "Maybe the fortune to be had is in black diamonds instead of black gold," he suggested. "What do you think?"

Stricklin gave a vague shrug as he paused to brush the nail shavings from his sharply creased slacks. "There have been rumblings from the Mideast about a possible embargo."

The gloom and doom forecasters had been saying the world would run out of petroleum if attempts weren't made to curtail consumption. Talk had never interested Dyson much except in relation to how it might affect the price of crude. But if the supply of petroleum were reduced, it would raise the demand for coal.

"I think it's time we started learning more about coal," he announced to Stricklin. "Cost of shipping to eastern markets, availability of railroads. Present and potential users, and how much competition we'll get from the Appalachian coalfields."

"I'll get right on it."

At the top of Dyson's mental list, there was a name. E.J. pushed the buzzer of his intercom.

"Place a call to Senator Bulfert, and let me know when you have him on the line," he instructed his secretary. The senator wasn't the source for his answers, but Dyson had other uses for the unscrupulous politician.

"Now, Chase, you have to admit our Texas winter is an improvement on the weather you left behind," E. J. Dyson chided as he passed him a tall glass of whiskey and soda.

Chase stood on the balcony of the luxurious condominium overlooking the Gulf. The tropical breeze blowing off the water was warm and humid.

"I admit it," he acknowledged as he raised the iced drink.

"I can't tell you how pleased I am that you and Maggie are here." E.J. stood beside him to admire the view. "I finally have the opportunity to return the hospitality you so graciously extended to me on numerous occasions."

"Maggie and Cathleen were both suffering from a bad case of cabin fever. So we decided to fly down for a few days and see Ty." On the beach below, he could see Cathleen busily darting all over the sand, picking up seashells and running to show them to Ty and add them to a small bucket. The third person with his son and daughter was a stunningly beautiful girl in a skimpy bikini, almost covered by a thin lace jacket. "You have a beautiful daughter, E.J."

"I think your son has fallen in love with her." He studied Calder over the rim of his glass to see his reaction. "So far, she's led him on a merry chase."

"Most women do." It was a somewhat nasty answer, but Chase couldn't explain to himself why he felt so negative.

"I can't say that I'd have any objections if there was a matrimonial merger of our two families in the future," Dyson remarked.

"Any objections would be premature. I don't believe either one of them is old enough to know what they want," he stated, throwing another glance at the young couple on the beach. "It isn't the right time for Ty to be getting serious about any girl."

"I quite agree," the Texan drawled. "Both of them have college to finish. And I want Tara Lee to spend a year abroad touring Europe, so that youthful thirst for adventure will be satisfied before she settles down. Like you, I don't want them rushing into anything. Unhappy marriages are hell, as you well know."

"That's right." The offhand response belied Chase's alertness as he tried to discern whether Dyson's comment had been a general remark or an observation of his strained relationship with Maggie.

In that first glow of reborn love, they had both been guilty of believing that love alone would smooth out all their differences and eliminate the rough patches every marriage encounters. Maturity and experience had changed each of them, yet it wasn't easy to let go of past images they'd had of each other. Sometimes it was difficult for him to relate to the sophisticated and highly educated woman Maggie had become. He was used to making decisions without consulting anyone, and she expected to be part of them. Adjusting to each other and adapting the old ways to their present needs required constant effort.

They had moments when things were right between them,

but those times were becoming less and less frequent. As long as Ty wasn't mentioned, they could pretend they didn't have any problems, but it was impossible for them not to talk about their own son.

There was a certain bitter irony in the fact that Ty had been responsible for reuniting him with Maggie, and now he was responsible for dividing them. Chase kept clinging to the hope that when Ty finished college and came home for good, his own conflict with Maggie would die a natural death.

Once he'd thought he could endure a marriage without any love or understanding from his wife. Perhaps without both, he could have. Although he knew Maggie continued to love him, he had to go to Sally for the understanding he needed. So far, he hadn't crossed that fine line of sexual faithfulness he observed.

"I've had the opportunity to become acquainted with your son since he has been attending college here in Texas," Dyson remarked. "As you know, he's occasionally spent weekends at my home in Fort Worth as well as here on Padre Island. He's an intelligent and sensible young man. I've become fond of him, even though I know he only comes to see Tara Lee."

"I've noticed Ty has a lot of respect for you, too." It was a diplomatic answer to conceal his resentment of the admiration Ty had shown toward the freewheeling entrepreneur. Ty seemed to put a lot of stock in Dyson's opinions. Chase had no complaints about his dealings with the man, but neither did he want his son using the man as a role model. That was the problem with college. It held up the wrong examples for emulation.

Chase didn't wish to continue this discussion. "I've been hearing a lot of talk about the new oil and gas discoveries being made in Wyoming. It looks like you'll have better luck there than you did in my country."

"The wells at Broken Butte will show a respectable return, a little below average but still respectable. But, yes, the rewards appear to be much greater in the Wyoming basin." Dyson nodded. "There's nothing left to find on your land except coal. I understand eastern Montana is underlaid with coal deposits. If the petroleum reserves ever gave out, you'd wind up a rich man, Calder."

"Maybe, but there wouldn't be a ranch left worth having." The idea was unthinkable. Chase bolted down a swallow of whiskey and soda to rid himself of the bad taste. "You only have to look at some of the coal states in the East to see how strip mines have desecrated the land."

"That's been true in the past," Dyson conceded, choosing his words carefully. "But with modern reclamation methods, the land can be turned back to original use as cattle graze. There wouldn't be any lasting damage."

"Is that right?" Chase eyed the man with a cool, challenging lift of an eyebrow. "When you cut somebody open and take out half his guts, then sew him back up, he's never the same again, and the scar never goes away. The homesteaders raped the land almost fifty years ago and it's still little more than a desert with scrub grass and weeds. That isn't my idea of graze."

"Chase Calder, how can you look at all that blue Gulf water and talk about grazing cattle?" Maggie chided him as she joined the two men on the balcony in time to catch the last of his remarks. "This is supposed to be a vacation, remember?"

"Sorry." The corners of his mouth twitched with a smile as she came to stand beside him. Once he would have automatically put his arm around her, but it had ceased being a natural gesture.

"Let me fix you a drink, Maggie," Dyson offered.

"I'll just have some tonic water with a twist," she said and leaned on the balcony railing to look down at the beach. "Cathleen is enjoying herself, isn't she?"

A broken sand dollar was added to the collection of shells in the beach pail that sat in the sand by Ty's feet. The two adults had tired of walking the beach and spread their towels on the sand to watch the five-year-old.

"Go find some more," Ty urged his little sister. Emerald-green ribbons were tied in bows to adorn her jet-black pigtails and match the bathing suit she wore. Cathleen was off with a dash, scampering back to the tideline with her pigtails bouncing.

"Your sister is a gorgeous thing, Ty," Tara declared,

silently marveling that a child could look so beautiful. "She takes after your mother so much."

"What do you think of my parents?" His shoulders were angled toward her, bared to the sunlight that played over the ridged muscles.

"Your father is almost the way I imagined he would be," she admitted. "But I was surprised to find your mother so sophisticated and modern. I guess I thought she'd be one of those dowdy, meek women who bake a lot."

"I told you she was special," Ty reminded her.

"Sons can be very prejudiced about their mothers," she countered, then studied him absently. "She doesn't look old enough to have a son your age."

"She was very young when I was born, still in her teens." It wasn't the time or the place to go into details about the past.

A slight frown marred Tara's forehead. "I always feel sorry for girls who become tied down with children when they are young. They miss so much." Her expression smoothed out as she suddenly smiled at Ty, giving him a message and softening its impact. "It's going to be a few more years before I tie myself down with children or a husband. There's too much out there I want to see and do first."

"Did it ever occur to you that a husband could see and do those things with you?" There was a taut edge to his question. She was a part of all of his dreams, yet she never seemed to consider including him in hers.

"A husband? Just one man? How boring!"

8

The needle on the gasoline gauge was flirting with the empty mark when Chase drove the pickup truck to the gas pumps that stood in front of the combination grocery store and post office of Blue Moon. Another dusty pickup

Chase recognized as belonging to the ranch fleet was already parked at the pumps.

As he stepped from the truck, Ty walked out of the store and paused, bending his head to light a cigarette. Chase had a second to study his son unobserved, and he liked what he saw. The dusty and sun-faded jeans, the scuff-toed boots with run-down heels and black marks where the spurs usually rode, the worn-soft chambray workshirt, and the sweat-stained cowboy hat on his head, all were the clothes of a working cowboy. Ty's hair had grown too long in back, but Chase was overlooking that.

Ty looked up as he shook out the match. There was a split second of hesitation when he saw his father; then he moved forward with an easy, rolling stride. Something seemed different about his father's attitude, as if for the first time in a long while they were meeting on neutral ground. They had been silently at odds ever since he'd announced his decision to attend college. But, a second ago, he thought he'd caught a glimmer of approval in his father's eyes.

"Did you just come from the Phelps ranch?" Ty vaguely remembered that, last night, his father had mentioned something about going there to look at some young horses.

"Yeah. I didn't have enough gas to make it to The Homestead." He paused as Emmett Fedderson squeezed his rotund body between the pumps and the pickup to fit the gasoline nozzle into the truck's gas tank. He lifted a hand in silent greeting to the operator of the establishment, then let his attention return to Ty. "It's your day off, isn't it?"

"Yeah." Ty narrowed his eyes against the cigarette smoke curling back into his face. "I was thinking about heading home so I can get cleaned up and have a bite to eat. Some of the guys are coming to Sally's tonight."

"A man named Jake owned the place when I was your age." His father smiled absently. "It used to be the only action for miles."

"Still is." Ty grinned.

"It's a far cry from the kind of night spots you're used to at college." It was a testing remark.

"It's true a man doesn't have to think too long or too hard about where he's going to spend his Saturday night around here," Ty conceded with an affectionate air. Chase relaxed slightly, relieved to hear that his son wasn't yearning for more sophisticated excitement. "If you're not in a rush to get back, we could go over to Sally's and I'll buy you a beer."

"All right. I'll pay Emmett for the gas and meet you there." Inwardly he was pleased, despite his casual acceptance of the invitation from his son. It had been a long time since there'd been any closeness between them. Maybe they needed to sit down over a beer and get acquainted again.

The first of the Saturday-night crowd usually started wandering in about suppertime, so when Ty moved his truck and parked it in front of the café-bar, other pickups were already on the scene. The early-evening patrons were usually older people and couples with young children. They came early to treat themselves to a meal out and stayed to have a few drinks. That group usually left to put the kids to bed about the time the partying crowd arrived.

When Ty walked in, most of the dining tables were filled. The jukebox was going full blast while youngsters raced back and forth between it and their parents, trying to wheedle more coins to keep the records playing. Amidst the clatter of silverware and loud music, there was laughter and lots of talking. The place had a warm atmosphere, comfortable and homey.

"Hello, Ty. What'll you have?" Sally Brogan asked the question before he'd sat down at one of the bare drink tables. She was on her way to another table, carrying two plates in one hand, a third balanced on her forearm, and a fourth in her other hand.

"Two beers." He pulled out a chair and sat in it, smiling at the friendly informality of the place.

Two more tables were served before Sally Brogan set down two foaming glasses of beer on their table. "How's things been?" No matter how busy it got in the café, nothing ever seemed to ruffle the quiet composure of the red-haired woman.

"Fine." Ty nodded. She was a pleasant woman, trim and attractive in a quiet way. She was everybody's sister or mother, depending on their age.

"How's college? I forgot what you're majoring in." She frowned.

"Agriscience and animal husbandry, with a minor in business administration. What else would a future rancher take?" he joked dryly.

"That's already over my head." She laughed in response.

"Sally?" The other woman waiting tables called to her. "DeeDee wants you in the kitchen."

He took a drink of the cold draft beer and wiped the foam from his mouth with the back of his hand. Her reaction was typical of what he encountered when the subject of college was raised. Around here, especially in the ranching community, a person was considered lucky if he had a high-school diploma, so they weren't comfortable talking about his advanced education. He'd been chided for using big words and jokingly told to talk in plain English, but there had been an underlying thread of seriousness in the jokes. For the most part, Ty had learned to suppress his knowledge in an attempt to put others at ease.

The café door opened and his father walked in. When he spied where Ty was sitting, he wended his way through the tables and folded his broad frame into the chair opposite him.

"Damn, that looks good," he said as he lifted the other glass. "Phelps talked me dry." He referred to the owner of the ranch he'd visited that afternoon.

"Did he have any good horses in the bunch?" Ty asked.

"A couple, but he wanted too much for them."

While they drank their beers, they discussed horses and exchanged opinions about ways of breeding out flaws. Chase drained his beer and set the glass on the table, hunching over it.

"Are you hungry?" he asked Ty. "This beer has reminded me I didn't have lunch."

"Yeah." His hunger seemed to sharpen his senses, making the smells from the kitchen seem all the more tantalizing. It was almost like being around Tara, although Ty doubted that she would appreciate the comparison. "Do you suppose Mom has started dinner?"

"Why don't you call and tell her not to fix anything?" His

father leaned back in the chair, straightening and looking around the busy café. "I'll have Sally throw a couple steaks on the grill for us. Is she here?"

"Last time I saw her, she was going into the kitchen." He hadn't noticed whether she'd come out.

"You go call your mother and I'll put our order in."

"Okay." Ty pushed out of his chair and dug a hand into the pocket of his snug-fitting denims, pulling out a coin for the pay telephone on the wall back by the rest rooms. While he walked in one direction, his father went in another, heading for the kitchen.

Cathleen answered the telephone at The Homestead. He was obliged to talk to his six-year-old sister a few minutes before she finally called their mother to the phone.

"Is something wrong, Ty?" Her voice was tense with concern.

"Nothing's wrong unless you've started dinner already," he replied.

"Not yet. I was waiting for your father to come home before I started frying the chicken. Why? I suppose you aren't going to be here for dinner tonight." She answered her own question.

"No. And Dad won't be home either," he informed her. "I ran into him on his way home from the Phelps ranch. We're at Sally's now, and we're going to grab a bite to eat, so you don't have to worry about cooking anything for us."

"Okay." Maggie's reaction wavered between pleasure because Chase and Ty were obviously getting along well enough that they wanted to prolong the time together, and uneasiness because Chase was at Sally's. Lately it seemed he had been stopping in there a lot, or maybe she was just sensitive because things weren't well between them.

"I don't know what time Dad will head back, but it'll probably be late before I get home," Ty warned her.

"Just try to be quiet so you don't wake Cathleen." Her son was of an age where she didn't attempt to dictate his hours.

"She wakes up every time I try to sneak in." He laughed. "I'm better off stampeding up the stairs. She never hears me then."

"Take care and drive carefully. The same goes for your

father." When she hung up, Maggie wondered why Ty had been the one to call her instead of Chase. But she didn't want to think about that.

When Chase pushed open the swinging door to the kitchen, he was greeted by the sight of Sally on her hands and knees, craning her head to look under the large dishwashing sink. DeeDee Rains, the tall Blackfoot woman who did the cooking, smiled and opened her mouth to speak to him, but Chase held up a silencing finger. Her smile broadened in understanding as he moved quietly in behind Sally and leaned on the sink.

"Did you lose a quarter?" he asked.

The unexpected sound of his voice startled her. She tried to sit back on her heels too quickly and knocked her head on the sink. She was rubbing a spot beneath the copper-red hair when she finally looked at him with accusing eyes and a forgiving smile. The kitchen heat and her exertions under the sink brought a slight flush to her pale complexion.

"I'm sorry, Sally. Did you hurt yourself?" Chase crouched beside her and reached out to feel her head where she'd banged it on the sink. His hand came away when he didn't find any knot.

"It didn't knock any sense into me, if that's what you're wondering," she replied, not able to mask the pleasure that glowed in her blue eyes.

He noticed the wrench in her hand. "What seems to be the problem?"

"Water started gushing out of the hot-water pipe," she explained with a heavy sigh. "Luckily it was just a loose connection. At first, I thought a pipe had broken, and I could see this week's profits literally running down the drain."

"Give me the wrench. I'll make sure it's tight."

"There's a lot of water on the floor," Sally warned. "Be careful you don't get wet or slip."

While he made a few more turns with the wrench to make sure the coupler was tight, Sally fetched a rag mop and began sopping up the pooling water on the linoleum floor. When he'd finished, Chase stood back and supervised her mopping of the floor.

"You missed a spot." He pointed to an area that still had a water sheen.

"Just what are you doing in the kitchen?" Sally swiped the mop at the spot, then leaned on the long handle. "Other than giving orders, I mean."

He chuckled at her question. "I came back to have you throw a couple of thick steaks on the grill."

"Two?" she repeated. "First Ty comes in and orders two beers, and now you're ordering two—" She stopped, the significance finally registering. "Are you and Ty together?"

He nodded as he sought out the quiet pleasure that ran through her expression. "I realized I hadn't talked to my son in a long while. I don't know whether it's because we're both away from the ranch or not, but there doesn't seem to be as much tension. I—" Chase stopped himself, realizing he should be saying these things to Maggie.

"I'm glad for you," she insisted quietly, then seemed to withdraw, too. "I'm glad for both of you." She half turned to call to the cook, "Burn two thick ones, DeeDee." Hesitantly her glance came back to Chase, then fell away. "I'd better put this bucket in the back room."

When she took a step, she forgot the wet floor would be slick. Her foot slid out from under her. Instinctively Chase reached out to catch her and haul her against his body to steady her. She pressed a hand to her breastbone and tilted her head to laugh shakily.

"My heart's going a mile a minute," Sally declared.

"Is it?" Chase was conscious of the woman's softness against him, the fullness of her hips and the heaving movements of her breasts. He laid his hand alongside her neck as if seeking its throbbing vein, but his thumb stroked her jaw. He felt the change in her at his caress, the sudden lift in tension.

"Chase," she murmured, warning him against the direction his thoughts were taking.

"There are times when a man gets tired of fighting and struggling all the time, Sally," he murmured, "when all he wants in his life is peace. You're a remarkable woman, so calm and tranquil. I need that strength."

"You always see me as being strong, but I'm not strong,

Chase. I'm weak. I know you don't love me and you never will. Yet I'm still here."

He sensed the giving in her—the giving that expected nothing in return—no lies and no promises. She didn't ask for his love, because she knew it already belonged to Maggie.

It would be so simple to have the comfort of her body—so very, very simple. His head came down until his mouth was poised above her soft, inviting lips. The flutter of her breath was against his face; the warm smells of food mingled with her scent. His hunger tempted him to take the sustenance being offered.

At the large, flat grill, DeeDee Rains turned the sizzling slabs of steak and stood back as the fat splattered into liquid grease, smoke and steam rising in a hiss of heat. She was aware of the couple behind her, finding themselves in the familiar pattern of an old affair.

The door to the kitchen started to swing inward, the movement catching her eye. For several seconds, it was held slightly ajar, then released to swing shut. It was likely the pair had been seen, but DeeDee didn't dwell on it. She already had a strong suspicion how it was going to turn out.

That Calder pride would bend most men's shoulders, but they put high stock in it. She knew it gave them no room. When the couple parted with embrace unconsummated, DeeDee wasn't surprised. No matter how it had ended tonight, nothing would have come of it. Pride was a funny thing. It would either break a man or make him stronger.

She said not a word to Sally when she came over by the grill and made busywork of replenishing the supply of bread. Her face was pale and her eyes were bright, close to tears. As DeeDee moved past her to grab a handful of french fries out of the freezer, she laid a hand on her shoulder and squeezed it gently. Sally gripped it to hold it there a second longer, then released it and brushed off the front of her apron.

"Sounds like we're going to have a busy night," she declared with forced brightness as voices and hearty laughter made a steady background din.

Ty leaned on the table, both hands wrapped around the second glass of beer. He'd taken one drink out of it, barely tasting it. The shock of seeing his father embracing Sally Brogan kept him numb. It was as if he couldn't feel anything, yet all the while his mind searched wildly through the blankness of his thoughts for something. There was a sense of being betrayed, but he didn't know how or why.

The other chair was pulled out from the table, causing Ty to look up. There was no expression in his father's face, but it looked closed as he sat down. The blood ran quicker through Ty's veins, breaking through some of the numbness.

"Did you get hold of your mother?"

"Yeah." His voice was stiff, with an abrasive edge, as Ty struggled to decide whether he should confront his father with what he'd seen. "What took you so long in the kitchen?" He flashed a challenging look at his father, then let it fall quickly away to the beer glass he held.

"The union had worked loose on a water pipe under the sink, so I gave Sally a hand tightening it." It was a simple, straight answer, an excuse so readily provided. Ty snorted out a short, low laugh.

"Is there something amusing in that?"

Doubt fought with his hot anger because a part of Ty didn't want to believe what he'd seen. He wanted to come up with some other explanation. Maybe his father had only been comforting Sally or she'd gotten something in her eye. Maybe it had only looked like he was going to kiss her. Ty cursed himself for not watching longer.

His father waited for an answer. Ty lifted the glass of beer toward his mouth. "I just can't picture Chase Calder as a plumber." He poured a swallow of beer into his mouth and held it there, rinsing off the bad taste that coated his tongue. Finally he let it run down his throat, never taking his gaze from the beer glass again cradled between both hands. "I always thought you were something special." His hands tightened knuckle-white on the glass.

The remark prompted Chase to recall Maggie's insistence that their son regarded him as some kind of mortal god. He couldn't feel less godlike than he did right now.

"I'm a man, Ty." Weariness pulled at him, weariness of everyone expecting him to be strong for them when he had trouble being strong for himself. "I get lonely and tired . . . and fed up just like everyone else."

Part of the reply struck a nerve. "Why should you feel lonely when you've got Mom?" This time Ty leveled a glance at his father, trying to flatten the dark glitter of anger in his eyes.

"Just because you love someone, that doesn't mean you stop being lonely," he replied while his narrowed eyes flicked keenly over Ty.

Sally Brogan approached the table carrying two plates mounded with french fries and draped with T-bones. Ty avoided looking at her and lifted his beer glass to drink it dry while she set the meal in front of him along with silverware wrapped in napkins, the steak knives lying across the crisply cooked meat.

He rocked his chair onto its back legs, observing his father while the red-haired woman placed a food-laden plate in front of him and paused at his side. "Anything else?"

"Not for me, thanks," his father refused with an air of reserve and swung her a brief glance that seemed hard with regret.

"How about you, Ty?" So calm-sounding and natural.

The chair came down on all four legs with a loud clump. "I'll have another beer." He pushed the empty glass onto the table in her direction but Ty never looked at her.

The salt and pepper shakers were exchanged without conversation. A fresh glass of beer was set in front of Ty and he mumbled a short thanks. The meal appeared to occupy the attention of both of them, but Ty's thoughts continued wrestling with this discovery about his father.

If his mother ever found out he was carrying on with Sally Brogan, she would be brutally hurt. How could a man love a woman and do that to her? Yet was it any different than his relationship with Tara: loving her while using other women to satisfy his body's lust? He instantly rejected the comparison. It wouldn't be like that after they were married.

He didn't know how to deal with the situation, on one hand hating his father for betraying his mother this way, and on the other trying to find excuses that would justify his father's behavior. Every time the hot bile of resentment rose in his throat, he washed it down with cold beer.

When they had finished the meal, his father ordered a cup of coffee, but Ty asked for another beer. "In a few weeks you'll be leaving again to start your last year of college." His father lit a thin cheroot and blew the smoke upward to join the hazy layer of air near the ceiling. "I guess you know I'll always think your time would have been better spent on the ranch. But at least it's nearly over and you'll be back for good." When Ty failed to respond, Chase lifted his head, sensing something was wrong. "Or do you have other plans that I don't know about?"

"No. None." The sweating beer glass left a wet circle on the table, and he turned it absently within that perimeter. "I'll be coming back after I graduate."

"You had me wondering for a minute." His mouth relaxed into a faint smile. There was a small break in the conversation, a lull that was filled by the growing hum of laughing voices in the background until his father spoke again. "Dyson will be flying up sometime next week for a visit. He called this morning to say he was going to be in Wyoming. Since he was so close he decided he'd take an extra couple of days and stop by the ranch."

"Will Tara be with him?" Ty had to ask.

"Not that he mentioned." He glanced at Ty while he tapped the slim cigar in the ashtray. "Are you serious about her?"

"I'm going to marry her," he stated.

His father took his time digesting this assertion as he idly rolled his cigar. "She's a beautiful girl." His glance moved with deceptive laziness back to Ty. "Are you sure you love her?"

No one had ever been able to explain to him what love was. With Tara, he had discovered it to be hunger—a driving hunger that ate away at him until he craved her the way a starving man would sell his soul for a loaf of bread.

"Yes, I'm sure."

"I won't tell you that you're too young for marriage, even though I think you are. If she's got you tied up in the kind of knots I think she has, you're beyond knowing what you feel or listening to anyone else. But if you do love her, bring her to the ranch before you marry her—for her sake."

"Why?" At the moment, Ty resented any advice from his father regarding marriage or women.

"Some people can't adapt to the isolation. Life out here won't be like what she's known. There aren't any fancy shops or theaters or country clubs, or so many things she takes for granted. You owe her the right to know what kind of life she'll have after you are married."

"Mother enjoys it here," he stated.

"Your mother was born to the country. Tara is city-bred."

"And that makes all the difference?" There was a trace of sarcasm in his voice at this constant preaching on the subject.

"If she doesn't like it here, you'll find yourself with an insurmountable problem," his father warned. "Every marriage has its problems."

"What's yours?" Ty demanded.

His father drew back, eyes narrowing. "That's a private matter between your mother and me, something we have to work out alone."

"First you have to want to work it out." The relationship between his parents had been strained for a considerable time now, ever since they had taken opposite sides on the issue of his college education. Maybe his father's solution had been to take a mistress.

"If you're hinting at something, say it out plain," his father challenged. "Otherwise, don't be trying to give advice on something you know nothing about."

The reprimand forced Ty to contain his half-formed accusations, but he did so grudgingly. As a twenty-one-year-old adult, he wanted to respect their privacy. Yet, as a son, he could not stand aside indifferently. He lifted the glass of beer, feeling sick and angry inside.

The other waitress came by the table with the coffeepot to refill Chase's cup, but he covered the top of it with his hand. "No more for me. It's time I was heading home before Maggie decides I've lost my way." He reached for the meal check that had been left on the table as he stood up. "The dinner's on me tonight."

After his father had left, Ty sat alone at the table a while longer. The beers he'd consumed were beginning to take effect. He had trouble keeping a run of thoughts going. His mind kept skipping back and forth from his father to Tara. He wanted to talk to her—to hear her voice.

Standing up, he shoved his hand inside his pants pocket and took out his change. The movement seemed to make the blood rush through him faster. He was suddenly feeling good, all loose and untrammeled. And if there was a little edge to his nerves, a little testiness, then it just heightened the other feelings.

The restaurant and bar had filled up. Some of the families with younger children were leaving while local cowboys and ranch workers filed into the café in twos and threes. Most of them Ty knew by sight if not by name. They hailed him with greetings which he returned as he worked his way to the pay telephone on the wall outside the rest rooms.

A cue stick was drawn back by its shooter bending over the pool table. Ty sidestepped it and jostled a towheaded boy of eighteen, his freckled face sunburned except for the white band of his forehead.

"Sorry, Andersen," Ty apologized to the son from the family that farmed some land adjoining the south boundary of the Triple C. There was a passel of kids, and Ty could never keep their names straight.

"It's okay." The lanky boy shifted, giving Ty a glimpse of the girl with him.

"Hey, Jessy." There was something taunting in his lazy smile as he slipped into the local dialect. "Hell, I ain't never seen you without a hat." He mussed her thick mane of hair, the dim light dulling its golden streaks. "Looks like the best damned roper on the Triple C has finally lassoed herself a date."

"Maybe someday I can teach you how to rope so you can be as good as me," she retorted.

Ty nudged the Andersen boy with his elbow. "Better watch her. She's a sassy thing." He took no notice at all of the white jeans she wore or of the plain cut of her shiny blue blouse.

Without waiting for a response from the quiet farm boy, he shoved off, aiming once again for the telephone. When the operator came on the line, he gave her the number in Texas and dropped in the amount of coins required for the call.

"Hello, I'd like to speak to Tara." He put a hand over his ear, trying to shut out the noise from the jukebox and the bar area.

"Who's calling?"

"Ty Calder." The same impersonal voice requested him to wait, which Ty did, impatiently.

"Hello, Ty? This is E.J. I'm afraid Tara Lee has gone out for the evening. Was it something important?"

The good feeling slipped away from him. A frown gathered as he tried to come up with an explanation for the call. "I just wanted to talk to her," he mumbled and repeated himself, "I just wanted to talk, that's all."

"Ty, are you drunk?" Dyson sounded almost amused.

"No, sir, not yet." But the urge was there to let the alcohol blot out all of his confusion. "Tell her I called." He felt a curl of anger because she hadn't been there. It put a stiffness in him as he hung up the phone.

9

Using a straw, Jessy stirred the ice in her Coke glass. Her glance often strayed to the pool table where Ty stood, a cue stick in one hand and a bottle of beer in the other. Somehow he managed to hold on to both, even when it was his turn to shoot, and usually there was a cigarette dangling from his mouth at the same time, making him squint one-eyed to aim through the smoke.

His long, muscled legs were unsteady under him. There was a barely controlled lurch and stagger to his movements. Jessy had no idea how many of those long-necked bottles of beer he'd downed, but he was on his way to becoming rip-roaring drunk. His laugh was loud, and so was his voice, yet the thin edge of anger seemed to run through him. She felt a surge of impatience and disgust at his behavior, although she ignored the cowboys with him who were in the same inebriated state.

Bending her head, she sipped the watery Coke through the straw. Leroy Andersen used the tabletop for a drum, beating his fingers in time with the music from the jukebox, his shoulders swaying in tempo. Jessy had given up trying to keep a conversation going with him, tiring of competing with the music for his attention. His beating fingers made a final slap to finish with the song.

"That was some rhythm, huh?" He rubbed his hands on his thighs and looked to her for agreement.

She smiled back wanly but didn't answer. Personally, she didn't like the song, but she hadn't liked any of the songs Leroy had selected.

"Wanta go pick out some more songs?" he suggested.

"Why not?" The choices of entertainment were limited, since Leroy didn't talk and, despite all that rhythm, couldn't dance. All her girlfriends made such a thing about having a date on Saturday night, as if it were some special honor, regardless of which boy did the asking. Peer pressure made her think there was something wrong with her if she didn't accept an invitation just on principle. But invariably, Jessy was bored. She had more fun when she double-dated or went with a group.

The jukebox continued playing preselections while Leroy tapped out the drumbeat on the glass front. Jessy wasn't sure why she was even looking at the record choices. They hadn't been changed all summer.

"Hey! Bring me another beer!" It was Ty who shouted the order, and Jessy turned. He was passing the pool stick to another player when he spied her at the jukebox. The record changed and the song "Cotton-eyed Joe" came over the speakers.

"How about this one?" Leroy asked and she looked to see which one he'd picked, already certain she wouldn't like it.

An arm hooked her around the stomach and hauled her sideways. Her breath came rushing into her lungs in stunned surprise. Ty smiled lazily down at her with that taunting gleam in his half-glazed eyes. Her hip was clamped to his thigh while her shoulder and arm were awkwardly trapped against his chest. She felt her heart knocking crazily against her ribs.

"I ain't seen you dancing once all night, Jessy." His husky voice had a faint slur to it. "Let's see if you're as good on a dance floor as you are on a horse."

"Ty Calder, you're drunk," she accused.

"I ask you to dance"—he frowned irritably—"not give me a lecture." Then he looked past her to smile with benign contempt at her date. "You don't mind, do you, Andersen?"

"I don't mind, Mr. Calder."

"Did you hear that?" A dark eyebrow was arched unnaturally high into his sun-browned forehead as he looked again at Jessy. "*Mister* Calder has permission from your date to dance with you." His head made a wobbly nod of mock formality.

"All right, we'll dance," she agreed. "If you can stand up that long."

She was loosened from his hold so they could move single file the few steps to the small cleared dancing area. When Jessy turned to face him, his circling arm once again brought her tightly against his body. Their hips were nearly joining as she straddled his thigh so there would be some place to put her feet without stepping on his boots. The contact signaled his every movement in advance, making it easy for Jessy to follow his lead, but the closeness that let her feel every ripple of his muscles was disturbing.

In the first few turns around the small area, he seemed to make a concentrated effort to coordinate his feet in the right pattern. Jessy was beginning to wonder if Ty was as drunk as she'd first thought. Then his concentration broke and he stumbled.

"Sorry," he muttered, then nearly stepped on her toe.

His hold on her tightened, and Jessy realized he was relying on her balance. His hat was pulled low on his forehead, shading his features so they wouldn't show his struggle for a moment's sobriety.

"Maybe I should lead and you follow," she suggested.

Ty stiffened. "I'll be damned if I'll let you lead." He started whirling her around the dance floor, hardly letting her feet touch the floor.

When the song finally ended, he stopped and let her go. Swaying unsteadily, he swept off his hat and tried to make a mock bow, but he staggered sideways. Jessy grabbed for him and helped him into a chair someone slid to them.

"Whew!" He tried to appear out of breath, but she suspected the room was spinning on him. "I need another beer."

"You've had enough," she stated.

"You're right," Ty agreed with her unexpectedly and stood up, but he made sure he held on to the chair back. "It's late. I gotta be gettin' home." He began groping in his pockets. "Where's the keys?" Then he shouted to the room, "Anybody seen my keys?"

"You're in no condition to drive home," Jessy announced while he swayed.

"I left them in the truck," he remembered and turned to lurch toward the door.

Someone grabbed him before he stumbled into a table, and Jessy darted forward to drape his arm over her shoulder and steer him in the right direction.

"Jessy, where're you going?" Leroy appeared at her side, frowning as he walked to keep up with her.

"Ty's too drunk to drive home. His truck is outside, so I'll take him back. It's late anyway." She struggled under his weight as he relied more on her than his unsteady legs.

"D'ya want me to come with you?" Leroy wasn't sure what he should do.

"There's no need of you following us all the way to the ranch, then have to drive home." Actually she was relieved to have a premature end to the date.

With the help of a couple other Triple C riders, Jessy was able to maneuver Ty into the cab of the truck. He protested when she slid behind the wheel, insisting he could drive, but she ignored him.

"You think I'm drunk, don't ya?" His words were slurred. When he tried to stare her down, her image started blurring as if it were trying to separate into two. Ty wasn't sure, but he didn't think she was even looking at him. "Well, I am," he informed her proudly and grabbed for the support of the door when the truck accelerated in a swinging turn onto the two-lane. "I'm a Calder, ya know." He braced himself for further unexpected turns that didn't come. "And a Calder always does what he sets out to do." He attempted to enunciate the words clearly. "Tonight, I set out to get drunk—and I did it."

"You certainly did," Jessy murmured.

His head felt large and heavy, its weight more than his neck could support. Ty slumped lower to lean his head on the seat back. His hat was pushed farther forward, angling down over his eyes.

The headlight beams tracked the rough pavement ahead of the truck, illuminating the high grass and weeds that choked the shoulder. Everything else was blackness. Ty stared into the edges of the scrubby growth, but it rushed by too quickly for him to focus on it.

All night long he'd put on a jocular show of good humor to conceal his anger, but now the show was ending. His tongue tasted acrid. Things were supposed to be so fine and so right, but not even his parents were happy. A dull rage rammed through him when he thought about his father, always so damned honorable and preaching his damned code. Everyone was supposed to live by it but him.

Drunkenly Ty cranked the side window down and let the outside air rush into the cab, then slumped back against the seat. After the first sweet smell of freshness, it was the pressure of the wind driving against him that he felt, never letting up, never giving him a rest. He was tired of always facing it, never turning aside for an instant for fear it would be interpreted as a sign of weakness.

The pickup slowed and made the turn into the east portal of the ranch. His groggy mind was slow to react to what his eyes saw. They were well past the simple gate before Ty realized where they were.

"Pull over." He had to make a couple of trys before he was able to sit more erectly in the seat. The truck's rate of speed didn't change. "I said pull over," he repeated the order.

"I can't stop in the middle of the road," Jessy explained. "You'll have to wait until there's room on the shoulder so we can pull off."

"I want you to pull over now!" He grabbed the wheel to turn it himself.

The truck swerved sharply for the ditch, the sudden motion throwing him away from the wheel. Jessy was able to wrench it back just in time, her heart catapulting into her throat before the headlights veered away from the yawning black hollow alongside the road. When he made a second grab for the steering wheel, she angrily shoved him away.

"You're going to get us killed." She was forced to slow the truck in order to keep control of it. "If you're going to be sick, just hang your head out the window."

"No. You stop this truck so I can get out." Ty groped for the ignition keys.

"All right. All right!" She was furious at his foolish and dangerous behavior as she pushed her foot on the brake pedal and the pickup skidded to a halt. "There, it's stopped." He was already turning and awkwardly searching for the door handle. Jessy gripped the steering wheel with both hands, flexing them while she tried to control the anger that had come from being frightened. She watched him lurch out of the truck. "I should just leave you here," she muttered. "The walk home just might sober you up."

But her threat went unnoticed as Ty weaved into the darkness, stumbling down the ditch and making a couple of tries to climb out of it before he succeeded. Jessy kept an eye on his black silhouette as he melded with the dark night. At first, she thought he was seeking the privacy of the darkness to urinate. Then she saw him stop and look around in a lost way.

When he lurched forward to walk farther from the road, she started losing him from sight. Hurriedly, she climbed out of the pickup to follow him. As drunk as he was, there was no telling what kind of crazy notion he had. If he slipped or fell somewhere out there, she'd have hell's own time trying to find him.

Thirty yards from the road, he stopped again, and Jessy paused, not far behind him. She'd left the truck lights on, their long beams shining out at right angles some distance behind her, but their light did her no good. She was surrounded by varying shades of blackness. The low, irregular line of hills in the distance thrust into the falling midnight sky, dusted with stars and lit with the silver horns of a new moon. Jessy was close enough to Ty that his dark shape was clearly outlined.

His arms were away from his sides, partially lifted in a supplicant gesture that was negated by the clenched fists of his hands. His stance was rigid, vaguely challenging, with his feet apart and his head thrown back.

"You're a lonely, stinking land!" The hoarse cry of anger came from some anguished depths of him. "A dream. That's what I thought I had." His drunken laughter was an awful sound. "It's been a nightmare from the start. You fool a man—make him see things that aren't there. You let him think there's just one more hill. You lead him on! You let him think it'll get better!" His voice fell. "And it gets worse. You twist a man until he keeps settling for less each time."

His legs slowly buckled under him as he sank to the ground, his head hanging in dejection. Jessy hesitated, moved by the gut-wrenching outpour of frustration and anger she'd witnessed. She knew that Ty hadn't wanted anyone to hear him. She waited until she was sure his silence would be lasting, then slowly made her way to him. He was sitting back on his haunches, his shoulders slumped and his head down. When she touched his shoulder, he looked up with a dazed glance.

"Come on, Ty." She was gentle with him as she bent down to help him to his feet. "I'll take you home."

"Do you know where it is?" he asked and struggled upright with her assistance. He draped an arm across the back of her shoulders while she kept a supporting arm around his middle and guided him toward the lights of the truck. A wide smile split his features; then he chuckled, amused by some thought. "I always wanted to be like him," Ty announced as he glanced down at Jessy, not really sure who she was. "Did I ever tell you that?" The irony in his voice bothered her.

"No." Jessy supposed he was talking about his father, but she didn't really understand what it was all about.

When they reached the pickup, she opened the passenger

door to help him inside. His foot made several passes at the running board before he finally managed to find it and haul himself into the cab with Jessy giving him a boost and shutting the door.

The effort seemed to expend all his energies. He was slumped in the corner when Jessy climbed into the driver's side. The noise of the motor starting roused him briefly.

"Damn, but I'm tired," he mumbled and settled his long body deeper in the corner between the seat and the door.

A quarter of a mile down the road, Jessy heard the deep sawing of his breath in sleep. She drove slowly over the rough patches in the ranch road so his sleep would be as undisturbed as possible. She attempted to convince herself that she was merely letting him sleep off some of his drunkenness before she got him home, but her earlier irritation with his besotted state had evolved into a tender concern. His dependence on her had stirred up those old dreams she'd had about him. They were still fresh. And if tonight he had let her down by not behaving in the manner of a strong, stalwart hero, he had shown himself to be human and, therefore, more reachable.

College hadn't changed him as much as she'd thought. It was true that he talked better than most of the cowboys— when he was sober—but deep inside, Ty was the same lonely young man she had once idealized.

One light was gleaming from the windows of The Homestead when she stopped the truck in front of the steps to its long colonnaded porch. It laid an irregular pattern of light onto the wooden planked floor. As she switched off the engine, Jessy glanced at Ty, but the cessation of movement and noise had not altered the deep rhythm of his breathing.

She slid nearer to nudge him awake. But he didn't stir under the prod of her hand. She gave his shoulder a little shake which produced a grunted protest.

"Wake up, Ty." Jessy used firmer tactics, grabbing his shoulders and attempting to pull him out of his comfortable corner. "Come on. We're home."

He was a deadweight, but she did succeed in rousing him. Ty stirred, mumbling unintelligibly and trying to snuggle back into his corner. Jessy persisted, moving closer to get a better leverage.

"Sit up, Ty," she ordered patiently and managed to tug him away from the door. "Come on, so I can help you into the house."

His head lolled as he tried to come awake and discover his surroundings. His hat was pulled so low he had to tip his head back to see.

"Where are we?" he asked thickly.

"We're home." She continued to use the plural the way an adult often does with a child.

The sound of her voice seemed to penetrate his consciousness for the first time, and Ty swung his head around to look at her. The high illumination of the yard light did not reach inside the cab of the truck, and the exterior light cast even darker shadows inside. Between the dimness and his own blurring vision, Ty couldn't clearly see the face of the girl with him. There was a vague impression of dark hair and the sheen of a curved cheek. He started to smile.

Satisfied that he was finally awake, or as awake as he'd ever be in his condition, Jessy started to shift away from him so she could climb out the driver's side and come around to help him out of the truck. "You stay here," she ordered. "I'll be right back."

"No." His hand grabbed her forearm, his fingers biting into it with careless pressure. "Don't go. You might not come back."

"Of course I will," Jessy chided him and twisted her arm to release it from his painful grip.

Instead of loosening his hold, he tightened it. "No." Determination hardened his mouth as he refused to let her go. His arm went around her, contracting like an iron band to gather her hard against his shoulder and chest. Jessy's resistance was tempered by confusion. He was clutching her to him the way a child possessively hugs a toy that had been lost. His face was burrowed into her hair.

"Don't leave me," he murmured in an aching voice that stirred her. "I need you. I always have."

"Ty." Jessy was stunned, an incredulous thrill running through her. She could hardly believe what she was hearing.

When he lifted his head, her face was shadowed by his hat, but he picked out the gleam of white teeth. She was smiling, but he couldn't tell whether it was to taunt him or welcome him. His intoxication lowered the barrier that usually kept emotion from showing in his expression.

Her breath caught, lodging in her throat, at the stark need she saw in his face. It was not another cruel joke he was playing on her. He meant it. Her hand trembled as Jessy reached up to trace the ridged angle of his jaw, made bronze by the reflected glow of the outside light.

The hesitant caress of her hand broke the lines of restraint. He had been too vulnerable to risk a rejection, but it wasn't a rejection her touch signaled. A deep, low moan of longing came from his throat.

His mouth opened moistly on her lips, taking them whole with a bold sensuality she had never before experienced. This was no awkward schoolboy, bumping noses with her, nor a brash teenager, coming on strong and crudely forceful. It unnerved her the way he hotly consumed her, needing and seeking with an urgency that made her feel raw.

Blindly she gave, trying to supply what he seemed to be desperately searching for. The invasion of his tongue brought with it the taste of beer and smoke, and the essence of something else. Everything quickened and rose, the heat of the blood rushing through her veins and the sudden intensifying of all her senses.

His arms never eased the pressure that pinned her to him even when his hands began moving on her body. She couldn't keep track of where his hands were as they roamed from shoulder to thigh, always pressing and urging. They seemed to only spread the raw intimacy of his kiss over more parts of her body. Passion was something she'd always known she'd possessed, but nothing had ever ignited it before except her own imagination.

She drank in air when he finally dragged his mouth away. But it wasn't the end; it was the beginning of a series of warm, wet kisses, one connecting to another in a trail over her features. His breath rushed over her skin, hot, moist waves engulfing her. Jessy was awash with sensation. Her hands had long ago found their way around his shoulders to hug and hold.

"You're mine." His low voice vibrated against her skin. "I knew it from the beginning."

Jessy didn't hear the faint slurring of his words, only the content. She had stopped believing Ty would ever feel the way she did. To learn it had begun some time ago for him as well was beyond her wildest dreams.

"So did I," she whispered with a certain fierceness.

"Oh, God, I've wanted you for so long." The groaned words were filled with pent-up longing as he sought her lips in rough need.

Eagerly she turned into the ardent hunger of his kiss. His arms tightened around her, pulling her with him as Ty gradually sank lower in the seat, sliding until they were both awkwardly lying on the length of the seat. Jessy was on the inside, pinned between the seat back and Ty's hard masculine body.

She was inexperienced, but not naive. What she hadn't learned observing animals on the ranch, she had picked up listening to bunkhouse talk. When she felt his hand move inside her blouse, seeking out her breasts, Jessy wasn't concerned with how far he was going, but whether he was going far enough. Her actions had never been governed by what other people regarded as proper behavior for a girl, and they weren't now.

His hat was pushed to the back of his head as Ty twisted down to nuzzle the small breasts and their tautly erect nipples. What they lacked in size, they made up for in sensitivity. The encircling lick of his tongue sent curls of excitement spiraling in ever-tightening coils through her body. His hand cupped the underswell of a breast and pushed it up to hold it in position while his mouth rolled onto its hard, flesh-brown tip, letting his teeth, tongue, and lips play with it. Her desire intensified to an ache, her hips writhing in search of pressure to relieve the ache.

Ty seemed to weaken on her, lifting his head from her breasts and swaying unsteadily on the support of an arm braced on the seat. Her hands tightened their hold on his shoulders so he wouldn't overbalance and tip backwards onto the truck floor. Their pressure brought him back to her lips.

"Don't stop now, Ty." There was an edge of frustration in her whispered plea, a faint anger that he'd aroused her to this point and might be too drunk to take her all the way.

His breathing was deep and labored. In his present state, more than half drunk and highly aroused, everything was fuzzy. She'd said something to him, but he'd already forgotten what it was. All he could remember was the insistence in her tone. From past experience, he knew that this was the moment when the protests usually came. Ty sought out her lips in the darkness.

"I've got to have you," he muttered against them and drove deep inside them without meeting any resistance.

His fingers tugged at the snap of her jeans, fumbling awkwardly with it before it finally popped apart. The ensuing urgency was mutual as he roughly worked one side of her jeans down over her hip while Jessy pushed on the other side. His weight moved onto her, their legs tangling as she banged her knee against the steering wheel. The heat of his body more than made up for her lack of clothes, her white jeans getting shoved onto the cab's dirty floor. At this point it didn't matter that he hadn't stripped. It was sufficient that he had unzipped his pants.

Even though Jessy didn't now exactly how to do it, she knew what to do. In such restricting confines, cooperation was required. Without hesitation, Jessy reached down and guided him into her, sparing each of them the awkward and frustrating probing. She had anticipated the sharp rip of pain and had her teeth clenched to check any outcry. It gradually dulled with his rhythmic movements, and the beginnings of pleasure silvered into the sensations.

All the discomfort fled as her enjoyment climbed to an exquisite level. Her arms were wound tightly around him, trying to clutch all of him to her while their kisses became rougher and hungrier, always demanding more from the other. Jessy had been silent in her pain, but she made no attempt to contain the raw sounds of pleasure that came from her throat when the climaxing storm of sensation shuddered through her body, turning her bones into jelly.

She had barely begun to recover some measure of sensibility when his arms gripped her hard to his body, her flesh absorbing the racking shudders that went through him. The stiffness slowly flowed out of him as he slumped onto her.

The position that had been so satisfying became uncomfortable; his body became a hot, oppressive weight; the quarters became cramped and her muscles protested against the hardness of the seat. She pushed at him, prodding him into moving off of her.

10

It took some maneuvering before both of them were upright again. Jessy began pulling on her clothes, forced by the steering wheel to angle her body into Ty's side of the truck. Inside, she felt all warm and loose, silky as cream.

With glowing interest, she looked at Ty. A smile tugged at her lip corners when she noted the hat still perched crookedly on the back of his head. She snapped the waistband of her jeans together and reached over to pull the front of his hat onto his forehead in a proprietorial gesture. His reflexes were slow, but Jessy made no attempt to elude the reach of his hands that gathered her to him. He was so relaxed she could feel the limpness of his muscles as she snuggled into his arms. The brim of his hat brushed her head as he bent to rub his mouth over her hair.

"You gotta marry me, Tara," he stated thickly, and Jessy went still.

"What?" She insisted he repeat it, hoping she hadn't heard him correctly.

But Ty took no heed of her request, not even noticing that he was caressing a body that had gone cold in his arms. "Tara, honey," he groaned. "I love you." His low voice was neither so thick nor so slurred that Jessy could doubt what she'd heard.

Gripped by a rigid numbness, she woodenly pulled out of

his arms. His lax hands made a feeble attempt to hold on to her, but it was a simple matter to elude them. Jessy did it without thinking, moving out of his reach to the driver's side.

Her fingers curled around the steering wheel in an ever-tightening circle that became a stranglehold. She stared at nothing; everything was focused inward on the devastating discovery that in his drunkenness he had made love to her believing she was someone else. And, fool that she was, she had thought all those things he'd said had been meant for her.

She had been used. It didn't matter how willing a partner she had been. Ty had used her to fulfill his own fantasy. A violent trembling started and her blood turned into hot ice.

"You bastard." Jessy turned her head to glare her hatred of him. She wanted to tear him apart with her hands. "You low-down, rotten bastard." The low fury of her words was pushed through her teeth, gritted so tightly together.

But it made no impression on him as he sat slumped against the seat, his chin tucked low against his chest. For a minute, Jessy was too blind with raging pain to notice the deep rhythm of his breathing. When the realization sank in that Ty had passed out, she wanted to scream.

There was no tenderness left in her when she grabbed his shoulders and roughly tried to shake him into consciousness. "Wake up, you son of a bitch." There weren't enough vile names to call him. But neither her cursing nor her shaking disturbed his sleeping stupor.

Jessy slammed out of the truck and stalked around to the passenger side. She jerked open the door and stared rigidly at his slumped and unconscious figure. His hat sat crookedly on the back of his bowed head, an insulting reminder that he hadn't bothered to take it off to make love to her.

"I oughta drag you out and leave you where you fall." Jessy wasn't sure why she didn't carry out that threat unless it was because her second choice had more appeal.

Pain usually had a sobering effect, or so she'd heard from bunkhouse tales of drunken cowboys. Cursing and shaking had failed to rouse him, but pain should.

Doubling up her fist, Jessy took aim on his slack mouth and chin and pulled her arm back. Her lips pressed together in a thin line of grim pleasure as she let loose her cocked fist. The impact was jarring, but when she felt his lower lip splitting against his teeth, she understood the satisfaction men got from fighting.

The blow jerked his head, instantly snapping him awake. A dazed frown claimed his features as Ty looked around, semialert yet not quite sure what had happened. It was a full second before he noticed Jessy or felt the pain in his mouth and jaw. He pressed a hand to his mouth, then looked at the smear of blood on his fingers with bewildered amazement.

"What the hell's going on?" The thickening influence of liquor was still in his voice, but he seemed almost sober.

Jessy said nothing and stood there waiting—waiting for him to remember what had happened between them before he'd passed out. But the yard light spilled over the roof of the truck cab and illuminated her features, accenting their strongly boned look. There were no distorting shadows to let him think she was anyone else.

"Who hit me?" Ty continued to frown at her while he licked at the cut and tested his sore jaw. "I don't remember a fight."

"I did," Jessy told him, the hurt and anger going deeper at his evident failure to recall what had transpired. She vibrated with the urge to hit him again, regardless of the sore throbbing in her knuckles from the last time.

The announcement startled him. "What the hell for?" No matter how sober he sounded, there remained a lack of coordination as he tried to get his long legs into a position that would get him out of the truck.

"You had passed out," she stated contemptuously and stepped back while he stumbled out of the cab. "And I wasn't about to carry you into the house."

"That was no damned reason to hit me," he muttered and gripped the open truck door to steady himself, wiping at his bloodied lip again. Then he pushed off, weaving toward the front steps with a staggering stride.

"You could say thanks," Jessy shot out. "I did get you home in one piece." Which was more than she could say for herself.

Ty stopped with one foot on the steps, his tongue loosened by the beer he'd consumed. "I could have driven home by myself." He resented being beholden to the tall, self-sufficient girl. "Why don't you wait until someone asks you for help instead of always buttin' your nose in where it isn't wanted? I never asked for your help—an' I never wanted it." In a sober moment, he would have been more tolerant of her solicitous actions on his behalf.

Jessy paled at this rejection of all she had ever done for him. But she had been schooled by the most poker-faced cowboys in the outfit not to let her feelings show in her face. Only the whitening of her flesh revealed that his words had made any effect at all.

In a pain-choked silence, she watched him start up the steps, trip on the edge of one, and stumble forward, cracking his knee and knocking himself sideways to land hard on one hip. Cursing savagely, Ty attempted to get his feet under him again, but they kept getting tangled. He was on all fours, trying to walk and climb up the steps all at the same time.

The ludicrous sight of him, clambering like a drunken fool, pulled Jessy to the steps. Her hands were rigidly clamped to her hips, refusing to make any gesture of help. His momentary shock of sobriety was wearing off. When Ty saw her standing at the foot of the steps watching him struggle, he flared in drunken irritation.

"Dammit, give me a hand," he snapped or tried to, but it came out with slurring force.

Smiling thinly, Jessy went up three steps and reached down to help him up. "It's a pity your precious Tara isn't here to see you like this." She didn't check the bitterness that curled through her voice.

"Tara." Ty looked around, as if expecting to see her appear. "I thought she was here." His head swung around to Jessy as he leaned heavily on her shoulders to negotiate the steps. "Wasn't she here?"

"No." It was a hard, flat answer.

A melancholia seemed to droop itself over him. "No. She had a date tonight . . . with somebody else. Always with somebody else." He was muttering to himself, unmindful that he was speaking aloud, or that Jessy could hear. "I must be drunk. It seemed . . . so real."

Jessy walked him across the wide porch to the front door, laboring slightly under the increasing weight on her shoulders. Listening to him and knowing what she knew, it hurt bitterly.

The front door was unlocked. With a kick of her foot, Jessy pushed the solid-core door to swing inward, then tried to squeeze sideways through the opening with Ty. He bumped a shoulder against the door's twin and careened off it. Unbalanced, he went staggering loudly into the foyer, dragging Jessy with him. It was several feet before she managed to dig her heels in and check their forward rush.

"You bumbling idiot!"

"I'm so damned tired," Ty mumbled, then turned to look at her, his tall body swaying as he pressed a silencing finger to his lips. "Mustn't wake Cathleen."

A light came on upstairs, throwing a track of light down the stairwell that opened to the living room. Chase Calder came down the steps and paused on the landing to survey the scene. He hadn't bothered to button his shirt or tuck its tails inside his pants. As he came down the last flight of steps and approached them, his craggy face was creased with puffy sleep lines. A hoary frost silvered the mat of hair on his chest, although this sign of graying hadn't yet reached his thick head of hair.

His disapproving glance slid off Ty to center on Jessy. "What happened?" Without pausing, he alleviated Jessy's burden by hooking one of Ty's arms around his neck and supporting him with an arm around his middle.

"He was too drunk to drive himself home from Sally's, so I brought him." She did not explain why she had volunteered instead of allowing one of the Triple C cowboys to bring him.

It seemed to take Ty several seconds to realize what had happened. "Well, if it isn't the mighty Chase Calder." He swayed backwards as if trying to bring his father into focus.

"That will be enough, Ty." He gave his son a hard, impatient look, then turned to Jessy to ask her something, but he was interrupted before he had a chance to speak.

"What's the matter?" Ty demanded. "Did I break some precious code of yours by getting drunk? I suppose a Calder isn't supposed to get drunk and have fun. He's got to be a man and hold his liquor." He made a mockery of standing up straight and tall.

"You're drunk," Chase stated flatly.

"Yeah?" The response was a taunting challenge. "You ain't so almighty righteous yourself."

Jessy glimpsed movement on the staircase. Ty's mother was silently gliding down the steps, hurriedly belting her robe. "Chase, what is it? Is Ty all right?"

The sound of her voice brought an instant change in Ty's attitude. The belligerence disappeared without a trace as he turned his head to watch her approach, a slack smile curving his mouth.

"He's fine."

"Don't worry about me, Mom," Ty inserted. "I'm just a little drunk."

"I was just going to get him up to bed," Chase said and nodded his head in Jessy's direction. "Make sure Jessy has a way to get home."

Maggie Calder glanced uncertainly after her husband and son before she looked back at Jessy. "I'll drive home in Ty's pickup and have someone bring it back in the morning," Jessy stated.

"All right." But there was hesitation in her voice as she took notice of the smears of dust on Jessy's white jeans and saw the taut pallor underlying her skin. "Ty's lip was cut. There wasn't an accident or a fight?"

"No." With a trace of self-consciousness, Jessy brushed at her jeans. "I guess I got dirty trying to get Ty out of the truck." When Jessy turned to leave, a consuming curiosity prompted her to turn back. "Mrs. Calder, who is Tara? Ty mentioned her name several times tonight."

"Tara is the daughter of E. J. Dyson." She seemed almost relieved by the question. "She's a lovely girl. I'm not surprised he mentioned her. He's been dating Tara for some time now."

"I see," Jessy murmured. "Good night, Mrs. Calder."

"Good night, Jessy. And thank you for making sure Ty got home safely," she added.

Halfway to South Branch, the tears finally began to collect

in Jessy's eyes and slide down her lashes. Her cheekbones glistened wetly, but there was no one to see except the thousands of stars in the sky or the luminous, shining eyes of a coyote trotting across the road in front of her truck.

At The Homestead, Maggie looked in on their daughter, who had slept soundly through Ty's noisy arrival home. Chase joined her in the upstairs hallway after manhandling their son into bed, where he'd started snoring almost as soon as he hit the mattress.

"Ty was right when he said Cathleen would sleep through it if he didn't try to be quiet," Maggie remarked in an amused tone as they walked to their bedroom together. At his silence, she lifted her gaze and probed his face. "Chase, surely you're not angry with Ty for coming home drunk, are you?"

He opened the door to their bedroom and let her pass, his cool eyes briefly meeting hers. "Are you happy to know your son is drunk and passed out in his bed?" he countered.

"I'm not happy about it." It seemed a ridiculous question to Maggie. "But it doesn't upset me either." With a ripple of impatience, she untied the knotted belt of her robe. "You're too hard on Ty. You always expect too much from him. Let him be young and enjoy himself while he can."

"It's always my fault, isn't it?" Chase gave her a look that was grim and calm. "I'm always too hard on him, but you're never too soft."

"I'm not soft. I simply understand—"

"And I don't?" he challenged.

"I never said that," Maggie denied and swung away from him, hating this quarreling. "You have to stop trying to mold him into your way of thinking."

There was a long silence, and Maggie waited for the explosion of angry words—the oft-repeated argument over their son. Instead, there came a loud breath, indrawn and released in a heavy sigh. Chase wadded up his shirt and threw it in a corner.

"We can't talk about this without arguing, can we, Maggie?" He sounded so tired and weary. When she turned to look at him, Chase was watching her, the width of the room separating them. "We're both so damned sure we're right."

"I guess so." Unconsciously holding her breath, she waited

for him to take that first step that would send her into his arms. She waited, but he didn't take it.

The moment of conciliation was lost, both of them bound by pride. "We'd better get some sleep." Chase finally broke apart the gaze and moved toward his side of the bed.

The bedsheets felt cold when Maggie slipped between them, too far away from Chase's body to be warmed by it. She ached inside, gnawed by the worry that Chase had offered her a compromise and she hadn't recognized it.

Summer passed quickly into September and Ty's last year at college. Only one clear memory of that night went with him—the scene with his father and Sally Brogan. The knowledge created an awkwardness in his relationship with both of his parents. When it came time to leave for college, he was glad to go.

After he arrived at the fraternity house, Ty made a desultory stab at unpacking before the anticipation of seeing Tara again got the better of him and he headed out of the room to the telephone. The hall was crowded with returning members, carting in luggage, tennis rackets, golf clubs, radios, and assorted vital items. He was constantly waylaid by arriving friends, shouting greetings and demanding to know how the hell he was.

"Hey, Ty!" He was nearly to the phone when he was hailed by another voice. He swung around with a trace of impatience, then broke into a smile when he recognized Jack Springer, who had become his closest friend at the university. "I was just on my way to look you up. Sappy told me you got in this afternoon."

"Yeah. Haven't even finished unpacking," Ty admitted, unconsciously edging closer to the phone. "How was your summer?"

"Hot and long, as usual." Springer's father owned a ranch in hill country outside of Austin. Ty had spent some weekends on it when Tara was otherwise engaged. It was a good-sized spread, a combination of a breeding operation and a game preserve, but it would have taken up only a corner of the Triple C. "Let's you and I clear outa here, grab us a couple of long necks and a pizza, and make a night of it."

"It sounds okay to me, but there's a call I gotta make first. I might be tied up." Ty hoped he was. It had been too long since he'd seen Tara.

A knowing look stole into the expression of the slimly built man. "Can't even finish unpacking before you phone a certain lady, huh?"

"Something like that." Ty grinned.

"If you're calling who I think you are, let me spare you a rejection. She's busy tonight," Jack informed him.

His statement made the smile fade on Ty's face. "How can you be so sure about that?"

"'Cause there's some big dinner going on tonight at the governor's mansion."

"So?" Ty frowned, his eyes narrowing.

"Tara will be there with her senator beau." His tone was both chiding and commiserating. "One of the problems with living in your isolated corner of Montana is you don't keep up to date. Tara Lee has grown weary of campus society and started traveling in more exalted circles."

"What do you mean?" A hard knot formed in the pit of his stomach.

"The newspapers around here have been filled with items about Tara Lee Dyson and the young and attractive bachelor Senator Mason Dodd the Third. I left out that his daddy willed him a fortune in oil stocks. The two of them have been the talk of Austin all summer."

Ty glanced at the telephone, wanting to pick it up and call her, find out for himself whether what Jack was saying was the truth or not.

"She dates a lot of people. It doesn't mean anything," he said.

"Once I would have agreed with you, but she's moved into the big time now. Come on, Ty. Surely you can see it. She's gone through this campus with a fine-tooth comb and raked off the guys who had something going for them—from star athletes to the big shots. She's made her conquests here, so now she's moving on to bigger game," Jack insisted. "You might as well forget about her the way all the rest of us have."

"That sounds like sour grapes to me, Jack," Ty accused.

"Hey, I've never pretended that I wouldn't have been

dripping at the chance to walk behind the barn with her. Hell, she wouldn't even have to crook her finger. I've taken my swipes at the string she trailed in front of me, but I'm smart enough to know she isn't going to let it lie there long enough for me to catch hold of it. And you should be, too."

"It isn't the same." He loved her. One way or another, he was determined to have her.

"It's the same all right. You're just too damned stubborn to admit it." The sandy-haired man shook his head in mock despair. "I'm just trying to be a friend, so it doesn't matter if you like what I'm saying or not. Little Miss Tara Lee gravitates to power like a duck to water. With a daddy like hers, she was raised to it. No one on campus is important enough for her to bother with now, including you."

The prediction didn't turn out to be entirely true. Tara usually attended any important social functions on campus with Ty as her escort, but most of her social life was centered off campus. Her dates ranged from young men holding political office to important lobbyists.

As graduation approached, the beginnings of desperation took hold of Ty. Another evening was drawing to a close. Standing alone with her on the private patio behind the Dyson home, he knew there weren't many chances left. He took a deep pull on his cigarette and held the smoke in his lungs, exhaling it finally through his nose in twin spirals. He felt a hand on his arm. Tara had a way of touching him with her fingertips that commanded all his attention.

"Ty Calder, I don't think you've been listening to a word I've been saying," she accused in her soft, drawling voice.

"That's only half true," he murmured, studying her through half-closed eyes in an attempt to screen the blatant desire he felt. "I've been listening to the sound of your voice. It reminds me of raindrops falling softly."

"Ty." The pressure of her hand increased slightly on his arm as a pleased smile radiated across her features. "You make a girl feel very special."

"You are very special—to me." He dropped the cigarette onto the cobbled patio and crushed it under his toe. "With a little encouragement, I'd consider telling you all the ways you're special to me." He slid an arm around her narrow

waist and made a quarter turn to face her and link his hands
together behind her back. "It might take all night, though."

"I'll bet you'd make sure it did." She laughed throatily and
ran her fingers under the lapels of his jacket. She looked at
him through the upward sweep of her dark lashes. "Did I tell
you that Douglas Stevens will be asked to join the diplomatic
staff at the American embassy in France?"

"No." Ty couldn't have cared less where the man was being
sent.

"Rumor has it that he's being given an important post."
She continued sliding her fingers along his lapel. "With Doug
there, I'll be able to stay at the embassy while I'm in France,
and probably attend a lot of the functions."

"Is that important to you?"

"Important? I'm not sure I know what you mean by that."
She tilted her head at a beguiling angle, the velvety darkness
of her hair blending into the midnight black making a cameo
of her face. "It will certainly be an unforgettable experience.
How many other girls would have a chance like that?"

"Not many, I suppose." Her smoothly innocent reply made
him feel churlish for harboring any resentment. "I guess it's
the idea of you seeing more of Stevens that I don't like."

"Jealous," she teased.

"Yes."

Tara laughed softly. "I don't know why I'm so surprised at
your bluntness," she declared. "You always seem to say what
you feel."

"Like I love you," Ty stated. When she started to cover his
mouth to keep him from saying more, he caught her hand and
held it against his chest. "No. I'm running out of time to say
all the things I want to say to you. I won't have many more
chances to see you before graduation."

"It's very late, Ty. Daddy will be wandering out here any
minute to shoo us inside so he can lock up for the night," she
warned him, but he saw the glitter of excitement in her eyes
and knew she wasn't really protesting.

"I can sum it all up in one phrase, Tara," he assured her
huskily. "I love you."

"Ty—"

There was a hint of withdrawal in her voice, so he didn't

take any chances about what her response might be. His head bent to cover her lips with the hungry warmth of his mouth. He tasted the honeyed gloss of her lips, pliant under his persuasive kiss.

"Tell me one thing." He rolled his mouth across her cheek, breathing in the sweet scent of her skin.

"What?" Her smallness was shaped against his hunched frame, her body bending like a supple willow. His roaming hands caressed the delicate curve of her spine and the rounded shape of her hips. The thin silk of her dress hid nothing of her body from him.

"Why have you kept me around? Why haven't you dropped me the way you did all the others?"

Her hesitation seemed sincere, as if she weren't certain of the answer. "You're not like them. There's something about you that's different."

"Maybe you love me?" he suggested and lifted his head slightly, their breath mingling warmly.

"Maybe I do." The breathy softness of her voice stirred him.

There was a break in her defenses; a concession had been made that hadn't been offered before. This time he kissed her man to woman with no artifice of persuasion or appeal. She responded warmly, but he sensed her struggle to keep from becoming too aroused. It was this vague reluctance he tried to batter down and insist she give herself freely to the passions that trembled through her body. But the more demanding he became, the less progress he made.

Tremors were shuddering through him when he finally ended the kiss. Tara swayed against him and bowed her head against his shoulder. An exultant smile lifted the corners of his mouth as his hands shaped her more fully to his length.

"You have to marry me now, Tara." The proposal seemed an echo of something from the past, familiar and used.

"Ty . . ." She lifted her head. This time he pressed a silencing finger to her lips, then reached into the outside pocket of his jacket.

"I had this made for you," he said. "I had to guess at the size, so I hope it fits."

Her small gasp of delight was a beautiful sound to him,

worth more than any words to express the genuineness of her pleasure. The patio torchlights caught the fire in the black opal, set inside a protective circle of diamonds.

"You had this made for me?" She seemed dazzled by it. Her hand was shaking when he slipped it on her ring finger.

"A rare gem for a rare beauty." In his present mood, he could have spouted love sonnets and not felt in the least ridiculous.

"It fits perfectly." She stared at it, unwilling to take her eyes off of it.

Ty was both amused and proud as he watched Tara admiring the ring, oblivious to almost everything but the play of light in the ring's fiery heart. "Does this mean you are accepting my proposal of marriage?"

Her limpid dark eyes looked at him, his question not immediately registering. "Yes. Yes, it does," she repeated with more certainty, then kissed him quickly and grabbed at his hand. "Let's go tell Daddy. I want to show him the ring."

It would have been his preference to stay on the patio and share a few more intimate moments together. But Tara had agreed to marry him. Now he could afford to wait.

"Hey, Ty!" Jack Springer stuck his head inside the door to Ty's room. "There's some gorgeous chick out here who wants to see you. You'd better get out here before someone steals her."

"Who is it?" He rocked his chair onto its back legs and rubbed the back of his neck, stiff from the hours he'd spent at the desk studying for final exams.

"Your ever-lovin' fiancée, of course," Jack declared. "I guess she's jealous of all the time you've spent the last two days cracking those books." Ty kicked away from the desk and headed for the door, hurriedly tucking his shirttail inside his jeans. "You sure picked a lousy time to propose—right before exam week," his friend chided and stepped away from the door. "'Course, I wouldn't have given two cents for your chances of having Tara accept."

In his eagerness to see her, Ty didn't waste time explaining that he hadn't seen much of his new fiancée because she had pleaded for time to study for her finals. It pleased him that she hadn't been able to stay away. Their engagement had become the hottest piece of gossip on campus, even though the official announcement wouldn't be in the paper until next week.

When he saw her standing near the foot of the stairs, he paused a second, the vision of her dark beauty making its impact on him. She looked up, her features so serenely composed, absent of any expression, yet so perfect in their construction. He ran down the last few steps and made to take her in his arms, but her hands kept them wedged apart.

"I've missed you, honey," he insisted and bent his head to kiss her, but she turned away. Ty straightened, puzzled by her reticence with him. "Is something wrong?"

When she looked at him, he had the feeling she was seaching for something. "Let's sit over here." She took his hand and led him to the settee tucked in the small alcove under the stairwell. Once they were seated, Ty was conscious of the distance she kept between them, angling her body on the cushion to keep him away. A run of uneasiness went through him, but he looked at the glittering black opal on her finger and was reassured. He took hold of her left hand and rubbed his thumb over the ring.

"I started to call you a half-dozen times—just so I could hear your voice," Ty murmured, aching to hold her. "I'm glad you came over."

"No, you're not," she said. Ty started to smile, but her next words wiped it from his face. "Because I thought it was only fair to tell you in person that I can't marry you."

"What?" It was a low sound, the beginning of a roar that was building in his head.

"I'm not going to marry you. There's too many things I want to do—too many plans I've made—and I'm not ready to give them up," she stated, clearly but softly. "I never should have accepted your proposal in the first place. I wouldn't have, but I was so overwhelmed by the ring that I lost my head."

"You don't mean what you're saying. I love you—and you love me," he insisted, his voice dropping with the intensity of his feelings. A raw hotness was coursing through his blood, the heat building.

"Ty, don't make this any more difficult than it already is,"
Tara flared. "Be a gentleman and accept the fact that I've
changed my mind." She had never been one to let her heart
rule her head. It was á ruthless determination that she'd
inherited from her father.

"Accept it. Just like that." Anger raged through his low
tone.

"Yes." She was irritated with him for turning this into an
emotional scene. It flashed in her eyes as she started to twist
the ring off her finger.

"Keep it," Ty declared hoarsely. He left her sitting there
and walked away in a numbed state of fury and pain.

11

After miles on the strip of highway that cut
across the empty reach of prairie, a handful of buildings rose
into view. There was something forlorn and forgotten about
them, rather like a battered suitcase left behind by a weary
traveler who figured it wasn't worth coming back for.

The ancient pickup truck slowed its rattling pace, which
had never been too speedy. Not much traffic went in this
direction, so Ty had been obliged to hitch a ride in whatever
came by. He sat loosely in the passenger seat, an elbow
crooked on the open window while he watched the buildings
of Blue Moon crowd close to the highway, desperately
clinging to their concrete lifeline. There was no show of
recognition on his face, and the position he'd held for miles
didn't change.

The scrawny, grizzled old man behind the wheel shifted
gears, slowing the springless truck more. He wasn't a talka-
tive man, hadn't said more than five words since he'd stopped
at the crossroads to give Ty a lift. The gray stubble of a
two-day growth of beard bristled on his hollow cheeks, and

his denim jean jacket and pants were faded to blue-gray, even their patches.

The only signs of life in the town were a couple of pickups parked in front of Sally's. The grizzled driver pulled the truck off the two-lane and braked it to a groaning stop. Ty finally roused himself and reached for the door handle.

"Thanks." He threw the man a quick smile and swung out of the cab. The old pickup truck vibrated like a jumping bean as the motor idled.

"You a Calder?" The land-worn man gave Ty a narrow, steely-eyed look.

Ty pushed the door shut and said through the open window, "Yep."

The old man nodded satisfaction at the accuracy of his guess. "Had the look of one." His sun-browned and age-spotted hand moved to the gearshift, an indication the conversation was at an end and he was ready to move on as soon as Ty got his case out of the back.

His bag sat in the battered rear bed of the truck, amongst loose straw, empty gasoline cans, and a dirty collection of spare parts. Ty hefted it over the side panel and stepped back, lifting a hand in salute to the driver.

The long afternoon shadow cast by the truck bounced away while Ty headed for the parked vehicles in front of Sally's. A running wind kicked up dust swirls and chased them across the bare ground ahead of him.

There had been two ways for him to reach the Triple C. He could have arranged to be dropped off at the east gate of the ranch, but if no one happened by to give him a ride, it would have meant a long walk of roughly thirty-five miles back to The Homestead. So he'd opted for Blue Moon. Sooner or later, someone from the ranch would come by the local watering hole and he'd be able to catch a ride back.

But his luck had run better than that. One of the pickups outside the café-bar belonged to the ranch. Ty threw his suitcase in the back of it and climbed the steps to the entrance of Sally's Place. The door opened before he reached it. Ty stiffened in place when he heard a throaty laugh he instantly recognized as his father's.

"See ya later, Sally." His father swung into view, emerging

from the dark shadows of the interior to cross the threshold and step outside. He came up short when he saw Ty, surprise shooting across his face. "How'd you get here?"

"I hitched a ride from Miles City and figured I'd be able to cadge a lift to the ranch from here." Ty wondered what kind of excuse his father had made to stop by Sally's. He'd heard that laugh and the warmth in his father's voice. It was plain that he was still involved with the woman.

His father moved forward, frowning. "Graduation is next week."

"I know." Ty swung around to descend the steps and drink in the untainted air. Another set of footsteps followed him. "I took the last of my exams yesterday. There didn't seem to be any point to hang around for a ceremony. They'll mail my diploma."

He'd tolerated the sympathy and the sad looks that told him everybody'd known all along his engagement to Tara wouldn't last, until he couldn't stand any more. The diploma was merely a document to please his mother and prove he'd achieved the objective he'd set out four years ago to attain. Pride had been his main reason for finishing out the last term, a pride that wouldn't allow him to crawl away and lick his wounds after Tara had broken their engagement.

It wasn't what Ty said but the things he didn't say, and the flatness in his voice and eyes, and the lack of any reference to Tara, that clued Chase in to the reason Ty had arrived unannounced. He didn't press for a more complete explanation as he climbed behind the wheel of the pickup and Ty settled into the passenger seat. It would all come out in its own good time.

Silence dominated the long drive to the Triple C, and Chase made no attempt to break it. They were nearly to the headquarters, the peaked roof of The Homestead thrusting its chimneys into the blue horizon, when Ty shifted his position, signaling an intention to speak.

"The engagement's off." Nothing more than that, and Chase didn't pry into the reasons, regarding them as none of his business.

"I guessed as much," he admitted and sliced a side look to his son. "I've never met a man who didn't get his fingers burnt or make a fool of himself over a woman at least once in his life. Wisdom only comes with experience."

"I suppose." Ty turned his head to look out the window. There was no consolation in knowing he wasn't the first or the last.

The doors to The Homestead burst open as the pickup stopped in front of it, and Cathleen came racing out, ropes of long black curls bouncing around her shoulders. She shrieked with joy when she saw Ty step out of the pickup and hurled herself off the steps into his arms.

"Hey, you're getting heavy, Cat." He smiled into her wide green eyes, beguilingly outlined with sooty lashes. She was remarkably beautiful for a girl who had just turned seven years old.

"Nobody told me you were coming home today." She pouted for an instant, then laughed and hugged his neck.

"They didn't?" Ty shifted her in his arms to smooth out the skirt of her ruffled white pinafore. "And I thought you were wearing this pretty dress just for me."

"I put it on for my Uncle Culley, but I would have worn it for you," she assured him quickly.

"Culley." Ty shot a look at his father, seeking an explanation, as he set his sister down.

"Yes," came the confirmation. "He's been released from the hospital. Maggie's bringing him home this afternoon."

"He's been sick," Cathleen informed Ty with an adultlike air and reached to take his hand and lead him up the steps to the house. "But he's better now. 'Course, Mommy said he still has to rest a lot."

"When did this come about?" Ty eyed his father, trying to discern his reaction. He was well aware of the bad blood that had been between his father and uncle, and seriously doubted that his father was pleased by O'Rourke's release from the mental institution.

"It's been discussed frequently these last few months, but the doctor notified your mother of his intention shortly after you phoned last week. We had planned to tell you when we flew down for your graduation." It was a statement of fact with no opinion offered, and none was visible as Chase

Calder opened the front door and the three of them trooped into the house.

"I've never seen Uncle Culley before. Have you?" Cathleen's patent-leather shoes made tapping sounds on the hardwood floor as she skipped along beside her older brother.

"Yes." But his memory was of a wild-eyed, paranoid man, trembling on the brink of madness. It was hardly an image he wanted to relate to his little sister.

"What was he like?"

"It was a long time ago, Cat. He's probably changed a lot since the last time I saw him."

Her look became thoughtfully troubled. "Do you think he'll like me?" Cathleen Calder was the darling of the Triple C, adored by everyone. With the sharpness of a child's perception, she had sensed the undercurrents surrounding her uncle's imminent arrival and guessed there was something about her uncle that made him different. Not having love and approval was the worst thing she could imagine.

Her question wasn't one Ty wanted to answer, because he knew how much Culley O'Rourke had hated anyone attached to the Calders in the past. But it wasn't something his little sister needed to know, and she wouldn't understand even if he attempted to explain.

So he merely laughed aside her question and playfully tapped the end of her button nose. "I'll bet he won't like you as much as I do." Cathleen beamed, finding reassurance in his avowal of affection.

"Nanna Ruth!" Cathleen spied the elderly woman as she entered the living room from the kitchen hallway, and let go of Ty's hand to run to meet her. "Look who's here!"

"Ty. My gracious." She rested a trembling hand below her throat, her voice weak with surprise. "I didn't know you were expected."

"I wasn't. I thought I'd surprise everybody." It was to become his standard explanation.

"You certainly surprised me," Ruth Haskell declared, then bit her lower lip. "We've been so busy helping Maggie get things ready for her brother that Audra hasn't had time to air your room or have clean linen put on the bed." Audra

Cummings was the wife of one of the cowboys employed by
the Triple C. She did most of the heavy cleaning at The
Homestead.

"Since it's my fault for not letting anyone know I decided to
skip the graduation exercises and come home early, I'll take
care of it," Ty volunteered.

"You're going to skip the graduation ceremony?" Her
brow became furrowed with lines of concern and regret.
"Your mother has been looking forward to seeing you in your
cap and gown."

"She'll have to be satisfied with the diploma." He smiled to
lessen the sting of his disregard for his mother's wishes.

"Did you bring your girl?" Ruth looked at him expectantly.
"Or will she be coming later?"

"No." Ty sobered, his expression hardening. "She won't be
coming."

"Oh." Ruth made a small sound as she realized her query
had been a mistake. In her lifetime, she'd seen many such
reactions—the closed-in look of a man whose feelings had
been deeply bruised.

The thick walls of the house muted the slam of a car door
that was closely followed by the sound of a second one. "That
must be Mommy with Uncle Culley!" Cathleen was about to
run to meet them, but Ty caught her by the shoulders.

"Let's wait for them here," he said and caught the glimmer
of approval in his father's glance before he turned to face the
entrance.

The man who walked through the door with his mother
seemed a shy shadow of the man Ty remembered. His
shoulders appeared permanently bowed in a protective
hunch, and the lank black hair that had covered his head was
now shot full of gray. He wasn't as thin as Ty's image of him,
but the added weight gave him a soft, puffy look—or maybe it
was the paleness of his white skin, so long shut away from
sunlight. The nervousness, the hair-trigger energy that always
seemed poised on the edge of violence, was gone. There was
something subdued about the way he allowed himself to be
guided into the living room.

A look of surprise flashed across his mother's face when she saw him standing behind Cathleen, but she didn't question his unexpected presence. That would come later. At the moment, her chief concern was to smooth the path for her brother's return to the world. There was tension on both sides.

"Hello, Culley." His father spoke first, neither offering false words of welcome nor offering to shake hands.

"Hello." His head bobbed in an abrupt acknowledgment.

Ty noticed how blank O'Rourke's eyes were, as if he were trying to shut out the identity of the man he greeted. His mother didn't press for more conversation than that, instead directing her brother's attention to him.

"This is Ty," she said in a bright and reassuring tone. "He's grown so much since the last time you saw him that you probably don't recognize him."

"He's taller, older—but I recognize him." His voice was clear and steady, hesitating only in its choice of words. While those shuttered eyes picked out the things he remembered about Ty, Ty was reminded of the old, grizzled man in the pickup truck who had remarked that Ty had the look of a Calder. "Hello, Ty."

"Hello, Culley," he returned and kept both hands on his sister's shoulders, like his father not offering to shake.

Cathleen twisted her head around to look up at him and hiss a correction. "You're supposed to call him *Uncle* Culley."

A dim sparkle appeared in the flat eyes as they fell to the little girl. O'Rourke crouched down, letting one knee touch the floor.

"You must be Cathleen." There was a softening that came to his mouth, almost a smile.

"Hello, Uncle Culley." Cathleen did not feel bound by the reticence of her father or brother. "I'm glad you're feeling better. Mommy said you were sick for a long time. It isn't fun being sick."

"No, it isn't." The innocent reference to his prolonged illness did not seem to bother him. Uncertainly, O'Rourke reached out and gently curled a hand under her fingers, being very careful, as if she were made of fragile bone china. There was something wondering about the gesture, hinting that it might have been a long time since he had touched another human, especially a child. "You are very pretty."

"Do you like my dress?" Cathleen took her hand away to hold out both sides of her green underskirt to show him. "I wore it for you. I would have worn it for Ty, but I didn't know he was coming home today. We got cookies. Would you like some?"

"I think that's a good idea, Cathleen." Maggie smiled, silently pleased at how much her daughter had achieved with her chatter. Her brother had been so ill at ease, watching everything he said so carefully. Culley had been used to his own company so long he had never learned how to relate. "Why don't we all sit down?" Maggie suggested, then said to Ruth, "Would you have Audra bring us some coffee and a plate of cookies?"

Over coffee, O'Rourke gradually started to loosen up, and Ty observed the slow emergence of the gray-haired man, old yet only in his early forties. Some of his initial impressions remained, but some altered.

"Wait until you see the room Mommy and I fixed for you," Cathleen declared. "Want me to show it to you?"

"You can take him upstairs a little later," Maggie inserted.

"It's nice," she promised. "You have your own radio, and a big chair, magazines, and everything. And it will be your room forever and ever."

Something flickered across his pale face, and he turned to look at Maggie, who sat on the sofa beside him. "Is something wrong, Culley?" she asked.

"Is this what you meant when you said you were taking me home?" he asked.

"Yes." She was puzzled by his question. "As Cathleen said, we have a room all fixed up for you—your own private place where you can be by yourself if you want or—"

"I don't think it's a good idea for me to stay here, Maggie." He swung a level glance at Chase. "You understand what I'm saying, don't you?"

"Yes."

"Culley, I want this to become your home, too," Maggie insisted and appealed to her husband to support her. "Chase and I talked it over and he agreed that you could stay here with us."

"I . . . appreciate that," Culley nodded, "but—it wouldn't work."

"Where else can you go?"

"Where I thought you were taking me—home to Shamrock," he said simply.

"But no one's lived in that old house for years," she protested. "There isn't any heat or lights . . . there hasn't been for seven years. You can't go there."

"I can fix it up—at least one room of it. Maggie, that's where I belong. I don't belong here." He looked around the big mansion-sized house. "There's too many rooms—too many people coming in and out."

Maggie sat stiffly on the edge of the sofa. "I'm not going to let you go back there."

There was a sad smile on his face. "If I stayed here, what would I do with myself? Sit around. I might as well be in the hospital. I need to work at something that's my own. The doctors call it therapy."

"I don't care what they call it."

"Do you have a ranch?" Cathleen was intrigued by the discovery.

"Yes. It's called the Shamrock Ranch."

"Is it as big as ours?"

"No. I don't think there's anything as big as the Triple C," admitted O'Rourke.

"I'll bet you wish it was," she stated.

"No, I don't think so, because I'd always have to worry about someone trying to steal part of it from me. Now, my ranch is so small, no one would bother trying to steal it," he explained.

"You can't make a living off of it," Maggie reminded him. "If it's work you want, Chase can hire you to work here."

"Let Culley decide for himself what he wants, Maggie," Chase advised quietly.

"But he isn't—" She didn't finish the sentence, stopping guiltily and looking apologetically at her brother.

"I'm not well enough. Is that what you were going to say?" he asked.

"Culley, I'm sorry. I didn't really mean it that way. It's just that it's been a long time since you've done physical labor. You're older and—"

"I want to go home, Maggie."

Chase took the matter out of her hands, knowing she would never agree. "We'll drive you over to the ranch tomorrow morning. In the meantime, you'll stay the night with us."

"Is your ranch far away? Can I come visit you sometime?" Cathleen wanted to know.

"We're practically next-door neighbors. You can come see me any time you want." Too long deprived of it, he seemed to feed on Cathleen's blithe innocence and ready attention.

"He sure has changed," Ty remarked idly and lit a cigarette. O'Rourke was upstairs, washing up before dinner.

"So it seems," his father murmured, but he appeared contemplative. "Just the same, I don't want your mother or Cathleen alone in the house with him. So I want you to stay here tonight while I drive up to the north camp and let Arch Goodman know that O'Rourke's moving into the Shamrock."

"Why?" Ty questioned the order. "The doctors released him, so they must be convinced he's harmless."

"No one and nothing is harmless, Ty." Dryness rustled through his voice. "There could be two reasons why he doesn't want to live here. One, he could know that the past can be forgiven, but rarely is it forgotten. The thought might have choked him to sleep under a Calder roof, eat Calder food, and drink Calder water. Two, he might be smart enough to know I'd have someone watching him all the time."

"Don't you trust him?"

"I'm just being cautious," his father said. "He's going to need help making that shack habitable again, so I want you to give him a hand."

"Me? Why?"

"Because I thought you might like to get off by yourself for a couple of weeks." No response was expected, and Ty didn't offer one. But it was true he needed time alone to come to terms with the broken engagement to Tara. And he suspected O'Rourke would keep pretty much to himself, so it would be the same as being alone. "We've been running Shamrock cattle on our graze, so I want to let Arch know he'll have to plan on separating them from our herd. O'Rourke never had much for saddle stock, so we'll see what we can spare as soon as he's got a corral built to hold them. He'll need tools, lumber, provisions."

"He's bound to know all this is coming from us," Ty pointed out. "What if he won't accept it?"

"He'll accept it. He's an O'Rourke, so he'll consider it his due."

The last of the cows carrying the Shamrock brand was separated from the herd and driven into a smaller holding pen. Jessy swung her sock-legged sorrel away from the gate as one of the ground men clanged it shut behind the animal. She pulled off her hat and wiped the sweat from her brow on a sleeve, then pushed the hat back onto her head. The sorrel gelding blew out a rolling snort, clearing the pen dust from its nostrils, and pricked its ears at the main body of the north herd being urged out the gate to scatter and graze. A confused calf darted the wrong way, and Jessy waved her coiled rope at him to chase him back with the herd.

After following the cattle and the pushing riders outside of the pen, she reined her mount around to the fence where two men sat on the top rail and stepped down. Reaching under the stirrup, she loosened the cinch to give her horse a breather.

"You've got 'em all, Arch," she informed her camp foreman in a terse fashion, then bobbed the rolled brim of her dusty hat in the direction of the older man, weathered and cracked with age. "H'lo, Nate."

"Jessy." He returned her nod of greeting. Nate Moore was the bachelor sage of the ranch. His bones were too stiff and brittle to tolerate the abuse of a saddle anymore, but his eyes hadn't failed him. And his eye for cattle made him the undisputed authority on livestock breeding on the Triple C Ranch. Since he couldn't ride the range anymore except in a pickup, he was always on hand whenever there was a gather on any part of the ranch to take a close-up look at the breeding stock.

"We'll hold 'em here overnight and drive 'em onto Shamrock grass in the morning," Arch Goodman decreed and pushed off the fence rail to hop to the ground, heading off to advise the other riders of his plans.

Nate stayed on his perch. "O'Rourke's gettin' back a better herd than he left." He took cigarette papers and a tobacco pouch from his vest pocket. Most of the old-timers still rolled their own smokes, but it was a trial for Nate, whose finger joints were enlarged and stiff.

"That's true enough." Jessy observed his awkward attempt to shake tobacco into the paper trough. "I'll do that for you."

He passed her the makings and watched her deftly shake the right amount of tobacco out. "Guess young Ty is at O'Rourke's helpin' him salvage something out of those tumbledown buildings on the place."

"I heard that." She caught the tobacco string between her teeth and pulled the pouch shut.

"That engagement of his sure didn't last long. It's off, ya know."

"Heard that, too." She rolled the paper around the tobacco and ran the long edge of the paper across her tongue to lick it shut.

"Jilted him, I understand," Nate observed. Jessy passed him up the handmade cigarette and he raked a match head along the underside of his thigh to light it. "Can't say I think much of a woman who'd give her word, then call it back."

"She probably had her reasons." She still felt raw inside at the way she'd been used by Ty, knowingly or not. And, in all honesty, Jessy couldn't say she was sorry at the way he'd been treated by his ladylove. There was a certain sweet revenge in it.

"Sidin' with her, are ya?" Nate observed while he cupped the flame to the cigarette and puffed it to life.

"Just sticking up for my own kind." She shrugged a shoulder.

"There are kinds—an' then, there are kinds." He stared off a ways, contemplating the vastness of the sky. "Most ranchers get all het up about havin' the best breedin' bull an' spend whatever it takes to get top quality . . . then put him to servicin' inferior cows. Now, if you want a good calf"—Nate pulled his gaze back to look at her with equal thoughtfulness —"ya gotta have a good momma. A lotta folks that claim to be experts don't realize a calf gets a lot more from his momma than from the bull that covers her. A rancher's money is better spent on a good cow than a bull. It's the female what counts, an' don't let anybody tell you differently."

"I'll remember that." It seemed odd to hear such advice when she'd been reared in such a male-dominated society, and especially coming from Nate Moore, a bachelor all his life. He should have been entrenched in the old views toward women.

"Heard ya got put on full time," Nate remarked.

"Yeah. 'Course, Dad didn't think it would look right if I worked under him, so he farmed me off to Arch." There had been hesitation before she was given the position of a regular hand, but no one could fault her ability, and everyone had pretty well gotten used to having her working on the range with them.

But Jessy also knew she was on trial. If being a woman caused any problems with quarreling among men too long away from the company of a female, she knew she'd get stuck in some tamer job at the barns or commissary. She had scoffed when her father hinted she had the kind of looks men might fight over, until he had explained that a face gets prettier when a man's desperate. And she was bitterly reminded that a man could be so desperate as to imagine she was someone else.

"It looks like they're getting ready to load up the horses." Jessy noticed the other riders congregating around the stock trailer and picked up the reins to her horse. "See ya around, Nate."

As she led the sorrel away, Nate gingerly maneuvered his stiff bones off the fence rail. He took a last drag on the cigarette, studied it, then glanced after the tall girl. "She rolls a damned fine smoke," he murmured to no one in particular.

III

Loving is something like dreaming
When it comes to the woman you wed,
So why does your mind keep turning
To one who's Calder born—
    and Calder bred.

12

"This is the most frustrating damned thing," Chase muttered under his breath, and the saddle leather creaked as he momentarily put weight on the stirrups to shift his position in the seat.

"What's wrong?" Maggie's attention strayed from the seeming chaos of the branding area to her husband. She had seen no cause for the impatience that ridged his jaw and hardened his eyes. He flashed her a look of ill-concealed disgust.

"When I was his age, I was bossing a crew. Ty is still taking orders." The roughness in his voice was an attempt to control a smoldering anger. "He'll be thirty before he gets any seasoning and experience at handling men."

With a mother's unerring eye, Maggie picked out her son among the riders roping calves and dragging them to the branding crews. His loop was running as straight and true as any man's out there. Like the others, Ty worked without letup, never slacking off. Everyone was feeling the pressure of the gray, overcast sky, looming so darkly over the afternoon with its threat of cold rain—or worse, snow.

"You talk as though Ty never thinks for himself," she reproved. "Have you forgotten it was his idea to alternate steel fenceposts with wooden ones when you were running new fence lines last summer to replace the old ones?"

"I haven't forgotten." His hardness eased slightly in remembrance. "But it can't be claimed as an original idea. It's been used by a few ranchers to keep their fence lines intact in areas where prairie fires are a danger."

In the event of a fire, wooden posts would burn, collapsing the fence and potentially allowing livestock to scatter. Using all steel posts prevented that, but it was also considerably more expensive. A combination of wood and steel, however, was a feasible alternative.

"But Ty did make the suggestion and ran all the cost projections beforehand," Maggie reminded him.

"Maggie, I'm not criticizing the work he's done or the way he's done it," Chase replied with a show of patience. "But I do know how much catching up he has to do, and that bothers me."

Although Chase had not made the remark with the thought of the four years Ty had spent away from the ranch at college, Maggie was sensitive to that issue and believed he was referring to that lost time. Ty had been back at the ranch for two full years, but Chase still wasn't satisfied. She went quiet on him, letting the bawl of the cattle and the shouts of the branding teams take over.

"Cat is loving this, isn't she?" There was a proud warmth in Chase's voice that she seldom heard in connection with Ty. While Ty seldom did anything right in his eyes, his daughter could do no wrong. Maggie didn't think it was fair, the amount of favoritism he showed their daughter. "It looks like riding herd got too tame for her. She's chasing down the calves with the ground crew now."

"I think she's more of a hindrance than a help," she retorted.

"She's having fun." And that justified it for him. "If she really starts to get in the way, the boys will boot her out."

Even though that was true, Maggie also knew the cowboys spoiled her as much as Chase did. It was amazing how one girl could wrap so many grown men around her finger, considering that she had only recently celebrated her ninth birthday.

It was difficult to keep Cathleen in sight now that she had dismounted from her flashy black-and-white paint horse. It was tied to the picket line, the hand-tooled black leather saddle and matching bridle adorned with silver conchos still on the small-built horse in case Cathleen changed her mind. She always had to be in the thick of things.

At nine, Cathleen was just as beautiful as she'd been at any other age. Even when she was playing tomgirl, as now, she

always seemed more girl than tom. Maggie suspected it was
the reason she appealed so strongly to the men. She was the
ideal, growing from a gorgeous child into a lovely young girl.

"Sit on his neck and hold him down, Cat!" Binky Ford
instructed with a wide grin as he straddled the calf he'd
flanked to the ground.

Laughing, Cat tried to sit sideways on the calf's neck, but it
was a hefty animal. Its struggles unbalanced her and she slid
to the ground with a plop. Not that it mattered. It was all a
game anyway. Her assistance wasn't required to keep the calf
down. The boys were just including her so she could be part
of the action. And Cat knew how to play it to get their
attention. The cowboys liked it when she mixed right in and
got dirty—and they laughed when she wrinkled her nose at
the stench of burning hide and hair, or when she flinched at
the dehorning.

The heifer calf was branded, tagged, vaccinated, and
released to go tearing back to the herd in search of its
momma. Cat dusted off her stiff new jeans and headed
toward the next melee of men converging on a roped calf. As
she trotted to them, she recognized the whip-slim figure with
a chunk of dusty tan hair hanging down the middle of her
back.

"Hi, Jessy." She stopped beside her and crouched down.
"Can I watch how you castrate that calf?"

A chortle of surprise came from one of the crew working
on the downed animal. "I swear you got the curiosity of a
cat."

"Why?" she asked in all innocence, but the man reddened
slightly and didn't answer.

Jessy bent her head to hide a smile and calmly passed a can
of antiseptic to the girl. "You can squirt some of this on when
I'm finished."

It amused her that these husky men were uneasy over the
prospect of the young girl watching a calf getting castrated.
But Jessy had been younger than Cathleen when she got her
first close-hand look at how it was done. Besides, the girl was
nine years old, so she knew *what* was done. The idea of it
wasn't new to her.

"Does it hurt a lot?" Cat asked, pulling her face together in anticipation of pain. There was a smear of dust on her cheek, which gave her a gaminlike charm.

"The trick is to do it so quick that by the time the calf feels the pain, it's all over," Jessy explained and cupped the scrotum in her hand to make the incision with her knife.

There was a hissing intake of breath from Cat at the first show of blood. Operating with the deftness of long practice, Jessy removed the male reproductive glands and nodded to the girl to apply the antiseptic. She started to rock back onto her feet away from the calf to toss the testes into the fire.

"Can I see them?" Cat asked, and Jessy heard one of the men muttering a protest at the child being subjected to such indelicacies. She wanted to laugh at the absurdity of it. Men didn't mind females knowing such things, but they didn't want to be around when they found out about them.

"Sure you can," she replied and noticed, out of the corner of her eye, how quickly the men became absorbed in their work.

Another team nearby had just removed the rope from the neck of their calf. Ty began coiling it up as he turned his horse back to the herd to catch up another. The striped-nosed gelding under him was fresh and eager to work. It sidestepped impatiently at the checking bit in its mouth, chomping on it noisily. The gelding's angling course brought Ty close to the second crew. He noticed his little sister among them and wouldn't have thought twice about it except that she was peering very intently at something Jessy was holding. He caught a glimpse of the bloodied organs and seethed with a kind of outrage.

"Cat!" He barked her name, and his sister jumped with an almost guilty start. "Get back on your horse!" She eyed him with surprise, taken aback and made wary by the sharp tone of command in his voice. It seemed wise not to question his authority over her at this particular minute, so she did as she was told. Still ignoring Jessy, Ty swung his glaring look at the other men. "How come you're letting her castrate the calves? That's no job for a girl."

"What's the matter, Ty?" Jessy asked in challenge. "Are

you worried my knife might slip and end up cutting a two-legged critter? Well, don't. I've cut more calves than you've got whiskers."

He threw her an angry look, then ordered, "Jobe, put her on the iron."

Jobe Garvey hesitated. "She's clean and quick with a knife."

His lips came together in a tight line. Jobe was head of the ground team, and it wasn't Ty's place to be changing assignments. He could only pull rank on the basis of being a Calder, and he wouldn't do that. There was no choice but to leave the matter to Jobe's judgment.

"I guess if she draws a man's pay, she can do a man's work," Ty declared roughly.

The calf was up and gone, and Jessy had discarded the testes and was on her feet, standing beside his constantly shifting horse. At his statement, the others moved off, considering the matter closed, but Jessy remained. There was an angry blaze in her hazel eyes.

"Which is it that bothers you most, Ty?" she demanded in a low voice that couldn't be heard by anyone else. "That I'm doing a man's work, getting a man's pay, or doing the job better than you?"

"Maybe I resent the way you keep showing off how good you are," he snapped.

"Dammit, I *am* good! And I'm not going to hide or pretend I'm not good just to please some man!"

"I suppose you're like some of those bra burners that want to be treated as equals." There was a derisive curl in his voice.

"If that means equal respect, yes!" she shot back.

"All right." Ty was hot, breathing deep and rough. Her accusations had stung him, hitting a little too close to the truth. He seemed to instinctively know just how to get even. "For a girl, you make a damned good man."

He saw her stiffen as he reined his horse to one side and booted it forward. Jessy glared after him, hurt by his insult. She had taunted him with her role in a man's world to remind him she was a woman. This summer she'd turned nineteen.

She had all the needs, desires, and longings of a woman. And he was too blind to see it.

A drop of rain fell on her cheek and splattered; then another came. Jessy lifted her eyes to the Broken Buttes, but their jagged outline was shrouded in a gray mist. The rain was on its way.

"Break out the slickers!" someone shouted.

Chase and Maggie sat astride their horses on a rise of the grassy plains to observe the branding process. He nodded an order to Maggie. "Better get Cathleen and head for the cook tent. There's no need in you two getting wet." He reached behind him to untie the yellow slicker from his saddle.

In the distance, there was a low hum that became steadily louder. Maggie had turned her horse to ride around the herd and take shelter at the mess tent before the scattered rain-drops became a downpour, but the sound became a low roar. Chase looked up almost at the same moment she did.

A twin-engine aircraft came out of the south, flying just below the low clouds. It wagged its wings as it thundered by them on the left.

"That's Dyson's plane." Chase recognized it.

"Were you expecting him?"

"No." He watched the plane dip a wing toward the ground and make a swinging turn, leveling out in the direction of The Homestead.

"He's awfully low." The plane seemed to skim above the tops of the rolling hills.

"He's probably flying over the gas wells," Chase guessed. "It looks like we'd better head home and meet our company."

The plane raced ahead of the rain, so close to the ground that all its undulations were apparent, belying its flat look. From the window, the land below seemed to slide by slowly for inspection.

"Look. There's a herd of cattle . . . and some riders." Tara pressed closer to the window, trying to see more clearly. She wondered if Ty was down there among them.

"It looks like they're in the middle of spring branding,"

E. J. Dyson observed. Their view of the scene was broken as the pilot made a slow wigwag of the plane's wings. When they leveled out again, Tara had lost sight of the gathering of animals, but she continued to look out the window.

"All this land," she murmured in a marveling tone.

"And we've only flown over half of it—not even that." It was difficult for him to look at it without thinking of the possible wealth lying beneath that grass, waiting to be exploited. It was not the potential for profit that excited him, but the thrilling challenge of putting a project of that magnitude together and making it work. It was the sheer adventure of it, high-stakes gambling at its highest. "The breadth of it is staggering."

"It is," she agreed. "And the Calders own every inch of it?"

"Every blessed blade of grass." Actually there was some question about that, but he intended to keep the information private, even from his daughter. "This land has quite a future ahead of it."

Leaning away from the window, Tara thoughtfully fingered the high-ruffled collar of her blouse while she gazed out the window at the slow-moving panorama. "It's funny. You've told me about this ranch so many times. And Ty talked about it endlessly. But I still never imagined anything like this."

"It's a kingdom, and not so small a one at that." He smiled dryly. "It's almost feudally run. I'm serious," he insisted when his daughter sent him a skeptical look. "Chase Calder is lord of the land. His word is law, make no mistake about that."

She lowered her hand to her lap, joining it with her other one in an attitude that seemed calm and poised, but her thumb was running over the smooth black opal gem, mounted in a ring. "Was anything ever said to you . . . about the broken engagement?"

"No—beyond Calder mentioning once that he thought you were both too young to be contemplating marriage."

"Good. I should not like to make things awkward by accompanying you on this visit," Tara murmured with a faint smile.

"Come, Tara Lee," E.J. chided her. "I'm not one of your beaus to be taken in by your modesty. You are hoping to make things very awkward. Admit it."

"Daddy," she scolded him, then laughed at how easily he read through her. "You're absolutely right. I only hope that's the way it turns out."

"My darling, no one can resist you," he assured her. "Not even a Calder."

A hint of satisfaction lay on the curve of her mouth as Tara turned thoughtful and silent. In the last two years, Ty had been frequently on her mind. It had simply been a matter of timing and priorities. It would have been so much easier if Ty had understood that.

Now was the right time and, by all appearances, the right place. She didn't doubt her ability to win back his affection. The mere fact that she had come to him gave her an advantage.

"How much longer before we land?" She flipped open the compact from her purse and checked her makeup in the small mirror.

"A few minutes."

The aircraft was sighted as it entered the landing pattern of the private airstrip, and a car was on hand to transport the plane's passengers to The Homestead. As they approached the pillared front, Dyson murmured an aside to his daughter. "A fitting cowboy castle for a cattle king, don't you think?"

Beyond an answering smile, there was no time for a comment as the massive front door opened and an elderly woman waited to welcome them. Dyson recognized Ruth Haskell from previous visits and smiled warmly. It was one of his rules of business to be friendly to the help; a man never knew when they might turn out to be an unwitting source of information.

"Ruth, it's good to see you again. How have you been?" He injected a hearty warmth into his Texas drawl. She murmured a predictable response, and Dyson was struck again by the impression that she was a faded wallflower, no doubt privy to a lot of Calder family secrets. "Tara Lee, I want you to meet Ruth Haskell. This remarkable lady has looked after things here for years. She's practically a member of the family."

"I'm afraid neither Chase nor Maggie is home at the moment," Ruth apologized for their absence and escorted the arriving pair into the house. "It's spring roundup time, you know, and they took Cathleen out to watch the branding. Word's been sent that you are here."

"We happened to fly over that section and noticed the roundup in progress." He hitched up his trousers and settled onto a rusty velvet chair in the living room, where a new fire crackled in the black marble fireplace. It warded off the gloom of the gray day and the cold rain that had started to fall outside. Tara wandered over to the cheery hearth.

"I'm sure they'll be here directly," the woman promised. "Audra should be here soon to prepare your rooms."

"That won't be necessary. Unfortunately I have to meet my partner in Calgary late this evening for a business meeting tomorrow morning, so this is going to be just a flying visit," explained Dyson. "I wasn't certain we had the time to spare to stop here, or I would have given Chase some warning to expect us this afternoon."

"You're always welcome," Ruth assured him, knowing from past experience it was true, but she slid a hesitant glance at his daughter. "May I bring you some coffee?"

"Please."

It was another hour before Chase and Maggie arrived at The Homestead. This gave Tara ample time to peruse the living-room furnishings without appearing to be snooping. Several items were unquestionably valuable antiques; others were old, but not quite as precious. Threads were showing in the patterned area rug that covered part of the hardwood floor where the furniture was grouped. The room gave her the distinct impression the clock had been turned back fifty years. It had a degree of charm and worn comfort, but, in her opinion, it could have been much more impressive.

After the greetings, apologies, and explanations were made, a rain-soaked and dirty Cathleen was sent upstairs to her room to wash and change clothes. After it was established that they would be staying for dinner, Tara thought it appropriate to ask about Ty. Neither of the Calders had mentioned him yet, perhaps because they didn't want to bring up a potentially awkward subject.

"Will Ty be joining us for dinner tonight?" She spoke very casually.

"No." It was Chase Calder who answered her question, studying her with a bland look that absorbed much more than it revealed. "The roundup crew will be spending the night at the holding grounds."

"Oh." She let her disappointment be seen and glanced at the windowpanes, sheeted with a driving downpour. "I thought with this rain they'd quit until it stopped."

The dryness of his amused smile was repeated in his dark eyes. "Once the roundup starts, it continues, rain or shine, until the last calf is branded."

"I was hoping to see him while we were here," Tara admitted and slid a quick look at her father before addressing Ty's parents again. "I know it must seem very forward of me to want to see him again after breaking our engagement. But Ty never gave me an opportunity to explain my reasons for doing it. I had hoped that now he'd be willing to listen. I regret what happened very much. I made a mistake, and I owe it to him to admit it."

There was much about the young and very beautiful woman that Maggie admired. She could identify with that strong sense of independence Tara possessed and with her strong will. She had always thought Ty and Tara were ideally suited, but she also knew how deeply Ty had been hurt. The broken engagement was still a subject he wouldn't discuss.

"It's a pity you aren't staying longer." Maggie was reluctant to comment on Tara's assertion of remorse.

"Perhaps . . ." She hesitated deliberately and glanced at her father, who was shrewdly observing her manipulations with an approving yet completely aloof eye. This was her game, to be played without his help. "If it wouldn't be too much of an imposition"—she turned an expressively appealing look on Maggie—"I could stay here a couple of days until Daddy and Stricklin finish their business in Calgary. Then I'd have a chance to speak to Ty." Her boldness in inviting herself to stay at the ranch was a calculated risk. Wisely Tara didn't press for an immediate answer. Instead, she let her attention come back to her father. "Would you mind stopping here again on your way back from Canada to pick me up? I know you didn't plan on it."

"Naturally I can come this way on the return flight," he replied. "It won't be any great inconvenience to me. I think it's a question of whether the Calders would care to have an uninvited houseguest at such a busy time of the season."

"I'm sorry." Tara apologized for being so thoughtless of their work schedule. There was still no reaction from Chase, but she could tell Maggie was weakening. "I'd forgotten how busy you are with the roundup and all. It just seems so awful to be so close and not have the chance to see Ty again."

"Of course you may stay with us for a few days," Maggie insisted without consulting Chase. But if she expected him to disagree with her, she was wrong. He thought it was high time that Ty faced this beguiling, beautiful woman and got her out of his system once and for all.

The rain had turned the churned-up ground into a thick gumbo of caking mud that wore down horses and men. The mire sucked at their feet with each step; no foot could ever be sure it was planted firmly. There was many a slip and spill of man and horse in the pursuit of a calf. The mucky conditions slowed down the branding pace considerably as mud-spattered and -smeared men and horses worked harder and accomplished less.

A smug sun sat high in the sky, drying the mud into stiff crusts on man and beast alike. Ty's mount stumbled tiredly, its head drooping as he walked it to the picket line where a fresh horse from his string was waiting.

"Hey, Calder!" Big Ab Taylor yelled at him. "The big boss wants ya!"

With a certain weariness, Ty lifted a hand in the cowboy's direction, acknowledging the message. He'd noticed the pickup truck that had arrived a few minutes ago but hadn't paid any mind to it. He reined his horse toward it, now spurring it into a reluctant jog.

The truck was parked near the motorized cookshack on wheels. His father stood in front of it, a cup of coffee in his hand, his long, husky frame propped against the hood and angled to one side. Checking his horse, Ty brought it to a halt beside the front tire and leaned on the saddle horn, pushing his hat to the back of his head.

"Ab said you wanted to see me." He could feel the spatters of mud drying on his face; his pantlegs were stiff with kicked-up clods.

"There's someone here to see you."

"Who?" His brows puckered together in a curious frown. Visitors were something he didn't get, and roundup time was a poor time to be calling.

"Tara."

Ty straightened slowly in the saddle, disbelief ringing through him. A quick search with his eyes found her, sitting on a campstool by the cookshack and watching the scramble of men and animals in the branding arena as if it all had been staged just for her entertainment. She still had that knack of taking possession of her surroundings and making herself at ease.

It took him a second to recover from the shock of seeing her. He swung out of the saddle with the unhurried manner of a man still trying to make up his mind. His spurs made no sound, cushioned with mud to silence their clanking jangle, as he crossed the stretch of ground, methodically pulling off his gloves. His father stayed by the truck, letting his meeting with Tara be a private one.

When she lifted her gaze to observe his approach, she smiled that same provocative, enigmatic smile that had haunted him for so many months of nights. He tried to hold himself indifferent to her vibrant beauty, but it reached down into his guts, as it always had. So utterly feminine in leg-hugging black pants, a long-sleeved blouse in scarlet silk, and a curly white sheepskin vest, she pulled at all his male instincts. Sheer pride alone carried Ty two steps to the side of her to the ever-full coffee pot.

"Hello, Tara." He was shaking inside as he poured himself a cup, but he kept his voice level. Ty barely looked at her, but he was conscious of her every movement, her every breath.

She stood with that regal grace, so flawless that he was instantly reminded of his grubby appearance, the stench of animal sweat and excrement that clung to his clothes, and a scratchy beard growth shadowing his cheeks. He bore little resemblance to the well-dressed college man who had waited attendance on her.

Her head was tipped at a considering angle as Tara contemplated the marked changes in him. The likeness to his father was so much more evident, almost a tribal stamp. The dark hair, thick and unruly, the granite chin and brow, the impenetrable darkness of those wide, deeply set eyes, the roughly molded cheekbones, and the ridged gravity inherent in the strong jaws, all were features they shared. The surface dirt couldn't hide the man he'd become.

"Hello, Ty." She finally spoke, her voice gentle—half humorous, yet so very confident. "I had hoped you would write, but I never heard a word from you. And I realized if I hoped to see you at all, I'd have to come to you. So, here I am—prepared to beg your forgiveness."

Her hands opened in a graceful gesture that seemed to give herself to him without reservation. Ty remembered well the subtle messages she could convey with her body movements, the many shades of meaning she could weave into words.

Too many conflicting reactions were going through him at once, too many emotions running raw for him to unravel. He wanted her; he hated her; he loved her; and he resented her being here and putting him through all this again.

"I can't imagine you begging for anything," Ty countered smoothly and lifted the metal cup to his mouth, never once changing his loose stance.

She laughed at his remark, admitting with a provocative, upward-peering look, "I don't do it well." Then that small smile claimed her lips again. "I rather like you in these surroundings. You were out of your element in college."

"Why did you come here?" he demanded, lowering his cup and staring into it. Not for an instant did Ty believe Tara was here to seek his forgiveness. She had never before cared whether her actions met with anyone's approval or disapproval but her own.

"I told you—"

"Don't play games with me!" Harshly he cut across her words. "You do it too damned well."

For a split second she doubted her ability to command the

situation. Then a hurt look flashed across her face as she dropped her eyes under the force of his gaze.

"I had hoped you might be glad to see me again." Tara lifted her head, throwing it back with regrouped poise and making her voice sound as if she didn't care. "I didn't come to make you angry. It's obvious I'm not welcome here." She paused, holding his gaze for an eloquent second. "I know it took me a long time to finally accept your invitation to visit, but I did come. I thought that might mean something to you."

His only reply was silence. As she made her turn to leave, the sun set fire to the black opal on her finger. The sight of it tore him loose from his rigid stand of indifference.

"Why are you still wearing the ring?" There was a betraying roughness in his voice, vibrating on an emotional edge.

Tara turned slowly back to face him, relaxing a little. And Ty knew he was still caught in the spell of her elusive beauty.

"Because you gave it to me," she said. His eyes made a feature-by-feature study of her, down to the last mole. And the silence lengthened. "What are you thinking, Ty?"

"That you're more beautiful than ever, but don't drag any more strings in front of me to see if I'll pounce at them," he warned.

"That's the second time you've accused me of toying with you."

"Didn't you?" The challenge was sudden and vehement, proof that she'd gotten through to him.

"Not consciously, no. Oh, I admit I made mistakes about what things were important to me. But, Ty—" Tara appealed to him in a half-bantering tone. "Isn't a girl entitled to change her mind about something more than once?"

The pressure of the moment got to him. He emptied the steaming coffee from his cup onto the ground with a downward fling of his hand, needing to release some of the coiled energy inside him.

"You say it so easily. It's just another game of yours. It was never a game with me. There hasn't been a day that's gone by that I haven't thought of you—wanted you. Never a midnight sky that didn't have your face in it. I never stopped wanting you. When Dad said your name a minute ago, I wanted you then."

"But I'm here," she insisted.

"You don't understand," he insisted gruffly. "I wanted you, but the wounds were licked dry. They haven't healed, they haven't gone away, but the bleeding has stopped. I'm not going to have you open them up again."

"Can I do that?" Tara mused playfully.

"You know damned well you can." Ty was serious. "But I'm on the road to getting over you, and I want to stay on it."

"Without looking back?" She let herself become serious. "Even when someone is calling for you?"

The shutters slipped, just for an instant letting her see his uncertainty. For her, the doubt fled. Reaching out, she grasped his roughly callused hand between her own.

"I didn't come here to open old wounds, Ty. It could be I came to see if I could persuade you to propose to me again."

"You already turned me down once. No, thanks." The touch of her hands seemed to harden him again.

"Can't you believe that I have realized I was wrong? Is it wanting too much to wish that I could have another chance?"

"So you can change your mind again?" Ty challenged. "I've been through that once, Tara. You're not going to put me through it again."

The wisdom of Eve made her wise enough to know it was time to draw back and not press the issue further. He had shown a moment's uncertainty; she knew he was vulnerable. She withdrew her hands, smiling resignedly up at him.

"I'm only going to be here a couple of days," she told him. "Daddy's in Calgary on business. He'll be coming back through on Wednesday to pick me up so we can fly back home. I wish there would have been time for you to show me around the ranch. After all you've told me about it, I would have liked the chance to see it with you."

"Maybe another time." Ty was relieved by her acceptance that he'd finished with the past and answered without thinking.

Immediately her dark eyes were dancing. "Does that mean I've been invited back?"

"It's one of the unwritten rules of the West—never turn a visitor away from your door; you might need the hospitality reciprocated sometime." He was careful not to make it sound like anything more than courtesy. "I stayed many times in your father's home. You're welcome to stay in mine."

A lone rider approached the camp from the opposite direction of the herd. Range-alert, Ty noticed him and centered his gaze on the rider to identify him. Tara looked in the same direction to see what had distracted him.

"Is something wrong?" The rider looked like just another cowboy to Tara.

"No. Nothing's wrong." But Ty wondered what Culley O'Rourke was doing this far into Calder land.

For two months, he'd spent night and day with the man, shared meals and chores, yet there'd never been any sharing of confidences. O'Rourke might have learned to tolerate a Calder, but he hadn't learned to like one. He kept to himself, on rare instances coming to The Homestead to visit Maggie, but always leaving as soon as Ty or his father arrived. There seemed to be a truce of sorts that existed, or, more accurately, a wary neutrality on both sides.

13

It wasn't considered polite to ride a horse into camp where it might possibly foul the ground where the crew ate. Instead of leaving his horse tied at the picket line with the other mounts, O'Rourke tied his separately, wrapping the reins around the rear bumper of a truck.

Although it didn't appear to be deliberately done, O'Rourke approached the open end of the traveling cook kitchen always keeping a vehicle between himself and any onlookers, as if shielding himself from prying eyes. Ty no longer believed it was caused by shyness. It seemed more likely a desire to escape being observed. O'Rourke didn't like people watching him.

"Hello, Culley," Ty greeted him when he rounded the cook truck.

"Ty." He nodded, his eyes shifting curiously to Tara. The outdoors had tanned his skin to a brown shade, making the gray in his hair more pronounced and the blackness of his eyes more compelling. O'Rourke was always careful about his appearance, wearing clean clothes and shaving every day. After two years, Ty was convinced his uncle was a little on the strange side, but harmless.

"What brings you down this way?"

"I got tired of cookin' for myself and remembered how good Tucker's food tasted." He looked at Tara again and briefly gripped the point of his hat brim. "Ma'am."

With a vague reluctance, Ty made the introduction O'Rourke was so obviously seeking. His stare remained fixed on her, which made Ty uneasy.

"You look a lot like my sister," he said finally.

At a distance, Ty supposed there was a resemblance between Tara and his mother. Both had dark hair and a small build. He wondered if that hadn't prompted O'Rourke to ride in, believing he had an ally in camp, only to discover he'd been mistaken.

"Think I'll find out when Tucker's going to have lunch ready." O'Rourke backed away at the first opening and ducked around behind the truck.

"It doesn't seem possible that man is your uncle," Tara murmured.

"Culley's had a hard time of it, one way or another," was all Ty replied. When he heard footsteps, he wasn't surprised to see his father coming toward them.

"What's O'Rourke doing here?"

"According to him, he got hungry for Tucker's cooking."

With Tara present, his father didn't pursue the subject. "The crew's going to break for the noon meal shortly." He glanced inquisitively at the girl. "Do you want to stay, or would you rather go back to The Homestead for lunch?"

"I'd rather stay here, if I won't be in the way."

"You won't be," he assured her but shot a curious look at Ty to see if he was of the same mind. Ty made no sign of objection.

"I'll let Tucker know we'll be having company for lunch."
Which was another way of saying his father intended to warn
the men to watch their language.

A line had already formed at the washbasins when Jessy
answered the cook's call to eat. Her clothes were stiff with
dried mud that broke off in crumbles as she walked. Her leg
muscles ached from constantly struggling against the sucking
mire. She made a halfhearted stab at wiping the gumbolike
accumulation off her boots onto the grass, but it hardly
seemed worth the effort. She moved up in line.

"We need some clean water!" A cowboy at the basin
impatiently bawled out the request. "Half of Montana's in
this one!"

"Yeah!" the rider behind him echoed. "We already had a
damned mud bath oncet."

The dirty water was thrown out as the rotund cook came
huffing and heaving with a fresh pail to fill the basin. He was
as round as a potbellied stove, but solid as one, too. His neck
was lost in the massive shoulders, and his bald head was
small, oddly out of proportion with the rest of his body.

"We got a lady with us, boys, so watch your language, or
I'll be knockin' some heads together," Tucker warned.

"D'ya hear that? He called our Jessy a lady!"

"How-de-do, ma'am." One of the cowboys tipped his hat
to her in exaggerated courtesy, and Jessy mockingly curtsied
back.

"Tucker ain't talkin' about her, ya damned fool!" Sid
Ramsey declared and batted at the man's hat. "The lady is
that dark-eyed lovely sittin' over there with Ty."

Jessy turned to look in the direction Ramsey had indicated,
and stared like all the others. She heard the low, suppressed
wolf whistles and the murmured comments of flattery and lust
the men exchanged to keep their virile images intact among
their peers.

But the sight of the raven-haired girl had the opposite
effect on Jessy. It didn't loosen her tongue. Instead, her
silence became deeper and deeper. A lot could be read into
the indifference Ty was showing the girl sitting beside him,
paying her none of the ardent attention the cowboys around

Jessy would so willingly have done. Ty barely looked at her. His expression was all closed up, everything shut in. Jessy could only think of one reason why Ty wasn't smiling and talking freely with a girl as lovely as this one. He'd been hurt by her in the past.

While the others were speculating about the girl's identity, Jessy was wondering why the girl was here. Behind all that beauty, there was a clever mind. There was a motive for her being here, and it wasn't a friendly social call. Jessy stepped up to the basin and dunked her hands into the murky gray water, scrubbing with the rough bar of Lava.

When it came time to eat, instead of loosely scattering around the camp, the hands began clustering in the center with the girl's campstool as the focal point. Nearly every one of them nodded to her, preening a little under the small smile she gave each of them. A couple of them nudged Ty, trying to prod him into an introduction. He was vaguely irritated by the stir she was creating among the men, even though he'd seen her cause the same kind of sensation many times before. She had the kind of beauty that made a man forget he had good sense. And he was angered at the way the men sniffed around her like a pack of fools, because he saw their weakness in himself.

An introduction couldn't be avoided, but Ty waited until the last man had left the grub line and found himself a place to sit. There wasn't any need to call attention to himself to begin, since all of them were waiting expectantly for him to do it.

"All you boys know E. J. Dyson. This is his daughter, Tara Lee." Ty omitted any reference to his past engagement to her. The regular riders would make the connection anyway. He glanced briefly at Tara. "I won't bother to tell you the names of this sorry lot of so-called cowboys. All of them think they're big, bad men, but there's a couple I oughta warn you about."

He looked around the suddenly downturned faces, agitation spraying through the ranks at the kind of outrageous remark he might be intending to make about them to this vision of beauty. There was a dead silence.

"Tiny Yates, the guilty-looking one over there." Ty pointed

him out to her. "He's a married man, but a lot of the boys claim that he keeps getting their wives mixed up with his." Notoriously tongue-tied around women, Tiny Yates went red from his neck up. "And Billy Bob Martin beats his dog every time he gets drunk. Liquor makes him downright mean." Someone choked on his coffee at that accusation. Billy Bob avoided drink like the plague. It only took a couple of beers to have him blubbering like a baby. Crying was a bigger sin than sobriety. "Ramsey struts around like he's cock of the walk. He's always crowing the minute the sun peeks up in the morning."

No one budged, afraid of drawing Ty's attention. The embarrassed and uneasy silence lay heavily in the air. Tara realized none of the things Ty had said were true, but she couldn't fathom his reason for making everyone so uncomfortable.

No one lingered over his food. They all ate quickly and began spilling away to dump their dirty dishes in the wreck pan. Ty observed their hasty departures with a faint grin of satisfaction.

"Why did you do that?" Tara murmured.

"It's taken me a long time to get even with that bunch," he replied and swilled his coffee.

"Get even for what?" She didn't know about the merciless hazings he'd endured at the hands of those same men.

"Nothing." Ty drained the cup. "It was just a joke among friends."

"Some joke." Tara thought he'd been unreasonably harsh on them. She'd never seen this side of him and didn't quite know how to take it.

"It's a rough brand of humor up here." He shrugged but didn't attempt to explain that none of the men bore him any ill will because of the things he'd said about them. Nothing personal had been intended, and they knew it. There was a slow ebb of men back to their horses. Ty flattened a hand on his knee and pushed himself upright against the desire that tugged at him to stay by her side. "Time I was getting back to work."

"Ty." She was on her feet, laying a hand on his arm to detain him a minute longer. As he looked down at her, she moved closer. He breathed in the clean scent of her body, its sweetness a soft contrast to the rankness of his own.

"Careful. You'll get dirty," he warned to push her away before temptation overwhelmed him.

"Do you think I care?" She laughed but took a step backwards. "Do you mind if I stay and watch the branding this afternoon?"

"Do as you please, Tara. You always have." Ty was curt, knowing it wouldn't make any difference if she stayed here or returned to The Homestead. She'd still be on his mind.

"Then I'll stay." Shrewdly she had observed the emotion that had sharpened his voice when he'd struggled to contain it.

"A piece of advice. Stay well back and upwind. It's a dirty, smelly business."

The afternoon's work had barely started when Sid Ramsey got two fingers fouled in the rope as he made his dally on a calf and broke both of them, clean as dry twigs snapping. A torrent of blue language rushed from him, a combination of pain and anger at making a fool's mistake like that.

It took a couple of minutes to get enough slack in the rope to unwind the wrap pinning his fingers to the saddle horn. Hunched over the saddle, Ramsey cradled his hand against his body and rode to the chuck wagon. A roper short, Art Trumbo yanked Jessy off the ground crew and ordered her into a saddle to fill the position.

Shaking out a loop, she adjusted her grip on the rope and walked her horse toward the herd to pick out an unbranded calf. Another horse and rider came alongside her. She glanced sideways at Ty and saw him looking toward the chuck wagon. She knew what drew his attention that way, and it wasn't Ramsey.

"She's the one who jilted you, isn't she?" Jessy looked straight ahead and said what others dared only to think. His mouth tightened, offering no reply. "I expect she wants to patch things up. Are you going to take her back?" She was very cool and very calm, but he gave no sign of having heard her question. "You're a fool, Ty Calder," she said and jabbed a spur into her horse, sending it after a calf.

Ramsey rode up to the chuck wagon and swung down.

"Hey, Tuck!" he bellowed for the cook. "Bring your black bag! I broke my damned fingers." He sallied around Tara, an arm hunched against his belly. "Beg pardon, ma'am."

A witness to his calamity, Tara followed after him, drawn by that curious fascination humans have for one of their kind in pain, attracted and repelled by it at the same time. She stood to one side and watched him gingerly pull off the leather glove, sucking in his breath with a hissing sound.

The forefinger and middle finger were both discolored and starting to swell. Tara drew back slightly, grimacing at the sight. When she glanced at his face, the skin was stretched tautly across his bones, ridging it white.

"You need to go to the hospital and have that X-rayed," she murmured.

"X-rayed? Hell, I already know it's broke." He tossed her a tight grin, scoffing at her suggestion.

"But they need to be set," Tara insisted.

"I don't need no doctor to do that. Ya just got to pop them back together and wrap them up with some tape." After thus assuring her of the simpleness of the matter, he turned to the ageless cook. "Ya got some of those ice-cream sticks in there?"

In horrified fascination, Tara watched the pudgy hands of the cook sandwich the broken appendages between a pair of short, narrow splints. Then Ramsey nodded to him. She heard the sickening snap of bones popping into place. Ramsey grunted, beads of sweat popping out all over his suddenly white face. Tara felt nauseated and weak. She swayed a little until the cook gripped her elbow.

"You okay?" The small eyes studied her closely.

"I'm fine." She stiffened determinedly and turned away, not staying around to watch the splints being taped into position.

The primitiveness of the incident had shaken her. She'd been raised in the conventional world where professional help was sought for the most minor medical problem. It was unthinkable to her that bones would be set without the aid of a doctor. For an instant she was assailed by doubts about being in such uncivilized country.

But she had only to look at Ty to have her decision

reinforced. Even though she had been raised in surroundings where she had been kept safe and protected, it didn't mean she couldn't be daring when the occasion demanded it. And she had dared to come to the ranch for the sole purpose of persuading Ty to take her back, although she was determined to conceal it behind a lightness of mood.

Her reasons for changing her mind about marrying him were nebulous, and Tara regarded them as immaterial, so she avoided analyzing them to find the truth. The decision was made. All her attention was now focused on making it come to pass. She intended to have him, even if it meant surrendering everything.

A slim, long-haired rider approached the herd alongside Ty. Tara didn't realize the rider was female until the face turned and she had a clear view of the classically refined cheekbone and jaw, smooth as honey. For the first time, she considered the possibility of local competition.

All morning the crew had worked in mire up to a horse's hock. By late afternoon, the sun and an incessant wind had dried it to a cementlike hardness, creating ruts and ridges to trip and stumble over. The hard, punishing ground used up a lot of horses; riders changed frequently to keep their mounts from becoming sore-legged.

Taking his saddle and pad from one horse, Ty threw it onto a buckskin and pulled the surcingle through the cinch ring. Saddle leather groaned behind him. He threw a look over his shoulder and noted his father, mounted on an iron-gray gelding only a couple of feet away.

"Want something?" Ty asked and ran the cinch up tight.

"Tara will only be here a couple more days. It's up to you whether you want to come home tonight or stay here with the crew."

"Okay." Reaching under the horse's belly, he buckled the back cinch.

His father chirruped to the gray and reined it in a half-circle. Metal shoes clanked as the horse was lifted into a canter. Unobserved, Ty paused in his saddling to consider the option his father had given him—to be with Tara or not.

The things he'd told her today were true. The wanting

hadn't stopped, but the bleeding had. For a change, she was doing the pursuing instead of the other way around. Ty took perverse satisfaction in that. Jessy had called him a fool, but how could a man want something for so long and not take it when it was finally offered to him?

The sound of her laughter drifted into the dining room, reminding Ty of the soft tinkle of bells. He wondered what his young sister had said to make Tara laugh. With an effort, he pulled his gaze from the doorway where she had gone, carrying dinner dishes to the kitchen.

All through dinner, the conversation had been lively and animated, his mother and Tara comparing impressions of European countries both had visited and enthralling Cathleen with reminiscences of their adventures. The three had behaved more like sisters. When it came time to clear the table, it seemed perfectly natural that Tara help, although Ty couldn't recall ever seeing her do domestic chores before.

He rubbed a hand across his mouth in a gesture that was both thoughtful and troubled. The blue smoke of a cigar drifted lazily above the linen-covered table. Glancing to the head of the table, Ty saw his father watching him.

"Don't make a rash decision, Ty."

The line of his mouth turned grim. "I think I'll go outside and get some air." He pushed his chair away from the table and rose. The house was too small with Tara in it to hold them both without something rash happening.

On the wide veranda, Ty paused to light a cigarette, then wandered to the edge and leaned against a tall white pillar. The black sky was alive with stars; one fell, making a white scratch. Overhead, a full moon gleamed with the luster of a giant pearl set among the diamond stars.

Dark and vibrant as the sky, soft and tantalizing as a breeze, Tara was a nightsong, full of all its mystery and elusive beauty. She was the essence of a man's dreams, feminine and alluring, as seductive as the night.

Taking a last drag on his cigarette, Ty flipped it into the air and watched the crimson trail it made arcing into the darkness. The front door opened, but he steeled himself not to turn. Light footsteps approached him from behind.

"May I join you?" Tara took his acceptance for granted as she slipped her hand through the crook of his arm and hugged it to her. The warmth of her body was pressed along his length, and Ty was all too aware of the contact his arm made with her breast, its rounded shape imprinted on his muscled flesh.

"You already have." Raw and tense, he swung his gaze outward.

Tara shrewdly studied his profile. She'd caught that flare of reaction deep in the wells of his brown eyes. His words might be cold to her, but he wasn't. She noticed the fine lines that had sprung into his face, cutting out the youthfulness. Its ruggedness was purely masculine now, roughly handsome. There was a comfortable certainty in her that eventually she would wear down his resistance as she turned her head to look at what he was seeing.

Lights from windows of the many buildings comprising the headquarters fanned out from the knoll of The Homestead like so many groundstars. The trees along the river made intricate cobweb shapes against the night's glow. From some barn, a horse whickered.

"It looks like a small city," Tara murmured. "So many lights. So many buildings."

"In a way, it is. We're practically self-sufficient with our own water supply, an auxiliary generating station, sewer system and all the utilities. There's two small fire trucks, a garage for repairing vehicles, not to mention a grade school for the younger kids, a veterinary facility, a totally equipped first-aid station, and a commissary."

"I'd like to see all of it." She sighed and snuggled closer. "It's cooler out here than I realized. Why don't you put your arm around me and keep me warm?"

"Why don't you go inside and get a jacket?" But Ty didn't object when she shifted his arm to curve it around her and buried herself deeper into his side.

"This is better, isn't it?"

"Stop it, Tara."

"I'm glad you came home tonight."

It was not the words so much as the way she said them, as if she had already made it her home and she would always be here waiting for him. Her upturned head made an invitation of her glistening lips. The urge was too strong and the habit of kissing them too deeply embedded in his memory. Before his mouth ever reached her lips, she was turning into him.

The heated contact jolted him and Ty started to pull back, but her slim hands were around his neck, their insistent pressure not letting him go. Her lips were all over his, breathing their drugging sweetness into his mouth and eating him until the blood was hammering so loudly in his brain he couldn't think.

He was suddenly angry, hating the weakness that made him putty in her hands. He gripped her wrists and pulled them down from his neck, breathing hard as he broke the kiss. But his anger didn't stop the need that trembled through him.

"No games," he insisted.

"Why must you be so dense?" Impatience broke through her before she made one of her lightning changes of mood. "You leave a girl no pride." Her drawling voice was provocative and gay. "I've come nearly halfway across the continent to tell you I was wrong—to try to make up for the mistake I made. What do I have to do before you'll ask me to stay?"

"For what purpose? To torment me all over again?" Muscles snapped along his jawline, tension running rampant through him.

"No." She tipped her head, looking at him in a way that both promised and withheld. "I know words aren't enough, Ty. But give me a chance to show you that I mean them."

He listened, beaten by the knowledge that he was unable to deny he wanted her to stay. "You have your chance, but I won't be batting at any more strings." He'd not give her an easy time of it.

She saw that. For a moment, she saw beyond that to a point in time where she would have to offer herself and accept his terms. Instead of dreading that moment of absolute surrender, she was stunned by the pleasurable rush of anticipation. She had stepped so carefully around her emotions for so long it was an exciting thought to let them take over just once.

"We'll have fun together. You'll see." Her dark eyes gleamed with knowing secrecy.

Ty didn't know what was going on in her head, but the look in her eyes, so confident and alluring, made his blood run hot. "We'd better go inside before you get chilled."

"Tell me, Daddy." Tara strolled along, linked arm in arm with her father as she escorted him to the waiting plane. She permitted a playful smugness to enter her expression when she looked at him. "Would you still like it if I became Mrs. Calder."

His stopover at the Triple C had been brief, not allowing any private moments between father and daughter until now. Dyson's look was proud and amused.

"Ty's come around, has he?"

"Not completely, but he will."

Tara surveyed her surroundings with a proprietorial air. Beyond the airstrip with its hangared aircraft and squatty helicopters, she could see the many roofs of the headquarter buildings and the stately Homestead, plus all the vast, open land that encompassed them. Dyson observed her expression with a dry smile.

"You're already visualizing yourself as lady of the manor, aren't you?"

"Someday I will be." She was certain of it, all confidence. Then she swung around to him, gay and bright. "You can stay away longer than a month, can't you? Surely you can find some excuse to delay your return."

"I could, but I have a couple of important meetings that I'm not going to postpone—even for you."

"Here? Who with?"

"A couple of Calder's neighbors. Actually I'll be back in about three weeks, but I'll be staying in Miles City, then fly up from there when I'm finished."

"If they're neighbors, why aren't you staying here?"

"Because I don't like to conduct deals in the house of a third party," he replied evenly. "Besides, I don't believe Calder would approve of my plans. It's better if he doesn't know what I'm doing until after it's done. He might try to influence his neighbors not to accept my deal, and I'd just as soon not lock horns with that range bull."

"What are you and Stricklin after?" He was being mysterious again, the way he always was when they were planning some big, new venture.

"Nothing that needs to concern you." He stopped when they reached the open door of the twin-engine aircraft, and kissed her cheek. Straightening, he winked. "I won't tell you to behave yourself. I'll merely wish you luck instead. You've kept Ty waiting by the car long enough, now scoot." He slapped her behind with fatherly affection to send her on her way, watched her for a thoughtful second, then climbed aboard the plane. Their separate plans might ultimately dovetail nicely.

Stricklin was already in the plane, buckled in his seat. Dyson nodded to him and took an opposite seat to strap himself in.

"I believe she is going to catch that young man, Stricklin," he said with a glance out the small window at the couple. "What do you think of the match?"

"It's ideal," his partner replied and meant it.

14

The spring roundup ended a week later, and it was arranged for Ty's duties to keep him around the headquarters instead of working out of one of the far-flung camps of the ranch. With Tara exercising her prerogative as a guest and sleeping late in the mornings, she seldom saw Ty until noon.

Most of the afternoons she was left to her own devices. Maggie Calder had given her a tour of the ranch facilities, taking her to visit the one-room schoolhouse and showing her the commissary with its assortment of grocery items, clothing, and miscellaneous hardware. Tara had found it all very fascinating, but she would have preferred that Ty had shown her these things. She spent irritatingly little time alone with him. Sometimes she wondered if he ever had a day off from ranch work.

With slow steps, she descended the stairs, absently trailing her hand along the railing while she wondered how she was going to fill this Saturday afternoon. The front door opened and shut with a bang and Cathleen came sailing in. Tara glanced at the girl with sudden interest. Maybe she could persuade Cathleen to guide her to wherever Ty was working this afternoon.

"Hello, Cat." She used the family nickname for the girl.

"Tara! I was just looking for you." She changed direction to come to the stairs, stopping at the base of them, bright-eyed and out of breath. "Ty said for me to tell you to put on some riding clothes. He'll be by the house in half an hour with the horses."

Just like that. He snapped his fingers and she was supposed to come running. With an effort, Tara smoothed the ruffled edges of her prickling nerves. "The lord commands and the lady obeys," she murmured.

"What's that?" Cathleen tipped her head, frowning in puzzlement.

"Nothing, my kitten." She shook her head and turned to retrace her steps up the stairs. "Half an hour doesn't give me much time. I'd better hurry." Flashing a round-eyed look of mock haste at the girl, Tara went to change.

It was a full forty-five minutes before she emerged from the house. The impatience on Ty's expression faded to reluctant admiration as she crossed to the horses, assuring her the extra time she'd taken with her appearance had been worth it. From the beaded fringe of her jacket to her designer jeans, from the feather-banded hat to her Italian-made cowboy boots, she was fashionably western dressed with the latest the exclusive Texas stores had to offer.

"I thought we'd go for a long ride this afternoon," Ty said. "You haven't really had a good look at the ranch, except flying over it or driving across it."

"I'd like that. It's something I've been wanting to do with you."

Ty gave her a leg up onto the back of the flashy blood bay,

made sure the stirrups were properly adjusted to her leg length, then mounted his own horse. Together, they rode north and west, their horses setting into a rocking canter that could be kept up for miles.

Buildings were left far behind as they traveled deeper and deeper into the land, rising and falling with the swells of the earth. The sun was a gold disk in the gigantic sky, and the horizon was a smoky blue haze of ridges. There was nothing out here but endlessly stretching miles of more of the same. Its emptiness was almost oppressive, surrounding Tara until she felt like a minuscule object.

Finally Ty reined his horse to a halt near the rim of a flat-topped butte and dismounted to hold the bridle of Tara's horse as she swung out of the saddle to join him. Leaving their horses ground-tied, they walked to the edge where there was a commanding view of the surrounding expanse of land. As Tara stood beside him, she felt overwhelmed by the silence and the vastness. A great well of loneliness seemed to fill her, and she edged closer to Ty. He glanced down at her briefly; then he took her hand, lacing their fingers together and unknowingly giving her assurance.

When he began pointing out the extent of Calder range, indicating the direction of far-distant boundaries, she listened to the quiet pride in his voice and absorbed it into her own feelings. From this plateau and in all directions as far as the eye could see, the land belonged to his family. And it was going to be her family.

"There's a certain magnificence about it, isn't there?" she said when he had finished, but she didn't mention the quality of melancholy it also evoked in her.

"It has a way of humbling a man and bringing him down to size," Ty agreed.

She didn't want to hear such talk. "But you're a Calder, Ty. You can do and be anything you want. With the Calder power and influence, someday you could be governor of this whole state."

After struggling so long to have his abilities recognized by his family, her praise and belief in his potential nourished his underfed ego. Yet he smiled, faintly amused by her suggestion.

"Did I say something funny?" Tara was a bit stung by his reaction.

"My granddad had a philosophy about politicians. My father explained it to me once," he said, humor lines wrinkling the corners of his eyes as he looked out at the land. "It went something along the lines of 'Why be governor when you can buy one?'"

Being the manipulating force behind the scenes was a tantalizing prospect. Her pulse quickened as she studied the intelligence in his features, the relentless determination and will to succeed.

"You're wasting yourself playing cowboy, Ty," she said firmly. "With your background and education, you could be so much more. My father has a high regard for you. I simply don't understand why you're here, working like a common cowhand, when you could be doing something important and worthwhile."

"I'm learning the ranch business from the ground up, you might say," Ty stated.

"Why? It isn't important that you know how to do everything as long as you hire people that do. Your father is a wonderful man and I admire him a lot, but his methods are sadly outdated." She tempered her statement. "I don't mean to be criticizing him. I just want you to be successful and important in your own right."

"I've made a commitment to my father. You may be able to back out of a promise without any qualms, but I don't find it so easy," he inserted stiffly and started to turn away.

"I've spoiled the afternoon, haven't I?" Tara said contritely. "I'm sorry."

"It's the first time you've said that." He paused, wanting to believe her, yet remembering how she had tried to press her ambitions on him.

"It is, isn't it?" She laughed. "I've made so many mistakes with you that it seems I shall always be begging your forgiveness."

He arched a brow. "Now, that would be a novel experience."

"There are a lot of novel experiences we haven't shared." She leaned toward him and tipped her head in an age-old gesture girls learned almost before they left the cradle. This time he gathered her into his arms and kissed her hard, breathing roughly when it was over. She ran the tip of her nail over his mouth. "You still love me, don't you, Ty?" The purring certainty in her voice was enough to put him off. He let her go and moved toward the horses to break the spell she'd woven around him again.

When Chase pulled his truck up in front of Sally's Place, he almost didn't see the camping trailer parked in the building's shade. Only the nose of the trailer hitch was poked into the sunlight, and Chase had caught the flash of light reflecting off its metal surface.

The sight of it brought him up short and changed his direction, and he went over to take a closer look. An electric cord ran from the trailer through the opened slit of the restaurant's kitchen window to hook the trailer to a power supply, and a wooden step had been set out in front of the trailer door to supplement the retractable metal ones. A thick film of dust and dirt covered the exterior, indicating it had traveled some distance since the last time it had been cleaned.

No one seemed to be about, but the windows were cranked open, a further indication someone was staying in it. Chase walked to the rear of the trailer. The license plate on the bumper was bent and half covered with road dust. The trailer was carrying Texas tags. He rubbed enough of the dirt off to read the numbers, then straightened, more puzzled than before.

Using the back entrance, he walked through the empty kitchen and out the swinging door into the restaurant side of the café-bar. There weren't any customers around, just Sally going around to the tables filling the sugar containers.

"Hello, Chase." Pleasure glowed in her quietly expressive face. "I saw you drive up and wondered where you had disappeared." She continued pouring sugar from the pitcher into glass containers. "I'll be through here in a minute. Help yourself to some coffee."

"I noticed that trailer parked alongside your building." He took a cup from the plastic rack and filled it with coffee. "Who does it belong to?"

"A man named Belton. Actually there's three men living in it, but I think Belton owns it." She screwed on the cap and wiped the outside of the jar before setting it down and moving her tray to the next table. "He came in . . . Saturday, I guess it was, and asked if he could park their trailer there and plug into my electricity. He offered to pay me seventy-five dollars a month, but I couldn't accept that much. So I just charged him fifty."

"What do you know about him?" Chase frowned.

"He's from Texas." She shrugged lightly. "I know they're working somewhere around here. All three of them wear those black engineer's boots. They look like those oil men that used to be out at your place—the way they dress, I mean."

"I don't like the idea of you having three strangers parked right outside your window, especially with you sleeping by yourself upstairs. It's not safe."

She smiled at his grimness. "What is the difference whether they are ten feet away or two hundred? They would have parked the trailer somewhere. Why shouldn't I get the benefit of charging them to park here? Plus, it's three more paid breakfasts and dinners, not to mention they asked me to pack a lunch for them the last two days."

"You're too trusting." Chase resisted her logic.

"It's good business," Sally returned calmly. "And I make sure all the doors are locked and bolted before I go to bed at night. And if worst comes to worst, I have a gun." She was quietly mocking him.

"How long are they going to be here?"

"Through the summer, I guess. Maybe longer. One of them was asking about the vacant houses in town. He wanted to know who owned them and whether any of them were suitable to live in now. I had the feeling they might be moving here for a considerable length of time." She filled the last container and walked to the counter where Chase stood sipping at his coffee. "It would be nice to have people living in some of those abandoned houses again. Some of them just need minor repairs."

"They didn't say who they were working for?" He persisted in his search for information.

"No. And they paid in cash—two months in advance." She smiled at his serious expression, inwardly pleased at his concern for her safety. A man's protective instincts were strong, always wanting to shield those he cared about from harm. Sally poured a cup of coffee for herself and walked around the counter to sit on a stool, prompting Chase to do the same. "Tuesdays are always so slow," she remarked, changing the subject. "What's the latest on Ty and his girlfriend? He brought her in last Friday night. Everyone in three counties is speculating on the outcome of that romance."

"I have the feeling he's going to marry her."

"You don't sound very happy about it," Sally observed. "She's a gorgeous girl."

"And used to a totally different way of living," Chase added dryly.

"That doesn't necessarily mean anything. I've seen the wildest bachelors become tame and respectable once they're married."

"And some stay wild and irresponsible—the way your husband did," he reminded her.

"What does Maggie think of her?"

There was a brief shrug. "Maggie is enjoying her company. All that woman talk about fashions and dinner parties and foreign places is something she's missed. Even the ranch women around here are more apt to talk about Junior's calf that he's showing or the baby's croup. Not very sophisticated topics." There was a cynical curve to his mouth. "Maggie and Tara get along very well."

"That's good. Maggie will be able to help Tara adjust to her new life—if she and Ty get married." Sally chose to see the positive aspect.

"Let's hope so."

It was late afternoon when Chase arrived back at The Homestead. He went straight to the study and picked up the receiver of the desk phone, dialing a number.

"Hello, Potter. Chase Calder."

"H'lo, Chase," came the laconic reply. "What can I do for you?"

"I have a license number I want you to check out for me."
He gave it to him.

"Texas plates? It might take me some time," the local
sheriff warned in a slow voice. "What's the problem? You
aren't havin' trouble with rustlers again?"

"No. There's a camping trailer parked outside of Sally's. I
want to know who owns it, where he works, and everything
there is to know about his background." He paused, then
added, "And have your men make some extra patrols past
her place at night after it closes. Call me as soon as you get a
rundown on that license number."

"Will do. By the way . . . I won't be runnin' for election
again. I'm gonna get me a fly rod and head for some of them
trout streams. I've got a good boy name of Dobbins all lined
up for the job. It'd be good if he had your support."

"I'll remember that, Potter." He hung up the phone and
turned around.

Maggie was standing in the doorway. "Were you talking to
the sheriff?"

"Yes. There was something I needed him to check on." His
hesitation was slight, barely perceptible, coming from an
unwillingness to communicate the nature of his inquiry.

"What is it? Is there trouble?" Maggie wasn't satisfied with
half an answer, nor with the bits and pieces of the phone
conversation she'd overheard.

"No." Smoothly he moved toward her. "I want to make
sure there won't be."

He was deliberately being evasive, and she could only think
of one reason why he'd do that. "Tell me, Chase," she
insisted, "does it have anything to do with Culley? Has he
done something?"

"This has nothing to do with Culley," he assured her.
"There's some strangers in town. They parked a trailer next
to Sally's and are using it as a kind of base of operations. The
sheriff's going to find out who they are and what they're doing
here. That's all."

Sally's. There was a leadenness in her heart as she searched
his craggy face. "When did you find this out?"

"I stopped by there this afternoon. When she told me

about the men, I decided to have them checked out." Chase eyed Maggie with a trace of irritation. "She does live alone above the café." There was a shortness in his voice.

"I'm sure Sally Brogan can take care of herself. She doesn't need you to protect her." Maggie was stiff with jealousy. A man protected what he regarded as his own. A couple of times Maggie had wondered whether the ashes of his old affair with Sally had been stirred. "Excuse me. I have to check on dinner." She made a retreat before she said something she might regret.

A night breeze fluttered the curtains at the bedroom window, then caught the lazy trail of smoke from Ty's cigarette and sucked it toward the screened opening. The hoot of an owl night-hunting on the riverbanks drifted into the darkened room, lighted only by the silvery shine of a moon on the wane. The midnight hour held the night in stillness.

Unable to sleep, Ty sat in bed. Pillows stacked behind his shoulders and back propped him against the headboard. His thoughts drifted; he was troubled. There had been a subtle change in his attitude toward Tara these last three weeks. Her beauty still captivated him; he still wanted her. But something was missing. Sometimes he had the feeling he was seeing her more clearly now, but he didn't know what that meant.

The faint scrape of a doorknob turning briefly aroused him; then he relaxed. It was probably Cat, stealing into his room to talk. She was something of a night creature, restlessly prowling or reading till all hours. Being ten years old was rough, he remembered, too old for childish games and too young for adult entertainment.

The door was pushed silently open. A shadow was thrown into the room with the rectangular patch of light from the upstairs hallway. Ty came to full alertness when a woman's figure slipped into the room, clad in a shimmering ivory satin robe. Ty crushed the half-smoked cigarette in the ashtray as he sat bolt upright. The bedcovers fell down around his hips, revealing his bare chest.

"Tara, what the hell are you doing here?" His voice was half-angry and half-stunned.

"I couldn't sleep." She glided toward the bed, the shimmering fabric rippling with her every movement, outlining her breasts and hips. "You couldn't sleep either, could you?" The knowing sound in her voice ripened his awareness of her.

"You shouldn't be here at this hour." But he didn't move as he watched her hands gracefully lift the skirt of her robe to set a knee on the bed.

The mattress dipped slightly under the weight centered on the point of her knee. The robe parted with a faint rustle, giving him a provocative glimpse of bare thigh; then the glistening ivory fabric came together again. Curling her body, she sat sideways on the bed and leaned an arm toward him.

"I kept thinking about us and I just had to see you," Tara murmured.

"Suppose my parents heard you come in here." All his protesting was done with words. The graceful sensuality of her body and the gripping beauty of her face were like drink to him, bringing back memories and making him heady with that old desire.

"I was very quiet. Nobody heard me." She slid nearer to him and reclined on the pillows that were still dented with his imprint. She lay there, so inviting, that near smile on her lips. "Relax, Ty. We'll just sit here and talk for a little while."

"You're crazy." He looked at her, his features tightening. "It's enough that we sleep under the same roof, but to have you in my bed—! Dammit, Tara, do you think I'm made of wood?"

Her soft, breathy laugh was like crystal pendants striking. "I hope not."

It prodded him. "You're getting out of this bed," he growled, remembering too well the number of times she'd tormented him with her body, always denying him, always letting him reach for the damned string and pulling it away.

His arm hooked her waist, meaning to heave her to the side of the bed, back the way she'd come, but she wrapped her arms around his neck. Ty had never guessed she had such strength. Both fell heavily onto the mattress. The feel of her body beneath him was a hot iron; he tried to back off from it, but her tightly wound arms wouldn't let him get far.

"Do you still hate me so much, Ty? Must I be totally brazen and shameless?"

His body was arched above hers, muscles straining to keep it there despite the relentless pressure on his neck. He was still, searching her face pooled in moonlight, while he tried to fathom her meaning without reading into it something that wasn't there.

"Say what you mean, Tara."

"You want me, don't you?" Her lips were open, her eyes on his mouth.

"I want you." All the hunger and loneliness of being without her rose up inside him as he looked at her. "You're asking to be raped," Ty accused roughly. He pried an arm loose from his neck and peeled off of her to lie taut and rigid on the bed, trembling inside. She rolled onto her side, facing him. Her slim white hand glided across his bare chest, her fingers running into the curling hairs.

"Ty, my silly love. Must I do the raping, too?" Her lips ran over the bunched muscle in his shoulder.

When she moved onto him, his hands came up to push her off, then stayed to hold the silken weight of her body while she ate at his mouth, her teeth biting at his lip in a hotly playful kiss. He endured its tormenting fire that teased and wouldn't satisfy, until he could take no more of the raw desire. He was made of flesh and blood.

With a twist of his body, he rolled her away and followed to pin her down, taking the satisfaction from her lips that she had withheld. She was all motion under him, restless and urgent. Her hands were in his hair, nails digging and flexing. Whispering sounds came from her throat, faint, sighing groans of pleasure and need.

He felt her skin against his, the satin robe coming apart and giving his body access to her nakedness. His hands made exploring contact with the rounded shapes of her body, territory he'd yearned to claim. Now it was being surrendered. The fevers heating him could not be dispelled to give him time to question her act.

Her breathing quickened under the caress of his hands. The rough texture of his callused skin was like sandpaper, leaving areas more sensitized than he'd found them. It was good what she was feeling, but the sensations had always been different with Ty. There was no need to hold back anymore. Her heart and her head were of one mind in this.

The pressure was building inside him, perspiration breaking out in little beads to dampen his skin. The hot desire pounding through his veins wanted no time wasted with preliminaries. There was a sane instant when Ty tried to consider the consequences of this moment and pulled back to discover if those vague doubts he'd had about Tara were important. But she clamped her legs around him.

"Ty, please."

"No."

"Ty!"

There was no seal of virginity to break. He was absorbed into her and she was all tight and warm around him. After that, it was mindless sensation driven by instinct that coupled them, forging chains that wouldn't be so easy to break.

Her breathing was settled as she lay half over him, her slim body feeling heavy. "It was good, wasn't it?" Her soft voice was thick and dreamy.

"Yes." His hand absently rubbed her rounded hipbone while he stared at the pattern of shadows on the ceiling.

Her fingers ran over the cord in his neck. "You aren't tense anymore," she observed. "You've been doing too much thinking lately, complicating something that's very simple. Now that edginess and tension are all gone. And it was so easy, too." .

Her body had taken it from him and given contentment. She had been confident she could erase the things that were troubling him, Ty realized. But there were other needs a man had—needs sex couldn't satisfy. He stirred, uneasy.

"Ty, what are you thinking about?" she asked at his silence.

"Nothing," he lied.

"It was what you wanted," she reminded him.

"Yes."

There was the game in it. He'd taken her, and now he was accountable for it. There was no forgetting what happened or turning aside from the consequences. When the hunger came to him, he'd want her again, and he knew it. Like a dog, he'd always return to the stoop where he'd last been fed.

The fact that she had come to him should have made a difference in her thinking. It had been as much her desire as it had been his. The blame should have been shared. But it was never that way with women—not women like Tara Lee Dyson.

This hadn't been a casual act. She'd laid her hold on his conscience. He had bedded her; now he was expected to wed her.

He let the thought settle into him. It was what he had wanted all along. Tara was the prize, the success—and she had come to him.

"I suppose you'll want the biggest, fanciest damned wedding Texas has ever seen," he said dryly.

She laughed in her throat. "You guessed it, honey." She leaned up to kiss him.

15

No amount of twisting enabled Jessy to reach the hook at the back of her dress. Frustration merely added to the irritability that she blamed on the early-morning August heat. It accumulated quickly in the upstairs bedrooms of the log home. She left her room and headed down the stairs. A whirring fan created a blessed stir of air in the living room, where her two teenaged brothers, Ben and Mike, were lounging in crisp new jeans and pearl-buttoned western shirts. Ben was painstakingly smoothing the creases in the crown of his good western hat. At the sound of her footsteps on the stairs, he looked up, then hit his brother.

"Would you look at Jessy?" His square face was split with a grin. "She's got legs!"

"Is that what those two white things are?" Mike quickly picked up on the oddity of seeing their older sister in a dress, siding as always with his brother to rib her.

"They look a sight better than those hairy things you two have," Jessy retorted.

"Wait'll the boys get a load of Jessy," Ben persisted with a wicked gleam.

"Wait'll they get a load of that fuzz on your face that you call a beard," she countered, accustomed to trading sibling insults.

Ben rubbed his chin defensively. "It's filling out and starting to look pretty good." But the new beard was sandy-colored and soft, which gave it a sparse appearance.

"Where's Mom?" Jessy glanced toward the kitchen.

"I think she's still getting ready," Mike replied.

The bedroom downstairs belonged to her parents. Jessy went to it and knocked on the door. "It's me. Can I come in?" Permission followed and Jessy entered, shutting the door behind her. Her mother was seated at an old-fashioned vanity table, wearing only a cotton slip trimmed with lace. The traces of gray in her hair only made its sandy color seem lighter. She leaned close to the mirror to apply her makeup and eyed Jessy's reflection in it.

"I can't fasten the top hook on my dress." Jessy crossed to the vanity table.

"I like that dress on you." Judy Niles looked at her daughter approvingly and returned her attention to the mirror. "I'm glad you decided to buy a new one for the party."

"A party for the new Calder bride is a special occasion." There was a faint edge to her voice.

"I wonder what she's like." She used a tissue to blot her lipstick.

"I wouldn't ask a man to tell you. They can't see past a pretty face."

"Jessy, don't you like her?" Her mother turned, surprised to hear that cynical note in Jessy's voice.

"I don't even know her. What does it matter anyway?" She sighed, trying to repress the impatience and irritation that pushed at her. She hurt inside. She didn't want to go to this party and meet Ty's incredibly beautiful bride face to face. All her life she'd been taught to stand up to unpleasant things, and pride wouldn't permit her to run from this.

"You'll never enjoy the party in that kind of mood," her mother declared and rose to her feet, standing as tall as Jessy. Placing her hands on Jessy's shoulders, she pushed her onto the bench. "Sit down and I'll brush your hair."

It had been a nightly routine when she was a small child—her mother brushing and brushing her hair until it glistened and shone—and Jessy could feel as beautiful as a fairy princess for a little while. She closed her eyes and let the rhythmic strokes of the hairbrush soothe her troubled spirits.

After a few minutes her mother began smoothing and arranging, pushing her hair this way and that. "I always thought when I had a little girl that I'd be doing things like this for her, but I had you instead," her mother joked. "You have nice eyes. You really should use some shadow."

"I'd look painted," Jessy replied, her eyes still closed. "Besides, I put on mascara."

"Let me try something." There was the rattle of her mother pawing through her makeup case. "Now keep your eyes closed."

"It's no use, Mom." But Jessy patiently let her dab here and there with an applicator, then a soft puff on her cheeks.

"Now look." A pair of hands turned Jessy's face toward the mirror and she opened her eyes to view the results. "There's an old saying," her mother murmured. " 'Ugly in the cradle, beautiful at the table.' "

Jessy stared at her reflection. The sun had streaked her hair to a glistening taffy color. It waved thick and full to frame her face. The makeup was barely noticeable, but her cheekbones stood out and her eyes seemed darker and more mysterious. The longer Jessy looked, the less she recognized herself. Just for a minute she was tempted—then she reached for a tissue to scrub it off.

"Jessy, you look lovely!" her mother protested.

"Mom, that's not me," she explained, somber and patient. "Would you please fasten my dress?"

The bedroom door opened and her father came in, frowning sharply. "Are you women still in here primping? We're supposed to be there early so we can help get things set up."

"I just have to put my dress on," her mother replied.

There were so many hands to set up the tables and chairs and get the barbecue fires going that nobody missed Jessy when she wandered away. As always, she gravitated to the horse barns, where it was shadowed and dark, musty with hay smells and horse odors. It was quiet except for the stomp of a horse and the swish of a tail at a fly.

Jessy wandered down the cemented walkway, swept clean of all but a few wisps of straw. Her low-heeled sandals barely made any sound as she walked by the stalls, pausing occasionally to rub a velvet nose curiously thrust at her. A horse in the far-end stall whickered and shifted agitatedly. Immediately Jessy heard a low, soothing voice croon to it.

A faint smile lifted the corners of her mouth as she guessed it was old Abe Garvey. It'd been a long time since she'd talked to him. He was quite a storyteller, always had tales to tell about the old days. She walked to the end stall and leaned on the board, careful to avoid the splintered edge.

"Hello," she said to the dark figure bent low, brushing the leg of a liver-red sorrel. The man straightened up tall, and Jessy stiffened in recognition of Ty Calder. "I thought you were Abe."

Ty's eyebrow briefly quirked at being mistaken for a stooped and crippled old man; then he went back to his brushing. "Abe went home to get cleaned up for the party."

"Oh. New horse?" Jessy was familiar with most of the horses on the ranch. This sorrel wasn't one she'd be likely to forget. It had good lines and an intelligent head.

"The filly's my wedding present to Tara. I was just getting her slicked down so I could give her to Tara this afternoon," he explained.

"Speaking of your bride, where is she?"

"Up at the house, I imagine." He patted the horse's sleek neck and came to stand beside the manger, opposite Jessy.

Her eyes studied him, scanning his features for some sign married life had changed him. He and his bride had gone straight from their Texas wedding on a three-week honeymoon. But there was no settled look about him, and his lazy eyes didn't give her any hint about what he might be thinking.

"You went off and got married so fast I never did have a chance to tell you congratulations," she offered.

"Thanks." His gaze wandered over her face, as if trying to find something that bothered him. "When are you going to get yourself a man, Jessy?"

"What makes you think I need one?" She was stung that he should ask her such a question.

His laugh was dry and throaty. "You always were self-sufficient, even when you were a kid." He swung a boot onto the manger and vaulted to the other side, landing next to her. The filly spooked, pulled back on her lead rope. "Easy, girl," Ty quieted the horse; then he turned to Jessy. "Guess it's time I got washed up and changed for the party." He was wearing a pair of old Levi's and a faded plaid shirt with the cuffs rolled back.

"See you later."

Ty started to walk past her, then stopped. "You're wearing a dress," he said. "That's what's different about you." He looked her over, discovering a female shape that was usually hidden by man-style clothes. "It looks good on you."

"I know it."

His brow drew together, creasing slightly. "I don't know if I'll ever understand you, Jessy," he murmured.

"You've got a wife now. It's her you need to understand," Jessy reminded him and watched him draw back slightly, then walk away.

"Where's Tara?" Ty asked as he entered The Homestead.

"She's still upstairs," Cathleen informed him. "I don't know what she's doing, but she's sure been making a lot of noise."

Taking the steps two at a time, Ty went up the stairs and straight to the master bedroom. When he entered, Tara was standing in the middle of the room, tapping a finger against her mouth and contemplating a chair. She was wearing a filmy yellow peignoir from her trousseau.

"Good morning, honey," she greeted him almost absently, sparing him no more than a glance.

"What are you doing?" There was a degree of indulgence in his look as he crossed to her. Tousled from bed and without a scrap of makeup, she was still the most desirable woman he'd ever seen.

"I'm trying to decide where to put this chair," she replied and pushed his hands away when he tried to slip them around her waist. "Don't, Ty. I'm trying to work this out."

"You've been rearranging the furniture," he observed with a glance around the room. "You're supposed to be getting ready for a party."

"It won't hurt if we're late." She impatiently waved aside his reminder. Just as suddenly, she was turning and grabbing both his hands. "You don't know how good I feel." She looked around the spacious room with a swelling pride. "This is our own private corner of the house, completely ours. I can hardly wait to start fixing it up."

"You'll have to wait, because you have to get ready for the party. It was very generous of my parents to give us the master bedroom with its adjoining sitting room," he agreed and changed the grip of their hands to pull her close enough to kiss.

After a brief touching, she drew back. "You smell of horses." She wrinkled her nose. "You'd better go shower before I smell of them, too." The drone of an airplane's engine sounded outside the window. "That must be Daddy and Stricklin." She dashed to the window. "Remind me to have him ship that antique secretary up here. It will fit perfectly in this corner."

Sheriff Potter had found a place in the shade where a breeze blowing in from the river could reach him. From his chair, he had a view of the tent and the wood pits, the cluster of tables, and most of the crowd. Without exerting himself, he could keep an eye on just about everything that went on. Thin-chested and wide-hipped, he was sprawled over the chair, his legs stretched in front of him with his feet crossed. The hair on his head had thinned to white wisps. Always on the edge of laziness, age had slowed him down still more.

Although he observed Chase Calder's approach, he neither straightened nor shifted his position. He continued sucking at his teeth, occasionally poking a toothpick between one gap or another. He waited until Calder had stopped in front of him before he bothered to nod.

"Glad you could make it, Potter." An empty chair was by the trunk of the shade tree. Chase brought it around and sat down.

"Wouldn't have missed the feed." The sheriff dug at his teeth again, then sucked out the bit of food. "I wanted to see the boy's gal, too. I've known four Calders in my time. Wonder if I'll be around to see the fifth one born."

"I wouldn't be surprised," Chase murmured dryly. The old man had a way of conserving energy and keeping himself going long after most people figured he was through.

"I've seen a lot." He slid him a look. "Been smart enough to forget most of it, too." The toothpick was left sticking out of his mouth to be rolled around and chewed on. "That engineering fella Belton that's got his trailer parked there by Sally's? I managed to do some backtracking on his company. Found out who hired him."

The initial check had come back more than two months earlier, proving the man to be reputable. Since no trouble had been reported, Chase had pushed the matter to the back of his mind. The sheriff obviously hadn't.

Chase glanced at him, mildly interested. "Who was it?"

"Another Texas outfit. A company outa Fort Worth, named Dy-Corp." He continued to watch the crowd with the ease of one accustomed to watching the world go by. "That's the same company that drilled them oil wells on your land, ain't it? Your son's new father-in-law owns it, I believe."

"Yes." Chase turned his gaze to the crowd and searched out the Texan. He didn't recall Dyson mentioning that he was planning any more drilling in the area.

"Remember that old Stockman place? Some company back east owns it and leases a bunch of federal graze. Dyson cut a deal this past June and leased it lock, stock, barrel, and mineral rights, includin' that government land." He chewed on the toothpick and flipped it to the other corner of his mouth as if his teeth got tired of holding it on the one side. "Just got one old buzzard on the place. Belton goes in and out every day. I don't know what's goin' on in there. It's real secret. But it ain't oil he's hoping to find."

"Water would be more valuable to him."

There was a long pause. "I see O'Rourke's here, skulkin' around the barn," the sheriff observed. "Queer fellow."

Chase followed the direction of the sheriff's gaze and located the slim, lanky man, leaning against the corner of the stable barn. He was like a coyote, curiosity bringing him close enough to see what was going on, yet with open space behind him so he could bolt and run.

"He does a lot of riding." Arch Goodman had reported on the frequency of fresh tracks crossing onto Calder land from the Shamrock. So far, there hadn't been any trouble. "It seems he can't stand being hemmed in anymore."

"Sorta like a wild animal that's been caged for a spell an' set free." Potter nodded his understanding. "Always gotta keep movin' now."

"O'Rourke was always a loner. Never wanted to fit in," Chase concluded.

"Now, that's a pair to keep your eye on—Dyson and Bulfert." The toothpick was taken out of his mouth as the sheriff focused thoughtfully on the two men, talking amiably amidst the crowd. "Yes, sir, Bulfert's the best money can buy, and he's been bought more than once. I bet he's turned more political tricks than a whore. And he's gone through his money 'bout as fast as one." There was another pause. "I heard he's retiring after this term. Wonder when he's going to check to see how well his pockets are lined."

"That sounds like a warning." Chase studied him, trying to read between the lines.

"Just an observation." The sheriff almost managed a tired smile. "Observing people is ninety percent of my business. I let the young fools chase the speeders at a hundred miles an hour and bring in the mean drunks. No, I just watch. That's how I've stayed sheriff so long—by watchin' and knowin'. I'm just passin' on to you what I see . . . for whatever good it might do you."

"I appreciate it."

"That partner of Dyson's—what's his name?" The sheriff

cocked his head toward Chase. "That tall, pale-haired fella with glasses."

"Stricklin."

"Stricklin." He repeated the name with a kind of satisfaction. "He's got clean hands. You ever noticed how clean they are?" He shook his head briefly. "I never trust a man with clean hands. I always wonder why he washes 'em so much." With a weary effort, he uncrossed his feet and made a project out of sitting up. "Guess I oughta pay my respects to the bride and groom and get back on the job."

"See you around, Potter." Chase stayed in the chair when the old man got up to shuffle down to the milling crowd. A lot had been said that warranted some thinking.

"Ty"—Tara leaned against his side—"who's that tall girl in the flowered sundress? Is she somebody important?"

There was only one tall girl he could see. "That's Jessy Niles. She works here."

"What does she do?"

"She works cattle with the men." He slid his wife an amused look and observed her expression of surprise.

"She isn't that grubby girl I saw on the roundup?" Tara frowned, not believing it was possible.

"The same." Ty studied the girl under discussion with lazy speculation.

Always level and direct, Jessy had eyes that could look right into the heart of a man. She was a serious and silent girl, and Ty was never quite sure what lay behind that solid composure, whether it was indifference or speculation or a more closely guarded feeling. There had been eruptions when she'd come out fighting.

The faint smile on his face began to fade the longer he watched her. For all her slim height, there was nothing angular about her. When sun rays became trapped in the mane of her hair and toasted it gold, Ty noticed the proud way she held her head and the innate strength in her features. Her body was supple-shaped, with a graceful way of stirring when she moved. She was completely woman, a fact he acknowledged with slow surprise. He'd seen her too long in a man's setting, and he suspected there was more to her that a man might not notice unless he studied her long and hard.

The discovery vaguely unsettled him. Pulling his eyes back, Ty looked sideways at Tara to search her expression. He found her watching him with cool interest. Ty quickly smiled to hide the idle interest that had been sparked.

"How would you like to see your wedding present?" His question banished all else from her mind, and the matter of Jessy Niles was forgotten.

Outside the stable, the wind howled, blowing a late-November snow across the yard. The bay mare in the large box stall nosed at the fresh hay in the manger, her ears swiveling restlessly, picking up every strange and new sound. She kept eyeing the coated man-figures studying her, their smells still new to her. She lipped at the hay.

"She's settlin' in," the wrangler Wyatt Yates predicted.

"We'll have to keep her in through the winter," Ty stated. "She's Texas-bred and not used to this kind of cold."

The mare was more than just a new horse. She was another addition to the brood-mare herd that Ty was establishing. Good cow horses with savvy and breeding were hard to come by. The Triple C had always done a limited amount of raising its own horses for ranch work, but Ty had convinced his father the operation needed to be expanded and a higher quality of horses bred.

Some of the Cougar-bred mares made good foundation stock. In the last two months, Ty had purchased three more mares, all of which had proved their cow sense as working horses and added their bloodlines to the herd. He was still searching for two top stallions. Until he found what he wanted, he planned to send the mares off the ranch to be bred to a selected group of stallions.

This search had meant a lot of trips, with more to come. Tara always went with him, invariably turning it into a combination of business and pleasure. If Ty was honest, he would admit that he enjoyed showing her off, knowing he was the envy of every man for having such a beautiful and loving wife.

Leaving the new horse in Yates's care, Ty left the stables and bucked the wind to reach the pickup. It was only a few hundred yards to The Homestead, waiting with lights shining in the gloaming of a winter dusk, but a man never walked when he could ride in this country.

On the porch, Ty stomped the snow off his boots on the bristled mat outside the front doors, then walked in. The house had a silent and empty feel to it. Cat was away at boarding school, which naturally made the house seem quieter than normal. Unbuttoning the sheepskin-lined suede jacket, he made a detour past the study and into the living room without seeing anyone. A glance into the dining room and kitchen found them equally empty, although there was the smell of something cooking.

He climbed the stairs to the second floor with slow deliberation and walked to the private quarters he shared with his wife. The two rooms were slowly being transformed by Tara, the heavier pieces of furniture moved out in favor of daintier ones. The four-poster bed had been replaced by a canopied king-sized one, pleated and draped in gold satin. New drapes at the windows, carpeting—something was always being added or changed. Ty was never sure what to expect when he walked in.

One table lamp was turned on a low setting, barely lighting the sitting room. After coming from the bright hall, it took him a second to adjust to the dim light. As he took off his hat, he noticed the flickering of the candlelight. The small round table, one of the more recent additions to the room, was covered with a damask cloth and set with china and crystal for two, and a pair of red candles in silver holders swirled with yellow flames in the middle.

Tara came from the bedroom, paused in its light when she saw him. As his gaze ran over her, again Ty was stirred by her beauty, clad this night in a gown of burgundy velvet, her ebony hair tumbling in ropy curls, diamond teardrops dangling from the delicate lobes of her ears. She glided across the room to him and he reached for her, so small and beautiful.

But she pressed her hands firmly against his chest and gave him no more than a brief peck on the lips. "You're all dirty. I have things all laid out for your shower."

His hands continued to hold her shoulders, not letting her go but not pressing an embrace, while he breathed in the fragrance of her hair, his attention slipping to her cleavage in the low-cut gown. "What's this?" Ty meant all of it—the candles, the table set for two, the evening gown.

"Tonight we have the house to ourselves, so I decided to do something different and intimate instead of sitting at that big old dining-room table again."

"To ourselves, hmm?" There was a darkening of desire in his eyes.

"Your father called around three to say he was going to be late and not to wait dinner. He was going to stop at some place called Sally's and eat," she explained, her reddened lips turning up to him provocatively. "When I gave your mother the message, she suggested that you and I might like to have dinner alone for a change."

"Where did she go?" His hold on her shoulders slackened as a sudden tension rippled through him.

"She said she was going to surprise your father and meet him at Sally's. She left about twenty minutes ago." She noticed Ty's sudden hesitation, the troubled grimness around his mouth. She tipped her head to the side. "Is something wrong?"

It was a long second before he heard her question. He loosened his grip, letting his hands fall to his sides. His interest in the intimate evening Tara had planned faded as Ty realized his mother must have guessed all along what was going on between his father and Sally Brogan.

"No. Nothing's wrong." Nothing that he could do anything about. He turned from her. "I'd better take that shower."

"I'll open a bottle of red wine so it can have a chance to breathe." Tara moved gracefully toward the table, unaware of the crosscurrents pulling at Ty. A gust of wind rattled a windowpane, and her mouth tightened at the howling, mournful sound. "I hate that wind."

Ty didn't hear her.

"What kind of heavy machinery?" Chase frowned at Sally's description of the equipment loaded on a big semi-trailer rig that had stopped to ask directions to the Stockman Ranch. "Do you mean drilling equipment?"

"No." Sally set her coffee cup on the table. The blustery, cold night had brought in few supper customers, and the drinkers wouldn't arrive until later. "It looked like construction equipment—those big earth movers, that kind of thing. They must be going to build something."

"It could have been road machinery," Chase suggested thoughtfully and cut into his steak. Headlights flashed through the large glass windows of the tavern-restaurant.

"That's probably what it was," Sally agreed and watched him fork a bite of meat into his mouth. "How's the steak? All right?"

"Perfect, as always." He smiled at her. His expression was warm and affectionate as a cold draft of air blew in when the door was opened. Chase glanced up idly and went still at the sight of Maggie striding across the room, smiling too cheerfully. He recovered quickly. "Maggie?" There was a faint question in his voice, a touch of wariness.

"Surprised?" She pulled out a chair and sat down at the table, glancing too briefly at the auburn-haired woman with him. There was a flash of fire in her green eyes, almost daring him to say anything, when she turned her gaze back to him.

"You know I am," he countered smoothly.

"I decided to join you for dinner tonight and enjoy someone else's cooking for a change," Maggie announced. "Besides, it will give our newlyweds some time alone."

Sally didn't lose her look of serenity, although her glance did run uncertainly to Chase for a second. "What would you like me to fix you, Maggie?"

"I'll have the same as Chase, only make my steak rare," she ordered, then added when Sally rose, "But come back and join us."

After Sally had brought Maggie's food, she refilled her coffee cup and sat down at the table. It didn't take Chase long to realize what Maggie was doing there. The longer he watched her action, the more amused and proud he became. In her own subtle way, Maggie was claiming him as her property and warning Sally to keep her hands off. It was all very ladylike, but the amiability was all on the surface. Underneath, she was fighting mad.

When it came time to leave, Chase spared a moment's pity for the quiet-natured Sally, who had become even more reserved. But she had long known the score, and tonight she had been outclassed from the start.

As they were leaving, two Triple C riders walked in. "Give me your car keys, Maggie," Chase ordered.

"Why?" She took them out of her purse.

"Grady!" He called back one of the riders and tossed the keys to him. "My wife's riding back with me. See that her car gets to the ranch—in one piece." Maggie made no protest.

"Yes, sir." The cowboy shoved them into his pocket and ambled for the pool table where his buddy waited.

His arm was on her shoulders as they walked out of the tavern. A chuckle started in his throat, gradually developing into a hearty sound.

"What's so funny?" Her breath came out in an angry puff, vaporized by the cold temperatures.

"You," he declared.

"I'm glad you find me so amusing." She was anything but glad as she moved out from under his curving arm and hurried stiffly down the steps to his pickup.

Chase caught up with her at the truck and turned her around before she could open the door. His look was warm and amused, undeterred by the snap in her eyes.

"You were jealous, weren't you?" he challenged knowingly.

"I don't know what you're talking about," she replied curtly and tried to twist out of his hold, but he merely rocked her deeper into the circle of his arms, bundling her as close as the thicknesses of their coats would permit.

"You had no reason to be," Chase informed her, not feeling the nipping cold. "Not even when we were having our hardest times. Oh, I admit I had a few thoughts in Sally's direction, but I couldn't forget you. I'd given you my word—my promise to love only you."

"Then why—?" Maggie shut her mouth on the question, not finishing it because she didn't want to admit she had been jealous and she didn't want to know why he had continually sought Sally's company for so long.

Blood surged exultantly through his veins with a young man's intoxication as Chase fell youthfully in love with her all over again. His fancies were wanting to sing and shout it out. All his senses were open to the excitement of the feeling, its heady flavors and sweet sounds. This proud, feisty lady was his kind of woman; none other could ever satisfy him, and none ever had.

"Why did I keep on stopping by to see her?" Chase knew the question she hadn't wanted to ask, strangely attuned to her thinking when he hadn't been for so long. "She offered comfort. And I was afraid I was losing you."

"Losing me?" There was blankness and confusion in her face at the implication she had somehow stopped loving him.

"I'm not sure I can explain." His mouth crooked ruefully. "Maybe it's your sophistication. I don't know. But I saw less and less of Maggie and more of the cultured Elizabeth, so cool and contained. I thought, when Ty went to college, you were wishing for your old life. That maybe you regretted . . . until you came charging into the café tonight, ready to do battle to keep your man." He grew tensely serious. "I am your man, aren't I?"

"Yes." She was so happy she hurt.

When he kissed her long and deeply, their renewed passion flowed freely. She wrapped her arms tightly around his neck and strained on tiptoes, holding on to this feeling they'd almost lost.

Their lips parted, but they stayed in the embrace, each breathing hard and smiling a little at this giddy rush of young love reborn. His hands moved over her back, vaguely irritated with the coat and the cold when he wanted nothing to interfere with this special closeness.

"Maggie, my love—my only love—let's go home," he insisted huskily.

She laughed, love rippling from her throat. "Oh, God, yes."

16

Heat shimmers made waves in the straight stretch of highway and distorted the buildings ahead. Speedzone signs were posted on the outskirts, the first hint of change. Ty slowed his pickup as he approached the town, noting the changes four short years since he'd married Tara had brought.

Blue Moon no longer had the look of a half-dead ghost town, crumbling on the roadside. The abandoned, run-down buildings with their broken backs and bulging sides that had stood forlornly by the two-lane, dying slowly for so many decades, were gone—bulldozed down and their rubble carted away for burial. In their place were mobile homes, the weed-choked yards cut down so children could play.

Three vehicles were already parked next to the gas pumps when Ty pulled in. One of them bore the insignia of Dy-Corp Coal, a subsidiary of Dy-Corp Ltd. Blue Moon was a company town, peopled mainly by the heavy machinery operators who manned the strip-mining equipment and their families.

Outsiders were eyed with curiosity, and Ty received his share of looks when he stepped out of the truck. Four years had made some changes in him as well. Muscles had filled out his chest and shoulders; he was a tall, imposing figure of a man. The sun and wind had toughened his face and etched craggy lines into his features. The deep-set eyes were more often hooded now, less expressive of his thoughts and feelings. And the black brush of a mustache added to his look of hard virility.

With those long strides that never seemed hurried, Ty left the truck and entered the store. The grocery section had been enlarged to carry more items, which left the post-office window crowded into a small corner in the rear. A couple of wives were shopping and trying to keep their children corraled.

As Ty approached the caged window of the post office, he heard voices and recognized them as belonging to two longtime residents of Blue Moon. The postal area also doubled as the private office for the store and station.

"Calder ain't gonna be happy when he hears about this," a man's voice declared, and Ty's steps slowed.

"Let him be upset," a second said. "He can rant and rave all he wants about protectin' the land and not damaging the environment. It's fine-sounding if you can afford it. But he never talks about the good things that come with this strip-mining."

"I know. Anna and I just about decided we were going to have to close down the store." It was Lew Michels, who owned the dry-goods and hardware store across the street. "We just weren't making any money until all these coal families moved into town. Now there's a good chance we'll be able to sell the business and have a nice nest egg for our retirement."

"This town was dying. All the young folks were leaving 'cause there wasn't any jobs for them. Now there's work and new blood comin' in. A man's got a chance to keep his head above water. Calder never did no more than throw us a bone from time to time. I say Dy-Corp is the best thing that ever happened to this town—and the land and Calder be damned."

"It's progress," Michels said. "Calder's gotta accept it. With the regulations they have on strip-mining, the land has got to be reclaimed. The president said so himself—it's in the national interest to develop our own resources. And we've got enough coal in Montana to heat the whole country."

When Ty appeared at the barred window, the talking abruptly ceased. "I think you have a package for my wife," he said.

"I sure do." Emmett Fedderson came to his feet, looking uncomfortable. "Just step around to the door and I'll give it to you."

The cardboard-boxed package was passed to him. Ty

hefted it under his arm and headed out of the store, the conversation he'd overheard lingering in his thoughts. He'd known feelings were running high on the issue of strip-mining coal, but he hadn't realized people were taking sides. Perhaps because he didn't share his father's passion on the issue. The older his father got, the more he resisted changing with the times.

As Ty climbed into the truck, he wondered what it was that his father wasn't going to be happy to hear. Dinner tonight was bound to be an awkward affair if the news turned out to be as unpleasant as Fedderson had indicated. Dyson was at the ranch visiting Tara and checking on the coal operation. It made for some strained evenings.

Seconds after Ty had walked in the door of The Homestead, he heard his father's angry voice ringing out from the den. "Dammit, you find out!" A telephone receiver was slammed down.

With a degree of resignation, Ty headed for the open doors of the study. There was no more wondering about what had happened. He was about to find out. But his mother was there ahead of him to ask the questions.

"What happened, Chase?" She bit her lip with concern.

His hand was a taut fist on the desktop, his head down and averted. "I don't believe it," he muttered. "All that work— all that money and effort spent to draft one of the toughest pieces of legislation to regulate surface mining—and what happens? The Interior Department in Washington has ordered the state of Montana to conform to federal regulations!"

Chase Calder had lobbied hard for the passage of that bill in the Montana legislature. It was a bitter blow.

"Dyson's behind this," his father announced grimly. "And I'd lay odds that Bulfert's sold out to him."

It was the suspicion of double-dealing that had infuriated his father more than the dilution of the mining bill, Ty realized. The clash with Dyson had never been personal. Each had applied pressure to stop the other, but on a business level. Losing to Dyson wasn't so bad, but the possible defection of the senator was not easy for his father to take. It was that old code surfacing that said, when you took a man's pay, you took his side. If a man rode for the brand, he fought for it, too.

The phone rang, and it was impatiently grabbed by his father. Now that he had learned the latest development, there was no more reason for Ty to stay in the room. He left, heading for the stairs.

"What are you doing up here?" Ty was slightly surprised to see Tara when he entered the suite of rooms on the second floor. Lately she had spent little time in them, complaining that they were too confining.

"Where else would I be?" she retorted irritably and rose from the damask-covered lounge chair.

Ty chose to ignore the remark. "I picked up that package for you."

"Put it anywhere," Tara said with disinterest. "It's just those boots I ordered."

"Maybe you should try them on," he suggested.

"Not now." She wandered to the window. "I wish your father would build a swimming pool or tennis courts. He certainly can afford it. At least then there would be something to do around here."

"This is a working ranch, Tara—not a resort," Ty responded with heavy patience. "If you want to go swimming, Cat is probably at the river. Why don't you join her?"

"I don't like to swim in the river." There had been a time when she enjoyed it, but that had been early in their marriage. Since the horse herd had been established and they had ceased traveling so much in search of that foundation stock, Tara had gradually become bored with the monotony of the ranch routine. She swung around to face him. "Let's do something this afternoon, Ty," she urged, a desperate edge to the smile she gave him.

"I was just on my way out to check on some possible sites for the new feedlot operation. Ride along with me," he invited with a slow smile and dumped the package on the sofa to cross the room to her. "You used to come with me whenever I went out riding. I don't think you've ridden your horse in over a month."

She turned to the window and lifted the curtain to look out. There was tension in her slim, motionless form. "Once you leave these buildings, there's nothing out there but land. No matter how much you ride, you go nowhere and you get nowhere." Her mood was somber, something rare for Tara. "Have you looked at that land, Ty? I mean really looked at it and felt it?"

"I don't know what you mean." He was puzzled.

"I have," she went on, responding to her own question. "It makes me feel small—like I'm nothing. Well, I'm something," she said with aggression.

"Of course you are." Ty was faintly amused by her dramatics, even though he realized she was absolutely serious. "I only suggested that you come riding with me because I thought you'd enjoy the outing. But if you'd rather not go, that's all right."

"Ty." The curtain was dropped as she pivoted to face him. She came to him, sliding her hands up the front of his shirt to rest on his chest. "Stay here this afternoon. You can look at those sites any old time. Today, you can stay with me instead."

"Tara, I can't." There was a weariness in his voice. This was old ground. Given a chance, she'd find some excuse to keep him by her side every hour. "I have work to do. I can't stay here and entertain you."

"What am I supposed to do?" she challenged.

"Mother doesn't have any trouble keeping busy."

"Your mother has a house to run and friends to see." She pushed away from him, hugging her arms in agitation. "All I have are these two rooms and a husband who is gone all the time. I don't know why we can't build our own house so I can have friends visit—and parties—and dinners."

"Tara, we've been through this before." His patience was wearing thin.

"I know. First you want to build this fancy feedlot of yours. Then, maybe, you might build your wife a house of her own." There was anger behind her smiling look.

"Look, you're the one who insisted on having a new house," Ty reminded her tersely. "You weren't satisfied to move into one of the empty houses here at the headquarters."

"Ty, really. How would it look for a Calder to be living in

some simple house like every other common ranch hand?" Tara challenged, impatient with a suggestion she found ludicrous. "That's not good enough for you."

"You mean that's not good enough for you."

"No, it isn't. I am a *somebody*, and I'm not going to live like a nobody!" She was rigid before him, her head thrown back in defiance. He saw her like that for a moment, needing the accoutrements of position and the recognition of social prominence. Then she crumpled and went into his arms, holding him tightly. "Ty, I didn't mean for us to quarrel over this again. I can stand living in your father's house, but I'm tired of seeing you stand in his shadow. I know how intelligent and capable you are, but you aren't being given a chance to show anyone."

"Tara, that's not true." He held her. "The horse-breeding program, the proposed feedlot operation—they were my ideas. Dad has let me take charge of them. They are my responsibility."

"I suppose they are." She reluctantly gave in, a smile forced onto her lips. "Darling"—she stroked his jaw—"the governor is having a private dinner tonight. Daddy is flying to Helena later this afternoon to attend. Let's go with him."

"I can't take off at the drop of a hat, Tara," he told her, grim-mouthed under the mustache.

"Surely you can go just this once," she coaxed with her most provocative smile. "It's been ages since we've gone anywhere."

"If you had said something sooner, I might have been able to arrange things so we could go. But this afternoon it isn't possible." There was a finality in his voice that didn't encourage any further use of feminine wiles. She had used her beauty and her body on him too many times for Ty to let their persuasions alter his decision. Yet there was also the knowledge that this party was an occasion she badly wanted to attend. Her protests of boredom made him feel guilty and hard-pressed to deny her the excitement she craved. "You can go to the dinner with your father if you like," he offered grudgingly.

"Do you mean it?"

He watched her eyes light up. "Yes." He smiled, but it

didn't reach his eyes. Somehow he knew it was the start of something, the first of many trips she'd take without him, the first of many reasons she'd find to leave the ranch and go back to a more socially active life surrounded by so-called important people.

"I already know which gown I'm going to take." She was busy planning. "Where's Stricklin? I'll need to let him know I'll be coming with them."

"I haven't seen him since breakfast this morning." He should have guessed Stricklin would be attending the dinner. Dyson never went anywhere without his second pair of ears.

"He might be in his room, working on those reports for Daddy." Tara headed for the door, belatedly blowing Ty a kiss. "See you tomorrow, Ty darling."

Ty was slower to leave the room.

The drone of an airplane broke the afternoon quiet. Ty reined his horse in atop a rise and looked up to see Dyson's twin-engine aircraft making its swing west with Tara aboard. There was a knotting of his muscles, a fine-honed tension that sharpened his nerves.

He'd finished his inspection of the site on the north range. It appeared to be the most promising of all, with an ample supply of water, good natural drainage, and only a short distance from one of the main ranch roads and the north camp bossed by Arch Goodman.

The plane grew steadily smaller. Ty soon lost it in the glare of the low-hanging sun. He sat a second longer on his horse, then lifted the reins to head for the north camp, where he'd left his truck and horse van.

As he started to send his horse down the slope, he spotted a rider leading a sore-footed horse along the shallow pocket. It was Jessy Niles who had been forced afoot. Ty rode down. Cowboy boots were not conducive to walking long distances. When she heard the drum of hooves, she stopped and extended the shade of her hat brim with her hand to block out the sun's glaring angle and identify the approaching rider.

"Trouble?" His dryly amused glance ran over her dusty face.

"Threw a shoe about six miles back," she answered

ruefully. "Wouldn't ya know I'd get nearly home before someone comes along."

Ty chuckled and took his boot out of the left stirrup. "Climb aboard."

Jessy passed him the reins to her horse, then stuck a toe in the empty stirrup and grabbed his saddle horn to swing up behind him. There was never any ease within her when she was around him. She didn't have it now as she had to grip the solid trunk of his waist to steady herself while she shifted into a comfortable position on the saddle skirt. Underneath all that casualness, she was as taut as a bowstring.

"Ready?" Ty wrapped her horse's reins around the saddle horn to eliminate the drag.

"Yeah." She took her hands off him and rested them on her thighs, balancing easily at the slow walk necessitated by her tender-footed horse. His shoulders were broad and well muscled. He smelled of horses and tobacco smoke. It was a full minute before Jessy realized he had turned off the path she'd been on. "Where are you going?"

"To the camp." He turned his head, giving her a view of his jutting profile, bronzed and sun-lined at the corner of his eyes. "Why?"

"If you angle to the north, it'll shortcut you to the edge of camp," Jessy said, knowing the area like the back of her hand. "I've got a cabin there, stuck in the woods."

"The old Stanton place?" Ty asked, neck-reining his mount in a northerly direction.

"Yeah."

"I thought you were still living with your folks," he remarked idly.

"I was up until last fall. I usually moved in with the Goodmans over the winter 'cause it's too hard trying to get from one end of the ranch to the other when the weather's bad. Old Abe Garvey had been living in the Stanton cabin. When he died last September, I decided to just move up here permanently so I wouldn't have to keep making that long drive back and forth," she explained matter-of-factly.

"You're completely independent now." It was an observation that said she had always been independent by nature, but cutting loose from her home made it total.

"My folks have the place to themselves now that Ben and Mike have both gone to work on other parts of the ranch. They used to complain it was too noisy in the house. Now they're saying it's too quiet," she said, smiling faintly and swaying with the rhythm of the walking horse. "I keep telling them they should be glad to get a twenty-four-year-old daughter off their hands."

"You're getting to be an old maid, Jessy." There was a smile in his voice.

"There's the cabin." She pointed over his shoulder at the low roofline in the shadows of the cottonwoods rising along the riverbanks.

When he reached the small log structure, he reined in the horse and Jessy pushed backwards to slide off its rump to the ground. Ty unwrapped the reins to her horse and stepped down.

"If you're not in a hurry, I can make some coffee," Jessy offered to return the favor that had saved her from walking the last half mile.

Ty hesitated only briefly. He had no reason to hurry back to The Homestead. "It sounds good," he accepted. "I'll give you a hand with the horse."

In short order, the horse was unsaddled and turned loose in the corral. Jessy entered the cabin ahead of Ty and motioned him to have a chair. It was just three rooms, orderly and simple. The walls were plastered white, and the bright chintz curtains at the windows stirred with the breeze rustling through the trees outside. There was a comfortable, lived-in air about it.

Unbuckling his spurs, Ty sat down in one of the curved-back wooden chairs at the table and hooked another one with his toe to prop his boots on. He leaned back and listened to the sounds coming from the kitchen—water running from the tap, Jessy's footsteps, cupboard doors opening and closing.

He felt the tension slowly drain from him. A feeling of comfort and quiet calmed him, loosened him. He took a cigarette from the pack in his shirt pocket and lit it, inhaling deeply on the smoke and letting it slide out slowly.

Ten minutes later, Jessy came into the room, carrying two cups of freshly brewed coffee, and noticed his relaxed and completely-at-home position. "It's good to put your feet up at the end of a long day, isn't it?" She set the cups on the table and pulled out the other two chairs, sitting on one and propping her feet on the other as he had done. "Especially when you've walked on them." She swept off her hat, dropping it on the table, and rumpled the thickness of her butternut hair.

"True." A smile tugged at his lip corners.

They drank their coffee without talking, without needing to talk. He watched her almost absently. He'd known her such a long time, yet he knew so little about her. Her lips were long and nicely full. He watched them as she drank from the cup.

Jessy rarely talked about herself, never gave anything away. That's why she was hard to know, Ty realized. She seemed straightforward and direct; yet sometimes when she looked at him with those steady eyes of hers, she seemed to be quietly waiting. It was that stillness which made him suspect there were emotions that ran strong and deep, but she either couldn't or wouldn't show them.

"You make good coffee, Jessy." He set the empty cup on the table and reluctantly swung his feet to the floor.

"There's more in the kitchen."

"No, thanks." He shook his head and rose to his feet, drifting toward the door, not really wanting to leave, but he couldn't find a reason for staying longer either. So he took his time about going. Jessy came after him, just as slowly, her hands stuck in the back pockets of her low-riding jeans. "You're quite a girl, Jessy." He eyed her, finding something attractive and strong about her face. "I can't believe you haven't had your share of proposals."

"Oh, I've had some proposals, all right," she admitted with a dry look. "But they weren't the marrying kind."

"I suppose you punched them in the nose." He smiled lazily.

"Actually I aimed lower," Jessy replied, a wicked gleam in her eye.

Her answer drew a hearty laugh from him, and Ty draped an arm around her shoulders as they went out the door. "There can't be anyone else on earth like you, Jessy."

"I guess the next debate is whether that's good or bad," she said and looked sideways at him.

Again, he sensed that waiting in her. There was an inner pulling at him, too. He became conscious of the arm he had around her shoulders and the lift of her breasts under the plaid shirt. She unsettled him—but she always had.

"I'd better be going." He brought his arm away and glided down the steps.

"See ya around," she said.

17

The feedlot was under construction at the site on the north range. Its grain silos had been erected; much of the conveyor equipment for mechanized feeding was installed. Fences were going up, dividing the cattle yard into lots. The chugging, revving engine of the posthole digger filled the afternoon, forcing men to raise their voices to be heard above it.

Stake trucks lumbered over the ground, loaded with fenceposts that were rolled off the back of the truck at regular intervals. More workers were following behind the posthole digger, righting the poles in the ground and tamping them solid. Adding to the racket was the pounding of hammers, nailing the board rails.

Standing back by the parked vehicles, Chase observed it all. His hands were thrust into the pockets of his open jacket and his head was drawn back in quiet satisfaction. Ty was amongst all those workers, supervising the project he had designed and organized.

"What do you think?" Maggie was at his side.

"I think there's no set time when a boy becomes a man. Some never do." He paused. "You know, it's hard for a father to recognize when that time has come for his son. You get so wrapped up in trying to handle everything for him, thinking you have to carry the whole load 'cause he can't cope with it, that you don't see he can." There was a faintly sad smile on his face when he paused. "Ty isn't a boy anymore, Maggie. And it's got nothing to do with age or size."

"No," she agreed, feeling a tugging inside at his words when she had expected him to comment on the way the work was progressing on this new operation. But Ty had been Chase's work—his project—teaching him, training him, trying to instill in him all the values Chase held important.

He put an arm around her shoulders and brought her closer to his side, his voice growing tight. "I always thought he had to do things my way, but he can't. He's going to be a better man than I am."

"Chase." There was so much she wanted to say, but she couldn't find the words to describe her feelings. She was proud of him for the man he was, and she felt a deep and abiding love for this proud husband of hers.

"Do you know what people will start saying when I walk down the street now?" He looked down at her, faintly smiling. "'There goes Ty Calder's old man.'"

"No, you'll always be Chase Calder," she insisted, but there was a part of her that knew he was right. The time would come, but not for a long while yet.

When she looked back to the scene, Ty was coming toward them, moving with that long, easy gait of his. He stopped once to direct a load of fence rails to a particular section of the yard, then came on. Chase let his arm slide off her shoulders and squared around to face his son, for the first time man to man.

"It's coming right along," Chase observed.

"Yeah. That load of fenceposts finally arrived."

Maggie listened to the run of their voices, not paying any real attention to their discussion. Chase's remarks were making her notice little things that had escaped her before. Ty was browner, leaner, and the mustache she had teased him about growing fitted the rough vigor of his features. When she compared him to Chase, she realized Ty looked stronger, more flatly muscled, and he was a good inch taller than his father.

Then her son's dark eyes were gazing at her, his features relaxed and at ease. "Has Tara called to say what time her plane would be arriving?"

Maggie hesitated. "She did call . . . to say she was going to stay in Dallas a couple more days and do some shopping—replenish her wardrobe."

Nodding, Ty looked away, a faint grimness underlying his expression. But there was nothing in it when he turned back, his reaction carefully hidden in a crooking smile. "I'll probably work late tonight, so don't wait dinner for me. I'll fix something for myself when I get there," he said and moved off to check on the workers again.

"She's too confident of him," Chase murmured, his gaze thoughtfully narrowed. "Or she wouldn't be gone so much."

"They seem happy enough." Together, they turned to walk to the pickup.

"She's a hungry girl," Chase observed grimly and opened the cab door on the passenger side for Maggie. "It doesn't seem to matter how much she has, there's always something more she wants."

"She loves him," Maggie said.

"In her way, I think she does," he agreed and helped her into the truck, closing the door.

Long after the workers had quit for the day, Ty stayed at the site, stacking lumber and preparing things for the next day's work. He needed to exert himself—to sweat and feel the pull of his muscles to rid himself of the bad mood.

It finally became too dark to see and he stopped, leaning against a section of finished fence to light a cigarette. There was a movement in the purpling shadows to his left, a silent stealth in it. Ty jerked his head around, nerves tensing, then easing slightly when he recognized the lean shape of Culley O'Rourke.

"Working late," Culley observed with a bright-eyed watchfulness, the premature gray of his hair showing almost white in the twilight.

"Just finishing up," Ty said and dragged on his cigarette, the red tip glowing brighter.

"Your wife's gone again." The statement carried a knowing sound that, in some way, suggested Ty wasn't man enough to keep her home.

"She's visiting friends in Texas." That was sufficient as an explanation for Tara's absence from the ranch, although Ty had trouble swallowing it. She was his wife; she belonged with him. Although he recognized her need for that other life, it wasn't easy to accept.

"Guess you'll be stoppin' by Jessy's on your way home again tonight," Culley said.

Ty's head came up as he tried to measure what lay behind that comment. Since construction had started on the feedlots, he had stopped at Jessy's cabin a couple of times for coffee and the company. Each time it had been when Tara was away, but it was only a coincidence.

"I might." He dropped the cigarette and ground it under his heel, then looked around. "Did you ride over?" He didn't see a horse tied anywhere.

"Yeah." But O'Rourke didn't volunteer where he'd left his horse.

"You do a lot of riding, Culley. Why?" Ty cocked his head to the side, curious about what went on in the man's mind.

Too many psychiatrists had asked probing questions about the workings of his mind. Culley didn't like explaining why he did things anymore, nor did he like revealing what he thought. Now he had his privacy and he guarded it jealously.

"I like it." He shrugged and edged toward the deepening shadows. "It's getting late. Better be headin' that way while the horse can still see the trail."

"Take care, Culley." The man was already a dark shape moving silently into the evening. Ty waited, listening, then heard the dull thud of hooves, nearly muffled by the distance. Turning, he walked to the lone pickup at the site and climbed behind the wheel.

The new road took him by Jessy's cabin, where welcoming lights gleamed from the windows. Ty almost drove past it, then whipped the wheel around at the last second and turned in. His headlight beams revealed another vehicle already parked there. By then, it was too late to change his mind about stopping without it looking odd.

Before he walked into the cabin, he had a look through the glass window in the door. The young cowboy sitting at the table with Jessy was a new rider. The Triple C didn't hire many outsiders except during the busy times, so Ty was quick to recognize the sandy-haired would-be Romeo with the hat pushed to the back of his head, leaning on the table to avidly study Jessy. He was the man hired two months ago, named Dick Ballard.

"Ballard." Ty nodded to the man, who looked anything but pleased to see him walk in. His mouth was pulled up at the corners, but it was only a movement as Ty swung his attention to Jessy, his look long and measuring. "Thought I'd see if you had any of that coffee made. I could use a cup before I make that long drive home."

"Help yourself." She waved him to the kitchen.

Ty poured a cup, then brought it back to the front room and sat down at the table. He lit a cigarette and smoked it as if it, and the coffee, were his only interest while he listened to the conversation between the pair. Ballard did most of the talking, and mostly about himself. Ty became impatient with Jessy, wondering why she couldn't see through the braggart's talk. The more he heard, the less he liked the man.

The rawness that he'd first tried to sweat out with physical work, then ease with some relaxing over a cup of coffee, was an irritable spur that goaded Ty into thwarting whatever Ballard's intentions were for the rest of the evening. When he finished one cigarette, he lit another, building up butts in the ashtray and showing no sign of being in a hurry to leave. The trip to the kitchen for his third cup of coffee finally got the message across to the cowboy.

"Guess I'd better hit the road, Jessy. I've gotta roll out at the crack of dawn in the morning," Ballard declared, trying to impress her with the long, hard hours he worked. The chair legs scraped on the floor as he pushed away from the table. "See ya, Mr. Calder."

"Good night." Ty returned to his chair while Jessy rose and walked out with Ballard.

Restless and edgy, he got up again. He could hear the low murmur of their voices outside but couldn't make out what they were saying. The coffee had gone very black and very bitter. He downed half of it and swirled the rest in his cup. He was in the same black and bitter mood as the coffee.

Jessy walked back in as a truck started up outside. Ty glanced at her and drank another swallow of coffee. He couldn't read her expression, and that made him even more irritable. The light played on her hair, making him notice the tawny streaks that ran through it.

"I didn't mean to drive away your company," he lied.

"That's okay." She calmly walked to the table, picking up the two empty cups. "I would have asked him to leave soon anyway."

Ty hesitated, then followed her into the kitchen with his cup. "This cabin sits a ways back from the others. It would be pretty hard for anyone from the camp to hear you if you needed help. Maybe you oughta change with somebody."

"I like being off by myself." She rinsed out the cups and set them in the sink. "I'm a big girl. I can take care of myself."

The confident statement irritated him. "You're always so damned sure you can handle anything," he said roughly, emptying his cup in the sink and setting it with the others. "Just what would you have done if I hadn't been here and Ballard had refused to leave when you asked him to go?"

"I'd have gotten rid of him one way or another." She shrugged indifferently at his hypothetical question.

"Would you?" His mouth tightened at that calm self-assurance.

"Yes."

Ty grabbed her arms, catching her off guard, and yanked her roughly against him. "How?" He pushed the challenge through his teeth. "Show me how."

His sudden grab had startled her. Before she could react, she was being crushed against him, her arms pinned between them. Fingers twisted into her hair to pull at the roots. In a few seconds, Ty had her virtually immobilized and at his mercy. But the heavy impulses driving him had no mercy.

His mouth sawed across her lips with bruising force, cutting them apart. He was venting all his pent-up anger on her, using her roughly and liking the fight she gave him. In a war of strength, he was unquestionably the winner. No matter how she strained, she couldn't avoid the hard thrust of his hips. He could feel her weakening, her body reluctantly relaxing against his. He eased the pressure, discovering the full and warm softness of her lips.

He had come to her cabin seeking a subtle comfort. But there was another kind to be found in her long woman's body and the moistness of her lips. Ty had a hunger for it. There had been too many previous occasions when frustration caused by Tara had turned him toward other women. There was no separation in his mind between those women and Jessy. His interest took on a passionate quality.

In that short lull with no resistance, Jessy had gathered her strength and violently pushed out of his arms. Breathing hard, she backed up, eyeing him warily. He took a step after her.

"It's her, isn't it?" Her voice was hoarse and angry, rough with the raging hurt of her emotions. "You're angry with her because she isn't here! And you're taking it out on me!"

Her words cracked across him like a whip. They stopped him—stunned him. Jessy had backed up against the counter, her hands reaching back to grip its edge. There was high color in her cheeks and the look of a wounded and cornered she-cat in her eyes.

"I'm Jessy Niles—not your wife!" She was trembling. "Don't ever make the mistake of using me for her again—or I swear I'll kill you."

Everything was held behind his expressionless features. "I know who you are, Jessy."

She turned her head, lowering it for the first time. "You'd better go, Ty."

There was the smallest hesitation before he did as she asked and left the kitchen, continuing straight out the door. When she heard the truck motor start, she went limp with relief, not fearing him but rather fearing herself.

It was one of those rare Indian summer days that tried to deny a bitter cold winter was just around the corner. Ty angled across the ranch yard, his father striding beside him. Coming from the direction of the barns, Tara's voice called for him to wait. Turning, he saw Tara and his sister hurrying to catch up with them.

"You're just the man I wanted to see," she declared and hooked her arms in his, sidling up to him.

"I'm glad to hear that." He smiled and started walking toward the pillared house on the knoll, his father and Cathleen a yard ahead of them.

"Let's go out to dinner tonight," she said.

"And where would you suggest?" Ty mocked. "In your extensive travels of late, have you discovered any restaurant in the area other than Sally's?"

"We'll go to Sally's. I don't care." She gave a blithe shrug, showing herself remarkably easy to please for a change. "It's Saturday night and I don't feel like staying at home."

"Are you going to Sally's tonight?" Cat turned, having been listening to their conversation. "Please, can I go with you?" she asked, all green-eyed eagerness.

"Cat, you shouldn't invite yourself," her father said in mild reprimand.

"But I want to go," she protested.

"Ah, that sounds like somebody's going to be there that you want to see," Tara guessed with an impish smile. "It couldn't be that Taylor boy, could it?"

"Tara!" Cat gave her a low-voiced warning, flashing her a look of annoyance while she glanced anxiously at her father to see if he'd heard.

"Taylor?" Ty frowned. "You don't mean Repp Taylor?"

"The very same." Tara nodded. "Cathleen has a crush on him."

"Why, he's twenty years old." Chase Calder frowned at his fifteen-year-old daughter.

"Don't pay any attention to Tara." Cathleen glared at her to be silent and faced the front with an angry little flounce of her head. "She doesn't know what she's talking about. Repp Taylor is much too old for me."

"I should certainly hope so," her father retorted.

"Can I go with them tonight, please?" She went back to her initial request, this time asking permission from her father first. "Other girls my age get to have dates, but I never go anywhere."

"It's all right, Dad Calder," Tara spoke up. "Cat can come with us, can't she, Ty?"

"I don't even remember saying that we were going," he replied.

"Yes, you did—just by not saying we weren't," she declared airily.

"Don't ever argue with that kind of logic, Ty," his father warned. "You'll never win."

Tara laughed. It was at times like these that Ty believed everything was going to work out for them, despite the frequent separations when Tara could endure the isolation of the ranch no more and left for a few days to return to what she laughingly called civilization.

When they were alone in their rooms, Ty queried her. "What's this about Repp Taylor?" He pulled on a clean white shirt, buttoning it. The young cowboy showed promise of being a good, solid hand, steady and reliable.

"It's simple. Cat is sweet on him." She turned her back to him. "Zip me up." Ty took a nibble of a white shoulder before he did, feeling the little shudder it sent through her. "I thought it would be fun to do our little bit in the furtherance of young love."

"Since you seem to know so much, how does Repp feel about her?"

"Adorably guilty because she's so young and a Calder."

The first person Ty saw when he entered Sally's restaurant and bar was Jessy, seated at a table with Dick Ballard. She looked up and met his gaze for an instant, then responded to some remark Ballard made. Ty was a step or two behind Tara and Cathleen as they walked to a vacant table. They were barely seated when Cat popped up.

"May I have some change so I can play the jukebox?" She held out her hand expectantly to Ty.

He dug in his pocket and gave her some. She was gone in a flash. Tara glanced at him knowingly and murmured, "Guess who is at the pool table?"

Repp Taylor stood tall and lean, with jet-dark hair and eyes. With a smile, he nodded to Cat, then ambled over to lean on the cue stick and check out the selections she was making.

But Ty didn't share Tara's interest in these opening moves

of courtship, even though she gave him a play-by-play description as it innocently unfolded over the evening. His mind was on other things, mainly the image of Jessy with that strongly expectant look burrowing into him. He hadn't seen her since the last time he'd stopped by her cabin. He still wasn't sure what had prodded him into kissing her, whether it had been out of anger at Tara, or something else. In many respects, Jessy was a sensitive creature despite her outward show of toughness. Now he wished he'd made amends for his behavior that night.

"You're very quiet tonight," Tara accused as they swayed with the music, their feet barely moving on the crowded dance floor.

"What?" Ty looked down at her blankly, then realized what she'd said. "Sorry, I guess my mind's on other things."

"It's not very flattering to be dancing with your wife and looking like you're a thousand miles away," she chided him without too much concern. "Did you see who is here?"

"You mean Jessy?" With so many newcomers in town, there were few other customers he'd recognized.

"Jessy Niles? Is she here?" Tara stiffened, looking quickly around the dance floor before locating the girl, dancing with a sandy-haired cowboy. "They make a nice-looking couple, don't they?" She didn't wait for a response. "I wasn't referring to her. I meant your uncle. He's standing over there by the back door."

A single crease rent his brow as Ty looked at Culley O'Rourke leaning against the wall by the back door, among the spectators watching the pool game in progress. His face was half hidden by the shadows cast by the light above the pool table, but that shock of gray hair was highlighted.

"I certainly never expected to see him here tonight," Tara remarked and shrugged indifferently. "But I guess the wolves have to come out of the hills sometimes."

The song ended. They were momentarily caught in the jam of couples trying to leave the small dance floor. Another record began a fast-tempoed song as Ty guided Tara through an opening.

He heard a male voice say, "Come on, honey. Let's you and I dance this one."

It was his sister who said a sharp "No!"

The stubborn and willful tone of her voice struck a warning, and Ty swung around. In a temper, his younger sister had no qualms about causing a scene. A husky blond had hold of her hand and was trying to persuade her to go onto the dance floor with him. The boy was trying to appear manly and forceful.

"I don't want to dance with you!" Cat stormed, never reacting well to force. But the boy just laughed. Ty saw trouble coming, but he was too far away. "Repp!" There was an impatient ring in her voice as Cat called for her would-be knight in shining armor to rescue her.

"What is it, Ty?" Tara was at his arm as he tried to push through the crowd to his sister.

"Just stay here." He lifted her hand from his arm.

By then, Repp Taylor was already on the scene. The crowd backed up, giving the pair room and tightening the press of people Ty had to get through. He never heard what was said, but a fist was swung and Cat screamed.

Bulling his way past the crowd, Ty made to break up the scuffling pair. Repp's nose was already bloodied and he was trying to throw all his weight into the husky blond and get him on the floor. When Ty tried to pry them apart, a rooting spectator jumped into the melee, thinking he was ganging up on the town boy.

Tara had made her way to Cathleen's side and put her arm around the girl. She watched in shocked silence as a man came hurling out of the crowd and straight at Ty. Swinging fists lashed out so quickly she couldn't discern who was hitting whom.

With a Calder in the fight, more Triple C riders came to his support. There were no more than a half dozen in the tavern, badly outnumbered by the local residents. But all of them seemed to be spoiling for the excitement of a fight.

As bodies crashed together and fists struck flesh and bone, Tara clutched Cathleen tightly and huddled close to the wall next to the jukebox. Ty was in the center of the brawl, blood pouring from a cut near his eye, his teeth bared below the black brush of a mustache and a killing look in his dark eyes.

All she could hear were the gruntings of breath, the

shuffling of feet, and the ripping and smashing of flesh. It was barbaric, the brutal violence sickening her, yet she couldn't look away.

"Somebody stop them!" she cried, but no one heard her above the din of the brawl and the blare of the jukebox.

Ty's lungs were heaving for air and he could feel the pounding of his heart. He hadn't been in a knock-down, drag-out fight like this since his college days. His head was swimming and there was a roar in his ears. He checked one blow from a nameless opponent; a second slammed into his shoulder. It was hard to see out of one eye, but he pressed the fight, smashing the flat of his knuckles into the man's face and seeing it roll out of his vision.

With that attack repelled, he staggered slightly to see where the next one would come from. He shook his head, blinking in an effort to clear the film from his eye. There was the shattering crash of a beer bottle being broken. He turned. The jagged neck was held in the hand of the man he'd just knocked down.

Ty backed up from it, crouching slightly and spreading out his arms. The fight had taken an ugly turn, no longer just a brawlfest. Some of the participants who had been in it just for fun retreated to the sidelines. Ty's mouth was dry, and he wetted it as they started slowly circling.

"Ty!" Someone shouted his name above the loud music from the jukebox. "Catch!"

Taking his eyes off the man's sweating face for an instant, Ty saw the brown shape of a beer bottle sailing through the air toward him. He made a one-handed catch of it and glimpsed Jessy on the inner circle of the onlookers.

Swift movement came at him and he jumped back, the jagged weapon slashing the air where he'd been. The closest thing to him was the jukebox. Ty brought the body of the bottle onto a metal corner with a hard swing, breaking it with a crash and turning to face his opponent, equally armed. He heard a woman's screaming sob, but it was far on the fringes of his interest as he dragged in breaths and fought the tiredness in his arms.

"Break it up! Out of the way!" A hard voice of authority barked the orders. "Break it up here!"

Uniformed men broke through the readily dividing crowd, grabbing and seizing Ty's opponent from behind. Ty straightened slowly, lowering his hands. His battered fingers loosened their grip on the bottle neck, letting it fall to the floor. He couldn't recognize any of the officers through his hazing vision.

Distantly, he heard one of them mutter his name. "It's Calder."

Swaying slightly, he turned, seeking something to lean against before his legs gave way. The roar was still in his ears. There was a pervading numbness in his body that temporarily kept him from feeling any pain. Some small body latched itself to him. He started to push it away.

"Ty. Oh, my God, Ty, you're hurt." It was Tara's sobbing voice that finally penetrated his haze. "Look at your poor face."

Impatiently he brushed aside the small hand that touched at his cheek. "I'm all right." His voice sounded harsh.

"You're not all right. Just look at you," she insisted.

He looked, rather stupidly, at his torn shirt, splattered with blood, but Ty didn't know whether it was his blood or somebody else's. He still felt a driving need for some kind of physical support. Suddenly, a voice took charge of his problem.

"Come on. Let's get him out of here." A strong arm went around his middle and a light caramel head ducked under his arm.

"Jessy?" He blinked, trying to see her through the filmy darkness that kept covering his left eye.

"It's me," she said.

It was a tired and wry laugh Ty released. "You always turn up when I need you," he murmured without being conscious of what he'd admitted.

For an instant, Tara was too stunned by his bloodied and battered face to react when Jessy appeared and started leading Ty away. Recovering, she followed quickly in their wake, irritated at the way her position had been usurped.

With the fight broken up, there was a mild confusion in the place as officers tried to separate the participants from the innocent onlookers. One of the policemen tried to stop them from leaving the scene, but Jessy firmly informed the officer Ty would be upstairs in the owner's private quarters if he was needed. She had a way of making men back down. An ache was starting in his muscles, a painful throb, or Ty would have made a joke of her easy dismissal of the man.

He had a glimpse of Sally Brogan leading the way to the private staircase in the rear, but all his concentration was centered on making his legs work.

A light was switched on and he was led to a chair. He sat down heavily. After the first blows had hit him, he had stopped feeling them. Now his body was beginning to react to the punishment it had taken. He leaned against the chair and let his head fall back, closing his eyes as the throbbing washed over him. His arms were draped loosely on his legs. There was a sticky wetness on his face, and Ty reached up tiredly to wipe it away from his eyes, then looked at the coagulating blood on his fingers with exhausted recognition. Something was set on the table beside him. He shut his eyes again, wanting only to rest.

"I have to go downstairs," Sally was saying. "If you need anything else, just help yourself."

A door shut. Then a wet cloth was dabbing at his face, accomplishing little. He tried to turn away from it. "Ty, I'm sorry." Tara was hovering beside him. "I know it must hurt terribly. You shouldn't have gotten involved in that fight. How could you stoop to brawling like that?"

Her tone of impatience chased away some of the mists. "You don't stand back and let someone else do your fighting for you." And it had all started because of his sister. He tried to take the cloth from her and do it himself, but there didn't seem to be enough strength in his hands or arms.

"If you don't know what you're doing"—Jessy's voice came from the side—"get out of the way and let me clean up."

"He's my husband."

"And at the rate you're going, he'll bleed to death." She pushed her way in and commandeered the damp cloth, pressing it hard on the cut above his eye. Pain stabbed through his head. Ty flinched, sucking in air through his teeth and swearing. Jessy took his hand and made him hold the cloth against the cut and maintain the pressure.

He opened one eye and looked at Tara, standing to the side now and watching the ministrations with a pained expression. "Where's Cathleen?" Ty questioned.

"I don't know." Tara shook her head blankly. "Downstairs, I guess."

"Go find her and bring her up here." He watched Tara hesitate, then reluctantly turn away to do as he asked. "The little troublemaker," Ty muttered when Tara had gone. "I oughta take a belt to her." Jessy had another cloth and was wiping the excess blood from his face, rinsing and wiping again. Then she lifted his hand and checked the cut.

"It's probably a good thing your wife isn't here," she said calmly, her lips tight-pressed. "That cut needs some stitches."

She made him apply pressure on the wound again and turned to the table to open a large first-aid kit. Ty glanced at her, things clearing up in his mind.

"You threw me that bottle, didn't you?" he said.

"Yes." She held a sterilized needle and suture in her hand when she turned back to him. "Hold still. This is going to hurt."

It was an understatement. Ty broke out in a nauseating cold sweat. No sound came from his throat except the loud, sighing breaths that forced their way through the tightly constricted muscles. Jessy worked swiftly and efficiently, mentally blocking out her emotions. It was a blessedly short cut, so she finished before the pain became unendurable for him. She watched the rigid tautness drain from him while she affixed a bandage to the sewed-up wound. Then she took the pack of cigarettes from his shirt pocket and lit one for him, placing it between his lips.

"Thanks." He looked up at her gratefully, took a deep drag on the cigarette, then took it from his mouth, blowing smoke into the air.

"You've got a couple more scratches on your face," she said and reached for a bottle out of the first-aid kit. "I'll put some antiseptic on them."

The smoke from the cigarette stung his bruised lips, but he smoked it anyway. Ty studied Jessy's face while she leaned close to him, concentrating on her task. Her face, her eyes, her nose, her mouth, all were expressionless, yet he sensed much going on behind what she showed him. The touch of her hand was smooth and pleasant. There was something steadying in having her there.

"What are you thinking, Jessy?" Ty wanted to know, his eyes narrowing with curiosity. "I never can tell what's going on inside you." She had a man's way of hiding it.

Her eyes met his for a scant second; then she returned her attention to the long scratch on his cheek. "I'm thinking that I could use a cigarette right now," she partially lied.

Ty remembered other things, the apologies he hadn't made. "Jess, I was planning to come by your place—with my hat in my hand—and tell you—"

But Jessy interrupted him as she finished and turned briskly to the table. "You don't have to tell me anything, Ty. No apologies. Nothing." She spoke with a man's bluntness, too. "Everyone on the ranch knows things aren't as good as they should be between you and your wife, with her going away so much. It's not something you can keep from them. But she's in your blood." The same way Ty was in hers. "When she's gone, if you get lonely and want company— that's fine. If you want to come to my place for a cup of coffee and some talk—that's fine. I won't shut the door on you if it's me you come to see." She snapped the kit closed.

Everything smoothed out inside him, all the twists and knots straightened. Ty caught her hand and drew her slowly back around to his chair, studying the look in her amber-brown eyes that seemed to absorb him.

"I'll be coming by for coffee—and your company," he said.

She smiled crookedly, her fingers briefly tightening around his hand. "One of us is a fool, Ty Calder," she declared with a rueful humor. "But I'll be waiting."

The door opened. Ty looked impatiently at the intruder. Tara stared back at him, her features sharpening. He felt Jessy withdraw her hand from his warm grasp, and he felt oddly guilty even though he'd done nothing wrong. It irritated him.

A rough-looking man in uniform followed Tara into the room. His belly appeared to be pushed up into his chest, giving him a swagger and a puffed-up look of importance.

The thickness of his facial hair cast a perpetual underlying shadow on his cheeks and jaw.

"We haven't met, Calder." The roughness of the man's voice, in itself, held a challenge. "I'm Sheriff Blackmore, recently elected by the good citizens of this county."

Ty was aware that Potter's picked replacement had lost the election, despite the support of the Triple C Ranch. The new group of residents in the coal-mining community had outvoted their choice and brought this man, from their ranks, to office.

"Sorry we had to meet under these circumstances, Sheriff." The expression of regret was an attempt to be polite. The man's attitude didn't exactly warm Ty to him.

"Maybe it's best we did," the new sheriff replied curtly. "You and your people have pretty well run things your way up till now. I'm the law around here—and you aren't going to be riding roughshod over anyone anymore. You cause trouble and you'll get trouble. Now, this fight tonight was started by one of your men."

"Sally knows I'll pay for whatever damage that's been done. And the fines will be taken care of, too." Ty didn't attempt to deny that the instigation had been on his family's part, but he didn't intend to drag Cathleen's name into it if he could avoid it.

"I don't know as money'll buy off your trouble, Calder," the sheriff stated, implying more stringent punishment.

"Excuse me, Sheriff," Jessy interrupted their conversation. "Have you been introduced to Mr. Calder's wife?"

"We met downstairs," he retorted impatiently.

"I thought perhaps you hadn't met Mr. Dyson's daughter." A cool smile touched her wide lips.

The sheriff's glance flicked to Tara, a stunned look of recollection striking through his expression before it assumed its former gravity again. "My respects to your father, ma'am." He touched his hat to her, then turned a stern look on Ty. "You'll be notified of the charges."

When the sheriff had disappeared out the door to clump down the steps, Jessy made a simple explanation to Ty. "This is Dyson's town. He put in the new water system, bought the fire truck, and graded the streets."

Ty began to understand her point. His father's fight to stop or severely regulate surface mining in the area threatened these people's jobs. It was Dyson who paid them and made certain they had a decent place to live. The sheriff would have written him up on every charge in the book—if his wife's maiden name hadn't been Dyson. Ty glanced at his wife. She, too, had grown more thoughtful at the turn of events that had stripped the Calder name of its weight.

"Where's Cathleen?" he asked, a certain weariness creeping into his voice.

"She's downstairs, fussing over Repp Taylor." Before Ty could ask why she hadn't brought her upstairs as he had asked, Tara hurried on. "It's all right. Her uncle is with her."

O'Rourke. In the fray, he'd forgotten the man was in the place. "Dammit, I told you to bring Cathleen up here," he muttered angrily.

"I'll get her, Ty." Jessy walked to the door, exchanging a long look with Tara before she left the room.

"She takes a lot on herself," Tara observed with faint criticism.

"Jessy's been doing that since she was ten."

18

The buzzer for the interoffice line sounded in the plush room. E. J. Dyson barely glanced up from his papers to motion to his partner to answer it. Stricklin picked up the phone, made an affirmative answer, and hung up.

"Bulfert's outside. He's being shown in," he informed him.

"Good." Dyson closed the report he'd been reading and sat back in his custom-designed swivel chair. "Have the cigars ready for him." Stricklin walked to a side cupboard and removed the box of imported cigars, placing them on the Texas-sized desk.

The doors to the executive office of Dy-Corp were opened and a statuesque blonde stepped aside to admit the heavily jowled politician. Excess weight had bulged his middle considerably, evidence of his self-indulgent ways. He mopped at his florid face with an expensive linen handkerchief. Dyson came out from behind the desk to greet him, submitting to the pumping handshake.

"Welcome to Texas, Senator." He paused, then smiled. "I guess I shouldn't be calling you Senator anymore since your retirement from office, but it's a habit I'm going to find difficult to break. I hope you don't mind—Senator."

"Not at all. Not at all," Bulfert replied with his usual show of aggressive joviality.

"Have a cigar." Dyson gestured to the box of the senator's favorite brand. "May I pour you a drink? How about some bourbon and our good Texas branch water?"

"Too early for me." He waved aside the offer of a drink. "But I will have a cigar." Stricklin offered him his pick from the box. "Thank you, Stricklin." He smiled at the darkly tanned man with sun-bleached hair, never completely comfortable with those steel-blue eyes on him.

"I try, Senator." Stricklin smiled back, ready with a light for the cigar the politician rolled between his lips.

"Sit down, Senator," Dyson invited and returned to his chair behind the desk. "We've had an opportunity to go over this . . . confidential file you left with us, and our findings concur with yours." His words were couched in polite terms, mocking what both had known from the start. "It would seem that the title to those ten thousand acres of land Calder supposedly purchased from the government was obtained by fraudulent means. It appears that this recently deceased"—Dyson paused to check the report for the name—"Mr. Osgood had no authorization to make the sale. His bank records show there was a sizable cash deposit made at approximately the same time the transaction occurred. And a similar amount was withdrawn from Calder's bank account some weeks before. An obvious case of bribing a government official."

"A terrible thing—violating the public trust," the senator agreed, smiling smugly. "So well documented, too."

"The government obviously has grounds to declare the sale of that land null and void," Dyson agreed.

"Exactly my thought." The cigar was clenched in his teeth as he responded to the assertion.

"As I promised, the file has gone no farther than this room. However, now that you aren't in office, I can think of no reason why it couldn't be arranged for this information to come to the attention of the proper official. Discreetly, of course."

"Of course." Bulfert nodded, the bagging jowls bunching out with the movement. "I'm sure, with your connections, you would have no difficulty obtaining the mining rights on that particular portion of federal land."

"We can certainly hope." Dyson smiled, admitting nothing.

The politician became serious, assuming a grave air. "You are aware that property is landlocked. Completely surrounded by Calder land."

"I'm sure the government can obtain the authority to demand and receive an easement access."

"Yes." Bulfert showed an uncommon interest in the fine ash building up on the end of his cigar. "I know Calder. He'll fight this every way he knows how. Injunctions, court battles, suits. Litigation could drag out for a long time. He'll fight over every inch of it. Never give for a minute."

"I expect he will." Dyson appeared calm.

"Do you?" Bulfert studied the Texan, wondering if he knew the breed of man he was tackling. "If he has to, he'll fight dirtier than the next man."

"He has that reputation. But that's hardly your problem, Senator." Dyson smiled. "I failed to ask how you liked your new office. Was it satisfactory?"

"Very nice. Quite comfortable." He tapped the cigar on the lip of the ashtray.

"Good. Of course, you have your own private secretary and a full expense account. The company won't be expecting you to keep any regular hours, since consulting work is an irregular business. But I know Advance Tech Ltd. is happy to have you on its staff." Both of them knew it was a manufactured position in a subsidiary company of Dy-Corp, with full salary and benefits, and no duties. "I expect it will take you some time adjusting to life in Texas after living in Montana for so long."

"I shall enjoy the warm climate. Montana's gotten too cold for these old bones." And the senator knew the atmosphere would soon grow colder for him back there, as soon as Calder realized he'd had a hand in this.

A few more pleasantries were exchanged before the senator took his leave of the two men. After he'd gone, Dyson stared thoughtfully at the closed doors.

"Calder will fight this," he said finally to Stricklin. "I wish there was something I could do to keep Tara from being caught in the middle of all this. I certainly don't want to cause her any unhappiness." An agitated sigh broke from him as he pushed out of the chair and strode from behind the desk, wanting to pace and trying to control it. "If Calder is as bullheaded as Bulfert says, this dispute is bound to affect Tara."

With his computerlike mind, Stricklin could sift through information, analyze it, and come up with specific answers, but only with the proper input. For a man who worshiped at the shrine of Tara, it was unthinkable that she should suffer any unhappiness.

"There must be some way of reaching Calder." He walked to the liquor cabinet and poured himself a drink.

"None," Dyson announced grimly. "The man's rooted in his opinions." He stopped in front of a large window, his hands clasped behind his back. For a long second, he stood silent. Then he swung away, disgruntled. "It would be so much easier if I were dealing with Ty. He's intelligent and reasonable . . . progressive in his thinking. You only have to look at the changes he's made at the ranch to know that. It would be a much simpler matter to convince him of the viability of our plans. Unfortunately"—Dyson took in a long breath and let it out—"Calder is in charge, not his son."

Stricklin swirled the liquor and ice cubes together and thoughtfully digested the information. Dyson paced into the middle of the room again, shaking his head.

"It's a peculiar set of circumstances, Stricklin." He stopped to look at the man. "All those Appalachian mines in the East are digging out tons of coal ore high in sulfur that burns dirty. With the pollution-control standards in force, the industries in the East are crying for clean-burning coal." Dyson shook his head again. "And Calder's sitting on top of all that low-sulfur coal. I'll never understand why on earth God put him there." Sighing, he walked to his desk.

"There's a lot of land in Montana that Calder doesn't own with coal deposits under it," Stricklin reminded him.

"If it were only coal I wanted, I'd leave him alone. It's his damned water I need," Dyson retorted. "A coal plant has a high demand for water, and Calder has the most plentiful and dependable source around. We can mine the ore and process it right on the spot. It's ideal." Half undecided, he fingered the file of documents on his desk. "What do you think we should do, Stricklin? Should I arrange to have it fall into the hands of our crusading friend in Washington? Even if it causes family difficulties? Or should I simply throw in my hand and look for another game in another place?"

"You want his coal; you want his water. That file will get it for you," the man stated. "You have a winning hand. Play it."

"Ah, Stricklin." Dyson laughed silently, shaking his head. "It amazes me the way you always see everything as black or white. Here." He picked up the file. "You know how to handle this."

A fire crackled in the simple brick hearth, but it didn't throw off as much heat as the wood-burning stove in the corner. Outside the cabin, a winter wind prowled in the cottonwood skeletons, rattling their limbs. Jessy sat cross-legged on a braided rug in front of the fireplace, an empty coffee cup in her hands. It had grown dark outside, but she hadn't bothered to turn on any lights, her thoughts absorbed by the news Ty had related.

His long body was stretched loosely in the plumply curved armchair, his face within the fringes of the dancing light from the fire. He was absently rubbing a forefinger across his mouth, the blunt ends of his mustache brushing the top of it. It was the troubled darkness within those hooded eyes that showed Ty was not as relaxed as he appeared.

"Even if the government can declare the sale invalid, surely there is something your father can do to maintain possession of that land," Jessy murmured, a determined quality in her level tone.

Ty brought his hand down from his mouth and took a deep, troubled breath as he leaned forward to rest his elbows on his knees and lace his fingers loosely together in front of him, bowing his head to study them. "He's meeting in Miles City with his attorneys the next couple of days to make some interim arrangements and decide what long-term action to take. He probably won't have any trouble getting temporary grazing rights." The corners of his mouth were pulled deeper into grimness. "He thought he held title to that land all this time. It was a blow to find out he didn't." Ty looked up at her, his mouth slanting. "The senator pulled some strings for him, all right. But it wasn't to shorten the red tape. He pulled open those purse strings for the wrong man."

"The senator has to be in as much trouble as your father."

"He's had time to cover his trail." Ty reached into the box of kindling near the hearth and took out a twig, absently snapping off pieces to throw, one by one, into the fire. "Since it happened so long ago, the government appears willing to overlook how the title was acquired. But if Dad fights for it, which he will, I have the feeling it's going to get messy."

There was a long run of silence. Jessy looked at him. She understood the stoicism that covered his face, hiding the tension beneath its angular surfaces. An impulse moved her. She reached out to clasp his linked hands, wishing she could lead some of that trouble out of him into herself. This desire to share some of it showed in her eyes. Ty was drawn by it; it was something he'd never seen in Tara's face.

"Maybe you should call your wife and talk to her," Jessy suggested, almost humbly. "You should be able to reach her at Dyson's home in Fort Worth."

"No." Ty rejected it absently. The warm pressure of her hand left his and he was conscious of its absence. The firelight wavered. "I'd better put another log on," he said and rolled to his feet, stretching slightly to ease the tautness of his muscles.

"I'll pour some coffee," Jessy said, rising also, her shoulders dropped, her head down.

The fire blazed cheerfully, lightening the room and the atmosphere when Jessy returned to it with two fresh cups of coffee. Ty was standing by the raised hearth, a shoulder leaned against the mantelpiece. Jessy handed him one of the cups and stayed, standing in front of the blaze, watching the yellow flames crawling all over the bark of the new log.

"The fire makes you forget there's cold weather walking around outside," Ty remarked idly and sipped at the hot coffee.

"It does." When a low chuckle came from him, Jessy glanced at him inquisitively.

"I was just remembering a winter tale old Nate Moore told me once," he said, smiling. The old cowboy had died a week before Christmas, joining Abe Garvey and other Triple C veterans who had gone before. It was the passing of an old order, making way for the new. It was with fondness rather than sorrow that Ty thought about these men and all they'd taught him.

"What was that?" Jessy asked with interest.

"As he told it, some greenhorn cowboy rode out to check cattle on a day that was about twenty below. A wind started blowing up snow, and he had a hard time seeing to find his way back to camp. When he finally rode in, he was frozen to the saddle. They had to use ice picks and chisels to pry him off; then they carried him into the bunkhouse and set him in front of the stove. According to Nate, when this cowboy finally thawed out, his legs stayed bowed like a wishbone. Every time he went outside, the cattle dogs would each grab a leg and try to pull him apart. He finally had to quit and go to work on a ranch that didn't use dogs. . . . You don't smile like that often enough, Jessy." Ty studied the way it softened her face and broke through the composure that could hold a man off.

Even after the smile faded, her lips lay softly together. "Nate was never one for idle conversation. He was either tale-telling or passing on some astute observation about life." The coffee was too hot to drink. Jessy set her cup on the mantel and held out her hands to the fire's warmth.

Ty studied the picture she made in the bulky knit sweater of dark green, slim-hipped and long-legged in thread-worn Levi's. "What is it you want in life, Jessy?" Everyone had ambitions and desires, and he wondered about hers.

She grew thoughtful at his question, pulling her hands back and shoving them into her hip pockets while she stared into the leaping flames. "Nobody gets very much in this world, Ty—not really. Sometimes, maybe something happens and, for an hour or a week, it looks like the rest of your life you'll be riding over smooth ground, with no coulees or high buttes in your way. They'll be there, though. You just can't see them for a little while. You'll have rough times, and you'll do your share of crying. You'll get through it because of moments like this." She turned her head to look at him, clear-eyed and silently strong. "What more can I want than I've got right now? A place of my own, a warm fire on a cold night, and someone to talk to. What's better than this?"

Her words, so simple and direct, moved him, cutting to the heart of life. Moving slowly, Ty set his coffee cup on the mantel next to hers, his gaze never leaving her face. There was an inner beauty shining through those strong features that was wholly woman.

He murmured, "Jessy," in a smooth, stroking voice and curved his hand to the back of her head, holding it gently. For a long, exploring moment, he looked at her and was drawn closer by this nameless, tender feeling that pulled at him. Jessy waited, realizing that she had gotten into his feelings. The pressure of his hand increased slightly as his mouth moved closer, his eyes continuing to study her features. She didn't fool herself into believing she had awakened a love. He was lonely, and Tara was far away. Ty had his morality and strong sense of honor, but he was, after all, a man. And she was close by, sharing his troubles and listening to his talk. That nearness had worn through the restraint which normally would have checked him.

Maybe she should have stopped him. Jessy knew he was on the edge of kissing her—kissing her, Jessy Niles. But she had meant it when she said that she might never have more than this moment. Too soon, Tara would return, and Jessy would once again have nothing. With a sweet and pure rush of defiance, she brought her hands to his middle and lifted her head that last inch to meet his mouth.

It was a long, slow warmth that gradually took possession of them. Jessy swayed into him, her body growing heavy against his while his enfolding arms gathered her in. Her heartbeat quickened, her blood running sweet and fast. There was something earthy and stimulating in the kiss that never lost its gently insistent quality. He was solid and strong, the smell of him mingling with fire smoke in her livening senses.

There was no hesitation on either side, no testing of the ground to see if it could support what was being built on it. It was the coming together of two equally strong forces, and in their seeking probe of each other, they touched depths of feeling where passion was not required to create intimacy.

It was too new, invading their systems too quietly for either to recognize its power. They came apart as slowly as they had come together, each seeking a reaction in the eyes of the other. Jessy turned again to the fire, feeling a wonderful calm and a steady glow within.

Neither spoke of the kiss, treating it as if it had never happened. Ty reached for his coffee cup, resuming his leaning stance against the mantel, and contemplated the fading flames of the fire. Taking her cup, Jessy moved to the armchair previously occupied by Ty and curled her long legs onto the cushion to sit crosswise. She, too, looked at the fire, completely comfortable, following her own track of thoughts.

After a long length of time, Ty straightened and drained the last of the coffee from his cup. When his idle glance swung to Jessy, she was watching him. "More coffee?" she offered.

"No." He shook his head, then looked at her with a steady, slightly curious regard. "How come you suggested I should call Tara and talk to her?"

"It seemed logical that you'd want to discuss what had happened with her," Jessy said, glancing briefly at her cup, then back to him.

"If I had wanted to talk it over with her, I wouldn't have come here." Ty sounded irritable, overtaken by a restlessness and agitation.

The moment of ease was destroyed. Something got between Jessy and her comfortable feelings. There was a hard, puzzled look in his eyes. The loneliness of the cabin pressed in on her again, abetted by the chilling wind that seeped through the walls and whistled through the crack in the door. She felt her spirits sinking.

That intense closeness between them was broken. All the uncertainties that had never entered her mind earlier returned now. Jessy watched him, knowing his mannerisms and silences and their meaning. His thoughts were heavy on his mind, shadowing his features.

"Jessy—" Ty began in a tone that was much too serious and loaded.

"I hadn't realized how dark it was in here," Jessy interrupted him, sounding casual but inwardly frightened by what he might be intending to say. Rising from the chair, she walked to the standing lamp and pulled its chain.

It was a calm exterior she showed him when she turned. She didn't want to hear any apology from him or an expression of regret—nor some false statement of his feelings toward her. They would only hurt. She didn't want his gratitude or his sympathy—nothing that might bind him to her. He was in love with Tara, whatever their problems. The shared closeness of that kiss might make him feel obligated to say something. And anything he said would only wound her.

Across the space, now illuminated by the lamp, he seemed to be measuring her, trying to judge something. Jessy moved, striving for resiliency.

"Ty . . . I told you once that you were always free to come here," she said quietly. "And you're always free to go."

As she met his eyes, Ty saw none of that deep feeling that had so oddly sprung between them. There was only that level-eyed calmness that seemed to attach little importance to what had passed. Yet he was relieved, too, that she'd given him an out. He had not meant for that kiss to happen—just as he'd not meant the other one, although the circumstances were completely different.

With a lifting of his shoulders, he seemed to gather himself and walked to the hook by the door where he'd left his hat and coat. "I guess it is time I was going to my own home," he admitted and shrugged into his coat. While he pushed his hat onto his head, Ty spared her a glance. "Thanks for the coffee, Jessy."

"Anytime." After the door had closed on the taunting howl of the cold wind, Jessy repeated her response, very softly. "Anytime."

19

The vision of Tara that Ty carried in his mind when they were apart was never as vibrant and stunning as the sight of her gliding toward him after another separation. So dark and compelling was her beauty, garbed in ermine against the late-winter Montana cold, that he could forget the loneliness of his nights and the hunger she always aroused.

Ty was impatient with the presence of her father and Stricklin, wanting her all to himself and knowing that moment had to be postponed until they were alone. His arm stayed possessively around her petite frame, keeping her at his side, while he turned to greet her traveling companions, her fragrance stirring him. He was too conscious of the constraints he placed on his own feelings to notice the trace of reserve in her attitude.

"Hello, E.J." He shook hands with his father-in-law. "To be truthful, Tara caught me by surprise when she phoned the other night to say she'd be flying back with you. I was under the impression you hadn't scheduled any trip north until April."

"That's true; I hadn't," Dyson admitted smoothly. "However, there was something I wanted to discuss with your father. I probably could have handled it by phone, but since Tara was returning, I thought I'd come along and speak to him in person." He sounded very casual about it, although the matter was obviously serious enough to bring him all this distance. Ty was too preoccupied with Tara's nearness to experience more than a passing curiosity over the possible subject.

"It's good to see you again, Ty," Stricklin greeted him with more warmth than he usually mustered.

While they stood on the unprotected flats beside the airstrip, the luggage had been unloaded from the twin-engine plane so it could be pushed into the shelter of an empty hangar shed. The mesa top offered a bleak landscape of snow-crusted brown grass beneath a massive sky. Its big blueness, icy and unforgiving, had its effect on Tara, making her feel even smaller in stature. A raw March wind was beating at her. She was glad of Ty's arm around her, stopping that wind from flattening her. She could not cope with these wild elements that cared nothing about who stood before them, nor that terrible feeling of inadequacy they evoked within her.

"Must we stand here to talk? It's brutally cold." Everything about this land seemed brutal to her whenever she was out of sight of The Homestead. There, at least, the stately structure was proof that someone ruled.

"I'd forgotten you aren't used to it after being in Texas." Ty smiled warmly, not realizing that she had learned to accept many things but she had never gotten used to them. He bundled her protectively against his side and led her to the car, the motor idling so the interior would be warm for its passengers.

Maggie Calder was on hand to welcome her arriving guests, relieving Ty of the obligation to act as host to Dyson and his assistant. Instead, he gave the cowboy a hand carrying Tara's luggage and packages to their suite of rooms on the second floor. She'd barely said anything to him, but her silence wasn't that unusual in the company of a third party, especially when that party was hired help.

Ty observed the silence, breaking it only to inquire where she wanted the packages left. "Anywhere is fine," she returned indifferently while she slipped out of her full-length ermine coat and took the time to hang it up in her bedroom closet. Ty gestured to the cowboy to leave them in the sitting room.

As soon as he'd left, Ty went into the bedroom. Tara was standing at the vanity mirror, removing the matching ermine hat and shaking out her long, silken black hair. He came up behind her and let his hands settle onto the soft points of her shoulders while he buried his face in the fineness of her hair.

"I'm glad you're home." His muffled voice was husky with need.

"I'm not."

The blunt, harsh answer stunned him. When she turned around to face him, Ty made no effort to maintain his hold on her. She must have seen the hard anger in his eyes. Her hands came up to rest lightly on his chest. There was an earnest, almost insistent edge to her expression.

"Ty, what are you going to do about what's happened?" It was almost a demand.

"I don't know what you're talking about," he said, brusque with his answer. The hunger was still in him, but he wouldn't show it to her now.

"This business with your father," she retorted impatiently. "Why didn't you tell me about it before? I wish you wouldn't keep things like that from me. It's very embarrassing to find out about them from someone else. It puts me in a very awkward position, and I don't like it."

While there was some consolation that she wanted his confidences, her complaint also touched a sore nerve. "Is it my fault that things come up while you're gone? Maybe if you stayed home more, you'd know what was going on."

"Why should I spend every day of my life here when you spend most of your time in some godforsaken corner of this ranch?" Tara flared at his criticism of her absences. "Just so I can be at your beck and call?"

"Yes!"

Temper claimed him, made quick by the hunger that sharpened his nerves. He caught her by the shoulders and hauled her roughly into his arms. Her protest was shut off by his hard kiss. For a moment, his passion had its way with her and she responded to its demands, kissing him back. But Tara wouldn't give in to it, not hers nor his.

Her arms pushed him back, stiffening to keep him there. "Ty, we have to decide how we're going to handle this," she insisted, despite the uneven rush of her own breathing. "I don't think you realize how important it is—what a problem it can become."

"You're awfully concerned about the ranch all of a sudden, aren't you?" Many things lay hotly and threateningly between them; not the least was Tara's strong will and ambition that could take precedence over the feelings in her heart.

"It's my home as much as it is yours!" she asserted, then instantly softened. "Ty, let's not quarrel over something as silly as this. We have to do something about your father before he ruins everything."

"How can he ruin everything by fighting to regain title to land he believed he rightfully owned?" Ty demanded, then wondered, "And what's your father doing here?"

"It was Stricklin's idea—not mine." Her disapproval was evident. "It was my opinion he should stay away and avoid being tainted by any of this."

"Tainted?" Ty found that to be an odd choice of words, but he had no opportunity to pursue the discussion as the door to their suite was opened.

"Tara!" Cathleen came breezing into the master suite, not regarding it as essential that she knock before invading their privacy. "I came to see what-all you bought this time. How was your visit? I'll bet it was warm down there. You beast, you have a tan," she accused enviously when she finally came to a stop in their bedroom. She would be turning sixteen soon. Beneath that youth, there was a woman's desires ready to make riot in her.

"Cat, would you mind clearing out?" Ty ordered. "I'd like some time alone with my wife. You can find out all about her trip later."

"I have plans for later," his sister replied, nonplussed by his attempt to evict her. "And I have to go back to school in the morning." Her green eyes took on a wickedly knowing gleam. "Besides, it's too early for what you've got in mind.

You'll just have to wait until it's time to go to bed to have your . . . time alone . . . with your wife."

"Cat's right." Tara sided with her. "There will be more time after dinner." She smiled at Ty and moved away. "All the packages are in the sitting room. Two of them are for you."

Overruled, Ty was forced to accept the decision and postpone the discussion until after dinner. He was brooding as he left their suite, the sound of Tara's voice and Cat's mingling in excited conversation over the purchases.

The dinner conversation that evening skirted controversial subjects and focused on safe topics. Since Dyson had started his coal-mining operations, the relationship between the Texan and Chase Calder had become strained. Chase still had reservations on the role Dyson might have played in this recent reversal of land title. He was suspicious, but without proof, so he'd kept them mostly to himself. Each time he looked at Stricklin's immaculately clean hands and manicured nails, holding the silverware, Chase was reminded of Potter's remark about not trusting the man.

"While the women are clearing the table, why don't we take our coffee to the den?" Dyson suggested. Chase hesitated, and Dyson took note of it. "I'd like a word with you in private, if you don't mind, Chase."

"Of course."

Ty folded his napkin and placed it on the table. "Unless you need me, I have a mare due to foal that I want to check on." It was a difficult line of loyalty to walk now between his father and Tara. Ty left it to his father's judgment whether or not it was necessary he participate in a discussion that might become heated.

It was a point Chase debated with himself, but he realized the conversation could be related to his son at a later time. "It's the first foal due out of your new stud, isn't it? You'd better check on the mare now. Tara won't thank me if you wind up taking part of her evening to do it because I claimed your time."

The doors were shut to the den when Ty left The Homestead to check on the mare's condition. Knowing his father, Ty doubted that he'd appreciate any advice from Dyson, and considering Tara's reaction, it was likely the reason for his visit. Dyson was protective of his daughter and always had been.

"Some brandy with your coffee, E.J.?" Chase offered as he unstoppered the brandy decanter to add a splash to his own cup.

"No, thank you." Dyson settled comfortably in an armchair in front of the fireplace while Stricklin carried his cup to an opposite chair.

It only left the sofa in the middle. With a wariness Chase couldn't explain, he remained standing to one side, not taking the seat that would put him in a position that was flanked by the two men. It was too exposed.

"What was it you wanted to talk to me about?" He dispensed with any pleasantries to come straight to the point.

"Information has reached me pertaining to the overturning of some land you purchased from the government several years ago." Dyson didn't hedge either.

"News travels fast," Chase murmured dryly.

"It isn't so surprising, really," Dyson insisted calmly. "I am engaged in business in this area. It's natural for something like this to come to my attention."

"I suppose." Chase conceded the possibility that Dyson could have recently learned of the invalidated sale through local sources, although the likelihood remained that, at the least, Dyson had foreknowledge.

"We've had our differences of late, Chase, but our two families are related. It's a fact we can't ignore."

"I am well aware that your daughter is my son's wife." It was the one thing that kept Chase from accusing Dyson outright of conspiring to deprive him of those ten thousand acres of land. There remained an element of doubt that Dyson would involve himself in such a way that could potentially harm his daughter.

"I am first and foremost a businessman, Chase. Only to a certain extent can I allow family considerations to prevent me from doing what I believe is important to my business. That's why I'm here." Dyson paused, studying Chase for an instant. "Normally I would not do this. I'd make a business move and let my opponent or competitor find out about it after the fact. Since there might be repercussions for Tara, I'm giving you advance notice of my intentions."

"And your intentions?" Chase inquired, faintly challenging.

"The government now holds title to those ten thousand acres. I am seeking the mineral rights and the use of its water for a coal plant. At the present, Tara knows nothing of this. I am aware that you are appealing the decision and seeking to regain title to that land. If the government retains possession, I wanted you to know my plans." There was another long, considering look before Dyson continued. "It's a business decision, Calder. I know it will be difficult, but I should like to maintain a peaceful coexistence for the sake of our children."

"You're right," Chase agreed, a tightness building inside him like a coiling spring. "It won't be easy. I'll observe a peace of sorts, but I'm warning you now—you'll pay bloody hell before you ever rip up one inch of sod on my land."

"We shall simply have to wait and see," Dyson said, with a resigned glance at Stricklin. The man was simply unreasonable.

After checking on the mare in the foaling barns, Ty returned to the house. Cathleen informed him, with a sly wink, that Tara had gone upstairs. He glanced at the study, but the doors were standing open. The discussion was obviously concluded, so his presence wasn't likely to be required. He went directly upstairs.

"Finally," Tara declared as he entered the sitting room. "How was your mare?" There was a trace of sarcasm in her voice.

"Fine." He didn't bother to explain it didn't look as if there would be a new foal this night.

"There are people hired to look after those horses. I don't see why you have to do it—especially at a time like this," she muttered impatiently.

"At a time like this," Ty repeated with humorless amusement. "I'd like to believe you're saying that because it's your first night home and it's my company you want, but that isn't the reason, is it?"

"It's part of the reason." She crossed the room to stand before him, her hands touching him, making contact to start the hungry pulsing while he breathed in her musky female scent. "You have to do something about your father."

"My father?"

"Yes. You've got to convince him to let this matter lie."

"Let it lie? What are you talking about? He paid for the land, bought it in good faith. Why shouldn't he fight to get it back?" Ty frowned.

"It's only ten thousand acres. Compared to the million he already owns, he won't even miss it," Tara declared. "Besides, he can still lease it to graze cattle on, so it's the same as owning it."

"It's never the same as owning it because it doesn't give him control." His eyes narrowed in speculation. "Why does the idea of him fighting for it bother you, Tara?"

"I don't think you have any idea what people are saying," she accused with a snap of her dark eyes. "They are using the words 'corruption' and 'bribery' when they speak about him."

"All that was a long time ago. Nothing can be proved."

"It doesn't have to be proved. The talk is enough. Don't you know how damaging that is to a person's reputation?" There was a kind of fury in her that she was being dragged down. "It's going to rub off on us, Ty."

"It doesn't bother you that he possibly made a payoff, does it?" Ty mused. "You're angry because he got caught."

"Don't you care what all this talk is going to do to the Calder name?" Tara demanded.

"Is that what's wrong, Tara?" he mocked. "Have your important friends started to shun you?"

"You say that as though you don't believe they are important." She was stiffly indignant, and slightly incredulous that he couldn't see the greater scope of the matter. "I don't think you realize what valuable contacts they can prove to be in the future. You certainly don't make any effort to cultivate their friendship. I'm doing it all so that when we take over the ranch there will be a network of people in influential positions that will be beneficial to us."

"You can't wait for the day when my father turns control of the ranch over to me, can you?" Pride and strong will had always been two qualities Ty admired in his wife, fitting characteristics for his life's partner. Tonight, her self-centeredness stuck in his craw.

"The sooner it happens, the better it will be for all of us." Tara didn't deny it. "We can't afford to have scandal attached to the Calder name. I won't have him destroy all the work I've done to make the name Calder mean something outside this state."

"If you don't fight for what belongs to you, the name won't mean anything in this state."

"That's your father's way of thinking," Tara condemned. "What does it matter what these local people around here think? They aren't important. The money your father is spending to fight this thing would buy another ranch some place else. The Triple C can become the first ranch of many scattered around the country, run by competent managers. The idea is to expand, and I don't mean by building feedlots. You have to stop thinking so small, Ty." She was insistent, urging and half angry. "Don't be like your father, Ty. You have to be progressive and modern like mine."

"That would solve your problems, wouldn't it?" A muscle leaped convulsively along his clenched jaw. "Maybe I should change my name to Dyson, too, so I won't be tarnished by anything that might blacken the Calder name."

"I never suggested anything of the sort! Why are you trying to twist what I'm saying?" Tara flung her protest at him, resentment flaring. "In this world, you have to look out for yourself. Your father's actions are going to affect us, Ty. They can hurt us. That's all I'm saying."

"You're asking me to side against my father." Behind all the smooth talk and an appeal for reason, it boiled down to that.

"I'm asking you to think about us." Her chin was lifted at

when Ty moved to the bed and turned to wait for her. His gaze drifted over her nude form, pale-shining and slender as a tall willow. She felt the touch of his eyes on her small breasts. Neither in looks nor form could she compare with Tara.

She had her moment of second thought; then his hand reached out to her. No more did she have to be strong; no more did she have to hide her feelings—her love. There was a wealth of passion in her going unused, too long suppressed. She had to give it or shrivel up inside and die. Its pressure was that strong. She went to him, to lie with him and live again.

20

After she had lighted two cigarettes from the ack on the bedstand, Jessy rolled back and passed one to Ty, nscious of his warm flank against hers beneath the sheet. e delicious curling sensation hadn't left her toes. Her body still tingling with the aftermath of their lovemaking. A smile curved the wide edges of her mouth.

shifted onto his side to study her, the caramel tangle of ir darkening the pillow under her head. "You're very pleased," he murmured.

not? You're feeling quite proud of yourself, too, ou had me." Jessy lightly teased the near smugness ession.

s no remembrance of that first time in his eyes. ked for it so often—waited to see it. Now she was e didn't remember. There had been too much one way or another. She wasn't going to tell o purpose would be served except to make him sorry. Whatever his feelings toward her, she e two things to be part of them.

became weighted with thought, somber

him, all her femininity sharpened into temper as she put her will against his.

"You think about us." His voice was low and heavy as he swung away to stride for the door. "It's your homecoming."

There was an instant when she could not believe he intended to leave. But the resoluteness was in his squared shoulders.

"Where are you going?" she demanded, her hands curling into fists.

Ty paused at the door, jerking it open, then looked at her in a glance that raked and stripped. "Out," he said simply.

The door was slammed to its frame. Tara stared at it, then whirled about to face the center of the room. Lately, Ty had started listening to her; then this had to happen.

Ty jumped into a truck and started driving, mindless of the blast of winter-cold air blowing in the opened windows. He had no destination, just an escape from the pressure of the thoughts crowding into his mind.

The right and wrong of something seemed to be all in the mind of the person making the judgment. Tara believed she was right. His father believed he was right. Where did his loyalties lie? In the past or the future?

He had no sense of time passing, no conscious choice of direction. It was a long time before Ty realized the truck had stopped moving. In the conelike pool of the headlights stood the log cabin where Jessy lived. The tension was still there, ruffling through him. He switched off the truck's motor and lights and walked onto the front stoop of the cabin.

It was completely dark inside. It took him a minute to find the light switch on the wall. "Jessy!" he called, but she didn't answer. The bedroom was empty, and the breakfast dishes were sitting in the sink. A glance at his watch gave him the time. She should have been home before this. She'd probably be walking in the door any time now, he told himself and fixed a pot of coffee to have waiting when she returned.

The cabin wasn't the same without her presence to give it that earthy peace. He stoked the wood stove in the front room, trying to put some warmth into the air. He rattled around in the cabin's emptiness. It was worse than being alone in the empty suite of rooms he shared with Tara.

"Dammit! Where is she?" Ty demanded of the four walls.

The headlight beams flashed over the ranch pickup parked in front of her cabin as Jessy drove up. Chimney smoke curled blue-white against the black web of tree limbs. Light spilled from the cabin windows to lay squares on the freeze-dried grass.

She wasn't exactly in the mood for company after a full day's work and an evening at her parents' to celebrate her mother's birthday. Besides, she knew Tara was home. There was no eagerness in her steps as she trudged up the steps to the cabin. The opening of the door brought Ty's voice to her.

"Where the hell have you been? Do you realize it's after ten o'clock? I've been here for almost two hours, not knowing where you were, not knowing if something might have happened. I've been half out of my mind!"

The cranky worry in his voice astonished her. There was an open possessiveness in his tone that he had never used with her before. And the dark scowl on his face when he confronted her at the door made it all the more blatant.

"It was Mom's birthday," Jessy said in a small, dazed voice.

His breath ran out in relief as he caught her and dragged her to him. She was shocked yet clearheaded, conscious of the strong arms around her and the temper that was thoroughly aroused. She realized just how deeply she had gotten into his feelings. It was in his voice and the constricting pressure of his arms.

"It's been a helluva lonely wait, Jessy," he muttered.

The roughness of his kiss was hungry and needing, and she returned it willingly and unreservedly. They were locked together, straining, made raw by this intolerable pressure inside them. But there was no easing of it.

Ty was breathing hard, his cheek pressed against the side of her hair, his arms binding her tightly to him. "Jessy. Jessy." In the muttering of her name, there was a question, a need expressed that his hard, muscled body had already told her.

"I know." She felt lightheaded. For all the pounding of her

heart and the almost violent ache inside, she felt a remarkable calmness, too. "Carry me?" she asked.

There was a moment when she sensed an uncertainty in him, when she thought honor might pull him back. Then his arms were loosening, shifting to scoop an arm beneath her thighs and pick her up. He stood there, holding her and looking at her shining face. There was curiosity behind his desirous look.

"I never thought of you as the romantic kind, Jessy." His husky voice throbbed.

"Why?" she asked softly as she stroked his cleanly shaven jaw, touching a fingertip to the brush of black whiskers above his lip. "Because I can ride like a man and do the work of a man, did you think I didn't have a woman's feelings? Why can't I like flowers and candy, too?"

"I don't know."

He carried her into the darkened bedroom and set her down. For a silent moment, they stood facing each other, tense and poised like a mare and stallion meeting. The pawing and mane tossing were finished; now the intense silence heralded nature's most precious and most and

Her face was lifted to him, conveying the age be kissed. Ty read it clearly and felt a splint The signals were all the same, whether they Jessy, or some other woman. Yet Jessy wa and he'd wanted it to be different.

Only it couldn't be different, beca things. She was a woman and he w level of communication was use were locked by the pattern. Ir stored the wonderful images varied. Slowly it filtered th matter.

Reaching, he pushe tossed it into the dar turned back, Jess fingers reached f

Her eyes were clothes come off to flesh, the clean male line lines drawing down his rugged features and bringing a troubled look to his eyes. "Jessy, sometimes I—"

"Don't say it, Ty." She cut in to stop him, firm and sure. "For both our sakes, don't say something you don't really mean. I went into this with my eyes wide open, knowing you would leave before morning came. Right now you're thinking that you don't want to go, but you will."

"How do you know what's in my mind?" Ty watched her closely, trying to fathom this woman who fitted him as comfortably as a second skin.

Just for a minute, Jessy dropped her guard and let him see the depth of love in her eyes. "Maybe because I've wished it, too." Yet her tone was near to a challenge.

Of all the times he'd made love to a woman without regrets, this wasn't one of them. There was a fierce surge of tender feeling that turned him raw. It was deep-seeded, as wild in its way as the stirrings Tara aroused in him.

That look almost made Jessy believe things could be different. Before she succumbed to the certain hurt it would bring, she swung her legs out of bed and sat up on the edge. It was not from any sense of modesty that she reached for the blouse at the foot of the bed and clutched it loosely to her small breasts. Clothes were a protection that kept others from seeing too much.

She crossed to the dresser and crushed the barely smoked cigarette in a glass ashtray. Ty sat up on one elbow, eyes drawn to the tightening play of muscles in her buttocks. When she turned, his gaze lifted past the triangular drape of her blouse with its apex at the valley of her breasts to center on the closed-in expression.

"Jessy, there's something I'd like to explain."

"I don't want to hear any explanations, Ty," she said with a shake of her head; then her chin came up. "I'm not as tolerant and understanding as you think I am. I'm not the cause of your problems with your wife, and I don't want to know what they are. I can't pretend she doesn't exist, but I don't have to listen to you talk about her. I'm more of a woman than she is, for all her pretty looks and frilly clothes— and I know that. So I'd say things about her that you wouldn't like to hear."

No matter how he was feeling now, Tara was the woman who held claim to his emotions. Part of it was her beauty, but the rest of it was Ty's dream. It was something Jessy understood too clearly. Ty had made Tara into the image of his wishes. Men dreamed the things they wanted into a woman. Even if Ty was beginning to see Tara was not all he believed, he was not ready to give up his dream.

In the semidarkness of the room, he caught the determined light in her eye, that unshakable courage to face a situation no matter how unpleasant it was. He left the cigarette to burn in the ashtray on the bedstand and rolled out of bed to cross the room. She half turned, avoiding his eyes.

"You'd better get dressed," she advised in a calm voice. "It's late, and she'll be wondering where you are."

"To hell with Tara right now." Ty used the name Jessy had avoided while unconsciously admitting he would be returning to his wife. "What about you, Jessy? Will you be all right?"

Jessy looked at him, and the desire to smile was strong. If she told him she wouldn't be, she foresaw how Ty would respond. Men were so pragmatic in their dealings with life, until it came to women. There they became thoroughly impractical, always promising to make life easy for them and fully believing that they could do it. Despite all her romantic fantasies, she had a woman's insight into life and knew there would be pain and loneliness in the years ahead as well as the blessings of times like this.

"I'm strong, Ty. I'll do just fine." She assured him instead of the other way around. She had made her bargain, and she was ready to pay for it. Tomorrow's heartache didn't frighten her.

He wanted to find something beneath that steadiness she showed him. It grated him slightly that she didn't need him, that she had a sustaining strength which enabled her to be independent of him. It was difficult for him to come to terms with her equality in things he considered male.

Yet there was no game playing in Jessy, no strings for him to chase. He couldn't help remembering that the one time Tara had been direct with him about her needs and demands, he had married her. The knowledge bothered him.

There was nothing he could say. He turned and walked

slowly back to the bed where his clothes lay. There was no figuring Jessy out. There was no figuring women out. But he knew he'd be back to seek the high sense of ease she gave him, and the good feeling that lighted a warm fire inside him. But he didn't say so. He didn't need to.

There was a faint noise in the upper hallway. Tara paused, ceasing to impatiently flip through pages of the magazine to listen intently, stiff and poised, for the sound of Ty's return. Another board creaked. She couldn't tell whether it was caused by the pressure of a foot or if it was simply the groanings of an old house. Rising, she dropped the magazine on the long daybed, the fur-trimmed robe of heavy satin falling softly about her legs.

She went to the door and pulled it open, a surfeit of pride showing in the high carriage of her body. But it was Cat who was creeping stealthily toward the stairs, bundled in a heavy coat, her black hair tucked under a white woolen cap. She raised a silencing finger to her lips when she saw Tara in the doorway, green eyes silently pleading with Tara not to give her presence away.

"Repp's waiting for me," Cat whispered. "Don't tell Daddy, please." After the fight she'd caused, Cathleen had been forbidden any contact with her older beau as punishment. Tara was not surprised to discover the young girl was defying the orders to keep secret assignations with her cowboy. It was also the least of Tara's interests, so she simply closed the door. Tensely lacing her fingers together, she paced to the window. The blackness of the huge night sky threatened to swallow her, and she turned back to the light.

When she reached the base of the stairs, Cat froze. There was a light in the den. Her heart seemed to trip over itself, unable to find its normal beat as she tiptoed past the light, peering anxiously into the room. She spied Stricklin clad in a high-necked burgundy sweater, standing at the bookshelves with his back to the door while he perused the titles.

Cat opened the front door a crack and squeezed through the narrow slit—the trickiest part was slipping outside without being heard. She winced at the small click the door made when she closed it. Then she waited, holding her breath and listening for the sound of footsteps coming to investigate the noise. A minute longer, and she expelled the breath in relief. The cold air turned it into a gray-white vapor that swirled and vanished on the night wind.

Moving silently, she traveled the length of the veranda and jumped to the ground, wrapped in the house's dark shadow. In a crouching run, she angled across the snow-crusted grass behind The Homestead, heading for the flat plateau and the isolated airplane hangar that had become their meeting place, far from observing eyes and chance discoveries. The cold air stung her lungs as she hurried to keep the rendezvous.

Hunkered down in a small pocket, Culley O'Rourke held the cigarette cupped in his hand, concealing the glowing red tip so its light wouldn't give away his presence. One by one, the lights had gone off in The Homestead, until only an upstairs light was burning. A minute before, he'd been about to steal away to where he'd left his horse tethered. Then a light had unexpectedly appeared in the den downstairs. He stayed to see if this stirring of activity was the beginning of something more.

Intent on the big house, he almost didn't see the dark shape moving furtively away from it. Motionless, Culley waited until it had passed his shadowy pocket of ground, catching a recognizable glimpse of Cathleen's oval face, and he trailed silently after her.

When she reached the hangar, Cat was out of breath, her face numb from the cold wind. The planes in the open shed stood silently in a row, looming shapes in the night's shadows. She walked swiftly between them, cutting through to the small office and storage area in the back. She opened the door and slipped inside, at last sheltered from the numbing wind. Her eyes searched the darkness as she paused.

"Repp?" Her whispered call brought the sound of movement from her right. Cat turned toward it as a dark form separated itself from the shadows.

"I had almost decided you weren't going to show up." The long wait had brought an edge to his voice.

"I know. I was afraid you might have left. I swear no one in that house goes to bed at a decent hour anymore." Impatience was in her voice, too. Her face was pasty and white in the office shadows, but they didn't dare turn on a light. "Tara was still up, waiting for Ty to come home, when I slipped out of the house. And Stricklin was prowling around in the den. Sometimes I wonder if he's human. I get the feeling he's a robot and doesn't need to eat or sleep like the rest of us."

"Are you sure you weren't seen?" Repp demanded, then muttered in a dark kind of irritation, "I must be crazy to let you talk me into meeting like this."

At last realizing that he would not bridge the space between them, Cat took the necessary steps and unashamedly wrapped her arms around the turned-up collar of his coat. She felt the pressure of his hands on her hips, neither pulling her closer nor pushing her away.

"I don't care how or where we meet as long as we can see each other." It was a dramatic declaration, but it was true. She would risk anything, even her father's wrath, to be with Repp.

"You don't know what you're saying." The low protest was almost groaned, the rashness of his urges threatening to overwhelm his control of them. "You are too young, Cat."

"I'm just as old as my mother was when she got pregnant with Ty." Cat tormented him with the knowledge.

"You oughta be spanked for goading a man with such talk," he accused roughly, more disturbed than he cared to admit, and she knew it. "You're just spoiling for trouble, aren't you? Someday you're going to say that to the wrong man and he's going to take you up on it."

"But I've never said it to anyone but you. You're the only one I ever want to say that to," she insisted and arched herself closer. "It's bad enough that my parents treat me like a child. I'm a woman, Repp. And I love you."

The soft declaration, coupled with her nearness, was too much. His hard-fought caution lost the battle with his driving impulses as his mouth came hungrily onto hers. The heated contact soon chased the numbing cold from their skin. The eager response of her lips broke through his restraint as he used her roughly, man to woman, without thought for her inexperience. She drew back, suddenly tense, then came again with her own rush of feeling. But he caught a breath of cold sanity.

"No, Cat." His fingers dug hard into the sleeves of her coat to stop her from coming against him. "That's enough!"

"Why, Repp? Why does it have to be enough?" she protested.

"You can't have everything you want," he told her.

Her shoulders sagged and she swayed toward him, nestling her head on his shoulder. After a long moment his arms went around her and he let his mouth come against the woolen cap covering her black silk hair.

"I don't want everything, Repp. I just want you," she said very simply without any dramatic elaboration. "Sometimes I just get to feeling desperate. Two years seems such a long time to wait." It seemed an agony of time.

"They'll go by fast," he lied. Something clanged outside in the hangar, and Repp stiffened. "Did you hear that?"

"What?" She lifted her head from the comfortable and intimate pillow of his shoulder.

"I think I heard somebody outside," he murmured and began untangling his arms from around her. "I'm going to check."

"There's no one out there," Cat protested. "You probably just heard the wind rattling the tin roof."

He ignored her explanation to glide silently to the office door. "Wait here," he whispered.

"No. I'm coming with you," she insisted. She spoke louder than she intended and it carried through the door Repp had opened.

"Sssh," he warned.

Cat kept a hand on him so she wouldn't lose contact as they stole out of the office into the darkened shed. A coyote wailed a lonely call from some distant hillside. A haze of stars barely cast enough light to make silhouettes of the planes hangared in the shed. Repp picked his way through the shadows, looking and listening.

Another faint sound came to them, unidentifiable. It seemed to have come from one of the ranch planes, the one Cat's father usually flew. They moved up alongside it.

"There." Cat pointed at the access door to the engine

compartment. It was open. "It must not have been latched properly and the wind blew it open."

"I guess so." He left her to shut the door and make sure the latch caught. When he came back, he looked around, not completely satisfied, instinct telling him someone else had been in the hangar or was there still. He started worrying about Cat. "It's late, nearly midnight. You'd better go back. I'll walk you partway."

"But—"

"Don't argue with me, Cat." His voice was firm, but he couldn't say why he felt this sudden urgency to get her safely away from there.

Something in his tone checked any further argument from Cat. His hand gripped her elbow to guide her out of the shed and across the short stretch to the knoll where The Homestead sat, its white exterior rising from the darkness.

After he'd left her, Repp couldn't explain what made him double back, taking a roundabout route. Halfway to the hangar, the wind carried to him the sound of hoofbeats. Briefly a rider was skylined on a crest against a dusting of haze stars. O'Rourke. It had to be. The bunkhouse gossip was full of talk about his restless wanderings over the Triple C. Even if he was Cat's uncle, the man gave him the willies. But at least his suspicions were satisfied. Repp turned and headed for the bunkhouse.

As Ty made the turn onto the driveway by the front steps, he saw a figure dart into the shadows of the house and recognized the white knitted cap. It didn't take much guessing to know where his sister had been and with whom. He didn't say anything until he was on the wide porch that ran the width of the front.

"There's no point in hiding, Cat. I already know you're there," he said quietly and heard a rustle of movement as she emerged from the shadows to haul herself onto the porch. "Sneaking off to meet Repp again? You're going to get caught one of these nights."

"Dad's too old-fashioned and too strict," she said with a resentful flash of her green eyes.

"You'll think he's too strict if he finds you going behind his back," Ty warned, but he wasn't really in the mood to be stern with her himself, so he let the matter lie. There were too many other things on his mind. He held the front door open for Cat to enter ahead of him, then walked in. "Looks like someone left a light on in the den." He started across the foyer.

"I think Stricklin is in there," Cat said, but she altered her course to accompany him and find out.

A book was opened and lying facedown on the armrest of the chair where Stricklin was seated. He had a pocket knife out and was meticulously cleaning beneath his nails. When Ty appeared in the doorway, he looked up with mild interest.

"Hello, Ty, are you just getting in?" Then the expressionless blue eyes looked past him. "I didn't realize Cathleen was with you."

"Yes. We have a brood mare that's due to foal," he said dryly, aware he was providing a mutual alibi. "I hope we didn't disturb you."

"Not at all," Stricklin assured him.

"Good night." Ty moved out of the doorway and headed for the stairs with Cat tagging along.

"That man is strange," she murmured.

"Why?" Ty was used to Stricklin's detached attitude.

"Who ever heard of cleaning your nails with a dirty knife?" she countered with a vague shrug.

At the top of the stairs, he noticed the sliver of light showing beneath the door to the master bedroom. He felt the tightening of his nerves, an alertness that ran through him and chased out the last vestiges of spinning tenderness. He didn't hear Cat's low-voiced "Good night" as he reached for the doorknob.

The sitting room was empty, darkened except for a lone lamp that laid its light on the door. Ty walked straight through to the bedroom, where Tara sat in front of a vanity mirror, rubbing a moisturizing cream into her smooth facial skin. Her eyes met the reflection of his in the mirror, coolly confident.

The satiny fabric of her nightgown exposed her white shoulders and enticingly outlined her round, firm breasts, erect nipples making a button pattern under the material. It was a feminine sexuality so understated that it was blatant. It irritated him that she had not doubted he would return to it. But it always seemed to be there—this heat that burned all the good feelings.

Her calmness had convinced him that she hadn't been waiting up for him. Ty believed it until he picked up the satin robe on the bed to move it so he could sit down and pull off his boots. The robe still held the warmth of her body, which indicated it had only been removed in the last few minutes. She hadn't wanted it to appear that she had been waiting up for him—another of her games.

"I'm glad you came home before I went to bed, Ty," she said and fixed the lid on the jar of cream. She straightened from the bench to walk toward him, all grace and slink. "I wanted you to know that I'm sorry for some of the things I said tonight. I was upset and spoke rashly."

Ty barely looked at her while she made her carefully rehearsed speech, reciting the lines so well. He pulled off his boots and set them on the floor at the foot of the bed.

Unable to endure his silence any longer, Tara laughed, exasperated. "I've apologized. Can't you at least say something?"

"What would you like me to say?" He stood up and began tugging his shirttail out of his pants to unbutton it. "I'm sorry about a lot of things, but that doesn't change them."

"I hate it when we quarrel, Ty." She moved in and began unbuttoning his shirt, so expertly coy and alluring. "Let's kiss and make up," she coaxed.

The heat of her kiss burned at the edges of his memory and taunted him with its closeness. It was always like this; he only had to be close to her to remember the fire of possessing this dream image. There was something blind about this desire.

And there was something about loving a person for so long a time that couldn't be stopped. Seemingly of their own volition, his hands curved onto her silken-smooth shoulders, absently caressing them. When he kissed her, Ty felt the start of a response; then she pulled back and swung away from him.

He hesitated, but in the end he didn't pursue her. Maybe

she had tasted Jessy on his lips. Women had a knowledge of such things, he'd learned. He let out a sigh and raked a hand through his hair.

Inside, Tara was seething with rage. She didn't understand this instinct that told her he'd come to her from the arms of some other woman, but she knew it. It was something in the way he kissed her, as if comparing. Only one woman came to mind—that she-bitch Jessy Niles.

"Ty—" She fought down the anger, smoothing out her voice.

"What?" She heard the heaviness in his voice.

"I—" Tara pivoted and watched his gaze travel down her. There was reassurance in seeing she still moved him. "I love you. This difficulty with your father . . . I know somehow we'll work it out."

"I won't go against him," he stated flatly.

"No." She could see that no amount of persuasion would make him do that. It was better if he didn't, now that she'd had time to consider it. An estrangement between father and son might not bode well for the future. Chase Calder was just stubborn enough to leave this mini-empire to his daughter instead of his son. "I can't ask you to do that, any more than you could ask me to defy my father. I realize that. But you don't have to become involved in the fight—not in a public way."

"I suppose not." It was a compromise of sorts. He suddenly felt very old and very tired and very troubled.

21

In the two weeks after Dyson had left, the weather went bad. Everything was thrown at them, from sheeting rain to sleet storms, snow driven by fierce winter winds to subzero temperatures. One system would come through, give them a short breather, and the next one would hit them. There was no holing up and taking shelter until better weather came. It was calving season, a round-the-clock operation in brutal weather that took its toll on man and beast.

After two weeks of eighteen-hour days, Ty was haggard and bone-weary, his nerves frayed. He stared with an absent envy at the closed eyes of the foal, lying in a thick straw bed, its body blanketed. Each breath it drew was a rasping, labored sound. It had entered the world with premature abruptness a week earlier when its mother slipped on some ice and went down, fracturing both front legs. The foal had been taken from her before the mare had been put down.

Since the horse colt was only two weeks early and a supply of mare's milk was on hand, there was a good chance they could have saved the foal. Then pneumonia had set in, and the chances for its survival were getting worse each hour as the foal's condition deteriorated at a rapid pace.

While Ty watched, the noise stopped. It was a full minute before his fatigue-dulled senses noticed the silence in the stall, and he realized the foal had died. He lowered his chin to his chest and swore silently and bitterly. The loss of both mare and foal virtually eliminated any chance the breeding operation might have shown its first profit this year.

There was a rustle of straw behind him, and Ty wearily lifted his head, turning it in the direction of the sound. Long hours, with little sleep in between, made his eyes appear more deep-set and hooded, and his hat was pulled low on his forehead, the rolled point of its front brim shading more of his face and adding to the impression.

"How's the colt?" His father came up to the stall, his breath making small puffs of steam.

"Lost it." With a slow swing of his body, Ty turned away from the foal and let himself out of the stall to join his father. No comment was necessary or expected. There was too much other work to be done for valuable time to be wasted discussing the death of one foal. "Was there something you wanted?" His father had rarely left the house, directing most of the ranch's operations from his desk or through instructions to Ty, while he worked on the land-title problem.

"I'm flying to Helena this afternoon. After so many postponements because of bad weather, the meeting with those officials from Washington has finally been scheduled for tomorrow morning," he stated, then added, "Your mother's coming with me. We'll probably be back by the end of the week, weather permitting."

"Okay." That meant Tara would be alone in the house. Somehow he'd have to arrange to spend more time there, or at least take his meals there. It was no good to urge her to get out and visit with some of the other wives similarly housebound. Only in desperation would she do it, and she usually returned more discontented than before.

"Where are you heading now?"

Ty paused, gathering the effort to answer. "I'm going to swing past the camp at Juliana and check on things there on my way up to the north camp."

"To see Jessy Niles?"

Ty's spine stiffened. He looked hard and direct at his father. "Arch has been having problems with the generator. I've got a crew up there, repairing it."

"Then stop by Jessy's place for coffee on your way home. Isn't that the routine?" Again that level tone, speaking calmly and saying volumes.

"Since Jessy has pulled the day shift and will be working at the calving sheds when I leave there, I'm not likely to stop by her cabin." Ty responded indirectly to the implied charge, neither confirming nor denying it.

"You're very familiar with her hours, aren't you?" his father challenged, closely observing Ty's reactions. "I've never made it a practice to pry into your personal affairs."

His temper frayed. "Then butt out of them now!" It exploded from him in a low rush, the anger barely checked.

"This talk about you and Jessy has gone too far when it's reached me," his father stated. "There's never this much smoke without some fire somewhere. You've made your bed, Ty. You're a married man. You've made promises to your wife, and you're going to keep them. I don't care how much of this is smoke and how much is fire. Just stay away from Jessy Niles. I won't tolerate any cheating."

"My God, that's the pot calling the kettle black!" Rage

vibrated inside him at the righteous-sounding order. "Don't do as I do, do as I say—is that it?"

"You'd better explain yourself," his father warned.

"I'll explain myself, all right," Ty promised in a rough-pitched voice. "In two words—Sally Brogan. Or don't you recall all those times you spent with her cheating on your wife?"

The backhanded swing of his father's gloved hand struck him full on the cheek, and Ty staggered backwards to crash against the upright posts of the stall. His hand was at his jaw, working it, while he glared at his father. Anger and resentment smoldered hotly in his blood. It drove him from the stall in a headlong charge that took both of them to the floor of the foaling barn, threshing and scuffling about like two giants locked in mortal combat, one in the prime of his manhood and the other wisened in battle.

Shouts came from some other part of the barn, followed by the thudding of running feet. A pair of hands grabbed at Ty, then two more, pulling and tugging. His blurred vision began to register other forms, stablehands getting into the fray to break it up and forcibly separate the two men.

Sanity returned slowly to him, and with it bitter remorse. His lungs dragged in air as Ty stopped struggling in the grip of the two men who held him. His lip was cut and bleeding slightly. He wiped at it with his glove, licking the inside with his tongue, while he glanced watchfully at his father. The older Calder shrugged off the hands with an impatient lift of his shoulders. He, too, was breathing hard and steadily eyeing his son. Then he looked around at the stablehands.

"Leave us," he ordered in a rough, winded voice.

There was an uneasy shifting of feet and exchanged glances before the men began a slow exodus from the scene of the fight. They were well away before either man moved or broke the heavy silence.

"Sally Brogan is a friend." A gloved finger was aimed at Ty to stab home his point. "Don't ever suggest again that I have been unfaithful to your mother. Sally was a friend when I needed one. And there was never anything more than that."

"I thought . . ." But it didn't matter what he thought, so Ty didn't finish the sentence. Reaching down, he scooped up his hat that had been knocked off in the scuffle and slapped it against his thigh to throw off the wisps of straw it had collected. Then he jammed it low on his head, tilting his head back slightly to meet his father's look. "I guess I was wrong," he admitted grudgingly.

"You sure as hell were." The force remained in his words, but there was a faint gentling of his father's stern expression. "You don't handle yourself too bad in a fight."

The near compliment seemed to break through the constraint. Ty came close to smiling, but the cut on his lip made him wince from the pulling action. "For an old man, you don't do too badly yourself." He pressed a finger at the cut, testing the degree of pain it inflicted, and winced again.

There was a slight pause, then: "About Jessy—"

"Don't ask." Ty shook his head. Right now, she was a kind of anchor for him, steady and calm, and he needed that.

"You're not fair to her," his father said. "You can only afford to have one mistress outside your marriage, Ty. And that mistress is the land. She'll give you all the satisfaction, and heartache, that you can handle."

They walked from the foaling barn together, long stride matching long stride. The stablehands watched and nodded approvingly to one another, their own anxieties eased now that the rift had been healed and there was harmony again between the head and heart of the Triple C Ranch.

Outside the barn, they parted to go their separate ways. "Let Tara know I'll be home tonight in time for dinner," Ty said and lifted a hand. "Have a good trip."

The sleek, fast single-engine aircraft made a banking turn and headed west into the gray gloom of a low overcast. The drone of its motor penetrated the walls and windows of the rebuilt house. Culley heard it and paused in the act of slicing a slab of roasted beef to combine a late lunch with an early supper. His keen senses recognized the sound of that motor. Leaving the half-sliced meat, he walked to the back door and stepped outside.

He looked up, searching the iron-gray sky. Finally he spied the plane, its markings barely visible at this distance. It was Calder's plane, all right. Once he'd sighted the plane, a certain indifference came over him. He turned and walked back into the house.

It wasn't until he'd set his plate down on the freshly laundered tablecloth that a thought started nagging him. He thrashed on it through the silent meal, cleaned and dried his dishes, then hauled out of the house and caught up a horse from the corral to saddle it.

The repairs on the backup generator were nearly complete. Ty left the two mechanics to finish up while he went by the calving shed to inform Arch Goodman of the work's status. At least, that was the excuse he used for going there.

Goodman was working right alongside the others, busy birthing a calf. "Help yourself to some coffee from the thermos," he invited. "Be with you directly."

A rickety cardboard table served as a coffee bar, stationed in a sheltered corner of the shed. Halfway to it, Ty spotted Jessy leaning upright against a roughed-out interior wall with her legs braced in front of her. He felt a small kick of pleasure.

Her long, slim body looked more rounded and firmly packed with its layer of insulated underwear and two layers of clothes beneath the winter jacket. A gold wool scarf was tied around her head, a dirty brown hat jammed on top of it. She saw him and, despite the tiredness in her expression, gave him the ghosting warmth of a smile. Ty had to stop himself from walking right to her and paused at the coffee urn instead, filling a paper cup.

"You should be sitting down," he observed over the rim of the cup he lifted to his mouth.

"No." There was a smile in her voice. "I wouldn't be able to get up again."

With the weather and the naturally busy time of year, the demands of work had gone too wild for Ty to see her more than twice since the last time they'd been together, and each of the subsequent times had been during the course of work. The heaviness seemed to leave his mind. There was something about her company that produced a warm ease in him, something solid that gave its own kind of heady glow. So different than anything he'd felt with Tara.

Ty wasn't conscious of how hard he'd been staring at her until she looked down. "I guess I'm a dirty, smelly sight, aren't I?" It was admitted with self-deprecating candor that had a rebellious ring to it. It showed clear when her eyes flashed upward at him. "You don't have to smile like that and make me feel even scroungier," she said in protest.

"Now I know you're a woman," Ty said and wandered closer, a humorous gleam in his eyes. "You're dead tired and dragging, but you're still worrying about how you look."

"I guess it shouldn't matter. You've seen me looking worse than this." There was a watchful expectancy in her expression, a waiting that always pulled at him like some powerful undertow.

"You look good to me," he said simply and discovered it was true.

With the scarf wrapped around her head and throttling her throat there was nothing to distract his gaze from the strong, pure lines of her face. Sun wrinkles made smiles at the corners of her clear almond-brown eyes, and the rounded ridges of her cheekbones stood out cleanly. Her wide lips lay comfortably together, warmly drawn and generous. His glance dropped much lower, to the bulky front of her jacket. A sudden wry smile pulled at one corner of his mouth.

"Why is it that every time I look at your mouth, I automatically glance at your breasts?" he mused aloud in a familiarly intimate tone.

"I never caught you looking at them." She gazed at him anew.

"All men look. They just try not to be seen looking," Ty murmured, a lazy caress coming into his tone. "You have such little ones—little and so very sensitive."

As he braced a leather-gloved hand on a rough board near her head, her breath quickened. He began leaning closer, his glance running more and more often to her mouth. She remained poised and motionless, under a spell and afraid to break it.

Someone shouted, and the voice sounded nearby. There was the scuffle and thud of boots climbing a pen fence. In that instant, Ty became conscious of their surroundings and straightened away from her, lifting his coffee cup to take a quick drink.

A heaviness settled onto her as grim knowledge entered her eyes. "Now that begins, doesn't it?" she said and didn't wait for him to ask what she meant. She'd seen his darted glance, that over-the-shoulder caution. "The wondering if we're being seen together? Who might be watching? When you come to my place, you'll probably have the urge to park behind the cabin where your truck can't be seen. And I'll start pulling the window shades. Still, we'll jump at every sound."

His tight-pressed mouth told its own story of agreement. "Are you sorry, Jessy?"

She thought about it a moment before she slowly shook her head. "No. Maybe it's wrong. But I never had even this much before. I'm not complaining, Ty."

But he was having regrets and misgivings. She could see it. His half-narrowed gaze was skimming the calving shed and its workers. Jessy looked out over the pens, and a small smile touched her mouth. Since Ty had joined her, none of the men had taken a break for coffee and a smoke.

"They all know, Ty," she said as she continued to look out. "You can't hide anything that goes on at this ranch from them . . . not for long."

"Have they said anything to you?"

"No, and they won't." Jessy faced him, calm and vaguely tolerant. "You should know that's not the way of things here. No, they'll just stand back and let me sort out my own problems. They don't make judgments as quickly as you might think. They wait and see."

"Is that why you look at me that way? To wait and see?"

"I know you're going to make a decision, or you're not the man I think you are." Part of her even knew what it was going to be. Tara's hold on him was strong; and a Calder lived with his mistakes, he didn't shuck them. Put those two facts together and the outcome was almost a foregone conclusion.

There were some on the ranch who questioned Ty's ability. He had been raised differently and educated differently. Some said he was too quick to discard the old way things were done in favor of a new one—too willing to accept change. The way he let his wife go off alone on trips had raised many an eyebrow at this example of a modern marriage.

But a lot of people overlooked the two qualities Jessy saw—his aggressiveness and his determination to succeed. They spurred him hard, harder than a lot of people realized. Jessy had glimpsed them beneath that mask of patience. She had yet to see whether these two powerful traits would overshadow his consideration of other people and things.

"It's time I was getting back to work." She pushed away from the wall and downed the rest of the now-tepid coffee in her paper cup before tossing it into a five-gallon pail.

"Jessy." There was a troubled urgency in his voice as a step carried her near to him.

"Yes." She paused.

A long, searching moment went by, and the intensity of it eddied around her. Finally he shook his head. "Nothing," Ty said and let her walk away. He wanted to keep her by him, but his father was right: it wasn't fair.

As Jessy walked away from the corner, Arch Goodman approached as if cued by her departure. No reference was made to Ty's slight preoccupation. The weight of Jessy's words were on him. Wait and see. But he was damned if he knew what all of them would eventually see.

The radio sat atop the refrigerator in the kitchen, its volume turned high to cover the silence in the house. Tara hummed the melody while she smoothly rounded the pâté in its serving dish. It was rare when she had the chance to plan the entire evening menu herself. It was hardly a challenge to cook for two, but she consoled herself with a silent promise that the time would come when she would be entertaining important guests at her table, people of position and influence in the furtherance of Ty's career beyond this ranch.

As she turned to carry the pâté to the refrigerator, she was startled by the sight of a man standing in the kitchen. Tara was shaken by the feeling he had been there for some time, watching her. A thready fear ran through her system even as she recognized the lean, black-eyed man with metal-gray hair. The Homestead sat on a knoll, too far from the other buildings for anyone to hear her cries, especially with the radio so loud. Tara reached up quickly to turn down the volume.

"How long have you been here? What do you want?" she demanded, masking her apprehension with sharpness. O'Rourke had always seemed such a silent and strange man to her. She had never regarded him as threatening, but she'd never been alone with him before. He had appeared so suddenly, so silently, that she felt an eerie chill.

"Where's Maggie?"

A breath of relief trembled from her as she realized he was looking for his sister. "She went to Helena with Chase. I don't expect them back until Friday."

He took a step toward her, his black gaze boring intently on her. There was something almost menacing about his expression. "Did they go by plane?"

"Yes." Tara drew back slightly, wary and trying not to show her alarm.

With a sudden turn of his head, he looked up as if he could see through the ceilings and roof of The Homestead to the sky. Something strained in him, like an animal tensed and waiting.

"You'd better go," Tara ordered. No man had ever seemed beyond the reach of her ability to control him. But she was nothing to O'Rourke. She made no impression on him at all, which was equally unnerving.

"Where's Cat? Is she in school?"

"Yes. Ty will be home soon, though," she said quickly, grabbing at his name as some sort of protection. She still wasn't sure from what. "Why don't you wait for him in the living room?"

"No." The way he looked at her made her blood run cold. It was as if she were being condemned for something.

She couldn't stand it and swung away, her breath running shallow. "I'm sorry I haven't time to visit with you," she said with forced lightness, "but I'm right in the middle of preparing tonight's dinner and I—" A sudden draft of cold air rushed over her. Tara pivoted in time to see O'Rourke slipping outside through the back door. The fierce grip she'd had on her composure snapped. "Don't you ever come into this house again without knocking!" she stormed. The door clicked shut on her frightened outburst, and Tara rushed over to lock it, not caring that her words and action went against Triple C custom.

The locked doors required an explanation when Ty had to knock to be let into his own home. Tara had managed to channel much of her fear into a kind of anger as she related the incident that afternoon with O'Rourke.

"I can't stand him," she asserted forcefully. "And I won't have him walking in and out as he pleases when I'm here alone."

"I'll speak to him," Ty promised to calm her down. "But he meant no harm. He just came to visit my mother."

"I don't care. I don't want him around." She rubbed her arms in agitation, remembering the eerie chill she'd felt.

She seemed vulnerable, in need of his protection. Ty came up behind her and put his arms around her. She turned into them, her face tipped to him. He felt again that stunned reaction to so much refined beauty and the clinging way she looked at him. The pull of her softly reddened lips brought his mouth down.

The next morning Ty climbed the steps, balancing a small serving tray with a glass of juice and a cup of coffee on it. Tara was still asleep when he entered the bedroom. He set the tray on the bedstand, then eased himself onto the side of the bed and kissed her awake. She lazily curled her arms around his neck and stretched like a sleeping kitten as she made a purring sound in her throat.

"It can't be morning already." She kissed at his lower lip, avoiding the tickle of his mustache. "Come back to bed."

"Can't," he said reluctantly. "You asked me to wake you up before I left the house this morning." For a moment, she couldn't think why she'd done that. Then she remembered O'Rourke and her desire not to be alone in the house and sleeping if he decided to pay another one of his unannounced visits. "I brought you some coffee and juice." Ty straightened, and she didn't try to hold him.

"That's lovely." She sat up in bed, plumping pillows behind her.

"Will you be okay?"

"Yes. I . . ." Tara hesitated. The thought of being alone in the house all day suddenly seemed intolerable. Her options were limited. "I think I'll take the car today and drive somewhere—maybe into Miles City. I understand there's a small gallery with the works of local artists. I'll be home before dark, though."

"I probably won't be back for lunch, then," Ty said. "We've got a batch of sick calves at the South Branch camp, and the infection is spreading faster than Stumpy can isolate them. More than likely, I'll be there most of the day." Ty headed for the door to leave, having tarried too long as it was. "Don't lock the doors," he admonished.

The veterinarian had a well-worn earthiness about him, and a face that carried a no-nonsense look as well as a simple gentleness. "The infection isn't serious in itself," he said to Ty in a voice that was weary and edged with frustration. "But it weakens the calves and leaves 'em open to pneumonia. So we're fightin' a war on two fronts." There was a faint twinkle in his eyes. "Niles's wife warned me that I'd better find some miracle drug to cure them, because there isn't room for another sick calf in her kitchen."

Ty chuckled, no more alarmed by the threat than the vet was. "She's like Jessy. She'd take the whole damned herd in the house if that's what it took to make them well."

"Ranchers' wives are about as crazy as the ranchers," the vet agreed, but looked away at the mention of Jessy. He nodded his head, calling Ty's attention to the vehicle pulling up in the yard. "Wonder what he wants." A ray of sunlight glinted off the badge pinned on the winter coat of the man climbing out from behind the wheel. "He sure likes people to know he's sheriff. As lazy as Potter was, he never threw his weight around like Blackmore does."

"The sheriff probably figures he's got it to throw around," Ty murmured as he straightened and turned to meet the officer walking toward them. "You're a ways off the beaten track, aren't you, Blackmore?" Ty asked idly. "What is this? A social call or business?"

"I'm here on official business, I'm afraid," the man said.

He seemed unusually solemn, lacking his usually abrasive edge, as he glanced around at the southern camp's buildings.

"If you're looking for my father, he isn't here. He's in Helena for a couple of days," Ty informed him.

There was a long, considering pause. "His plane didn't make it to Helena," the sheriff stated in a brusque yet flat voice. The first wave of unreality hit Ty. "It went down seventy miles this side of it—in some rough country. A sheepherder in the area saw it crash-land and went for help. A rescue party reached the site early this morning."

"How can you be sure it was his plane?" The sense of disbelief demanded the question as Ty stared, unmoving, at the officer. Then the second realization hit him. "You haven't said anything about survivors."

"Your father's been taken to a hospital in Helena. The only word I had from the authorities on that end was he was badly injured."

"And my mother?" Ty demanded.

"She was killed outright." His head bobbed downward, unable to meet Ty's gaze. "I'm sorry."

Beside him, the vet murmured a stunned "Sweet Jesus."

Ty held himself tightly together, braced against the shock that tried to reject all he'd been told. A scraping rawness clawed at his insides, but he couldn't give in to it—not yet.

"My sister—she'll have to be told." His mind seemed to detach itself from his feelings. "I'll go by the school on the way to Helena. She'll want to come with me. My wife has gone shopping today, in Miles City, I think. Would you put out an emergency bulletin for her, Sheriff, and have her call home immediately?"

"I'll do it." The sheriff nodded affirmatively.

"Bill." Ty glanced at the vet, his voice turning on the husky side. "Tell Stumpy he's in charge until I get back."

"Will do, Ty." It was a quiet answer, respectful and subdued.

There was a weakness in his knees and legs as he left the two men without another word and crossed to the pickup. It was a long drive to The Homestead, and it would be an even longer drive to Helena with a detour to the school to break the news to Cat. Until then, he had to keep his feelings at bay.

IV

Trouble's got a way of picking its time
To keep you from mourning your dead.
Look to the land for the answer,
'Cause now you're Calder born—
    and Calder bred.

22

All the while he was on the telephone, Ty stared at the empty leather chair behind the desk. Despite the things the impersonal voice on the phone was telling him, he found it difficult to believe his father was in some surgery room fighting for his life. The feeling of him was strong in this room.

The voice finished its report. Ty absently thanked it and hung up. Instantly the stillness of the house crept in and put its pressure on him. The shaking started and he reached for a cigarette, but his coat was still buttoned and his hands were still gloved. In a kind of suppressed agitation, he pulled off the gloves and jerked open the buttons.

He watched his hands tremble as he lit the cigarette, then dragged the smoke deep into his lungs. The action seemed to shatter the stiffness that had held him so erect. He sagged against the edge of the desk, sliding off his hat and leaving it on the desktop while he combed a hand through his hair as though trying to rake out the knowledge that clawed at him.

It hurt to breathe. He caught himself listening for sounds—any sound that would tell him there was life in the house, not just hollow echoes of it. Its silence seemed to tell him louder than the sheriff's words that he'd never hear his mother's laughter again. The front door opened, and Ty attempted to throw off this depression that weighted his body. Straightening, he turned to meet the sound of quick footsteps.

"Ty?" Jessy halted in the doorway. For a long second, she simply stood there, looking at him, her coat hanging open. He appeared all withdrawn and forbidding, invisible barriers surrounding him to shut her away. Then she saw the stark despair in his eyes and slowly crossed the room to stand in front of him. "Have you heard anything more about your father?"

"I just talked to someone at the hospital." The cigarette tasted too pungent. He stabbed it out in the desk's ashtray. "He's in surgery now. They're talking about multiple broken bones, possible spinal injuries, collapsed lung, and a concussion." There was no emotion whatsoever in his voice, but Jessy wasn't fooled.

"You'll want to shower and change clothes before you leave," she said. "You can't go to the school looking like that. It would only frighten your sister more."

"There isn't any easy way to tell her."

"There never is," Jessy agreed. "Maybe by the time you're ready to leave, your wife will be back so she can go with you. A woman might cope better with Cat's tears."

"How did you know? How did you get here so soon?" His eyes seemed to take her in, just now realizing she should have been elsewhere.

"The telephone lines across the ranch were all busy from the minute you left South Branch. I came as soon as I heard." There was no reason to tell him that she had bolted from the calving sheds and stopped at her place long enough to throw on some clean clothes when she'd learned there was no one with him. Maybe it wasn't her place and maybe it wasn't proper, but she didn't give a damn about that.

His hand reached up to touch her face, as if to make certain she was real. In the next second, she was being gathered into his arms and crushed hard against his body. She could feel the awful tension in him and pressed herself more fully to his length, trying to absorb some of it. His face was buried in her hair.

"I can't believe it, Jessy." His mouth moved against her hair, the words issued in a hoarsely painful voice. "I just can't believe she's dead."

"I know," she whispered and held him all the tighter, crying for him because he wouldn't cry for himself. She felt the shudder that racked his shoulders.

The smell of her was sweet and strong, striking deeply into

him. While all around him hung the cloud of death, here was life. He tightened his hold on it and moved his head to drink deeply from its full cup. He kissed her roughly, unable to slake his thirst or find a bottom to the well that poured back. There was pain, urgency, and the vitality of life all wrapped together in a harsh embrace.

He tasted the wetness of her tears and drew back, breathing raggedly. She quickly lowered her head and wiped them away before he could see them clearly. He bent his head, trying to see the glitter in her eyes and identify the tears, but she pulled back with a short, sharp shake of her head.

"You'd better get cleaned up." Her voice was low but even.

After a moment's hesitation, Ty left the study. The telephone rang, and Jessy answered it. The phone call was the first of a series of inquiries that came. Jessy told them all she knew. After the last phone call, she walked into the large living room to see what was keeping Ty. As fast as the news was traveling, there was a risk someone at the school might learn of it and inadvertently say something to his sister.

The front door opened, and Jessy swung sharply around. A tall, lean cowboy was pulling off his hat. "Repp, what are you doing here?" She crossed the foyer.

"Does Cat know yet?" The concern in his eyes was apparent.

"No. Ty's going by the school to pick her up. He'll tell her then," she explained.

"Do you suppose it . . . Do you suppose it would be all right if I was there, too?"

"Yes. I have a feeling Cat will need you."

"Thanks." He fingered his hat, then set it firmly on his head. "I'll wait outside."

As Repp Taylor opened the front door, Tara was crossing the porch. She threw him a surprised glance; then her gaze lighted on Jessy and darkened. Repp held the door open for her and waited until she was inside before going out himself.

The silence stretched between the two women for long seconds as they studied each other. A tension lay heavily between them, a tension time would never erase. Tara's vibrant looks and poise allowed her a dominance against which Jessy was reserved and silent, yet alert to every change in the woman's expression.

"What are you doing here?" Tara demanded with thinly concealed hostility. Her dark glance flashed by Jessy to the stairwell. "A policeman stopped me and said there was some sort of family emergency. Has Ty been hurt?"

"Not the way you mean," Jessy replied. "There was a plane crash. Maggie's dead, and Chase is critically injured."

"How terrible!" Just for a moment the shock of the tragedy pushed aside her other thoughts.

"Yes, it is. Ty is upstairs now, changing clothes so he can leave immediately to pick up Cat at school and go to the hospital in Helena."

"I suppose you've been consoling him." Her tone was quick and hard.

Jessy didn't bother to respond to that statement. "If you'll excuse me, Mrs. Calder, I'll be leaving. Now that you're here I won't be needed anymore."

"I don't think you were ever needed," Tara said sharply, her chin lifting at a higher angle.

"Yes. I was."

Tara stiffened at the tone. "You sound very sure of that."

"I am." Jessy was direct. "You don't like to hear that, do you?"

Tara was not without her poise as she eyed her opponent with cool speculation. "But I hope you don't think you are the first woman Ty has used for consolation. Of course, the others were not foolish enough to think it meant anything."

"Why do you let him?" Jessy demanded, showing the first traces of temper. "Why do you go off and leave him to get lonely? You're taking a terrible chance. Don't you realize I wouldn't have been here if you had been home? You're in his blood, and I don't deny it. Maybe that makes you happy to know it. But I have no respect for you. You can't help being what you are and living the way you want. But you're hurting Ty. You want to have him and everything else, too. Well, you can't."

"Neither can you," she retorted.

"The difference is, I know it." Jessy became calm again. "If

Ty asks where I am," she continued, "tell him I've gone to Ruth Haskell's house. Chase was like her own son. She's taking this pretty hard."

On that assertive note, Jessy walked past a silent and stiff Tara to the front door and let herself out.

Upon arrival at the hospital, Ty went directly to the intensive-care unit. Tara followed him, a supportive arm wrapped around Cathleen, whose face was strained white and whose eyes were red and puffy from tears. A tension surrounded all of them as they stopped at the nurses' station.

"I'm Ty Calder. My father—" He wasn't given an opportunity to complete his inquiry as a man in a doctor's smock interrupted him.

"We've been expecting you." He passed a patient's chart board to one of the nurses and slipped his pen into the breast pocket of the long jacket. "I'm Dr. Haslind. We spoke on the phone earlier today."

The voice on the phone had sounded as if it belonged to a much older man, but Haslind appeared to be in his early forties. Despite an air of professional competence that kept him tall and straight, there was a drawn and tired look about his face that suggested long, tense hours without rest.

"My father—" Cat's demand quavered on a high-pitched note. "How is he?"

"Under the circumstances, he's doing as well as can be expected." The response had an emotionless quality, as if repeated by rote, which made it meaningless.

"What are his chances?"

"Your father is alive." It seemed the one hope he was willing to offer them, but he appeared reluctant to say more in front of the obviously distraught Cathleen. "More surgery will eventually be required, but it will have to wait until his system is better able to take it."

"Earlier today, you mentioned possible spinal injuries." The possibility that his father might be incapacitated was something Ty had difficulty accepting.

"Yes." The doctor nodded affirmatively. "There are indications of some paralysis, but at this stage it is impossible to gauge the extent of it or if it might be permanent. It's simply too soon."

"I want to see him," Ty requested.

"Of course." Haslind nodded again, this time giving permission. "However, I must restrict your visit to two minutes."

Ty hesitated. "Does he know about my mother?"

After an uncomfortable pause, he answered, "No. I deemed it ill advised to tell him when they brought him in this morning."

"Doctor?" An approaching nurse summoned him to the side. He excused himself and stepped away, but they were still within range of Ty's hearing. "You asked me to notify you when Mr. Calder began to regain consciousness," the nurse was saying. "He's coming out of the anesthesia now."

"Good."

A splintering crash violated the hushed silence of the special ward. For a shocked second, no one reacted except to look toward the door of the room from which the loud noise seemed to have originated. Then both the nurse and Dr. Haslind were hurrying toward it. Ty followed, only a step behind.

As they pushed the door open and charged inside, Ty had his first glimpse of the trouble inside the room. A nurse was trying to strap a struggling patient into his bed and at the same time prevent him from ripping off the array of tubes and wires attached to his body. Beside the bed, an IV stand had been overturned, its bottles of solution on the floor, still rocking from the fall.

The patient's head was wrapped in bandages, as was most of his naked body, a cast enclosing the lower half of him virtually from the waist down. Myriad cuts and bruises made his face almost unrecognizable, and his head rocked from side to side in a frustrated protest at his inability to move, never giving Ty a clear look at him. Only one arm appeared to be fully functional, since the other was in a cast; but judging by the havoc that had been raised, one was enough.

At the last minute, he tore his arm loose from the strap before the nurse could fasten it securely. "My wife! Why won't you tell me where she is?" His voice was so weak and hoarse, it was barely above a loud, rasping whisper. It finally hit Ty that this battered and scarred man was his father.

The doctor joined the nurse, lending his efforts to firmly subdue the patient. "Calder, you've got to lie still," he ordered impatiently. "A lot of us have worked hard to put you back together. You're going to undo everything we've done."

Ty approached the bed in a kind of daze, trying to reconcile this person with the indestructible image of his father he carried in his mind. The man he'd practically idolized, and whose respect he'd valued above that of all others. So tough, so strong, so helpless now.

"I've got to know if Maggie's all right." It was as near to a plea as anything that had ever come out of his mouth. His arm was strapped down, immobilizing him, but still he strained in resistance. No one listened to him. They were too busy trying to put everything back in order, righting the IV stand and reinserting the needles into his veins and attaching the monitoring equipment.

"Let's concentrate on getting you better," the doctor said in an almost absent response to the hoarse demand as he snapped impatiently at the nurse filling a hypo needle. His glance flicked across the bed at Ty, irritation showing. "I'll have to ask you to leave."

"No." It was a flatly voiced refusal, and the doctor chose not to argue. Ty bent closer to the man in the bed. "Dad? It's me, Ty." His voice was level, all emotion pulled out of it. "You've got to do what they tell you."

The brown eyes that were turned on him were the same as his father's, hard and piercing when they wanted to be. And they were now, despite the glaze of pain.

"Ty, they won't tell me. Your mother . . . is she alive?" Desperation clawed at the edges of his weak and gravelly voice.

There was a long moment before Ty could push out an answer, his throat gripped too tightly by emotion. Finally he looked away to say thickly, "I think you already know the answer to that, Dad."

"Yes." The word was long and slow in coming, so soft Ty

almost couldn't hear it. A wet shimmer covered his father's brown eyes before he closed them to hide that gathering of tears.

"Mr. Calder"—one of the nurses firmly but politely nudged Ty out of the way—"we're going to have to put this tube down your throat. It's going to be very uncomfortable, but it will be easier if you don't fight us."

There was no resistance left in him as his father mutely gave himself up to their ministrations. "You'd better leave," the second nurse suggested to Ty and blocked him away from the bed. "There's really nothing you can do here. Take your family somewhere and try to get some rest. Just leave word where you can be reached and we'll contact you if there is the slightest change in his condition."

It was sound advice, although it wasn't easy to convince his sister of that. She wanted to stay at the hospital so she could be close to her father. In the end, Ty relented when Tara agreed to stay with her. But he couldn't allow himself the luxury of such a gesture. Too many other things required his time and attention. He had seen first to the living; now it was time to make arrangements for the dead and put into motion the adjustments necessary for the continuation of the ranch's operation.

A place to stay had already been arranged. Dyson kept an apartment in Helena for his occasional use, and Tara also had a key. She gave it to him.

"I don't understand him," Cat murmured tautly as she watched her brother stride away from the waiting room. "How can he leave when our father might be in there dying?"

Personally, Tara was heartened by the control he exhibited over his emotions. It seemed to make a mockery of Jessy's claim that he had needed her.

"I don't think you're considering the number of responsibilities that have fallen to him now. He has to act as the head of the family as well as take full charge of the ranch." It was the realization of a dream for Tara, and there was a streak of guilt that she found a cause for rejoicing in this tragedy. "There are many arrangements he has to make."

"You mean . . . for my mother, don't you?" Cat said in a small, grief-tormented voice; then agitation lifted it. "It isn't fair." she protested in a stormy outcry. "She had no right to die! Not like this—with no warning! How could she have done this to us?"

No logic could combat those words of bitter rebellion against fate. Pain-charged emotions were being released through anger, so Tara simply let the girl rant on until the tears came. Then she held Cathleen in her arms and let her cry to the point of hiccoughing exhaustion.

On the way to the apartment, Ty stopped at the local mortuary where his mother had been taken and made arrangements for her body to be sent home for burial in the family plot. After that, there was a long list of phone calls he had to make. He started by tracking down which hotel Phil Silverton, the attorney who handled all the Calder interests, was staying in.

"How is your father, Ty?" the man asked after Ty had reached him by phone. "The hospital wouldn't give me much information."

"Not good," Ty admitted, still struggling himself to face the reality of that. "I spoke to him briefly, but— The doctor is unwilling even to say what his chances are."

"What do you want me to do about this meeting with Hines from the Interior Department? Naturally, when we heard about the plane crash, everything was put on hold. However, I know he's still in town."

"I'll meet with him," Ty said. "See if you can schedule something for tomorrow morning."

"Right." It was an affirmative answer, followed by a short pause. "I haven't heard any official word about the cause of the accident. An eyewitness thought the plane had engine trouble. Was your father able to tell you anything?"

"No. I didn't ask." The cause had been the least of his concerns. He was still trying to deal with the aftermath of it.

"Ty—I hate to bring this up, but . . . some decisions have to be made. From what you've told me, your father is going to be out of commission for a long time, even if he survives. You are going to have to be empowered to act as head of the company. There are two choices. If the doctor can certify that your father is aware of his actions, we can have him sign a document turning control of the company over to you. Or we can petition the courts and have you appointed to manage his interests. The first is the best way if it can be done."

"We'll talk to Dr. Haslind about it in the morning." Ty understood the necessity for it. In all but fact he had taken over, but making it legal sounded so final.

"I'll draft a document tonight."

After he had concluded his business with the attorney, Ty phoned Dyson at his home in Fort Worth. Despite business conflicts, Dyson was Tara's father, therefore a member of the family and entitled to be notified of the accident. Ty gave him what details he knew, embellishing none of them.

"If there is anything I can do in the meantime for you, please call," Dyson said in parting and hung up the phone, sobered by the news.

"What is it?" Stricklin removed his wire glasses and sat back in his chair to study his solemn-faced partner.

"Calder's plane crashed yesterday." Dyson rose from the desk and crossed the room to pour himself a drink. "His wife was killed."

"And Calder?"

"He's in very critical condition."

Stricklin reached for the telephone. "I'll contact our pilot and make arrangements for us to fly up there."

"Yes, do that." Dyson nodded absently.

Ty called Stumpy Niles at the ranch and apprised him of the situation; then he made a separate call to the Haskell house. Jessy answered, and he repeated again the words he'd said so often that they'd lost meaning to him.

"How's Ruth?" he asked in a voice that was heavy.

"I don't know," Jessy admitted on a troubled sigh. "She keeps demanding that Vern take her to the hospital so she can be there to look after your father, insisting it's what Webb would want her to do. She talks about your grandfather as if he were alive yet. Then she rambles about all the illnesses she nursed Chase through as a child." There was a slight pause. "The doctor's given her a sedative, so hopefully she'll rest."

Ty rubbed his forehead, trying to erase the dullness. "Has anyone been to O'Rourke's place to notify him about the accident? I should have done it before I left but . . ." A broken sigh came from him as he left the sentence unfinished. Too many other things had crowded any thought of his uncle from his mind.

"No, I don't think so. I'll go see him," Jessy volunteered.

"Thanks." Just the sound of her voice was somehow oddly reassuring. It was the one steady thing in this upheaval that surrounded him.

Few stars were shining in the inky black of a moonless night when Jessy drove into the yard of the Shamrock Ranch. The house was darkened, no light showing from its windows. Her headlights failed to pick up any sign of life in the yard; the usual tall yard light was not lit.

When she stepped from the pickup cab's warm interior into the chill of the night, her breath billowed in a steamy vapor. She hunched her shoulders against the sudden drop in temperature and looked around, searching the dark shadows of the barn and corral. At this hour, she doubted that O'Rourke would be out riding. She turned toward the house, and a voice jumped at her out of the shadows.

"Are you looking for me?"

Jessy swung around, staring into the darkness, barely able to make out the motionless black form against an equally black background. No sound betrayed his presence, and he offered her no silhouette against the faint stars in the sky.

"Yes, I am." She took a step in the direction of the voice, then paused. For reasons of his own, he didn't want to be seen clearly, or he would have come forward. So Jessy didn't press him. "I'm sorry, but I have some bad news." No sound prompted her to tell him. There was only a waiting silence. "There was a plane crash." It was an uncomfortable feeling to talk without being able to see the person she was addressing. "Your sister . . . was killed."

There was a trace of gray against the black; a breath that had been long held was released. It was the only reaction as the silence lengthened.

"She's coming home tomorrow." Her voice gentled with compassion. In this, she couldn't be blunt. "Ty asked me to tell you that the funeral is being scheduled for the day after. He would have come himself, but he's at the hospital. His father is badly injured, and they aren't sure he's going to make it."

"He'll make it, all right." There was a leaden sound to the voice that came from the shadows. "Them Calders have as many lives as a cat." The statement seemed tinged with bitter acceptance.

"I'm sorry about your sister, Culley. I know how close you were to her." Jessy felt a reluctance to leave him. She frowned slightly, trying to penetrate the shadows and gauge how well he was handling the news. "Would you like me to stay awhile? Maybe fix some coffee?"

He was a long time answering. "I'd rather be alone," he said finally.

There was nothing left to do but crawl back into the truck. As she reversed the pickup onto the rutted lane, the beams briefly swept the motionless figure of a man, hands thrust in the pockets of his dark coat and the brim of his hat shading his face.

For a long time, Culley didn't move from his position. The sound of the truck had faded into the night and silence enclosed him before his motionless stance was finally broken. He lifted his face to the heavens, the wetness of tears glistening in his dark eyes. A groan came from his throat.

With a mournful cry, he wailed her name. "Maggieee!" Guilt bore down heavily on him, driving him to his knees.

23

The throng of people attending the funeral had thinned out until only family was left at the gravesite. All the headstones bore the name Calder, including the newest, inscribed with the words Mary Elizabeth Calder, My Beloved

Maggie. Ty felt keenly the absence of his father, the one who mourned her passing the most.

A slim, softly gloved hand slipped inside the crook of his elbow. Ty roused himself to glance at his wife, a dramatic vision in her ebony fur and a turban-style hat. The cold had rouged her cheeks with color, giving an added vibrancy to her looks.

"It's time we went home. Cathleen's already at the car waiting for us," she prodded him softly.

"Yes," he agreed on a heavy breath and lifted the black Stetson to put it on his bare head, pulling it low.

Together they turned to walk across the frozen ground to the car. "I wondered whether he would show up here since he didn't attend the church service," Tara murmured.

Ty located his Uncle Culley O'Rourke, the object of her remark, as he angled across the small cemetery to the pickup parked all by itself. The black suit he was wearing made him appear a slim, dark shadow. His head was bowed, and there was a look of utter loneliness about him.

"Uncle Culley!" Cat had noticed him, too, but her call went unheeded. She left the car and hurried down the narrow path between the graves to intercept him. "Uncle Culley, wait!"

He slowed and finally turned to meet her. The cold air had taken some of her breath. She paused to catch it again while she searched his stony face. There was a haunted bleakness about his eyes, the only sign that revealed the extent of his grief. She was moved by it.

"Will you please come home with us?" She felt, oddly, that she was talking to a child, despite the gray of his hair. "A few people who were very close to Mother are stopping by The Homestead for coffee. You should be there, too."

"No." He shook his head slowly, his glance sliding briefly past her. "I'm not welcome there."

His reason momentarily stunned her. "Yes, you are," Cat insisted. "You'll always be welcome, the same as when Mother was alive."

"Nothing's the same."

"Please come. I know how much you miss her." Her voice became choked, breaking on a sob. "So do I."

Gently, the way someone would caress a delicate petal, he touched her cheek. There was a sadly adoring look in his eyes. "You look so much like her."

All through the memorial service and the graveside ceremony, Cat had struggled to hold back the tears, trying to wrap an adult privacy around her grief. But at sixteen, she wasn't as mature as she wanted to be. The little gesture of love from a man so lonely and alone as her uncle unleashed the awful ache. Without caring how childish it looked, she threw her arms around him and hugged him tightly, burying her face in the warm collar of his coat and needing the silent comfort of a pair of arms around her.

Culley held her close. The ache inside him was so great it hurt to breathe. Yet there was solace in the way she needed him that filled a void. She was a part of Maggie. He still had that. A faint smile touched the corners of his mouth as he silently thanked Maggie for giving him this.

But he was also conscious of the couple standing by the car, watching them. As always he was aware of all things that went on around him. Gently but firmly he held Cathleen away from him and wiped at the wet trail of her cheeks.

"I'll always be close by if you ever need me," he promised her. "You'd better go now. Your brother's waiting."

She started to turn away, then stopped to plead one last time, "Won't you come?"

"No. I'm not good around people," he said gently and urged her along with a motion of his hand.

"I'll come visit you—soon," Cat promised and headed for the car, glancing over her shoulder now and then to see him standing there, so alone.

"You should speak to her, Ty," Tara murmured in disapproval of the emotional scene between uncle and niece. "I don't think that sort of thing should be encouraged."

"I wouldn't be concerned about it if I were you." He opened the car door and helped her inside. "They're just sharing their grief."

As Cathleen reached the car, she explained, "I asked him to come to the house, but he wouldn't."

"It's probably just as well, Cat," he said and walked around to the driver's side.

At The Homestead, Ty stopped the car and climbed out to assist Tara and Cathleen, but he didn't accompany them up the front steps. Halfway up, Tara paused to see what was keeping him.

"Aren't you coming in with us?" she queried sharply.

"No. I'm going to stop over to see Ruth Haskell for a few minutes," Ty explained. "The doctor wouldn't permit her to attend the services today, so I thought I'd pay a call on her."

On the surface, it seemed a thoughtful gesture, yet Tara kept remembering that Jessy Niles had gone to comfort the old woman when the news had come about the plane crash. There was no reason to believe Jessy had gone there after the funeral, but the nagging suspicion wouldn't leave her, even though it seemed inconceivable that Ty might be going to the Haskell home in the hope of seeing her.

She crossed the porch to the front doors, letting Cathleen go ahead of her. She paused in the doorway to watch Ty driving away from the house.

"Tara Lee, is something wrong?" Stricklin came to the doorway, his flat blue eyes looking out at the sight that had captured her attention.

"No." It was a quick answer as she turned smoothly away. "Nothing at all." She stepped inside, briskly tugging off her gloves. "Where's Daddy?" she inquired calmly, then saw him talking with two other people in the living room. She went forward, at long last the mistress of the Calder Homestead.

"Hello, Vern." Ty shook hands with the sullen-faced man who admitted him into the Haskell home. "How have you been?" He removed his hat and unfastened the top buttons of his charcoal-dark topcoat.

"Poorly." The old and stooped man leaned heavily on his cane and hobbled to a rocking chair. "Not that I ever asked for sympathy," he declared sourly and lowered his arthritic body into the chair. "You'll be wantin' to see Ruth. She's in her room lyin' down." He pointed toward a door with the end of his cane; then his expression took on a sly look. "The Niles girl is with her, which maybe you knew and maybe you didn't."

"Thanks." Ty let the last remark pass without comment

and crossed to the door. Meeting Jessy had not been his motive in coming, but he couldn't deny the warm tingle it had given him when Vern informed him she was here. He rapped lightly on the door, and Jessy's voice bade him to come in. As he stepped inside and quietly closed the door behind him, he caught the small leap of light in Jessy's hazel eyes and was pleased. Her long, straight hair was coiled in a shimmering knot atop her head, adding dignity to her strong features. Her dress of mourning was a simple blue wool, a warm color like the sky between dusk and night.

Ty walked to the bed where the ever-thinner Ruth Haskell sat, propped up with a stack of soft pillows. An old-fashioned quilted bedjacket trimmed with lace covered her bony shoulders.

"Hello, Nanna Ruth." He used Cathleen's pet name for her as he bent to kiss a withered cheek. "How are you feeling?"

"I'm fine," she insisted, and he couldn't recall ever hearing her complain. "I so wanted to come today." Her trembling hands clutched at his while her teary eyes looked up at him. "Jessy told me what a fine service it was. So many people came. I only wish . . ." Her weak voice trailed off, then found a new subject. "I feel so badly about Chase."

"I spoke to the hospital this morning. They said he was doing much better." "Holding his own" was actually the phrase that was used, but he chose to sound more optimistic with Ruth.

"He is like a son to me. What a pair of boys I had," she declared, smiling in fond reminiscence. "Chase and my Buck. Buck should be here. He could always make Chase smile. He was so outrageous sometimes—and the tales he'd come up with." She clucked her tongue in loving affection, then sobered slowly and looked anxiously at Ty. "He never meant to be bad."

"I know," Ty said to assure her, but kept his own counsel on that subject.

"I think you should take some of the medicine the doctor left for you, Ruth," Jessy suggested, "and see if you can't get some rest."

"Maybe I should," Ruth agreed hesitantly, showing uncertainty and a willingness to be told what to do.

"Here." Jessy shook two pills from the prescription bottle and handed them to the woman, then poured a glass of water from the pitcher on the bedstand. After Ruth had taken her medicine, Jessy rearranged the pillows so she could lie down in comfort, then pulled the window shade to darken the room.

"I'll come by to see you again," Ty told the woman and moved quietly to the door. Jessy followed him, then paused short of the door. "Aren't you leaving now?" he asked in a low murmur.

"No, I'll stay until she sleeps. Have you learned anything about the crash? How or why it happened?"

"Nothing certain. The initial reports from the wreckage indicate a broken oil line as the possible cause, but they're still trying to determine if it had ruptured before or after the crash." And his father had been able to provide the authorities with only scant details. "I have to leave." There was a reluctance in his tone. "There's company at the house, and I can't let Tara entertain them on her own."

"Somehow, I don't think she'd mind," Jessy murmured cynically.

A vague irritation rippled through him at the implied criticism. "You don't know her well enough to judge that."

"You're still defending her," she observed.

"She's my wife."

"I know." It was very quietly said as Jessy turned away and walked back to the bed.

Ty hovered indecisively between anger and regret, then reached for the doorknob and let himself out. The dark scowl on his face didn't go unnoticed by Vern Haskell, who smiled to himself. He'd always been treated like a kind of outsider by the Calders, even though he'd married into one of the old families. When his son had gone bad, he knew they had blamed it on the Haskell blood in him, not the good Stanton blood from Ruth's family. It did him good to see a Calder getting denied something he wanted, and his little talk with

Jessy Niles had obviously not turned out the way he'd planned.

A full month had gone by since the funeral. Between hospital visits and the full load of the ranch management resting on his shoulders, Ty had been going from morning until night. Plus there had been meetings with the attorney, in connection with both the disputed title to the ten thousand acres of land and his mother's estate, made complicated by some of her California holdings.

A lot of the routine paperwork and reports had been shoved to the side and allowed to pile up. Unable to postpone the deskwork, Ty had finally closed himself in the study to wade through it. At first, he merely glanced over the monthly balance sheet and its accompanying profit-and-loss statement. When the figures finally registered in his mind, he felt a glimmer of alarm. He went to the files and extracted the previous six months' statements for comparison. His concern mounted.

"Ty?" The door to the study was pushed open as Tara stuck her head inside, then knocked on the door. A blue silk bandeau shimmered around her black hair and across her forehead. "Can I interrupt you a minute?"

"Sure." He breathed in deeply and leaned back in the chair, almost welcoming the intrusion that broke up the whirl of figures in his head. She walked into the study, holding something behind her back. "What is it?"

"Do you remember this old photograph you showed me a long time ago?" She held it out to him. "The man in the middle was your great-grandfather, isn't that right?"

"Yes. Chase Benteen Calder. My father was named after him." Ty nodded that the tall man in the broadcloth suit was his ancestor, or so his father had told him. "What about it?"

"The woman with him—didn't you say she was some English lady?" Tara prompted.

"Yes." He frowned slightly, not recalling that part of it too well. "Duncan or Dunhill, something like that. In those days, it was fairly common for a rancher to have a European backer, a financier of sorts." His puzzled but interested glance held a trace of amusement. "Why?"

"I was packing away some of your mother's things, and I went into the attic to see if I couldn't find room in some of those old trunks upstairs. While I was going through them, I found this." She showed him a second photograph, this one of a young woman. The edges of it were burnt, as if it had been in a fire. "Doesn't she look familiar?"

At first, Ty didn't understand what she meant. Then he noticed the similarity between the two women in the photographs. "It's hard to tell, but there is a resemblance."

"They are the same person, and I'd bet on it," Tara stated; then a light glittered in her eye. "Do you know who she is?"

"Lady Dunhill or Duncan, I've forgotten her name."

Tara shook her head. "According to the back of this photograph," she said, indicating the one of the younger woman, "she is Madelaine Calder, Benteen Calder's mother."

"I was told she ran away when he was a small boy." He frowned, doubting Tara's discovery.

"She ran away and obviously married into some titled English family, then came back. Imagine that, Ty," she declared with a suppressed eagerness. "You are descended from English royalty. Well, not exactly." She shrugged her shoulders to dismiss the lack of real blue blood. "But a little family scandal is always more exciting, especially when it's connected to lords and ladies. I can hardly wait until the Franklins arrive this weekend so I can tell them. They'll spread the story around like wildfire. You'll be the talk of everyone who is anyone."

"The Franklins?"

His blank look brought a trace of exasperation to her mouth. "Ty, I told you at dinner last week that I had invited them for the weekend."

Maybe she had, he conceded. Most evenings he had been either too tired or too preoccupied to listen. "Sorry. It slipped my mind. You know, of course, I'll be going to the hospital on Sunday."

"Surely you can postpone your visit one day," she urged.

"Can't. Spring roundup starts," he announced. The knowledge of the full schedule ahead of him seemed to prod him back to the monthly reports spread across the desktop.

"I suppose that means we won't see a thing of you all weekend." The impatient edge was in her voice, honing out the drawl that usually softened it. "Lyle Franklin could be very helpful to you. Put someone else in charge of overseeing the roundup. Considering the number of people you have on the payroll, one of them should be qualified to do it. If none of them are, it's time you hired someone who is."

"It's my job and I'm going to do it," Ty informed her patiently and glanced down at the damning figures on the papers. "It seems I have enough problems without arguing with you."

"Problems? What do you mean?" She was quick to catch the troubled note in his voice. Her expression was instantly serious and intent.

"It appears the ranch operation has been steadily losing money over the last few months." He gathered the reports together. "And I think it's time I found out just how long this has been going on, and whether it's as serious as it looks."

"I can't say I'm surprised, considering the way your father has run this ranch," she said, careful to keep her criticism from becoming too sharp. "He's still paying people who are too old to work. It's a very noble gesture if you can afford it, but it would be much cheaper to set up a pension fund for them. Most of these old fogies around here should have retired years ago."

"They do what work they can." Ty rose from the chair.

"Where are you going?"

"To see Bob Crane. He prepared these reports, so it will be a lot faster to get to the bottom of them by talking to him, and find out whether it's payroll or something else."

After two hours in the accountant's office, Ty discovered there were many factors that had contributed to the present situation.

"As you can see," Crane pointed out to him, "if it weren't for the income from the wells that are pumping out at Broken Butte, we wouldn't have broken even the last five years. It would have been a struggle under normal operations, but to throw in two large capital expenditures with the feedlot and the horse-breeding facilities and stock . . . the expansion simply came at the wrong time."

"I can see that," Ty agreed grimly, aware both had been his programs.

"Of course, there have been abnormally high legal costs this last year as well, because of that land dispute with the government. And it hasn't been resolved yet," the accountant reminded him. "And this doesn't show the medical costs that are being incurred every day your father is in the hospital. I've heard"—he glanced hesitantly at Ty—"that with the operations and therapy he's going to require, it might be as long as a year. That's going to cost a small fortune."

"My father must have seen what was happening," he insisted, his forehead creasing in a frown.

"Yes. But he was gambling on an upturn in the cattle market that didn't materialize."

"There don't seem to be many options," Ty noted, "except to pare down expenses or create an income stream by selling off expendable assets."

"That's about the size of it," Crane agreed. "Sorry, Ty. I would have said something to you, but I thought you regularly saw the reports."

"I saw them, but always separately. I never recognized the trend they were showing." The corners of his mustache were pulled down by the grim curve of his mouth. He rolled the reports in his hand and tapped them absently on the desk as he rose. "Thanks, Bob."

His steps were heavy when he entered The Homestead, weighted by problems he hadn't expected. Some hard decisions had to be made, and they needed to be the right ones. He walked straight to the study and tossed the reports on the desk. Crossing to the wet bar, Ty poured himself a shot of whiskey, then wandered over to the large stone fireplace with its mounted set of longhorns. Tara called to him, but he didn't answer.

"Ty, didn't you hear me? Dinner will be ready as soon as you've showered and changed." She appeared in the doorway and paused to skim his brooding look. "Bad news?" she guessed and crossed the room to his side.

"It wasn't good," he admitted and poked at the fireplace ash in search of a hot coal to rekindle the fire.

"Why don't you tell me about it?" She watched him, a certain complacency entering her expression.

"I have some thinking I need to do." He lifted the shot glass and tossed down part of the whiskey.

"You can think out loud," Tara urged and masked it with an idle shrug. "Maybe I can help. I do know something about business. I am my father's daughter."

"Beneath all the Dior and diamonds." Ty mocked the elegant afternoon dress she was wearing and the diamond studs in her ears.

"There are brains, yes." She smiled with slow provocation, using the combination of wiles and charm that served her so well.

"I don't doubt that there are business areas where you are knowledgeable, but you don't understand how this outfit is run."

To be so lightly regarded goaded her. "I understand that it's been run the wrong way, or it wouldn't be in the trouble that you've found it," she retorted. "It hasn't been operated like a business. It's been run like some benevolent society where everything but profit comes first."

"This is a working ranch, and you can't base its operations on short-term profits. You have to look at long-term gains." His patience was on the thin side.

"How can you do that when the ranch is operating under methods that are twenty years old, if not older than that?" Tara argued, but she kept a reasoning tone. "Times change, and methods have to change with them. You don't still see longhorn cattle grazing out there on that land, do you?" she said, gesturing toward the curved and twisted horns above the mantel. "You need to start throwing out these outmoded ideas and begin modernizing. It has to be run more efficiently."

"You say that as if there's nothing to it." A muscle ridged along his jaw. "I'm faced with the problem of finding a way to cut costs or create a new source of income, preferably both. The kind of program you're suggesting would be damned expensive to implement. And I can't go out in the back forty and sink a well to pay for it like some of your Texas friends, because there isn't any oil or gas there!"

"But there's coal, Ty." She said it quietly, eyeing him closely and containing the eagerness that vibrated inside. "Tons of it. Enough to make you so rich it wouldn't matter if this ranch earned a penny. You could become the coal and cattle king of the whole country."

"No." It was a hard sound, poised on the edge of anger. "You know damn well how my father feels about surface-mining."

"It doesn't matter how he feels. He has no say in it. You're in charge," Tara reminded him with that same intense quiet. "You have absolute control of everything."

"For the time being." He qualified it even though there had been no time restrictions set forth in the documents his father had signed. His power was limitless.

"Be realistic, Ty," she insisted. "Your father is going to be hospitalized for at least a year. And after that, you know as well as I do that he'll never be able to take this kind of stress and strain. There will be a limit to what he can do. So it's your ranch from now on. And it's up to you to decide how best to run it."

"It's going to be hard enough on him when he learns that I'm dropping the suit to regain title to that land." Ty stared at the whiskey in the bottom of the glass, a coiled tautness about his expression. "I'll have to, at least for the time being, in order to cut the high legal costs. But to tear up Calder land for coal—that's something else."

"Tear up the land! You make it sound like a sin," Tara chided him. "It's only dirt and grass, which can be put back. You studied all about land reclamation in college, Ty. Don't be like your father and condemn the idea without looking into it. Talk to my father; let him show you his operation. I know he could help if you'd let him."

"I'll think about it." It was a tersely low statement, designed to end the conversation and commit himself to nothing.

"My father is flying up here in a couple of weeks. I can call him and tell him that you want to speak with him. I know he'll arrange to spend a couple extra days here," she said confidently.

"Dammit, Tara! I said I'd think about it." The heated

words tumbled from his throat. "Don't push it!" He swung away from the fireplace, shoving the whiskey glass onto the first table he passed.

"Where are you going?"

"Some place where I can think in peace." He grabbed his hat and jammed it on his head, snugging the front down on his forehead.

She went icy with temper. "Where is that? Jessy's, maybe?" It was a cloyingly sarcastic suggestion.

It stopped him, stiffening his frame and closing in his expression behind a ruggedly indifferent mask. "I hadn't considered it until you mentioned it. It just might be the place I'll go."

The totally unexpected response flamed her. "Then go to her! And go to hell on the way!" It was wounded pride that insisted on rejecting him before he could walk out on her. When long strides carried him out of the room, she was spurred by her temper into following him. "You are a fool, Ty Calder!" she declared in an angry, wavering voice. "I can give you so much more than she can! She'll never be able to help you the way I can!"

The door was slammed with violent force. Tara stopped, dragging in sobbing breaths of impotent fury and hurt. A small noise came from the dining room. Tara jerked around, stiffly trying to contain all her emotions. It was the young ranch wife who cooked and kept house for her, standing hesitantly in the archway to the dining room.

"I'm sorry," she apologized. "I was just coming to ask about dinner."

Humiliation flooded through her as Tara realized the woman had overheard nearly everything. The thought of the story being spread around was unbearable. None of the women liked her anyway. They'd tell it just out of spite because she was somebody and they weren't.

"Get out!" Her hands were clenched into rigid fists at her side. "Get out of my house!" She was near to crying. "I won't be spied on! Now get out!"

She managed to hold herself rigid until the woman had disappeared from her sight. Then she began to crumple, the silence of her tears shaking her body.

"I hate you." Tara sobbed her defiance at the disapproving stillness of the house. "I hate all of it. I hate this place and I hate this land."

The telephone rang, forcing her to choke back the bitter sobs and attempt to swallow them. She made an effort to regain her poise as she carried herself erectly to the phone, sniffling back the tears and wiping at her face.

"Calder residence. Mrs. Calder speaking." Her voice was level and controlled.

24

The hem of her chocolate-colored chenille robe brushed her ankles as Jessy came out of the bathroom, fresh from a shower, her bare feet leaving damp tracks on the linoleum. Vigorously, she toweled the long, wet strands of her hair, scattering droplets of water on the floor.

When she entered the kitchen, she immediately sensed a presence. Before she even saw him, she knew it was Ty in the room. It was something in the air that she instinctively scented. He stood motionless just inside the back door, fingering the crown of the hat in his hand. The unruly thickness of his dark hair showed the rake of his fingers through it, and his hooded eyes were watchful and brooding.

"The coffee's fresh." Jessy resumed rubbing her hair dry with the towel. "Help yourself to a cup."

There was a faint hesitation; then he hooked his hat on a peg by the door and tugged loose the buttons of his coat, letting it hang open. A thinly leashed energy seemed to lie beneath each move as he took down a cup from the shelf of a cupboard and poured coffee into it from the pot. Turning, he leaned a hip against the counter and took blowing sips from his coffee while he watched her. Jessy could feel his eyes following her as she walked to the refrigerator.

"I was just going to fix some supper." She draped the damp towel around her neck and opened the refrigerator door. "Have you eaten?" She took out a package of ground beef and a dish of boiled potatoes.

"No." Ty shifted slightly as she set them on the counter near him.

"How about a hamburger steak and some American fries?" For all her outward calm, her nerves were tingling.

"Not for me." The coffee cup was abruptly set down. "Jessy." His voice was low and insistent.

When she looked up, his arm hooked out to catch her waist and haul her to him with an urgency that made her blood run quick. His mouth came down heavily onto her lips, the clipped ends of his mustache scraping at her skin as his mouth ground onto hers. She felt his hands digging into her flesh and the viselike bite of his arms that wedged her against his long, muscled body and walled her in with the thickness of his coat. The seething force inside him gave no quarter, brutal in its demands.

Anger ran through her like a two-edged sword. She twisted from beneath his driving kiss and pulled back to glare at him, breathing roughly from the smothering pressure.

"You had an argument with her, didn't you?" Jessy accused. "That's why you're here."

"I'm here. It doesn't matter why," he insisted.

"The hell it doesn't!" she flared and pulled the rest of the way out of his arms. The chenille robe became tangled around her long legs as she strode to the back door and jerked it open, mindless of the cold draft of air on her bare feet. "Get out!"

Crossing the room, he jerked the door out of her grasp and slammed it shut. "Like hell I will!" He gave her a hard and knowing look. "And you don't want me to go."

"Like hell I don't!" The same expletive was being flung back and forth, strong wills clashing and hurling back to clash again.

"It is hell," Ty said through his teeth, catching her again and ignoring her vigorous resistance to take her in his arms again. "It's hell wanting and not having the right to want. It's hell being with you and knowing it's wrong."

This time when his mouth rolled onto her lips, his need was a hungry, growling thing—tonguing and insistent. She was indecisive—wanting and not wanting him, liking it and loathing it. But she stayed with the kiss.

And the bands of restraint inside him began to break. This need that was blind and unfair, without a conscience, took control. Ty became intent on sweeping her beyond the limits she tried to impose. He molded her closer and felt the stirrings that took the weight from her body, making it supple and light.

As if realizing what was happening, she broke away from the kiss. Her fingers dug into his jacket while she turned her head aside. Then she lifted it, exposing her throat and the gaping front of her robe, and the small breasts heaving beneath it.

"Sometimes I hate you, Ty Calder," she said in her throat. The glitter in her eyes was halfway between anger and tears.

Then she came at him with the same fierce aggression he had shown, her mouth hungry and demanding while she pushed the rest of the way inside his coat. Ty scooped her off her feet and carried her to the first empty space he found, the large braided rug in front of the fireplace. Crackling yellow flames laid a gentle light on it.

He set her on it, his mouth clinging to hers while he unknotted the chenille sash of her robe. Her shoulders hunched to shrug out of it as he pushed it down her arms and laid it out behind her on the rug. Then it was his jacket, clothes, and boots that made a pile on the floor while she reclined on the robe-cushioned rug and watched him strip.

The firelight played golden over her nude body, shadowing its valleys and shining on its rounded curves. Her still-damp hair was slicked away from her face, throwing her strong, bold features into sharp relief. Her long arms lifted to gather him in when he came to her.

Heat surrounded them, pressure pushing from inside and out as his mouth moved from her lips to her erect nipples, finding succor in each. She writhed under him, hips urging.

There was harmony in their mating, something earthy and good in their coming together. It spiraled through him, sweet and clean as the air after a rain. And that was the way she looked to him when she rolled him over and sat atop him, fingers linked tightly in his grasp, her movements graceful as a willow. Her strong looks were of the land that bred her, proud and indomitable.

In an instant of clarity, Ty knew it was her strength of body and spirit that Tara could never match. He could be rough and forceful with Jessy because he knew she could give it back, if not better than she got. But Tara would have been frightened by so much emotion. She couldn't give all her love like this—like this.

It was his weight and his arms that shifted her onto the rug again, and the driving pitch of his needs that made the sounds in her throat. Hot sensation dragged them both into its blissful undertow where minds ceased to function and bodies did all the communicating that was necessary.

After slipping her arms into the sleeves of her robe, Jessy loosely draped the front of it shut. She tunneled a hand under the nearly dry hair at the back of her neck and lifted it from beneath the robe. Ty came padding into the living room in his stockinged feet, clad in a pair of Levi's but bare from the waist up. He sank onto the braided rug where she was seated and handed her the hairbrush he carried.

"You're sweating," she observed and picked up the towel to blot at the sheen of perspiration on the muscled points of his shoulders.

"It's the fire," Ty murmured, a lazy light gleaming in his eyes.

"Which one?" Jessy inquired in a dryly teasing voice and laid the towel aside to begin brushing the tangles from her hair.

His hand stopped her and tugged persuasively to urge her to lie back. He was raised up on one elbow, and she lowered herself to rest her head on his muscled forearm. His half-closed eyes studied her while he traced a slow circle from her cheekbone to her jaw to her lips, the skin around them reddened by the scratch of his mustache.

"Still hate me?"

The faint smile stayed on her lips, but the light in her eyes became more serious. "Sometimes." She fiddled thoughtfully with the hairbrush. "It seems I've hated you on and off ever since I've known you."

"Such as?"

"That time you kissed me as a joke, then . . . there have been a couple of other times." But she chose not to elaborate.

A grimness took over his expression. "Like when I married Tara, I suppose."

"That was one of them." Jessy sat up again to resume brushing her hair. Ty rolled over and reached for the pack of cigarettes in his shirt pocket.

Everything had been so infinitely pleasant and comfortable between them. Now the old irritation was back, the ugly twinges of guilt and unease. The match wouldn't light, and he swore bitterly under his breath. Then he simply held them, the matchbook and cigarette in one hand, the match in the other.

"I've tried to stay away from here. You know that, Jessy."

"I guessed it," she admitted, neither of them looking at the other. She stopped brushing her hair and simply studied the dark bristles.

"It isn't fair to you," he said.

"I think it's up to me to decide whether a bargain is fair or not."

"Maybe I know you deserve more than you're getting."

"Old Nate Moore told me once that you should never do any heavy talking on an empty stomach." Jessy uncurled her legs to rise to her feet. "Are you sure you don't want to change your mind about supper?"

It was a deliberate change of subject, turning aside a topic she didn't want to discuss. Ty breathed heavily, grimly admiring her guts. Not once had she asked him to lie to her or make meaningless promises.

"No, thanks."

As she started for the kitchen, the telephone rang. She changed direction to answer it, holding the front of her robe shut, but the bottom gaped about her long, shapely legs.

"Hi, Dad," she said the instant she recognized the voice on the other end of the line. "What's up?"

"Mrs. Calder just phoned me." There was an edge to his voice. "She was looking for Ty and broadly hinted that I might know where to find him. Is he there?"

"Ty?" she repeated his name for Ty's benefit and saw his head come around to narrow questioningly on her.

"Yes, Ty," her father said, none too patiently. "If he's there, tell him to get home right away."

"What is it? Has something happened?" Her questions brought Ty to his feet and across the room to take the telephone from her.

"What is it, Stumpy?" he demanded. A frown of surprise broke across his expression. Briefly he covered the mouthpiece to tell Jessy, "It's my sister. She's missing from school." Then into the phone he said, "I'm on my way," and hung up.

"What do you mean by missing? Was she kidnaped, or did she simply run away?" Jessy queried.

"I don't know." Ty was hopping on one foot while trying to tug on his boots. "Tara didn't give him any details. Damn, this is all I need. If she's run away, I'll wring her spoiled little neck."

"So, Mr. Niles did manage to locate you." Tara was smoldering when he walked through the front door. She was gowned in a filmy black negligee and a matching robe with thick ruffles forming the collar and running down the front to the hem. "If you ever do this to me again, I'll leave you," she threatened, her voice trembling.

"What's this story you told him about Cat?" Ty demanded. "What's happened to her?"

"I don't know. The school called right after you left to say she was missing. They don't know for how long." Her answer came back angry.

"Did she run away or what?" At the moment he was more concerned about his sister than he was about his wife's outrage.

"That's the way it looks, but they aren't sure. They think a couple of her girlfriends covered up for her this morning," Tara explained tersely.

"My God, has she been gone that long?" His frown was

deeper and angrier as Ty crossed to the telephone and picked it up, dialing a number. "Who is this?" he demanded when a voice answered. "Jobe, I want you to roust Repp Taylor out of his bunk and get him up to The Homestead *now!* And if he isn't there, I want you to get up here on the double!"

"You surely don't think—" Tara began.

"I wouldn't put anything past her," Ty cut in and clicked the phone to clear the line, then dialed another set of numbers.

"Are you calling the police?"

"No. She might have gone to the hospital to see Dad." He waited impatiently for someone to answer. The hospital operator came on the line and switched him to the appropriate nurses' station. The response to his initial question brought a flurry of more queries. When he was satisfied nothing more could be learned, he hung up. "Cat was there the latter part of the afternoon." The information was absently passed on to Tara, his thoughts tracking along another course. "She left shortly after the change of shifts. As far as anyone remembers, no one was with her and she said nothing about returning later."

The muted thump of booted footsteps crossing the wooden floor of the long veranda filtered into the house. As they registered with Ty, he ran a critical eye over Tara's appearance.

"Go upstairs and change into something decent. I won't have you walking around dressed like that in front of my men," he stated tersely.

"I didn't think you had even noticed what I was wearing." And she had changed for his benefit, a spiteful attempt to show him what he'd missed when he'd stalked out of the house.

"That was the whole point, wasn't it?" he taunted with no humor. Tara swung away, even that satisfaction lost to her as she crossed to the stairs. "When you come down, put some coffee on. It's going to be a long night," Ty called after her.

The order infuriated her more. He was treating her like she was some kind of servant. Maybe other ranch wives waited on their husbands like little slaves, but she was different. She had talents that were more valuable to him than anything these women around here could offer him, and she knew it. She wasn't going to be reduced to the position of serving him coffee. When Tara reached their suite of rooms, she stayed there.

After observing the anger in Tara's carriage, Ty pivoted to face the front doors as one opened to admit two cowboys. Repp Taylor came forward, a puzzled look in his expression, with Jobe Garvey following him into the living room, intently curious about this urgent late-night summons.

"Jobe said you wanted to see me right away," Repp said, gesturing to the older man behind him.

"I came along just in case you needed me," Jobe added in quick explanation for his presence.

Ty didn't waste time, his gaze drilling into Repp Taylor. "Where's Cathleen?"

"Cat?" A stunned look flickered across his lean features. "Isn't she at school?"

His reaction seemed genuine. Ty threw a question at Garvey, who was foreman of the crew Taylor worked in, but didn't take his eyes from the maturing cowboy. "Where was Taylor today?"

"He was right here at headquarters, checking the remuda with the rest of us." The stocky-built Garvey quirked an eyebrow, a furrow deepening in his forehead.

"What's happened to Cat?" Repp demanded.

"The school has informed us that she's missing," Ty stated, continuing to watch for any sign that Repp knew more than he was telling. "It appears she has run away, and I thought you might . . . know something about it."

"Of all the—" Repp turned his head aside, containing the rest of the comment with a visible effort. Then he slowly shook his downcast head, as if it were beyond his understanding. "I didn't know anything about it. Since the plane crash, she's talked about running away from school, but I swear I never thought she'd do it."

"Why? Did she give a reason?"

There was a vague shrug. "She wants to stay on the ranch and she talked about getting a private tutor if you wouldn't let her quit school altogether. Losing her mother and all . . . I

CALDER BORN, CALDER BRED

guess it's got her scared that something might happen to her father—or you. And she wants to be home if it does."

"That little idiot." It was a muttered aside that Ty made, finally convinced the explanation was the extent of Repp's knowledge. "She's been to the hospital. Where she is, or where's she planning to go after that, I don't know." Grimness was in his voice. "What about her girlfriends? Do any of them know you?"

"I've met a couple," Repp admitted.

"I want you to get on the phone and call them. See if you can find out anything. They'll talk to you before they'll talk to me or the authorities." After all, Repp was Cathleen's boyfriend.

"Yes, sir." He moved to the phone extension in the living room.

"Find out if they can tell you how much money she had with her," Ty added. "And whether she planned to travel by bus or hitchhike." Then he turned to the foreman, Jobe Garvey. "I want a man posted at every gate into the Triple C, in case she's on her way home. In the meantime, I'll contact the authorities so they can start searching for her."

The new moon was a cold sliver of light in the night-black sky. There wasn't enough star glitter to make more than jagged silhouettes of the rough rimrock country against the horizon. Black shadows and dark shapes constantly loomed in front of her and on either side as Cathleen trudged along the rutted, little-traveled track, stumbling on the uneven ground she couldn't see.

A thousand times she wished for a flashlight. And a thousand more times she wished she hadn't left the highway. The farther she walked, the more uncertain she became that she had picked the right ranch lane. She should have asked the driver who'd given her a lift to wait until she'd checked to be sure, but she'd been so positive. If she got lost out here, she'd never hear the end of it.

The sudden flapping of wings startled her as a night bird, disturbed by her passing, flew from its roost in a nearby pine tree. Cat paused to catch her breath in the cold night air. She was winded and physically exhausted, already regretting the impulsive actions that had brought her to this point. At the time she made her decision, such drastic measures had seemed necessary. Now her bravado was fading.

Something rustled in the needle-covered ground next to the rutted lane. Cat started forward again. Her legs ached as if she'd walked for miles, and she'd turned her ankle so many times it was sore. There had to be something at the end of this lane, so she kept walking rather than turn back.

After another mile that seemed like two, dark objects began to take shape against the blackness of the ground. They resembled small buildings, and Cat started walking faster. There weren't any lights showing. At this distance, she couldn't tell whether they were abandoned or if the occupants were asleep.

A horse whickered suspiciously from the corral, and Cat was reassured the buildings weren't vacant. As her approach carried her closer, the place began to look more familiar, even in the dark. Renewed confidence gave her a fresh burst of energy, and she broke into a stumbling run the last thirty yards to the house.

"Who's that?" The voice came from the porch shadows of the darkened house.

"Uncle Culley? It's me, Cat," she rushed, out of breath. "I was just about convinced I was lost."

Boards creaked beneath his feet; then his dark shape moved out of the shadows and came down the steps to meet her. The starlight in the clearing finally gave form and a face to him.

"Cathleen. What are you doing here?" He gripped her shoulders, then reached a hand to turn her face into the dim starlight. "Are you hurt?"

"No, just tired. I walked all the way from the road and I—" Her aches and exhaustion weren't important now. She quickly switched from complaining to the reason she was here. "At the funeral you said if I ever needed help, I could count on you. Did you mean it?"

"Yes, I meant it." Just for a minute, he fiercely and protectively hugged this precious image of his sister. Then Culley pulled away, made self-conscious by the physical contact. "You say you walked all that way. You must be tired and half frozen. Let's get you in the house and put some hot coffee down you."

"Thanks." She felt humbled that he hadn't even asked what kind of trouble she was in. Since she was involving him, it seemed only fair to tell him. She made her confession as they walked up the short flight of steps to the front stoop of the small house. "I ran away from school. I just couldn't stay there anymore." Her reasons were too flimsy when voiced aloud, but they were very real to her. "I know my brother is going to be furious with me when he finds out . . . and I'm just not ready to face him yet."

"He can be as mad as he likes." He opened the door and reached inside to switch on the overhead light before letting Cat precede him into the house. "But I'll see that he doesn't make you do anything you don't want to do."

"I wanted to go home, but I can't. He's just going to insist that I go back to school, and I don't think I could face that. I thought, maybe . . . I could stay here with you until I could figure out something."

A tenderness seemed to radiate through his face. "This is your home. You're welcome to stay here as long as you like."

Inside the house, he sat her down at the table, insisted on hanging up her coat for her and bringing her coffee, eager as a pup to please her any way he could. "Are you sure I can't get you anything else? Maybe something to eat?"

"No, I ate at the hospital." The warmth from the stove was seeping into her aching body and driving out the chill. All the tension and anxiety over the possibility of facing her irate brother tonight was melting . . . enough so that she reconsidered his offer. "Do you have anything sweet—like chocolate cake or anything?" The minute she asked, Cat doubted a bachelor would go to the trouble of baking for himself.

"No." Disappointment flickered in his expression. "But I've got some store-brought cookies." He went to the cupboard and returned to the table with a sealed container holding less than a dozen shortbread cookies. "There you are." He watched her anxiously to see if the alternative met with her approval.

Even if she hadn't liked them, Cat would have eaten them. She took a couple, dunking them in her coffee and nibbling at the coffee-soaked softness of them. "They're good. Thanks," she assured him, and he smiled with a degree of relief. Cat ate the cookies and talked, telling him about her decision to run away, the visit to the hospital, and the ride she'd cadged as far as his lane. When she reached for another cookie, she realized there were only two left. "Here." She pushed the container to him. "You better have these before I eat them all."

"Go ahead," he insisted and shoved it back. "I'll get more."

After a small hesitation, she gave a little shrug of her shoulders and took the last two cookies and started dunking them in her coffee. "Nobody understands the way I feel." She sighed.

"You know I was just about your age when my momma died," her uncle said. "Things just never were right after that."

"I'll never understand why their plane had to crash." The anger and frustration of deeply held pain began to surface as her tiredness made her more vulnerable. "Why did that oil line break? Why did she have to die? I'm so tired of everyone telling me it was God's will. It wasn't. It couldn't have been. Why would He want to do that? It wasn't right!" Her chin began to quiver as she lowered it and fought back the tears that welled in her eyes.

"It wasn't right," he agreed and got up from the table, uncomfortable with her tears. "But I'm going to do something about that. I've got it all planned out, so don't worry about nothin'. I'll take care of it."

"Take care of what?" Cat frowned in bewilderment as she lifted her head, tilting it to one side. "I don't understand."

But he clammed up and wouldn't explain. "After the long day you've had, you must be pretty tired. I'll put clean sheets on my bed so you can turn in."

"But—"

"I don't sleep much anyways," he said before she could protest. "When I get tired, I'll just catch a nap on the sofa."

"Then let me fix the bed."

"You just sit there and finish your coffee and cookies," her uncle insisted.

25

The sheriff leaned forward in his swivel-based office chair, his barrel chest pushing at the edge of the desk he rested his arms on. "Look, I'll explain it to you again, Mr. Calder," he said with weary patience and began ticking off on his fingers the points as he made them. "Now, the law says you can't file a missing-persons report until the individual has been missing for twenty-four hours or more. And the school told you that they didn't discover your sister was not in her room until suppertime last night, which is only fourteen hours ago. You gotta wait ten more hours to file your report. Legally there's nothing I can do until then."

"Then, dammit, do something illegal!" Ty demanded, coming to his feet and placing his fists on the desktop to lean on them. "I want her found! And I don't intend to wait ten hours before someone starts looking. I'll finance a private search for her if I have to!"

"You have to understand the law's position." The sheriff settled complacently back in his chair. "Juveniles run away all the time. After a night alone, they usually call home, crying and saying how sorry they are. You go on home and wait for that phone call," he urged with a touch of smugness. "If she don't call in ten hours, you come back and see me."

"If anything's happened to her, I'll come back to see you in hell!" Tired from no sleep and frustrated by the lack of cooperation from the authorities, Ty swung away before he followed his threatening words up with action.

Long slicing strides carried him out of the newly renovated sheriff's office, courtesy of the new tax revenues generated by Dy-Corp coal workers. Blue Moon was expanding as fast as they could put in streets, sometimes faster, with mobile

315

homes sitting on a plot of ground fifty yards from a road and accessible by a path worn into the grass.

In his pickup, Ty gunned the motor and pulled onto the dirt street. A dog ran out, barking angrily and biting at the tires, chasing the truck until satisfied it was leaving the neighborhood. When Ty reached the two-lane highway, he had simmered down. It was plain he wasn't going to get any efficient outside help to look for Cat. He'd have to organize something himself.

After he swung the pickup onto the highway, he made almost a full U-turn to park in front of Sally's Place. He rubbed his eyes tiredly as he climbed the steps and entered the café. The place was half full with morning coffee drinkers. None of them he knew, but he heard his name being passed around. He paused at the counter, not taking a stool.

"Hello, Ty." Sally Brogan looked mildly surprised to see him. "How's your father? I was up to see him last week and he seemed to be doing so much better." Without asking, she poured a cup of coffee and set it in front of him.

"He is improving. My sister hasn't been around here, has she? Last night, maybe?"

"Cathleen? No. Why?" She noticed the haggard and raw lines in his face, and concern began to filter into her expression.

"She's missing—ran away from school." He took a quick sip of the hot coffee. "Can I use your phone? I want to check back at the ranch and see if they've heard from her."

"Sure. Just go on through." She motioned toward the swinging door to the kitchen. "I'll ask around the tables and see if anyone here remembers seeing her."

"Thanks."

When he entered the kitchen, the cook, DeeDee Rains, gave him a big smile. "It's been a long time since you've been around. What can I fix for you? Bacon and eggs? Some hashbrowns, maybe?"

"Nothing, thanks," Ty refused as he reached for the wall phone just inside the door.

"I made doughnuts this morning." She wiped her hands on the white apron and used a napkin to wrap two frosted doughnuts. "Your uncle came to the back door earlier and took a batch home with him while they were still hot. He wouldn't come inside and eat anything, though. That crazy Culley, he's quite a character."

The doughnuts still had a warm smell that reminded him he hadn't eaten in some time, so he smiled his thanks to her and accepted the doughnuts she handed him. The distant ring of a telephone finally stopped and a voice sounded in his ear.

"Yeah, let me speak to Stumpy." With his forefinger, he pushed at the front of his hat brim to tip it to the back of his head.

"Is that you, Ty?" The voice belonged to Jessy.

"Yeah, it's me. Has there been any word from Cat?" He tiredly leaned an elbow against the wall.

"Nothing as of twenty minutes ago," she said. "Same for you?"

"Yeah. Let me speak to your father."

"Sure."

There was a clunk of the receiver being set down. In the background, there was the low murmur of voices, the words indistinguishable. Then Stumpy Niles was on the line.

"I spoke to the sheriff," Ty said. "And he was about as much help as a drop of water in the desert. So we're on our own."

"I could have told you that," Stumpy offered dryly. "It's not wise to count on getting help from anyone but yourself."

"I know, you can't wait for somebody else to solve your problems." Ty repeated the saying that he'd heard time and again. "We're going to start actively looking for Cathleen ourselves. I want you to organize the boys into pairs and drive every inch of highway between here and Helena. I want them to hit every road stop and bus stop along the way. I'll be at The Homestead by eleven. We'll use that as the headquarters. If they find anyone who *thinks* they have seen her, they're to call immediately. Got that?"

"I'll have them on the road in less than twenty minutes," Stumpy promised, glad some action was finally being taken.

Before he left the kitchen, he called a thanks to DeeDee again for the doughnuts. Sally passed the word that no one in the restaurant remembered seeing Cat but they'd keep an eye out for her. Ty flipped some coins on the counter to pay for the coffee he hadn't drunk and walked out of the café to his truck. He swung into the cab and jammed one of the doughnuts between his teeth as he started the motor. The second he left in its napkin on the seat. The doughnut was so fresh the first bite nearly melted in his mouth as he started to reverse onto the highway.

A horn honked. "Hey, mister!" A man shouted from his car. "You got a low tire in back."

Ty waved a thanks and pulled over to the gas pumps next door, not wanting to be delayed by a flat on the way home. Emmett Fedderson plodded out of the store. "What d'ya need?" he asked.

"Just some air in the rear tire. One of them's low," Ty said and hopped out of the truck to check it himself, still munching on the doughnut.

"Is that one of DeeDee's?" Emmett asked as he pulled the air hose around to the back of the truck.

"Yeah." Ty crouched down and unscrewed the cap from the valve.

"Your whole family's got a sweet tooth this morning," the man observed and passed Ty the air hose.

The remark instantly put him alert. "What do you mean? Was my sister by your store this morning?"

"Your sister, no. It was your uncle—O'Rourke." He shook his head, mildly amused by his own thoughts. "That crazy Culley was waiting outside when I unlocked the doors this morning. He bought two sacks of cookies, a chocolate-cake mix and frosting, as well as a ten-pound bag of sugar. I never knew him to buy that much sweet stuff in a year."

"Chocolate cake." Ty wasn't even conscious of saying the words out loud. It was Cat's favorite. In his mind, there was a vision of Cat embracing O'Rourke at the funeral . . . sharing their grief, he'd said at the time.

"Aren't you gonna put air in that tire?" Fedderson prodded him.

"Yeah . . . yeah." It was an absent response, and he fitted the hose connection onto the valve with equal absentness. It was incredible. He would never have looked for Cat at the Shamrock Ranch in a million years. With the tire filled, he straightened. "Do me a favor," he asked and didn't wait for

Fedderson to agree. "Call the Triple C and talk to Stumpy Niles. Tell him not to send the men. Tell him I'm on my way to O'Rourke's place and not to do anything until he hears from me."

"Sure." The request made him curious. "What's going on?"

Ty didn't take the time to answer him. Right now, he just wanted to get to O'Rourke's place and find out if his hunch was right.

The second doughnut lay forgotten on the seat. In this country, there was no such thing as short distances. Ty had an hour's worth of traveling or more ahead of him.

After she had slipped the cake pan into the preheated oven, Cat walked back to the counter and picked up the mixing bowl. With her finger, she wiped the sides and wandered to the kitchen table, licking the chocolate batter from her finger.

"This is the best part," she told Culley, her tongue darting out to clean the corners of her lips, and offered him the bowl. "Want some?"

His mouth curved with indulgent humor as he shook his head in quiet refusal. "You go ahead." He'd smiled more in the last few hours than he remembered smiling all his life. Pleasure and contentment ran through him. A light glowed in his dark eyes. He'd passed the fifty mark and once again life seemed worth living.

With the bowl wiped clean, Cat licked every last bit of batter from her fingers and carried the bowl to the sink. "It's been ages since I've messed around in the kitchen," she declared. "It's fun."

"Your momma used to do a lot of baking," he recalled. "She'd go out and work on the ranch all day long, just like a man, then come home an' cook our meals an' clean the house." But he didn't want to dwell on the past. "There's still a couple of doughnuts left."

"I couldn't eat any more," Cat insisted. "I must have eaten a dozen already. Besides, I have to save room for the cake. What I need is some exercise." She laughed. "After that long walk last night, I never thought I'd say that again."

"Maybe later I can saddle a couple horses and we can go riding, I can show you around the ranch. It's pretty country, but it's not much good for raising cattle—not enough water and not enough grass."

"I'd like that, but"—she looked down at the regulation pleated skirt—"I don't have anything to wear but this dumb school skirt. I was going to have the school send my clothes home. I'm afraid this won't work for riding horseback."

"I wish I'd thought about that." Culley frowned. "When I was in town, I could have bought you some everyday clothes to wear."

Cat tipped her head to the side, looking at him with wondering affection. "You would have done that, wouldn't you?"

He turned the empty coffee cup in front of him, liking the way she looked at him but made self-conscious by it, too. "Crazy, huh?" he said. "Ole Crazy Culley." He heard the protesting sound she made and lifted his head, shrugging one shoulder to show indifference. "I know that's what they call me." And he also knew they'd never take the word of an O'Rourke. And Crazy Culley—they wouldn't believe a thing he told them if he swore on a stack of Bibles.

"It isn't true." He saw the flash of spirit, the indignation on his behalf.

"Don't worry your head about it." He smiled proudly.

Culley had lived too long in this place not to know every sound that belonged in and around it. And his senses were too keenly trained not to notice the intrusion of an unnatural sound. It was faint and still some distance from the house, but it brought him to his feet and carried him to the window. His sudden alertness brought a quick end to the conversation.

"What is it?"

"Someone's coming." He stared out the window at the break in the trees where the vehicle traveling up the lane would first come into sight. Cat crowded close to look, too.

"It's my brother." Even though she hadn't been able to see the driver clearly, the pickup unmistakably belonged to the Triple C. "I know it is."

Culley turned, eyeing her closely. "Do you want to see him?" He observed her indecision, the reluctance and dread taking dominance. "Get into the bedroom and shut the door. I'll handle it. You don't have to go home until you want."

"I—" She couldn't finish it, her teeth sinking into her nether lip. After another second's hesitation, she turned and hurried to the bedroom.

There were still a couple of minutes before the truck rounded the turn and entered the yard. Culley waited until the bedroom door was securely shut, then headed for the small front porch. Just before he walked out of the house, he hesitated and reached for the rifle on the low rack mounted on the wall by the door. At his age, he was no match for a young buck like Calder. And if Cat's brother got persistent, Culley might be in need of an equalizer.

He made sure the front door swung quietly shut behind him, silent movement a habit with him. Culley walked as far as the steps and stopped to lean the rifle against an upright post, out of sight and within reach; then he faced the mouth of the lane.

Before the engine had stopped, Ty was out of the truck and coming around the hood to confront O'Rourke. "What brings you over here on a warm spring morning like this?" O'Rourke inquired conversationally.

Ty halted short of the steps. "I'm here to get Cathleen." He made it a positive statement.

"Cathleen!" O'Rourke feigned mild surprise, but he was no actor.

"I know she's here, so don't pretend you don't know what I'm talking about," Ty challenged.

There was a short silence while O'Rourke debated the best way to handle the situation now, even though he couldn't figure out how Calder could be so absolutely certain.

"All right. She's here," he admitted finally. "She showed up late last night—cold and tired—and asked if she could stay. She didn't want to go home because she knew you'd be angry about what she'd done and she was afraid you'd send her back to school. I told her she was welcome to stay with me as long as she liked—and I meant it."

The explanation only added to his impatience with Cathleen. "She has stayed as long as she's going to." Ty took a step forward, intending to go into the house and get her.

With a sly quickness that belied his age, O'Rourke scooped up the hidden rifle and aimed it level from his waist. "I don't think so," was all he said.

Ty froze in his tracks, a wariness tingling through him as he glanced from the rifle barrel to the man holding it. "Let me by, Culley. I'm not leaving without her."

The lever action sounded unnaturally loud as a bullet was pumped into the firing chamber. "You're on private property, Ty," O'Rourke said. "And I'm telling you to get off." There was a sudden quirk of his mouth. "Things sure take a funny twist, don't they? A long time ago, it was a Calder who had my sister and ordered me off his land. Now I got a Calder's sister and I'm the one telling you to git."

Don't back down from anything, his father had once told him, because it only makes it easier to back down the next time. And Cathleen was in that house. Taking a calculated risk, Ty released an angry sigh of disgust and half turned away.

"Damn that girl!" he muttered and swept his hat off his head to rake a hand through his hair. Then he turned back to address his complaints to O'Rourke. "The whole damn ranch has been up all night and half the state is looking for her. She's got me and everybody else worried crazy, thinking something might have happened to her. And all the while, she's been warm and safe over here at your place"—his hands and his hat gestured wildly as he made his points—"and she didn't so much as even send word that she was all right. You're damned right I'm upset with her!"

The last was issued with an upward swing of his hat that hit the rifle barrel and pointed it skyward. A deafening explosion roared in his ears as his arm completed its arc and knocked the rifle out of O'Rourke's grasp. Ty charged up the steps as the gray-haired man backed up, half crouching into a fighting stance.

Cathleen came hurling out of the house to throw herself between the two men, protectively shielding O'Rourke. "Ty, no! Don't!" It was a frightened and angry command. "He was only trying to protect me!"

"He wouldn't have had to protect you if you hadn't hidden in the house like some damned child!" Ty raged. "Were you afraid to come home because you thought you were going to get a spanking? You spoiled little brat! You've never had a spanking in your life—and that's what's wrong with you now! You didn't want to stay in school, so you ran away! Don't I have enough to worry about with the ranch and Dad lying in some hospital without having to worry about where the hell you are?"

"I'm sorry." Tears were stinging her eyes as she faced him.

She looked so damned vulnerable, but his exasperation with her wouldn't allow him to be moved by it, although it took his anger, leaving him with impatient disgust. "Grow up, Cathleen," he ordered roughly. "Nobody held my hand when I was your age, and I'm sure as hell not going to hold yours." He swung off the porch to stride to the truck.

Not immediately following him, Cat glanced hesitantly back at her uncle. "You don't have to go with him," O'Rourke said quietly.

A sad little smile touched her mouth. "Yes, I do." Impulsively, she leaned up and kissed him on the cheek, whispering a tremulous "Thanks." Then she ran down the steps after her brother.

The motor had started and the pickup was reversing out of the ranch yard before Culley remembered. "What about the cake?" he called after his niece, but she didn't hear him above the engine noise.

He kept it for days until the chocolate frosting dried and cracked and the cake became too hard to eat. Finally he threw it away.

"The spring roundup went well." Ty sat in the chair beside the hospital bed. Dressed in a western-cut suit, he idly turned the Stetson hat in his hand, trying to find an easy way to lead up to the matter he dreaded to tell his father. "Our winter losses were minimal."

"That's good." His father grabbed the overhead bar with his one good hand and tried to shift his position in the bed slightly. The twitching grimaces he tried to control indicated he was in considerable pain. His big frame seemed gaunt and pale, the deep tan faded after these long months in the hospital. The accident and Maggie's death had aged him, graying more of his hair until the temples were completely silvered. When the pain had subsided to a tolerable level again, he glanced at Ty. "Did you bring me any cheroots?"

"I thought the doctor said you weren't supposed to smoke," Ty reminded him. He'd suffered a collapsed lung in the plane crash; then infection had set in, further weakening his breathing.

"The doctor also told me I wasn't supposed to live," his father countered dryly. "Which just shows you how much he knows."

The reference to death brought a different kind of pain into his eyes as he briefly turned away. Ty knew he was thinking about Maggie. He still hadn't gotten over losing her, and probably never would. Without her, his father had lost interest in so many things and seemed to go through the motions of living, with no more purpose than to get through each day.

It seemed wise to change the subject. "Some of Tara's friends from the East came to stay during the roundup. They got a kick out of watching how it was done in the 'Wild West.' As a matter of fact, they're still at The Homestead. That's why Tara didn't come with me today."

"How's Cat? Did she come with you?"

"Yes. There was some shopping she had to do, and she didn't want to leave it too late in case the stores closed," Ty explained. "She should be here before long." One corner of his mouth lifted in a faint smile that crooked the line of his mustache. "She received her grades from school, and I'm sure she has every intention of showing them off to you."

"One time she talked to me about staying at the Triple C and having a private tutor," his father recalled vaguely. "Look into that for her." The accident hadn't altered her father's willingness to indulge his daughter's every whim, regardless of its extravagance.

"We can't afford it." Ty looked grimly at his hat, then lifted his gaze to his father. "I've been cutting expenses everywhere I can."

"You're running the show. You do what you have to." Along with everything else, his father appeared to have lost interest in the operation of the ranch.

"I am," Ty stated and took a breath to finally make his announcement. "You might as well know I've dropped the suit for title to the disputed ten-thousand-acre parcel. In the meantime, I've negotiated an interim lease on it."

For a few minutes, he had his father's undivided attention. "Why?"

"The legal fees were too expensive. Maybe, if the cattle market changes, I'll be able to afford to go after the title again."

"But possession is nine tenths of the law. That land has been in the Calder name, in one form or another, for a hundred years," his father protested, but not vigorously.

"And it still is. That's why I waited until I had a signed lease before I dropped the suit. It can be filed again," Ty assured him.

He sank back on his pillow. "Maybe you're right." There was defeat in his voice, and it hurt Ty more than an angry dispute over his decision could have. "Maybe it isn't worth fighting over. If I hadn't been so determined to get it, there would have been no reason to fly to Helena and your mother wouldn't have been killed."

"Don't talk that way. You can't blame yourself," Ty insisted.

"You can't deny it's true." It was a humorless smile he turned on his son. "Light me a cigarette."

After hesitating, Ty reached inside his suit jacket and took out a cigarette from the pack in his shirt pocket. He lit it and passed it to his father. A long, dragging puff was taken from the cigarette and blown at the ceiling.

"Did you talk to Dr. Haslind when you arrived?" He studied the smoldering tip of the cigarette.

"No. I missed him. Why?"

"I'm scheduled for surgery Monday morning. They think they can relieve some of this pressure on my spine."

For a long minute, Ty couldn't say anything. "I'll be here."

"You have a ranch to run"

"I'll be here."

When they wheeled him down the hospital corridor to the operating room, Chase was all prepped for surgery. A nurse had given him a shot earlier, and he felt heavy and groggy. With blurring vision, he searched the faces above him. Ty had said he was going to be there.

"My son . . ." he murmured thickly.

"Your family is in the waiting room outside surgery, Mr. Calder," a woman's voice assured him, but it seemed to come from far away.

There was something he'd meant to tell him. It was important, but he had trouble remembering what it was. "Tell him . . ." It was almost there. He strained, fighting the cloudy softness that drifted around him. ". . . mineral rights." He remembered, but his voice was very low and slurred. ". . . get mineral ri . . ."

"What did he say?" A surgical aide glanced at his partner to see if she had understood.

"Something about minerals." She shook her head. "Some of the patients come up with the craziest things."

26

It was late in the afternoon when Ty arrived at The Homestead from his third trip to the hospital in slightly over a week's time. He was tired, well aware there was a backlog of paperwork waiting for him in the study.

Tara was at the door to greet him when he walked in. "Welcome home." She kissed him lightly. "How is your father doing after his surgery? You gave him my love, I hope."

"Yes, and he's doing fine, recovering nicely, so far." Then he glanced about the living room. "Has E.J. arrived? I explained to Dad that you didn't come with me because your father was flying in."

"He and Stricklin arrived shortly after lunch. They're over

at the mine this afternoon." She paused, eyeing him critically. "You look tired."

"I am." He headed for the study, hoping to get some of that paperwork knocked out before Dyson and Stricklin returned.

"You shouldn't have made the trip to the hospital so soon after the last one. Both of us were there for his surgery. We even stayed until the next day," Tara reminded him.

"I thought it was necessary," Ty stated and didn't explain his reasons. When he entered the study, he saw a middle-aged woman in a navy-blue dress and white apron polishing the liquor cabinet. Tara came alongside him as he stopped abruptly. "Who are you?"

"Ty, I want you to meet Mrs. Thornton. She's keeping house for us," Tara explained.

An eyebrow shot up as he frowned. "Since when?"

"Since I hired her . . . and an excellent cook named Simone Rae. You'll have an opportunity to sample her culinary skill at dinner this evening." She seemed almost totally indifferent to his chagrined surprise at the news.

"How do you do, Mr. Calder." The new housekeeper respectfully inclined her head in his direction.

"Mrs. Thornton." He kept a tight control on his displeasure. "You can finish the cleaning in here another time."

"Of course, sir," she murmured and quietly withdrew from the room.

"What's the meaning of this?" He turned on Tara when they were alone.

"I told you I needed extra help," she reminded him with a small laugh of confusion.

"And when you told me that, I thought you meant you were going to hire a local girl here on the ranch."

"Ty, you know we need properly trained staff," she insisted. "And Doug Stevens and his party will be arriving next week. After all the time he spent in France, I couldn't serve him poorly prepared meals. I had to find a decent cook."

"Dammit, Tara," he muttered impatiently, turning his head aside, then slicing her an accusing look. "You know I've been trying to trim expenses everywhere I could."

"You simply can't entertain cheaply."

"Unless you don't entertain at all!" he countered with more than a trace of anger.

Her dark eyes fairly snapped. "If you would spend more time with our guests instead of traipsing all over this godforsaken ranch—"

"I don't have time to entertain your guests!" Ty interrupted. "I'm trying to run this ranch and find money enough to pay to feed all these people who keep arriving—at your invitation."

"I ask them here so you can meet them and get to know them." She was struggling not to lose her temper. "If you want to get ahead, it's not what you know—it's *who* you know. Surely you can't be so blinded by all this sun and sky that you can't see that. Someday these people might be useful to you."

"How? Useful the way the good Senator Bulfert was useful to my father?" he challenged.

"One of them might have the influence to help you regain title to that land your father thinks is so important." She knew he was still sensitive about that, and she used it to win her argument. Tara saw the indecision warring in his expression and let her own soften. "Look, Ty," she began, again in a reasoning tone. "I can't rope cows or brand calves. I can't do bookwork. So let me help in the way that I can. I know a lot of important people. Please, when the Stevens party comes, spend more time with them."

"You can be as beguiling as a witch," he muttered.

"A beautiful one, I hope." She laughed softly and linked her arms around his neck. He was drawn down by the shiny invitation of her lips.

The rumbling roar of the huge, diesel-powered earth mover vibrated through the air as it peeled away the grass and soil to expose the seam of coal. Elsewhere, power shovels were scooping up chunks of coal, broken up earlier by explosions of dynamite charges, and loading them into large coal trucks for transport to preparation plants. The ebb and flow of men and machines was as constant as the deafening noise.

The land had the gouged and desolated look of a battle-field. The plant life that still survived at the edges of the pits was coated with layers of dust.

As Dyson and Stricklin emerged from the temporary offices on site, there was a slowdown of activity. The line of empty coal trucks returning for new loads growled to a stop.

Dyson turned to the mine director, Art Grinnell. "What's the problem?"

His glance flickered briefly at Dyson, a frown gathering. "I don't know," he murmured, but his tone lacked something. "I'll see." He excused himself and went to check out the cause of the backup. "Hey, Rhodes!" he called to the man in coveralls walking back from the line of trucks.

As Dyson watched the two men conferring, he said to his partner, "Let's see what it is." Something didn't smell right to him. When a man had made a living relying on his instinct as much as he had, he didn't ignore a funny odor when he caught the scent of one. They crossed the stretch of hard-baked ground to where the two men were talking. "What is it?"

"Just a mechanical problem with one of the trucks, Mr. Dyson." Grinnell assured him it was nothing he needed to be troubled about, but he didn't meet his eyes when he said it, sliding a short glance to the driver named Rhodes instead.

"As I recall"—Stricklin spoke up—"there's been a rash of mechanical breakdowns of late. That's why the productivity was down this month, you said." The tacked-on phrase was faintly accusing.

There was a smile in Dyson's eyes when he glanced at his partner. It was always reassuring when Stricklin reached the same conclusion through reasoning that Dyson had come to through instinct. Both suspected something in this situation, but each came at it from a different angle. That was what made them such a potent combination.

"That's true. There have been," Grinnell admitted, and Dyson sensed the man's reluctance to discuss the subject.

"What seems to be the problem with the stalled truck up ahead?" Stricklin put the question to the driver.

There was a moment when the driver, Rhodes, looked to his boss for directions; then he pressed his lips tightly together. "The oil line's been cut."

"Cut?" A sudden frown crossed Stricklin's usually expressionless face. "How can you be sure?"

"I'm not for certain—not until the mechanic gets a look at it. But it's for sure the oil line's broken, and if it's like all the others, it's been cut."

"You're saying it was deliberately cut?" Dyson wanted the implication verified.

"Yeah, and if the guy doing it hasn't got time to cut the oil line, he dumps sugar in the gas tank." Frustration and anger vibrated in his half-muttered answer. The driver glanced again at Grinnell, aware that he'd spoken out of turn but also determined to get this out in the open.

"That's all, Rhodes," the manager dismissed him. "Go see what you can do about getting that truck towed to the garage." He watched the driver walk away, then hesitantly swung his attention back to the owners of the company.

"How long has this sabotage been going on?" Stricklin demanded.

"A little over a month." He shifted uncomfortably. "I've already doubled the security at night."

"Then triple it," Dyson ordered.

"Do you have any idea who's doing it or why?" It was Stricklin, who rarely took part in cross-examinations of reports, that was doing most of the questioning.

"I have a pretty good idea who I think is behind it and why," Grinnell responded grimly. "It's obvious he wants to slow us down and create as many problems and delays for us as he can. When a machine breaks down, it's not only costly to repair, but it also means time lost. He probably figures if the mine gets too costly to operate, we'll shut it down. And he probably figures if he can't stop us one way, he'll do it another."

"Who exactly do you believe is behind it?" Stricklin removed his glasses and began cleaning them with a handkerchief from his pocket.

There was a pregnant silence as Grinnell looked uneasily at Dyson, then shifted his weight to another foot. "No disrespect to your daughter, Mr. Dyson, but . . . it has to be Calder." And he quickly rushed to defend his reasoning before either man could comment on his conclusion. "He's been giving you grief ever since he learned about your coal operation here. Some of the other ranchers in the area have supported him, but none have come down as hard as he has. He's tried every legal means he could. And from what I've heard from the locals around here, the Calders aren't above making their own laws and carrying out their own kind of vigilante action."

"Impossible!" was Dyson's reaction. "There is no way Chase Calder could have engineered this sabotage from his hospital bed." Stricklin replaced his glasses, pushing them onto his nose. "Besides, I've seen him and talked to others who've been around him. There's no fight left in him. And as for my son-in-law, he has never been as stridently opposed to this as his father, and he wouldn't stoop to this kind of tactic."

"Maybe you're right," Grinnell conceded, but he wasn't convinced. "It's for sure you know your son-in-law better than I do. Except I remember seeing him get into a fight once at Sally's Place in town. He went after one of our guys with a broken beer bottle, which tells me he'll fight dirty if he has to."

"I want to hear no more talk about the Calders being responsible for this," Dyson stated. "Somebody else is doing it. Either catch him or make the security so tight that he won't risk attempting any trouble."

"Yes, sir." It was a tight-lipped answer, acknowledging there would be no more discussion of the subject. "If you don't need me for anything else, I'll be getting back to the job."

"That's all." There was a moment's pause as Dyson somberly watched Grinnell head back for the office; then he seemed to rouse himself and glance at Stricklin. By silent agreement, they both started for the car parked a few yards away. "What's your opinion, George?" E.J. finally asked.

"It could be just a coincidence that somebody's cutting the oil lines on our machinery—and that Calder's plane crash was caused by a broken oil line."

"Or someone could be trying to throw suspicion on the Calders," Dyson suggested.

"But why?" Stricklin murmured to himself and opened the car door to slide behind the wheel.

The windows were rolled down, but the interior of the car still had that hot, sunbaked feel of stale air. Stricklin flicked the air-conditioning fan on high. Driving slowly through the congestion around the mine area, he approached the main road to the old Stockman ranch house and stopped the car to let a large tank truck loaded with water turn across the road in front of him.

"Every time I see one of those trucks, I shudder when I think how much it's costing us to haul that water." Dyson's sigh was heavy with displeasure.

"It's an investment," Stricklin replied and turned the steering wheel to follow the tank truck.

"Well put." Dyson leaned to the side in an attempt to look around the truck and get a first glimpse of their investment.

After the dull, coal-dusted earth of the barren land around the strip-mining area and the yellowing grass of the surrounding range, the sudden patch of green made a healthy contrast. It was the first of the mine's reclaimed areas, seeded and watered to grow a thick stand of new grass. Stricklin stopped the car to watch while the tank truck drew to a halt by a portable water-storage tank hooked to the irrigation system.

"It's certainly shut up the complaints from the environmentalists and silenced a lot of the ranchers," Dyson stated, nodding with approval at the scene. "Of course, it's the most expensive grass in the country, too. It should be green."

"But it serves its purpose. It's a showcase reclamation project. We spend the money now and we won't have to spend as much later. We can leave it to Mother Nature instead." The economics of the situation were plain to Stricklin. There was no other viable alternative. "Ty needs to see this, especially now that he's dropped the suit contesting the land titles." He said no more than that, trusting Dyson to have a sense of the right timing. After all, he was the promoter.

"Yes." It was a thoughtful agreement. "I thought I might feel him out, so to speak, this evening. Tara has indicated they're in a financial pinch right now, so it just might be the time to approach him with a deal."

The mention of Tara brought a warm light to Stricklin's metal-blue eyes. "Tara has really come into her own since she's become the *lady* of the house." He placed a slight emphasis on the word "lady," because that's the way he saw her—as a lady, with position and dignity. "She is so skillful at managing her guests and ensuring their stay is flawless. She was born to the role."

"Indeed," Dyson agreed, proud of his daughter for so smoothly taking charge of the household and slowly changing it from being merely the grand home of a big rancher to being the center of a whole new social life that attracted a lot of influential people. Ty would do extremely well with her. And Dyson also knew he could count on her as an ally without ever putting the matter to her. He and his daughter thought too much alike.

"Excellent meal. Simply an excellent meal," E.J. assured his daughter.

"Thank you, Daddy." She hugged his arm as they left the dining room, trailed by Ty, Stricklin, and Cathleen. "I told you my cook was a real find. She'd worked at the governor's mansion for years. It was lucky for me that the restaurant she opened in Helena failed. I had dined there once. So I scooped her up the minute I heard she was in the job market again. And she highly recommended Mrs. Thornton, whose credentials were impeccable anyway. It made it very convenient that the two of them were acquainted, since it meant they could share quarters." Plus it kept them fairly isolated from the other ranch employees and lessened the amount of gossip spread about what went on in The Homestead, but Tara didn't mention the other objective she had accomplished with her new, imported staff.

"Brandy in the study?" Ty suggested, drawing level with the father-daughter pair as they reached the living room.

"You obviously aren't including me in that offer." Cat grinned, since only on special occasions was she allowed to even have wine at dinner. "So I won't join you. I think I'll brave the insects and take a walk outside instead."

"May I join you, Cathleen," Stricklin inquired. "After all that delicious food, I need some exercise."

"Sure." Her shoulders lifted in a shrug that assured him she had no objections.

"I guess that leaves you and Daddy," Tara declared. "I need to plan out the next week's menus and check with Simone to be sure we have everything that she'll need when Doug Stevens arrives with his party."

There was a general, unhurried parting as they branched off in different directions, Ty and Dyson wandering into the study. The brandy was poured and the two men settled comfortably into matching armchairs. Dyson cupped the snifter glass in his hand and slowly swirled the liquor to warm it.

"I was hoping I would have a few minutes to talk to you alone on this visit, Ty." He made his opening gambit.

"Oh?" Ty sent him a mildly curious look.

"Actually, this is a bit awkward for me," he confessed with a small, self-deprecating smile. "I don't want to create any problems, yet at the same time I'd really like to have you as a partner."

"A partner?" His head came up in brief surprise.

"It isn't simply because you married my daughter. I want you to understand that, although it is an additional reason why I'd like to see it come about—to keep it all in the family, so to speak." His smile deepened slightly as he observed no resistance to the idea in Ty's expression. "But I've always liked you. You've got a head on your shoulders and you know how to use it. I respect that. And it's exactly what I want in a business partner."

"Another thing you need from a business partner is his time," Ty said. "I've got my hands full with the ranch."

"Problems?" Dyson made the inquiry rather than have Ty think his daughter had dropped some hints to him.

"A few."

"Yes, I understand the cattle business is in a slump right now." He nodded with a show of understanding. "And the flow from the wells at Broken Butte has dropped off considerably, so that income won't be taking up the slack anymore."

"Unfortunately," Ty agreed and took a sip of the brandy.

"You have another ready source of income available to you—coal." Dyson saw the protest coming and held up a hand to stop it. "I know all about your father's feelings on the subject of mining coal, especially on Calder land. Believe me,

I've heard it all before, and not just from him." He laughed to show how little attention he paid to such talk. "The same things were said by ranchers in Texas when they first started drilling wells. They were certain it was somehow going to ruin their land or interfere with the grazing of their cattle. And the fishermen screamed that offshore rigs would drive away the fish. I could go on and on. But every time their fears proved to be groundless. I'm not telling you anything you don't already know."

"You've made a very good point," Ty agreed. "However, the same can't be said for strip-mining. You only have to look at some of the places in the East to see what it's done to the land."

"In the past, yes. But you know how strict the regulations are now. You'll have to come over to the Stockman place and see our reclamation project. By next year, you won't know that land was ever disturbed," he insisted. "This is certainly the time to be getting into the coal business, too, with all these energy programs that are requiring the big power plants to convert to coal as their fuel. The demand is going to be high, and the price will go right along with it."

"I have no doubt there is money to be made from it." Neither did he dispute the other claims Dyson had made about the stricter regulations on strip-mining and the advanced techniques in reclaiming the soil. He was not the skeptic his father was.

"The partnership I have in mind is a joint venture to mine the coal on that ten-thousand-acre parcel of land. I can easily obtain the mineral rights to it through my company." Dyson didn't tell him that his request had already gone through government channels and the approval was virtually guaranteed by his contacts. "Because your father feels justified in his claim that the title to that land is rightfully his, I couldn't, in good conscience, begin mining the coal under that parcel unless there was some arrangement between us to share in the profits."

"I appreciate the sentiment—" Ty began with a faint negative movement of his head.

"I'm not asking you for an answer right now," Dyson insisted before the offer could be rejected. "I'd like you to think on it. It's going to put you in direct opposition to your father's wishes if you agree, and I'm aware of that. I've said it before—your father is of the old school. He's slow to accept change, unwilling to accept new ideas and new directions. But this country is going to need the coal under this ground. Someone is going to mine it; it's inevitable. But your father simply doesn't want to admit it."

"I know." He studied the brandy in his glass, feeling the conflict between a logical and an emotional point of view.

"Enough talk about business." Dyson settled into his chair, confident about how smoothly the discussion had gone. "What do you think of the new senator who won Bulfert's old job?"

A half-moon had begun its ascent into the night sky, changing from gold to silver. A splatter of stars dotted the blue-black canopy, as if some giant hand had taken a handful of diamonds and hurled them into the air to scatter and sparkle. In the quiet, the wail of a coyote was a homeless sound amidst all this emptiness.

The main lights of the headquarters were behind them as the pair wandered as far as the road heading east from the ranch buildings. Cat stopped to let her gaze stray over the blackness of the ground where it met the distant horizon. A stiff breeze blew her dark hair into her face. She shook her head to toss it away and turned into the night wind.

"It's a good thing there's a strong breeze tonight," she murmured to her silent companion. The moonlight silvered his blond hair, the color already making a graceful transition from gold to silver-gold and concealing his age. His features remained smooth of lines, and his trimly muscled physique still gave him the look of a younger man.

"Yes, it makes it seem much cooler," he said.

"I wasn't thinking of that." Cat laughed softly. "It keeps all the flies and mosquitoes from having such a feast on us. Sometimes they get so thick, I swear, they could eat you up."

"They can be a terrible nuisance," he agreed.

"Look." She pointed at the sky. "There goes an airplane. See that red light moving across the sky?"

"Yes." He watched it for a minute. "Tell me, did they ever

learn what caused your father's plane crash? The last I heard, it was some sort of engine failure."

"A broken oil line." Her tone was subdued as she lowered her chin, the subject stealing some of her pleasure in the evening walk.

"Does anyone know what caused it?" Stricklin continued to study her profile.

She shook her head, glancing at him briefly. "It just happened, I guess."

There was a slight pause; then Cat studied him curiously. "With all the flying you do, doesn't it bother you that something might go wrong with your plane?"

He held her look for a long second, probing into her green eyes. "No," he said finally. "I've never given it much thought." He reached in a side pocket and withdrew a small knife.

Cat watched with amusement as he ran the blade under the ends of his nails. "Why do you spend so much time cleaning your fingernails?" At least this time the knife was clean, she thought to herself.

Stricklin briefly appeared startled by her question, then shrugged. "It's a habit, I guess." He looked off into the night. "Are you still seeing that young cowboy?"

This time she looked at him and frowned. "Repp? How'd you know about him?"

"Did Tara let something slip that she shouldn't have?" he countered. "Sorry, I didn't realize I wasn't supposed to know."

"It doesn't matter." She shrugged, then became curious. "What did she tell you anyway?"

"Nothing, really, I assure you," Stricklin promised. "I believe she merely mentioned once that you liked a particular cowboy but your father didn't believe you were old enough to be dating. I think she hinted that she occasionally helped the two of you meet."

"I did see him a couple of times that my father doesn't know about," Cat admitted, underplaying the number of times she'd slipped away to meet Repp. "He thought I shouldn't date until I was sixteen, and I didn't want to wait that long."

"That's typical of young love, I understand." There was a very faint curve to his mouth. "Secret meeting places. All very romantic—that sort of thing."

"I guess so," she agreed, able to look back on that time with a somewhat amused eye at the high drama she had given to those stolen moments. Of course, she was sixteen now and able to date Repp openly.

"Did you have secret meeting places?" he queried.

"Now, that would be telling," Cat chided, reluctant to reveal that their special place had been the office shed at the hangar. It was a private thing between her and Repp, not to be shared.

"I'm sorry. I was prying, wasn't I? Naturally you wouldn't want to divulge the location." A smoothness seemed to overlay his voice, so little feeling ever expressed in it. "Did you ever get caught?"

"No, or it wouldn't still be a secret." But she remembered the time Repp had thought he'd heard someone outside. It had turned out to be the wind blowing the access door to an airplane engine that had been left unlatched.

Somewhere close by, a horse snorted. Cat turned toward the sound, then caught the almost muffled thud of hooves softly swishing through thick grass. Her sudden alertness to something in the night attracted Stricklin's attention. It was difficult to make out anything in the immediate darkness of the land surrounding them. Saddle leather creaked.

"Who's out there?" Cat demanded. For a long minute, there was nothing but the rustle of the breeze in the tall stand of grass. Suddenly a dark shape loomed, and Stricklin stiffened at the man's silent approach. "Uncle Culley." She laughed softly at the start he had given her. "I didn't know it was you."

"You okay?" he asked while his dark gaze flicked suspiciously to Stricklin.

"Sure. We were just walking off a big dinner," Cat explained. "You've met my uncle before, haven't you, Mr. Stricklin?"

"Of course. How are you, Mr. O'Rourke?" His mouth curved into a smile, but there was no more than that to it.

"Fine." Culley nodded his head, but his gaze never wavered from the man for a second.

Cat sensed an awkwardness in the air, a kind of tension that made her uneasy. "Are you going to be home tomorrow, Uncle Culley?" She spoke to ease the strain of the brittle air. "I was thinking about riding over to the Shamrock."

"If you're coming, I'll meet you by the river and ride with you," he said.

"I'll leave you two to make your plans," Stricklin said, taking a step to move away toward The Homestead. "I enjoyed the walk, Cathleen."

"Good night, Mr. Stricklin," she said and absently turned to watch him retrace his steps to the house.

"How come you were alone with him?" her uncle questioned.

"Alone?" She hadn't even considered that she had been alone with the man, not in the kind of context he seemed to be indicating. "We just went for a walk after dinner. That's hardly being 'alone' with someone."

"Maybe not," he gave in grudgingly. "But you'd best stay away from him. I don't trust him."

"Stricklin? I've never seen him take a second look at a woman in all the times I've seen him." Cat scoffed the idea that he might get amorous ideas about her. "Besides, he's too old. And I'm dating Repp anyway."

"Just keep in mind what I said," Culley insisted. "Are you really coming tomorrow?"

"Sure. I'll meet you at ten o'clock by the river."

27

It was one of those hot, lazy summer afternoons that didn't encourage much physical activity. It was a time for slow moving and slow talking. When Jessy climbed out of the pickup she'd parked in front of the ranch commissary, there was a raucous group paying no heed to the warning of the broiling sun overhead. The noise of shrieking laughter and mirthful shouts echoed from the river that wound through the headquarters. It came from the current group of houseguests frolicking in the clear-running water.

The sun had baked the metal of the pickup door. It burned her hand as Jessy pushed it shut and walked around the truck to the screened entrance to the commissary. The opening swing of the screen disturbed the flies crawling on the dark mesh. They buzzed noisily as she slipped inside the building.

"Hello, Sid," she greeted the cowboy leaning on the counter, hip-locked with all his weight on one leg.

"'Lo, Jessy." He threw her a look, then resumed his pose, appearing hot and tired and thoroughly disgruntled with life. A large fan sat on the floor, whirring noisily and chasing the air around the rows of canned goods, food supplies, and varying assortment of stock.

"Where's Bill?" Jessy glanced down the length of the long ranch store for the wheelchaired Bill Vernon who ran the commissary with the help of his wife.

"In the back," Ramsey replied, his head jerking in the direction of the rear storeroom. "He's lookin' to see if he can't find me some chewing tobacco. Those damned dudes in here from New York came in and bought him out. Now I'm probably gonna have to drive all the way into Blue Moon for tobacco."

"That's rough," Jessy sympathized and reached into her

340

shirt pocket for the list of supplies she needed to restock her shelves at the cabin.

"This place is supposed to be for us," the cowboy complained. "But it's been turned into a damned tourist store for those dudes she keeps bringing in." There was no need to explain that "she" was Ty's wife. "They come in here so they can buy the 'gen-u-ine' article. Bill swears he's sold more pairs of jeans, shirts, and hats in one month than he usually sells all year. 'They want to wear what the cowboys wear.'" He pitched his voice higher, speaking with sarcastic mimicry. "I told Bill he oughta set up a souvenir stand and we'll bring him in some cow chips. Those fools'd probably pay five dollars apiece for 'em. Hell, we could make a fortune."

Jessy laughed. "I wouldn't be surprised."

"Do you know what she's having Bill do?" There was that "she" again as angry disapproval showed in Sid's eyes. "She told him to charge double the price on anything he sold to her friends—more if he thought he could get it."

"Maybe she figures they can afford it," she offered with a small shrug, not wanting to join the criticism of Tara. She was hardly impartial. "Besides, everything here is sold practically at cost. Even at double, it would still be a fair price."

"Maybe so." Ramsey pushed off the counter, straightening to hitch up his pants, but his expression still had a disgruntled look to it. "I just don't like what's happening to this ranch. It ain't the same anymore."

It wasn't the first muttering of this sort she'd heard, and it worried her. The discontent seemed to be growing. "What do you mean?" She feigned a casualness.

"This is supposed to be a cattle ranch. Do you know what I'm doing?" he challenged and pressed a finger against his chest. "She's got me taking her 'guests' on trail rides! Half of 'em have never been on a horse in their life and hang on to the saddle like it was gonna sprout wings. And the other half *think* they're riders and wanta go galloping hell-bent-for-Mary across the plains in the heat of the day! And all of 'em oohin' and aahin' about how 'buu-te-ful' it is!" It was a biting mockery. "It's enough to make a fella sick." He turned back to the counter. "You're lucky, Jessy, that you're working up at the north camp an' don't have to put up with all this."

"I guess I am." She hadn't come in contact with any of the guests, but the ranch grapevine kept her apprised of the continuous arrivals and departures of each group.

"You know what I'm supposed to do now?" Ramsey didn't wait for Jessy to ask. "None of those dudes can get up early enough to see the sunrise. So I got orders to arrange a late trail ride so they can watch a sunset out on the range. And they wanta sit around a campfire. A campfire!" he repeated with a snort of disgust. "Can you imagine that, with the grass as dry as it is! They'd have a fire, all right. If there was any wind at all, they'd have a whole damned range fire!"

"You explained that, didn't you?" Jessy frowned.

"Yeah. That part of it has been nixed," he grumbled. "This batch of guests must be real dandies."

"Why?" Her question seemed to make him uncomfortable for a minute.

"From what I've heard, a couple of the guys must be fairies," he muttered.

"What?" Jessy tried not to laugh.

"Yeah. Bud Jebsen, the guy who mostly works on the windmill crew, is a carpenter. She's got him buildin' a zebo down by the river."

"A zebo?" She frowned bewilderedly. "What's that?"

"I dunno. Bud showed me a picture of what it looks like. It reminded me of a round bandstand with a roof on it. He didn't quite get the right of it, but said it sounded like a zebo is a place where gays sit."

"I never heard of such a thing," she declared in a murmur of confusion.

"Neither did I." There was a grim shake of his head. "I tell ya, I just don't know. I always liked Ty, but I don't much cotton to the way he's running things, cutting good men off the payroll while his wife hires some highfalutin cook and a maid. Do you know he even quit fightin' to get that land title?"

"I'd heard that," Jessy admitted.

"I just can't understand." Ramsey pulled in a deep breath and let it rush out. The storeroom door opened and Bill Vernon maneuvered his wheelchair through the opening. "Didya find any, Bill?"

"Sure did." He picked up the small round box on his lap and tossed it to Ramsey.

"Maybe the day ain't gonna turn out so rotten after all," the cowboy declared and dug into his pocket to slap some change on the counter. "Thanks, Bill." He angled for the door with a springing step. "See ya later, Jess."

"What d'ya need, Jessy?" Bill inquired.

"Just about everything. Coffee, eggs . . ." The list went on.

"It's a damned shame the security man didn't get a good look at the guy." Dyson rubbed his chin in irritation, his arm resting on the car's window frame. "He couldn't even get a good description of him—just a slim cowboy on a dark horse."

"It isn't much to go on," Stricklin agreed and slowed the car as they entered the ranch yard of the Triple C.

"Maybe nearly getting caught will keep the guy from trying it again," Dyson offered hopefully. "He's caused enough trouble already." His mouth was pressed tightly shut, a furrow of concentration creasing his forehead. "Damn, but I just can't think why he's doing it. Why does he keep coming back time after time? Do you have any ideas?"

"None." He turned the wheel to drive up the knoll to The Homestead.

"I don't know how much longer we can keep this under wraps," he said grimly. "Ty mentioned to me when we were here a couple weeks ago that he'd heard we had some trouble on the site. I downplayed it, treating it as malicious vandalism. But I can't have him thinking he's going to inherit trouble if he agrees to the deal I made him."

"Has he indicated which way he's leaning on the deal?" Stricklin asked as the car rolled to a stop by the front steps.

"No, but I have a feeling it's going to depend on how financially strapped he is." Dyson climbed out of the car and halted, looking across the roof of the vehicle, his attention caught by the laughing group approaching The Homestead. "Here comes Tara Lee."

Stricklin paused by the driver's side of the car and watched the swimsuited and toweled figures, singling out the green-eyed girl with wet black hair.

The man walking with Cat paused at the base of the knoll and glanced at the slope with weary assessment. Just past thirty, he was plainly out of condition. His thickening waistline was beginning to develop into a paunch which he had ceased attempting to hold in, muscles and energy flagging. When Cat realized he wasn't keeping up with her, she turned back.

"Are you coming, Mr. Macklin?"

"Do I have a choice?" he countered wryly, puffing slightly from the walk from the river. "I'm going to have to talk to your brother. Either he needs to move the house closer to the river or the river closer to the house. Nobody should have to walk up a hill like that after swimming all afternoon."

She laughed at his joking complaint and came back to his side. "Maybe I'd better help you," she declared, treating the situation in the same light vein, and he draped his arm around her shoulders in a mocking show of dependence.

Laughing, they started up the hill as a trio of riders entered the ranch yard. The instant Repp Taylor recognized Cat and failed to recognize the half-naked man in swimming trunks with his arm curved so familiarly around her shoulders, he spurred his horse away from the other two and aimed it at the slope. The drumming sound of approaching hooves quickly made itself heard and slowed the steps of the returning party as they glanced around with mild curiosity.

When Repp reined his horse to a stop a few feet short of Cat, his lean and rugged features wore a displeased look that had nothing to do with his hot and dusty appearance. "I want a word with you, Cat," he declared in an ominously flat voice and swung out of the saddle.

A little bewildered, Cat stepped away from the houseguest, whose arm had already slid off her shoulders. But her smile showed no confusion. "I'll be along directly." She assured the onlooking party that they needn't wait for her and went to meet Repp.

They started up the knoll again with Tara in the lead. "He's Cat's boyfriend," she murmured in explanation to her guests, showing an amused tolerance for the intensity of young love.

"What did you want, Repp?" Cat asked. Instead of looking at her, he was watching the party ascending the slope to the parked car. "Is something wrong?" She glanced hesitantly over her shoulder in the same direction.

He waited until the group was out of earshot before saying anything; then it was a low, rough demand. "What was the idea of letting that stranger hang all over you?"

"Mr. Macklin?" Her stunned reaction was quickly followed by an urge to laugh aloud at the realization Repp had been jealous. "That was a bit of harmless fun. He was joking that he couldn't make it up the hill, and I pretended to help him. That's all."

"Don't be so damned naive. That was just an excuse to get his hands on you." Impatience rippled through him like an angry wind. "You have no business being with a man twice your age to begin with."

"I wasn't 'with' him." She didn't like the way he was attempting to dictate to her. "All of us had spent the afternoon at the river swimming."

"That's the worst of it—you parading around half naked for a bunch of strange men to leer at you."

"I'm not going to listen to that kind of talk." Her lips were pressed firmly together as Cat turned stiffly to leave, infuriated by his attitude. But Repp grabbed her arm and swung her back.

"You stay away from them," he ordered.

"They're our guests," she insisted.

"Did you invite them?" Repp challenged.

"No, but—"

"Then it's not up to you to entertain them," he snapped.

With an angry jerk of her arm, she broke free of his grip. "Don't try to tell me what I can do, Repp Taylor," she warned.

"It's time somebody did." His voice lifted.

"Well, it isn't going to be you!"

"I'm telling you to stay away from them," Repp ordered again.

"No!" It was an angry refusal as she pivoted on her heel to stride away.

"You haven't proved anything! If you go on, all you're

going to do is get yourself into trouble!" Angered by her stubborn disregard for his warnings, Repp refused to trail after her.

Cat paused long enough to hurl a salvo back at him. "Then that's my problem, isn't it? I don't need any help from you!"

Snatches of their argument were carried on the lazy stillness of the afternoon air, but only one person was listening closely to the content. Dyson came around the car to stand beside Stricklin, both watching as Cathleen hurried to catch up with the others just cresting the knoll to the driveway.

"A lovers' spat," Dyson murmured in an amused aside to his partner.

"So it would seem," Stricklin agreed. No more was said on the matter as the party reached them and the talk became taken up with greetings and social banalities. In a loose collection, they moved toward The Homestead. Stricklin lagged behind to follow Cat into the house. "I hope the quarrel with your boyfriend wasn't a serious one," he murmured.

She paused, briefly surveying him with a cool and assessing eye. "I wouldn't let it concern you, Mr. Stricklin," she replied coldly, disliking his probing into her private affairs. Instead of joining the others for the refreshments awaiting their return, Cat went straight upstairs to her room, nursing her hurt and wounded outrage at Repp's criticism of her behavior.

The silence of the house pressed into the room. A pitch blackness outside made mirrors of the windowpanes in the study. Ty laid down his pen and wearily rested his elbows on the desktop to try to rub the tiredness out of his face and eyes. Then he paused, a hand covering his mouth and mustache, to stare at the summer-cold hearth of the stone fireplace. A fatigue that was both mental and physical pulled at him. Too many pressures from too many sides were crowding in on him, making him long for the contentment of other times. In his mind, Ty could see the leap of yellow flames on fireplace logs, and Jessy—the strong beauty of her features and that waiting look in her eyes. He ached to feel

Maybe it was finally coming to grips with reality. Maybe it was finally growing up and acknowledging that he had a responsibility to Tara . . . and to the marriage they had made. If he couldn't find the comfort he desired in his marriage, he had no right to seek it elsewhere. He owed it to himself and to Tara to prevent their marriage from becoming a sham. If the soul and the spirit had gone out of their relationship, leaving only the fiery side, then so be it.

The conviction in his voice gave Tara a sense of victory. All her confidence in ultimately winning out over her competition had been justified. Flushed with success, she bent her head to kiss him. Ty had a glimpse of the black hearth of the fireplace before her dark beauty blocked out any images that might have lingered for him. The warmth of Tara's body seemed to soak through him, bringing the fever—the hot hunger that was not nearly as consuming as it once had been.

A gate had been installed in the fenceline that separated the Shamrock Ranch from the Triple C range, providing easy access from one to the other. With practiced skill, Cat maneuvered her flashy paint gelding so she could open, then close the gate behind her without dismounting. She let the horse set its own lunging pace up the slope to the crest of the rimrock, spotted with clumps of pine. A faint trail led into the broken country, and Cat followed it.

She was still smarting from her argument with Repp, and dejected by it, too. At times like these, it seemed she had no one to whom she could turn. Once she could have gone complaining to her parents, but her mother was gone. Her father, who had always seemed strong enough and powerful enough to solve any problem, had become someone she wanted to protect from anything unpleasant. Ty was too busy, and Tara, who was sometimes exactly like an older sister, still regarded Cat's feelings as childish and never took them seriously. More and more, when the loneliness and insecurities crept in, Cat found herself seeking out her uncle so she could have the company of someone who cared.

Always in the past, Culley had intercepted her somewhere along the trail and they had ridden to his small ranch house together. This time she rode all the way to the yard without seeing any sign of him. Although she had never understood how he'd known she was coming the other times, it bothered her that he hadn't shown up yet. She dismounted in front of the house, scanning the empty yard, and tied the reins to the post supporting the roof of the front stoop. She walked to the screen door and tried to peer through the wire mesh to see inside.

"Uncle Culley?" she called out hesitantly. There was something eerie about the silence. "Uncle Culley!" Her voice lifted imperatively.

A small sound came from inside the house. There was something vaguely alarming about the situation. Although it hadn't crossed her mind before, it suddenly worried Cat that her uncle lived alone, completely isolated and far from help. If he were hurt or sick, who would know it?

"Uncle Culley?" She yelled loudly in case he was in the barn. "Are you here?" Somehow she didn't think he was outside, so she entered the house, closing the screen door quietly behind her and listening for any sound. "Uncle Culley?" Her voice sounded hollow in the silent house. The bedroom door was shut. She had barely taken a step toward it when it opened and her uncle came out, looking pale and disheveled, his shirt unbuttoned and half tucked inside his pants. His gray hair was springing in tousled disorder and gray wool socks covered his feet.

"I didn't expect you today, Cathleen." His voice didn't sound right, and he seemed stiff and awkward as he approached her. "I'm afraid you caught me napping."

He did appear to have just gotten out of bed, and some of her concern faded with his explanation. "I was starting to worry," she admitted. "I thought something might have happened to you." Then she caught a glimpse of something white wrapped around his middle where the unbuttoned front of his shirt gaped open. "You are hurt," she said in sharp accusation.

"Nothing for you to worry about." The waving gesture of his hand dismissed her concern. "I just banged up some ribs when a horse kicked me."

"You'd better let me have a look at it." There was a brisk

insistence in her voice as she reached for his shirt to see if he'd bound the injured ribs properly.

"No!" There was a sudden blaze of rejection in his eyes. "I told you I just bruised myself some. Now leave me alone."

"Look here, Culley O'Rourke. I can be just as stubborn as you," Cat warned.

"If you come over here to visit, we'll visit. But if you're just here to pry your nose into things that ain't your affair, you can just leave."

Cat stiffened as if she'd been slapped. Her uncle had never spoken to her like that. "It's plain to see I'm not wanted or needed. Nothing I do is right anymore." She swung away to walk to the door, her pride hurt and her feelings.

"Cathleen, I'm sorry. I—" The last was abruptly cut off by a stifled groan of pain, followed by the grate of a chair leg under some weight. Alarmed, Cat pivoted to see her ashen-faced uncle gripping the back of an armchair. She rushed to his side.

"You *are* hurt. I don't know why you tried to pretend it was nothing," she accused impatiently and helped him into the chair. When she attempted to lift aside his shirt, he protested weakly and tried to stop her. But it was too late when she saw the crimson stain seeping through the white. cloth bandage. "You're bleeding," she accused in a mixture of puzzled shock and alarm. "I thought you said you just bruised your ribs."

"It's just a scratch," he insisted as the faintness that had attacked him began to pass. "I'm okay, I tell ya."

"I'm not taking your word for anything," Cat retorted and began untying the crudely knotted bandages that held the cloth in place. She tried to be as gentle as she could be, but it obviously hurt when she lifted the pad off the wounded area. The sight of the long, jagged line of purpling red flesh ripped open nearly made her sick to her stomach. It was all she could do to keep from gagging. "Uncle Culley, you've got to go to the doctor and get this treated." Her limited experience in minor first aid didn't include a wound as serious as this.

"No." He shook his head, his face pale and drawn. "Just pour some disinfectant on it and put on a clean bandage."

"Uncle Culley, please," Cat pleaded with him to listen to

her. "I know you don't like doctors, but this isn't a scratch. Let me go get the doctor and bring him here. You could get poisoning or something."

"No. I can't go to a doctor. I can't let him see this." He gripped her hand, nearly crushing the bones of her fingers together. "Cathleen, you've gotta promise me you won't tell anyone about this."

"Why?"

Again, he shook his head. "Don't ask questions. Just promise me," he begged.

She looked into his pleading eyes, then at the raw, open wound, and slowly shook her head. "I can't promise that." It hurt her to deny him. "I don't want anything to happen to you. I've got to get the doctor." She started to pull away from him so she could ride to the ranch for help.

"No." He tried to call her back. "You don't understand, Cathleen. The doctor would have to report this to the sheriff."

"The sheriff?" Cat hesitated a foot away from him. "But why?"

There was a long moment when he seemed torn between answering her and keeping his silence. "Because . . . it's a bullet wound."

An incredulous light entered her eyes. "What?" His answer had completely thrown her. "But . . . why would anyone want to shoot at you? And why does it matter if the sheriff finds out?"

"Just believe me." He struggled against her questions. "I don't want you to get involved in this."

She came back to the chair and dropped onto her knees in front of him. "If you don't tell me what this is about, I'll go to the doctor and the sheriff myself," she threatened, because she was frightened by the failure of any of this to make sense. Culley was talking and acting mysterious and wild.

"I don't want to leave you, Cat." Tears shimmered in his eyes, but they weren't caused by pain. "But if the sheriff finds out, he'll arrest me . . . and I'll never see you again."

"But why would he arrest you?" she persisted.

"Because I . . . I know who killed your mother."

For a moment, his statement lay in the absolute stillness of the room while Cat stared at him. "What?" It was a small, little sound. She was almost convinced he was crazy. "She died in a plane crash."

"Caused by a broken oil line." He nodded. "But it didn't break on its own. It had help. Someone cut it partway through."

"How . . . how do you know that?" She was skeptical and hesitant, yet he sounded so convincing.

"Because . . ." An anguish swept through his expression. "Remember the night you met the Taylor boy in the hangar and you thought you heard something?"

"Yes." She nodded slowly. "Was that you?"

"No. It was him. I saw him tampering with something in the motor. After you and Taylor left and he'd sneaked away, I checked. I figured he'd done something to it, but I couldn't tell what."

"You mean . . . you knew something was wrong with that plane? You knew and didn't tell anyone?" She stared at him, drawing back when she realized the crash that had killed her mother and so severely injured her father could have been prevented.

"I didn't know for certain . . . I didn't know if he'd had enough time before you heard him. If I had known Maggie . . ." The torment was in his voice, a wretched sound to hear. "Don't you see, Cathleen? That's my punishment. I thought something was wrong with the plane, but I never told anyone. And . . . she died. Not your father. *She* died."

"How could you!" She began to sob angry tears, hurting all over again. "How could you kill my mother!" Her fists beat at his legs and thighs as she cried passionately and released all the stored-up violence that had been churning inside since her mother had died so suddenly.

Culley cried with her, more silently but with no fewer tears. When she had finally exhausted herself and lay crying on his knee, his hand touched her hair, barely stroking the shiny ends.

"Please don't hate me, Cathleen," he whispered hoarsely.

"Why? Why didn't you tell somebody?" It was a plaintive demand.

"Who would have believed me?" he reasoned sadly.

"Maybe he was clever and cut it where it wouldn't be seen. Maybe they wouldn't have found it even if I told them. And if they had found it, it was only my word that he'd done it. And they would have started asking what I was doing there . . . saying I did it." There was a long pause. "A lot of things happened before you were born, but it's never been a secret that I've never cared whether your pa was alive or dead. Folks have long memories around here. They remember ole Crazy Culley, and they'd have believed I did it, not him."

"Who did it, Culley?" She raised her tearstained face to look at him.

"Stricklin was in the hangar that night, probably carrying out Dyson's orders."

"No." She looked at him with disbelief.

"You see? Even you don't believe me."

The sadness in his eyes was touched with irony. Cat slowly began to understand his dilemma. Who would believe such a tale—especially coming from her uncle, who had been institutionalized for so many years? She felt the frustration of his hopelessness.

Conceding it was the truth, she had to ask, "But why would they do it?"

"Calder had something they wanted and he wouldn't let them have it, so they tried to get rid of him. Maggie just happened to get in the way." That's how he'd figured it. No matter how innocent a victim she had been, it didn't lessen his desire for revenge. When he attempted to shift his position in the chair, the movement pulled at the wound in his side, making him wince and go white with the splintering pain. Culley pressed the loosened bandage against the fleshy part of his waist.

"Let me put a clean dressing on that." Cat wiped the tears from her cheeks and rose to fetch new bandages. "How did this happen? Do you know who shot you?"

While Cat cleaned the wound with disinfectant the best she knew how and folded a torn section of a freshly laundered bedsheet, Culley answered her questions between grunts of pain. "Some security guard . . . over at Dyson's mine. I've been visiting there . . . nights and cutting the oil lines on . . . their equipment. Sometimes . . . pouring sugar in the gas tanks if . . . I haven't got time for . . . nothing else. I thought it might spook 'em and . . . flush them out into the open where they'd show their hand. I spooked 'em, all right. That place has . . . got more guards than a criminal ward. And I still can't prove nothing."

She taped the new dressing in place with small strips of adhesive. "I've done the best I can." The worry showed in her eyes that it might not be good enough. "But it really looks bad, Uncle Culley."

"No doctor," he repeated.

"I'll speak to Ty, explain everything you've told me to him and—"

"He isn't going to believe you." He shook his head sadly at the hope she placed in her big brother. "He's married to Dyson's daughter. He isn't going to believe anything against the man without proof."

"But what are we going to do? We just can't let them get away with it."

"They aren't going to get away with it," Culley assured her. "I'll think of something. They gotta be plenty uneasy now 'cause they know somebody knows something. We just gotta keep 'em worried. You work on a man's nerves long enough and he'll break. They're bound to be real jumpy right now, not sure who suspects what they've done. That's why you gotta promise not to tell anyone about this—not your father or brother—not the Taylor boy—no one," he insisted. "We can't risk letting anything slip."

"But—" Cat wanted to protest this secrecy, but she had no adequate argument against his reasoning. Who would believe a story like this, without proof? She had difficulty swallowing it herself, but she was convinced her uncle believed it.

"Do I have your word?" His earnest gaze searched her face.

"Yes," she agreed after a second's hesitation. She bit at the inside of her lip, still trying to figure out what she could do about doctoring his wound. "I'll fix you something to eat," she said. "Then I'm going to ride back to the ranch and see if I can't get some sort of medicine from the vet's office. I'll come back later tonight."

"Better not. If somebody sees you with it, they'll start

asking questions and they just might check up on any story you give 'em," he warned.

"I have to do something." Her frustration came through in the vehemence of her statement. "If you get infection—" She stopped, unwilling to voice the possible consequences. "I'll be careful. No one will see me, I promise. I'm just as good at it as you are." She tried to inject a light note into the conversation. "Look at how many times I slipped out to meet Repp without anyone finding out."

When she returned to The Homestead, the situation took on a terrible unreality. Twice after dinner, she almost called Ty aside to confide in him so he could tell her it was a lot of foolishness and make it something to laugh about. But her desire to protect her uncle was stronger. Regardless of his reasons, he could be arrested for what he'd done; maybe they'd put him away again. He trusted her, and she couldn't betray him like that.

With her head whirling with large doubts and small suspicions, she avoided spending any time in Dyson's or Stricklin's company, worried that she might unconsciously stare at them. There were plenty of houseguests to occupy their time as well as Ty and Tara's, so she doubted that her absence was noted when she took the key from the study and left The Homestead to get some medical supplies from the vet's office.

There were only two means of transportation available to her—a ranch vehicle or a horse. Using one of the ranch pickups might lead to questions about where she was going and the necessity for a nighttime visit to her uncle. Only in theory did she have the run of the ranch and could do just about anything she pleased because she was a Calder. At sixteen, she still faced certain restrictions, and permission might be withheld if her reasons were insufficient. Cat didn't want to make up any more stories than she had to in order to conceal her reasons. A late-evening horseback ride, supposedly for pleasure, was unlikely to arouse any curiosity, even though it would take a lot more time.

It was well after midnight when she returned to the ranch headquarters. Darkness had forced her to take more time on the way back. She rode straight to the stable, unsaddled her horse, and rubbed it down.

Only a couple of lights showed in the upper-floor windows of The Homestead, indicating the occupants had just recently retired. Guests invariably meant late nights, so Cat wasn't surprised to discover not everyone was in bed. She slipped into the house and moved through the darkened living room to the lighted staircase. Despite her try for silence, the steps creaked now and then under her weight.

At the top of the stairs, she turned to the hallway leading to her room and walked close to the railing where the flooring was more solid and the boarding was less inclined to grind together under her footsteps. The door to a room opposite from her was opened, and Cat turned with a guilty start. Her heart leaped into her throat when she found herself staring into Stricklin's opaque eyes. For an instant, panic raced wildly through her.

The lateness of the hour and the silence of the rest of the house made all the things Culley had told her about the man she faced seem very believable. He'd always struck her as being a cold fish; now that impression seemed especially chilling.

"You scared me." She finally forced out the honest admission. "I'm not supposed to be out past midnight. I thought I'd been caught." Cat watched him closely while she faked a smile, trying to see if he was going to buy her implication that she had been out with Repp.

The corners of his mouth curved upward, but she wasn't sure what that meant. "I was just on my way downstairs to see if I could find a book to read." He spoke as softly as she had, avoiding any comment on her weak explanation.

Cat was afraid to prolong the conversation, wary that the suspicions Culley had imbedded in her mind would not allow her to behave normally with him. Neither did she want to bolt from him like a frightened rabbit. A noise from one of the rooms offered her an excuse.

She glanced toward the sound and whispered a quick "Good night," then stole softly down the hallway to her room. Once the door was safely shut, Cat nearly laughed aloud with hysterical relief.

Stricklin was slow to descend the stairs, his mind clicking over the small details he'd noticed—the horsehair on her clothes, the length of time she'd been absent from the house, and the fear he'd seen in her eyes, not merely alarm. The vindictive pranks at the strip mine were just the kind of thing a teenager would dream up.

Alone in the study, Stricklin dialed the telephone number at the mine. The security chief answered.

"This is Stricklin. Has it been quiet so far tonight?" he asked.

"Quiet as can be," the guard assured him. "With all the floodlights we've got trained on the equipment, it's like daylight out here. There's no way anybody could get within thirty feet before they're seen."

"Good."

For a long time after he'd hung up, Stricklin sat in the chair by the desk and cleaned his fingernails. He wished for Dyson's intuition on the matter. As in a defensive chess game, he had blocked his opponent's initial strategy; now he was waiting for the next move, certain it was coming, but he lacked his partner's ability to anticipate where.

28

It began as a dark bruise on the sky, a gentle rumble of thunder in the distance. Then it spread, churning black clouds rolling to block out the sun with the suddenness and violence that accompanies the spawning of a thunderstorm on the plains. The hot, lank air caught a sudden cool breath, sweet with the smell of rain. The wind died, and absolute stillness settled onto the land.

Darkness rapidly descended under the fast-moving storm, and the air was suddenly split with ragged bolts of lightning, blue-white tongues of fire raining a death dance over the ground. The claps of lightning and booms of thunder came one on top of the other, vibrating the earth, while slanging rain sheeted down in torrents. It was a dramatic and awesome display of nature's violence. In fifteen minutes, it was over and past.

Thirty miles away at the Triple C headquarters, there had been no more than a whiff of rain smell in the air. Standing in the feedlot with puddles of water soaking into the sponge-dry ground, Ty looked at the destruction the storm had left in its wake. The carcasses of ten dead steers were crowded in a corner of the lot where they had bunched in a frightened, bawling mass during the storm, a large target for the ball of lightning that had exploded on them. The weight of their bodies had collapsed a section of fence, and the rest of the fat cattle in the lot had stampeded through it, three more steers trampled to death in the panicked melee. The sophisticated feeding machinery had been hit as well as the grain elevator. Half the grain in it was likely ruined by the inpouring rain.

The cost of the damage was staggering, none of it insured. With an operation the size of the Triple C Ranch, the theory had always been that it was big enough to absorb its losses. But there had been too many other drains on its reserves. There wasn't anything left to cushion the blow.

"I don't know what to say, Ty," Arch Goodman offered grimly. "I'll let you know how much grain we can salvage. With feed prices today, if we have to buy more grain, the fat cattle aren't bringing in enough on the market to offset the increase. We'll wind up going deeper in the red."

"We'll have to fatten most of them on grass and finish them with a couple weeks' worth of grain." It seemed the only viable alternative, even though it meant the cattle wouldn't bring top prices. More and more, circumstances were pushing him toward another decision.

"You aren't going to get top dollar for 'em that way," Arch warned, voicing what Ty had already considered.

"Do you think I don't know that?" Impatience put a sharp edge on his reply.

Goodman stiffened slightly at the harsh tone. "Looks like they rounded up the rest of the steers." He observed the trio of riders herding a small band of cattle toward the feedlots, his attitude stilted and cool. "I'll go give 'em a hand with the gate."

Tight-lipped, Ty simply nodded and covered his silence by lighting a cigarette while the man walked away. He shook out the match and dropped it on the wet ground where there was still enough moisture on the surface to make the match head sizzle faintly. A truck was backing into the yard to load up the carcasses of the dead cattle. Ty left the men to their job and angled to the fence to look over the steers being herded into an adjoining lot.

One was lame. The rest were probably a few pounds lighter from the run—valuable pounds. Ty made a climbing vault of the fence and stood on the other side to watch. Without conscious effort, he picked out Jessy among the trio of riders. When the gate had swung shut on the last of the animals, he waited. It seemed there was no end to the unpleasant decisions he had to make.

Jessy was on the outside of the riders as they came to the fence and dismounted. Her caramel hair was tucked under her hat, giving him a view of her long, slender neck. She gave him a clear-eyed look which skipped away to the feedlots. Then she turned her patrician-strong face to him.

"Some storm," she remarked idly.

"Yeah," he agreed. As he looked at her and heard the stiffness in their exchange, there seemed to be a lot of things he didn't need to say. Yet some things had to be said to make it final.

"This just adds to your problems, doesn't it?" Jessy said and looked again at the destruction the storm had left, some of it visible.

"Yes, it does." He struggled to find an easy way to lead into the things he wanted to say to her. He didn't want to be blunt. "There's been some grumbling among the boys. Some of them aren't happy about the way things have changed lately." She rested her gloved hands on the top rail of the fence, gripping it slightly and rocking back from it. "They claim they're spending more time catering to your guests than they are cowboying."

"They're lucky they're working at all." Irritation made his response sound curt. "I can just barely cover the payroll for the regulars now. Have they been complaining to you about their working conditions?"

"No. I've just heard talk. I thought I'd pass it along in case nobody had said anything to you." A shoulder lifted, attaching little importance to her knowledge of the issue.

And it did gall him a little to learn there was dissatisfaction among the ranks and he hadn't known about it till now. "There's not much I can do about it."

Jessy eyed him through shuttered lids. She sensed that he'd managed to lose touch with some basic things, not so surprising considering the pressure and responsibilities that had been heaped on him of late. Not to mention the constant stream of guests that had been at The Homestead. It was all those other demands on his time that she'd blamed for his not coming by her place. But looking at him, at the aloofness he wore like a barrier, she wondered if those demands were the only reasons.

"I suppose not," she said.

"Jessy—" Something in his voice flattened her heart, and she mentally braced herself. "What we had was good." Past tense.

"Yes, it was." She turned to meet him square on. "And I have no regrets."

Ty had some, but it seemed pointless to voice them. "I never set out to hurt you. I know I have."

"It doesn't matter." She slowly shook her head, her wide lips turned upward at the corner in a sad shadow of a smile. "I've always known she came first with you." She'd known it much longer than he realized. The sting of tears was in the back of her eyes. She looked away at the horizon, squinting a little to keep them in check. "It's probably best if I hand in my notice the end of the month."

"You once told me I was free to go or free to stay, whichever I wanted. Now I'll say the same to you." Ty didn't want to think of her being anywhere else but right here, where he could keep an eye on her and watch out for her. But it wasn't his right to ask that.

"Thanks, Ty." Her throat hurt, but pride insisted on a show of lightness. "I'd better get back to work before I'm accused of loafing on the boss's time."

When she climbed into the saddle, her head was held high. It was the only way to keep her chin from quivering. It hurt to breathe; it hurt to live. A long time ago her mother had told her that no woman had ever conquered loneliness. It was an endless battle, especially in these lonely spaces.

As Ty watched her ride away, he swore he'd never met a more honest woman. There had been no commitments, no promises between them, and she had not pretended she had been wronged by him. She was as honest about this as she had been about her emotions. He felt the lesser for it. But Tara's ripe beauty waited for him—the kind men spun dreams around.

Halfway to the headquarters, he spied a wet-looking and bedraggled Cathleen riding her paint horse along the road's grassy shoulder just ahead of his pickup. He slowed the truck to a crawl as he pulled alongside her.

"Did you get caught in that downpour?" He smiled at the sodden state of her clothes. It would take them a long time to dry even in the warm sun.

"How did you guess?" she shot back with a snap of sarcasm, wet and miserable.

"Tie your horse to the tailgate and I'll give you a ride."

Cat wasted no time accepting his offer as she reined her horse to the rear of the truck and dismounted to knot the reins to the bumper. Then she hurried to the front and climbed into the passenger side of the cab, her feet squishing in her wet boots.

"Cold?" Ty flicked a glance at her.

"No. Just wet." Everything stuck to her as she tried to settle back in the seat. "I was just crossing that open stretch between Culley's gate and the river when the sky opened up. I tried to make the trees, but I was soaked to the gills by the time I got under them."

"You were at Culley's again?" Ty drove slowly, glancing frequently into the rearview mirror at the reflection of the paint horse. "You've been going there nearly every day this week."

She nervously licked her lips. No one had commented on it, so she didn't think anyone had noticed the frequency of her visits. "He . . . hasn't been feeling well."

"Why didn't you say so?" Ty frowned at her.

"It was just a mild case of the flu," she said quickly. "He was up and around today. I think he liked me coming over and fussing with him, which is probably why it took him so long to get well."

"More than likely," he agreed, smiling vaguely as his thoughts began to wander to other, more pressing matters.

The minute Dyson got off the telephone, he summoned Stricklin into his office. He had a drink poured and ready to put in his hands when he walked in.

"What's this?" Stricklin looked blankly at the drink he'd been given.

"You've heard the old superstition that bad news travels in threes. Well, so does good news," Dyson declared and clinked his glass against his partner's. "First, it's been nearly two weeks since we've had any trouble at the plant. Second, we were granted the mineral rights to that parcel of land on the Calder ranch. And third—" He paused for effect. "I just talked to Ty on the phone. He's been considering my proposal for a joint venture on this strip-mining operation and wants us to come so we can discuss it in more detail."

"He said that?" Stricklin was slow to join Dyson's celebrative mood.

"We've got ourselves a deal." He saluted Stricklin with his glass and downed a swallow, smiling broadly. "And you were so worried a week ago," he chided. "So certain there had to be some reason why Ty was holding out. I told you there was no cause to be suspicious. We have a kingdom of coal and all the water we need now that he's joining forces with us."

"Maybe there's another reason why he wants us to come to Montana. Maybe he's just using the deal as an excuse," Stricklin suggested, his mind cautiously turning over the possibilities.

"No." Dyson shook his head in a very positive fashion. "He's buying the deal. With Chase out of the picture, it's happening just the way I knew it would."

"Yes." It was a somewhat absent agreement from Stricklin as he took a contemplative sip of his drink, then a second with more confidence in his manner. "I'll begin rearranging our schedule so we can leave for Montana first thing in the morning."

Cat watched the car pull away from The Homestead with her brother at the wheel, again accompanied by E. J. Dyson and his partner, George Stricklin. The trio had been practically inseparable since Dyson's plane landed at the Triple C's private airstrip the day before.

It was becoming more difficult for her to believe the pair had perpetrated the deed her uncle suggested. She had known E. J. Dyson all her life, Stricklin, too, for that matter. Even before Ty had married Tara, Dyson had been a friend of the family. Her father had strongly differed with him over the issue of strip-mining, but he had continued to show respect for him.

None of her uncle's suspicions seemed plausible. She knew how much Culley had loved her mother—worshiped her almost. Cat was nearly convinced he was trying to blame someone for her death because it was the only way he could reconcile her passing in his mind.

"Cat, what's the matter with you?" Repp's impatient voice cut into her thoughts.

She half turned, looking at him blankly for an instant. "I'm sorry. I was just . . . thinking." His dark gaze tried to peel away the layers of her preoccupation to find the source of it. She wanted to tell him the awful secret Culley had given her to carry, but it had begun sounding too incredible.

Her troubled eyes bothered him. A week ago she had assured him their jealous argument was forgotten. But something was still gnawing on her mind and she wouldn't tell him about it.

"Thinking about what?" Repp probed. "Your father? When you visited him Sunday, you said he was doing much better."

"He is. There's a numbness in his legs, and the doctor said that was a very good sign because it means he's getting some feeling back." There was still the need for more operations, more therapy. Recovery was still in the future.

Even if she had wanted to sound out her father on a few of

the things that were troubling her, she hadn't been given the opportunity. Ty had taken up most of their visiting time bringing him up to date on the situation at the ranch.

"Then what is it?" he persisted.

"Nothing, I told you." Cat tried to laugh off the questions that made her uncomfortable and glanced past him at the pickup idling a few feet away. The cowboy at the wheel impatiently gunned the motor. "You'd better go. I'll let you know about the party Saturday night."

"Do that." Repp was almost curt with her, irritated by her stubborn refusal to admit anything was wrong when he knew damned well there was. He walked to the truck and swung onto the passenger seat. He didn't look at her again until the truck was driving out of the yard. She was wandering aimlessly in the direction of the airstrip. Maybe she was still depressed over her mother's death. It might account for her moodiness.

Cat hadn't set out with the intention of going to the private airfield, but when she saw the hangar shed, she gravitated toward it, drawn by the memory of that night when the deed was supposedly done. A midday sun was broiling the flat stretch of earth, creating wavy heat lines on the hangar's tin roof. The wind made the only sound, running across the ground and billowing the directional windsock.

When Cat wandered into the cool shade of the hangar, the peaceful quiet was broken by the clang of something metal being dropped. She froze. "Who's there?" she demanded.

A head popped up from behind the cowling of the twin-engine airplane parked in the shed. Dyson's pilot appeared nearly as startled as Cat. "Hello," he said. "I didn't hear you come."

She ducked under a wing to walk around to his plane. "What are you doing?" she inquired curiously. A tool kit was at his feet, and grease-stained tan coveralls protected his clothes.

"Just checking the motor." The blue-eyed man had the slim build of a man much younger than his forty-plus years. His business was flying and he took it seriously, giving the plane his attention even as he responded to her inquiry. "Stricklin didn't think it sounded right when we flew in yesterday. He's gotten downright nervous about safety—wants everything checked and double-checked. I guess he forgets I'm flying in this bird, too."

"There's something I've been wondering about. Maybe you could answer it." Cat chewed hesitantly on her inner lip, trying to word her question cautiously. "After a plane's crashed, how can they tell what caused it?"

"Well . . . they piece together the wreckage. A good mechanic can usually tell you what was damaged on impact and what probably malfunctioned before the crash, presuming the cause was mechanical." He paused to wipe his hands on a rag before shutting the access door to the engine's motor. "Now, you take your father's plane crash, oil would have spewed everywhere when that line ruptured."

"But . . . could they determine why the line broke?"

His eyebrows lifted at her question. He considered it a minute, then shrugged diffidently. "I suppose they could. But I don't know what they'd accomplish by doing it unless they were checking to see if it was a factory defect or something like that."

"Are you saying that once they find a cause they don't investigate it further . . . unless they have reason to believe something else might be wrong?" A small frown made lines in her forehead.

"They make their decision on a collection of information. The wreckage, eyewitness accounts, and, in this case, your father could verify the sudden drop in oil pressure since he was piloting the plane." He shifted uncomfortably. "It's pretty well cut and dried what happened. Private planes go down all the time. It isn't like a big airliner where a lot of lives are involved and liability has to be determined."

"I see," Cat murmured thoughtfully, then glanced at the man, smiling vaguely. "You're right, of course."

"Listen, I—" He was bothered by her questions about the plane crash, concerned that he hadn't given her satisfactory assurances that the investigation had been handled properly.

"No, it's okay," she interrupted him. "I understand."

He hesitated, studying her; then his attention fell to his dirty hands. "Guess I'd better wash up. I got that grimy oil under my fingernails. It really takes some digging to get them clean."

A mental image flashed before her mind's eye of Stricklin sitting in the study that night cleaning his fingernails . . . with a dirty knife! She had forgotten all about that until the pilot's comment reminded her of it. It didn't exactly prove anything, but still . . .

"See you later," she said to the pilot and left the hangar, walking swiftly toward The Homestead.

There was no one about the front room when she entered the house; both Tara and the new housekeeper were occupied elsewhere. Cat slipped into the study, unseen, and closed the doors. She was determined to either prove or disprove her uncle's suspicions about the cause of the crash and end this agonizing doubt once and for all. It took her several phone calls before she finally reached the man who'd been in charge of investigating her father's plane crash.

"Yes, I remember the case." He assured her of his familiarity with it. "We completed the investigation and we filed our final report a couple months ago. It was a mechanical failure, as I recall, a ruptured oil line."

"But what caused it?" Her hand tightly gripped the receiver. Cat sensed the hesitation on the other end of the line. "Could you tell if someone had tampered with it—partially cut through it or something like that?"

"Well, I hardly think—" His tone of voice was attempting to dismiss the idea.

"Please," Cat interrupted him before he could reject the possibility. "I have to know if that happened."

"Do you know what you're suggesting?"

"Yes," she said firmly. "That someone deliberately caused that plane to crash."

"I tell you, Ty, I couldn't be more pleased that we've all agreed on the same site," Dyson declared as they gathered in the dining room to take their places for the evening meal. "Out of the possible locations we could have selected on that parcel, I believe we've picked the best for the new coal plant. We have a dependable water source right on the doorstep and a wide underseam of high-quality bituminous not a hundred yards away. In the first years, we can mine almost in a circle around the new plant. It will make for a highly efficient and economical operation, as well as a highly profitable one."

"How soon do you anticipate generating an income from this?" Tara asked, then motioned to the housekeeper-maid to forgo the tasting of the white wine and fill the goblets around the table. She smiled at Ty, her dark eyes gleaming with pride and excitement for the further realization of her dreams.

"That's the beauty of it." Dyson was in ebullient spirits. "With our existing operation at the Stockman place, we have the men and machinery on hand to begin mining the coal as soon as we have access roads graded to the site. The coal plant itself will obviously require some construction time, but we'll use the Stockman plant during the interim. The cash turnover will begin almost immediately."

Cat had been listening to the business discussion with only half an ear, paying little attention to what was said. Her thoughts were preoccupied with the phone conversation she had had, as well as struggling against the prickling awareness of her dining companions. She reached for the linen cloth at her place setting to unfold it and lay it across her lap.

"Since your attorney will have the papers ready for our signature tomorrow," Dyson was saying as he picked up his wineglass, "I don't think it's premature to drink a toast to our new partnership, do you, Ty?"

His action attracted Cat's attention. Startled by his announcement, she accidentally knocked her salad fork off the table. It clattered noisily to the floor, drawing everyone's attention to her.

"Sorry, I—" She didn't bother to finish the apology as she stared at Ty. "What's this about a partnership?"

"E.J. and I are going into the coal business together," he replied smoothly. His rawly handsome features held an expression of calm decision, irrevocable and firm, as Ty lifted his glass to Dyson.

"I've looked forward to this day ever since you and Tara were married." Dyson wore a very self-satisfied look, and Cat stared at him, hearing the trace of premeditation in his statement. Her glance swung to Stricklin and fell away immediately when she saw he was watching her from behind those thick lenses of his glasses. Harassed by doubts and unproven suspicions, she kept silent.

All through dinner she listened to their talk of coal with growing trepidation—the potential tonnage that could be mined annually, sale negotiations with various high-usage companies, the fortunes to be realized. All the while the fear kept nagging at her that her brother was going into business with the two men who might be responsible for their mother's death.

At the meal's conclusion, Cat managed to waylay Ty before he could follow the others into the living room for coffee. "You can't do it," she insisted, trying to keep her voice low. "You can't go into business with them, Ty."

"It's done." His glance was hard, although his voice held patience.

"You haven't signed the papers yet," she reminded him earnestly. "It isn't too late to change your mind yet." She knew she had to give him a reason. Without proof, she was reluctant to tell him of her suspicions, brainwashed by Culley's many protests that she wouldn't be believed. "You know how Dad feels about mining coal. You can't do this."

"Financially, I have no choice." His mouth thinned out. "I'm in charge, Cathleen. You were at the hospital last Sunday. You heard him say it was up to me. It's my responsibility to see that we start bringing in some money, any way I see fit. Which is exactly what I'm doing. There isn't any room for sentiment in business decisions, although you're probably too young to understand that."

"It isn't that at all," Cat protested. "What if I told you that—"

"Ty?" Tara appeared in the archway. "Aren't you having coffee with us?" She glanced from Ty's hard features to the desperate and beseeching look on his sister's face. "What's the problem, Cathleen?" She smiled indulgently. "Won't Ty relent on his midnight curfew edict for the party Saturday night? I'll speak to him about it for you. In the meantime, I'm going to steal him away from you. Daddy has a lot of details he wants to discuss with him."

Her chance was gone; so was the urge to tell him what she and Culley suspected. Just seeing Tara reminded Cat that her brother was unlikely to believe his wife's father was capable of doing such a thing. She wasn't sure herself.

29

No announcement was made; no word was given out. But when the first surveyor stepped onto Calder land to stake out a new road, the news reverberated across the Triple C like a shock wave.

The pickup had barely rolled to a stop in front of The Homestead when Jessy came charging out of it, up the steps and through the front door. A tautness claimed every long inch of her as she demanded of the first person she saw, "Where's Ty? I want to see him."

Tara stiffly faced her, icily controlled. "I don't think he wishes to see you."

"I don't give a damn what he wants, and put your claws back in," Jessy retorted, having no time for petty jealousies. "I've already handed in my notice and I'll be drawing my pay and leaving at the end of the month. Where is he? In the study?"

"He's busy." She tried to block the way to the open doors of the study, but Jessy moved lithely around her.

"This won't take long," she promised grimly.

The half-raised voices had already aroused Ty's attention. He was just stepping out from behind the desk when Jessy burst into the room and stopped, her hands resting on her hips in a challenging stance.

"There's just one thing I want to know." Her voice was flat and hard, like the look in her hazel eyes. "Is it true?"

There was a second's pause when Ty almost pretended not

to know what she was talking about. Then he dropped his gaze and made a half turn to the desk to pick up some papers. "Yes, it's true. The Triple C is now in the coal-mining business." The tension in the room was thick and oppressive, licking at his nerves.

"I didn't want to believe it when I heard it," Jessy declared. "I thought you were a Calder. I thought you had some feeling for this land."

His decision had raised a clamor of disapproval among the veteran hands. It rankled Ty that he was being made to feel an outsider again when his sole interest was in keeping the ranch from going broke. It hardened his stand against her.

"Was there anything else you wanted?"

"I want you to take a ride with me. There's something I'd like to show you," she stated, not altering her challenging stance one degree.

"I'm busy just now." Ty didn't wish to argue with her over his decision. It seemed simplest to avoid any opportunity to do so.

"You aren't so busy that you can't spare one hour." Anger trembled through her control. "Have I ever asked you for anything, Ty?" she demanded when he hesitated. "Well, I'm asking *this* from you now!"

A heavy breath came from him. "All right. I'll go with you." With a gesture of irritation, he shoved the papers onto his desk, then reached for his hat to jam it onto his head and follow her out of the room. Tara was instantly at his side, subtly attempting to detain him. "It's business, Tara." He sharply brushed aside her veiled protests and left the house with Jessy.

Not a word was exchanged as he climbed into the passenger side while Jessy slid behind the wheel. With smooth efficiency, she put the truck into motion and swung it away from The Homestead and onto the ranch road leading east from the headquarters. She showed him no more of her face than the strong-boned lines of her profile, her skin tanned brown and sun creases spreading out from the corner of her eye.

For a long time, the only sounds were the rush of wind over the truck and the loud hum of the motor. Behind him, a rifle rattled in the gun rack mounted across the cab's rear window, a fixture in nearly every ranch vehicle. The grass-covered plains yellowing under the summer sun were a blue smear outside his window as the truck sped along the road. Ty thoughtfully rubbed his mouth, his mustache scraping the top of his finger, as he tried to guess at the unknown destination.

"Where are we going?" he finally asked after they had turned onto the highway, then shortly turned off of it again to bump along a rutted, overgrown track.

"We're almost there." She was equally abrupt.

The rutted tracks disappeared into a tangle of thistle-choked weeds. The truck bounced to a stop when it ran out of trail in the middle of nowhere. Jessy switched off the motor and climbed out of the pickup without explanation. Impatiently, Ty put a shoulder to the passenger door, opening it and swinging down.

A debris of rotted, broken wood and torn strips of black tarpaper was scattered about the weeds. It appeared to be an old dumping ground for trash. Ty looked around him with an expression of disgust and scantly concealed irritation for being brought here.

"Watch where you step," Jessy advised him when he started forward. "There's an old cistern buried around here somewhere."

"What is this place?" His glance sliced to her.

"This is where your grandmother used to live," she told him. "She was a homesteader."

Ty looked again at the scattered debris. He knew little about his grandmother, other than the fact that she had died shortly after his father was born. There was so little he knew about his family's background. Jessy was more knowledge-able about his family's history than he was. It grated nerves that were already irritated.

"In those days, they called them honyockers or nesters." Her gaze was turned out to scan the sparse and scrubby plant life. "I wanted you to see what the plow did to this land. It used to be covered with grass—as thick and tall as the grass you find today on the Triple C."

His glance ran over her tight-lipped and angry expression.

She stood tall beside him, stiff with resentment. When she turned her narrowed and clear-eyed look on him, he noticed again the strength in her features, clean of any makeup.

"Look at it," she ordered. "Because this is what happens when you rip up this earth. It's eroded and windburned; not even the weeds can hold it together. Three hundred acres could maybe support one cow."

"It needs to be seeded . . . reclaimed." Ty conceded the land was in sorry condition, more desert than plain.

"Do you think it hasn't been tried? Millions of acres of land were torn up like this." Her voice vibrated with her effort to keep it controlled. "The native grasses wouldn't come back. New kinds have been planted; some of the hardier ones have taken hold, but it takes a lot of care and work and water. It's been fifty years and there's still places like this. Are you willing to destroy the land for the coal underneath it? Destroy it not just for your use but your children's, too?"

"Dammit, Jessy! I don't have any choice!" he snapped under the increasing pressure of her censure. "I need the money to keep the ranch going."

"What ranch?" she argued. "There won't be anything left when they finish gobbling up all the coal. What are you saving, a place that will be a scrub desert in thirty years?"

"You don't seem to understand." He tried to control his temper.

"No, you don't understand!" Jessy retorted. "You are doing it for money—for profit. It's business, you say. It's progress. You've been given a legacy, Ty. A tradition that has prided itself on caring for the land and people. You're going to lose both because you think money is more important. People built this ranch. The only way it could ever be destroyed is from the inside. And you're the core of it. If the heart is no good, the rest of it will slowly die."

It was a long moment before Ty offered any response. "You've made your point," he said.

In silence, they made the long drive back to the ranch headquarters. Her words hammered in his mind all the way. When Jessy dropped him off at The Homestead, nothing was said; simple courtesies seemed superfluous at this point.

Tara attempted to besiege him with questions, but Ty stayed in the house just long enough to get the keys to the single-engine aircraft, then left again. After taking off from the runway, he flew over the site picked for the jointly ventured coal plant, surrounded by rolling, grass-covered terrain with its rich deposit of low-sulfur coal inches below the surface. The road surveyors were colored dots in the grass, their vehicles the size of a child's toys viewed from the plane's altitude.

Banking the plane to the east, Ty continued his flight over the scrub prairies where grass struggled for survival against the erosion of wind and rain, and against the sturdy weeds. Then he changed his course to fly to the Stockman place.

A large green blanket of carefully nurtured grass offered a marked contrast to the black coal pit with its haze of dust and crawling machinery. But the reclaimed area suddenly appeared small when compared to the trail of chewed-up earth the monster shovel had devoured as it followed the underground coal seam.

When he returned to The Homestead, there was a lift to his shoulders and more authority in his rolling stride. He went straight to the study, called his father at the hospital, and advised him of his decision to break the contract with Dyson.

"I'm glad." His father's voice sounded choked, but it came back strong. "What are you going to do now that you won't have that money?"

"Cut down to a bare-bones operation." Ty told him some of his plans, to which his father added his suggestions. Together they arrived at a workable program. It wouldn't solve the ranch's financial woes, but it gave them a chance to ride it out to better times.

"What about Dyson?" his father questioned. "He'll fight you—son-in-law or not."

"It's possible," Ty conceded.

"Don't wait to find out," his father advised him, and they discussed the best way to block any moves Dyson might make. "You'll have to watch him. He's clever, very clever."

"I will."

After the phone conversation with his father was finished,

Ty began making calls to summon the managers of the various operations and outlying camps to the headquarters.

Over the next hour and a half, they trickled in one by one from their various districts. Most of them were stiff and cool toward him, ready to take his orders but not ready to like them. They had lost trust in his judgment; his previous decision had gone against the values they'd been brought up to believe. But their opinion underwent a change once they heard what he had to say.

"When a man's made a mistake, he's got two choices." Ty said the same thing to Wyatt Yates that he'd told the others before the manager of the horse-breeding operation had arrived. "He can grit his teeth and bull his way along, pretending that he's right. Or he can own up to his mistake and do his damnedest to change it. I thought mining coal was the answer to the financial problems we've been having. But it's only going to bring more problems. I'm going to break the deal and fight to stop it."

"Do you think you can do it?" Yates eyed him, still wary.

"I won't know if I don't try." Ty wisely didn't claim he could do anything. "In the meantime, I want you to get on the phone and start calling breeders around the country and sell those two studs. Find buyers for all the young stock you can, except for that two-year-old stud out of that San Peppy mare. We'll keep him back for future foundation sire. Keep the Cougar-bred mares and sell the rest."

His instructions to Arch Goodman were similar when he came. "Sell off all the fat cattle in the feedlot and save the grain to fatten our young stuff coming off the range this fall. We're cutting our losses now before the cattle market drops any lower."

"Dumping that many cattle in a depressed market is liable to drive the prices down still more," Arch warned.

"At the moment, I can't worry about what lower prices are going to do to the other guy. Make arrangements to get the cattle shipped, and get the best price you can for them."

As Arch left the study, Tara came in. There was curiosity behind her smile. "What's going on here this afternoon? People constantly coming and going all the time?"

"I'm implementing some more cost-cutting measures, ranchwide," he replied, still businesslike in his tone, although the look in his eye gentled under the stroking touch of her hand. "Some of which you aren't going to like."

"Such as?" She cocked her head to one side.

"You're going to have to give your cook and that house-keeper notice that we won't be needing their services after the end of the month," Ty stated.

"You can't be serious." The smile left her face as she reacted first with incredulity, then with indignation. "You can't do that. I need them. We have guests coming nearly every weekend for the rest of the summer."

"You'll simply have to explain to your guests that they'll either have to make their own beds and wash their own dishes or entertain themselves while you do it. This is a working ranch, not a hotel equipped with maids and room service."

"I have never heard anything so absurd in my life," Tara flashed. "These are important people. I can't ask them to come out to the kitchen and wash the dishes."

"Who knows? They might get a kick out of it." He shrugged lightly.

"Well, I'm not going to find out," she informed him, breathing deep and fast in anger. "Neither Simone nor Mrs. Thornton is leaving. This is my house, and you're not going to tell me how to run it. I don't tell you how to run the ranch."

"You're wrong. This is *our* house and *our* ranch. The house isn't strictly your domain and the ranch mine. Both belong to both of us," Ty argued roughly.

"I don't care about the ranch or what you do with it. I've told you dozens of times to hire a manager and let him run it, but you wouldn't listen to me."

"I listened and disagreed."

"Then I'm disagreeing with you about letting Simone and Mrs. Thornton go," Tara countered.

"I've had to cut expenses all the way across the board—that includes the household budget. So if you want to pay them out of your own money, that's your business."

"Why are you so worried about money again?" Impatience and confusion ran hotly through her voice. "I thought the

partnership with Daddy settled all that. There will be more than enough money for everything once you start selling the coal."

"There won't be any money because there isn't going to be any coal sold," Ty stated flatly as the front door opened.

"What do you mean? Since when?" But her questions were interrupted by the sound of Dyson's voice calling out her name. "In here, Daddy!" she answered and started across the room to meet him when he entered. "Ty was just telling me some nonsense that you wouldn't be selling the coal. I—"

Ty interrupted her before she could go further, standing as Dyson darted him a puzzled glance. "I'm glad you're here, E.J. I was just about to explain to Tara that I've decided to back out of our deal."

"I don't understand." Dyson laughed his confusion. "It's all been agreed. What is it? Aren't you satisfied with the terms? Do you feel you're entitled to a larger split?"

"I'm not objecting to the terms. It's the use of the land I don't like. There isn't going to be any strip-mining on Calder property." Ty made his announcement and glanced at Stricklin standing in the doorway, listening and letting Dyson do all the talking. "I suggest we dissolve this partnership amicably and forget it."

"She had something to do with this, didn't she?" Tara accused. "You were in favor of it until she came to see you this afternoon."

"Let's leave Jessy out of this discussion." It was a quiet warning. He refused to let her name be dragged through a family argument. "She may have opened my eyes to a few things, but the decision was mine."

"We have a deal, Ty," Dyson reminded him, dropping his cajoling attitude. "It's all signed and legal."

"And I'm telling you I'm breaking it. Now, we can either do it amicably or not. It's up to you." His gaze leveled on the man, offering the opportunity to avoid an unpleasant confrontation.

"You're not thinking straight, boy," Dyson insisted. "In my business, a deal's a deal. It's a little late to change your mind now."

"It's never too late," Ty corrected. "Maybe I need to make myself clear. You have twenty-four hours to get your surveyors off my land. There will be no road. There will be no strip mine. There will be no coal plant."

"And I'm telling you we have a legal agreement," Dyson tersely reminded him.

"Then you'd better sue me for breach of contract!" Ty snapped.

"You're forgetting something. I hold the mineral rights to that land. I don't need you for a partner. I made the deal with you because I thought it was the honorable thing to do so we could all share in the wealth. But if you're going to welsh on the deal, you don't deserve any of the money. There's a fortune out there, and if you're too dumb to see it, I'm not." It was almost a threatening tone, advising Ty that he was going ahead with the plans with or without him. "I thought you had some smarts, boy. But this is a dumb move. We're going to take that coal out of that ground. And the way it stands now, you aren't going to get a dime."

"Now it's you who's forgetting something," Ty replied in a deadly level voice. "That chunk of ground you're talking about is landlocked. And you'll play hell crossing Calder property to get to it."

"I've done my best to avoid a fight with you—for Tara Lee's sake—but you've backed me into a corner," Dyson warned. "Whatever happens, it's your doing—you started it." Stiff with anger, he turned to his daughter, a turbulent figure of contained fury at his side. "I'm sorry, Tara Lee, but you see how it is." He threw another dark look at Ty, then swung to his partner. "Come on, Stricklin, let's get out of here."

As the two men left the study, Ty watched Tara struggling with her temper, all the volatile emotions enriching the vibrancy of her dark beauty. Slowly she crossed the room to him, the reluctance in her body showing that it went against her pride to plead with him.

"How can you do this?" Then suddenly, unexpectedly, she was pressing her body against him, her fingers curling into his shirt with a kind of desperation. "Don't do it, Ty. Please."

His arms went around her as he bent and kissed her silky black hair. "Try to understand, Tara. It's not what I want to do. It's what I *have* to do . . . for the ranch . . . for the heritage of the land."

With a negative swaying of her head that brushed his chin, she resisted the finality of his words. She lifted her determined, insistent dark eyes to his face while her hands came up to stroke his jaw in frantic little caresses.

"It isn't too late to change your mind, Ty," Tara urged. "I can talk to Daddy and smooth it all out. I'll just explain to him that you were confused for a little while." Her hands tugged at his head to force it down while her hot, eager lips rushed onto his mouth, kissing him in a wildly anxious way. "He'll understand." Between bites, she breathed the words into his mouth. "I know he will." Her heated lips worked on him, awakening the heavy impulses that made him tighten his arms around her. "Everything will be all right. You'll see." Confidence ran through her.

"Tara, no." The rasping pitch in his voice showed his level of disturbance while he roughly trailed his mouth across her cheek. "I'm not going to change my mind."

Her hands pushed at his chest to arch her body away from him. "But you made an agreement with him. You gave him your word on it. I thought your promise was supposed to mean something."

"I have a prior commitment that's in direct conflict with the deal I made with your father." His voice was still husky as he tried to convince her. "It has to take precedence."

"How can you be such a fool?" Tara broke out of his arms, angry and disgusted with him again. "Do you realize how rich we could be? There's a fortune lying out there."

"And that's where it's going to stay."

"No, it won't. Daddy's company will take it—all of it. And half of it can be yours if you'll only listen to me."

"No." Ty was adamant, unswayed by her appeals or demands.

"If you can throw away a chance like this, then our marriage obviously means very little to you." She stood indignantly erect, proud and strong-willed. "You're willing to sacrifice our future, which means you don't care if we have one. I think you've made that very plain."

"Tara—" A heavy sigh broke from him.

"When my father walks out of this house, I'm going with him."

It irritated him that she was using this issue to test his love. "Don't make idle threats, Tara," he snapped.

It was the wrong thing to say. He had called her bluff and forced her into playing out her hand. Ultimately, they both would be losers in the game. With an anger that was almost regal, Tara walked from the room. Ty couldn't call her back, because neither of them had left room for compromise.

An hour later, he was on the telephone when he heard the bang of suitcases on the stairs. His attorney's voice barely registered in his mind as Ty listened to the sounds of departure—the footsteps, the opening and closing of doors, car doors, and trunks, and the starting of a motor.

Suddenly, the front door opened and light footsteps entered the house. Just for a minute, Ty let himself admit how much he needed support and understanding from his wife at this crucial juncture. But it was his sister, Cathleen, who appeared in the doorway.

"Where's Tara going? She didn't say anything to me about leaving." Cat had to wait for her explanation until he was off the phone.

With the passage of the first twenty-four hours, a tense waiting game began. Sooner or later, Dyson was going to make a move. For Ty, it was a matter of trying to anticipate when he would make it and what it would be, so he could be prepared to block it. Everyone on the ranch was put on the alert with orders to first report the presence of any outsider to headquarters, then escort the trespasser off Triple C range with whatever force was necessary. Ty shifted all the hands he could spare from their regular duties into the northeast district of the ranch. It involved a major reallocation of riders, which included Jessy being temporarily transferred to the lower east camp at Wolf Meadow.

Her route across the ranch had her traveling over a section

of the main road leading east to Blue Moon. Dust plumed behind the pickup as she headed into the high-angling light of a morning sun. Her attention was on the road, watching for the south turnoff. She wouldn't have noticed the hidden vehicle at all if the sunlight hadn't hit its window just right and reflected a glare into her eyes.

Wincing at the painfully brilliant flash, she jerked her head to the side to avoid it. At the same moment, she became alert to her surroundings and slowed the truck to scan the rugged, rolling land to locate the cause of that sudden glare. Jessy was almost ready to decide it had been some broken glass along the roadside and her brief alarm had been unnecessary when she spotted a four-wheel-drive vehicle. The squatty-nosed jeep was well hidden, back from the road in a wide coulee, its dark green color blending in with thick-growing chokecherry bushes.

With no hesitation, she shifted the pickup into low gear and turned off the road to bounce over the rough terrain to search for the driver. In the meantime, she reached for the mike of the citizens'-band radio and relayed the news of her discovery back to the base station at the headquarters. The trail turned out to be so simple to follow, it was almost laughable. Stakes with little red flags marched out in a row, leading Jessy directly to the surveying crew.

The rattling rumble of her truck bumping over the rough ground gave them ample warning of her approach, but they boldly remained in the open, the three of them grouped around the tripod-mounted trans. Jessy circled them to stop in their paths, then reached behind her to take the .30/.30 from its window rack before climbing out of the truck. The rifle was held loosely, the butt tucked under her armpit and the muzzle lowered at the ground. Thirty feet separated her from the men.

"You're trespassing. Take your gear and get moving," she ordered smoothly.

"We're on government land. And we're here doing a job." The man in the khaki jacket made the response.

"You're inside the Calder fenceline." Jessy didn't argue the rightful ownership of the land. "My orders are to escort any trespassers off Triple C range." She shifted her hold on the rifle to bring the barrel level. "I'll tell you again to get moving."

Next came that instant of anger when a man's been physically threatened by a woman. "I suggest you put that rifle up before you find yourself in trouble!" the surveyor retorted.

"You're the one that's in trouble, mister." When he took an angry step toward her, Jessy cocked the rifle and squeezed off a shot that whined two feet above his head. He stopped short, cautiously trying to decide whether that had been purposely or accidentally close. "I've owned a rifle since I was twelve, and I've collected my share of bounty on coyote hides. Now, if you want to know whether a woman can shoot what she aims at, you just take another step." This time she had the rifle butt by her shoulder. "Now get your stuff and start walking."

There was hesitation as the three of tnem glanced at each other. Jessy swung the rifle barrel to the right, took aim on a red flag just beyond them, and felt the butt jump against her shoulder when she squeezed off a second shot. The whang of the bullet snapping off the head of the stake convinced them. When she put a third one at their feet, they were assured she meant business.

"You crazy woman," the man in khaki muttered angrily as the other two hastily began assembling their equipment and picking up the sack of flagged stakes.

Already the roar of gunned motors had reached Jessy's hearing. It was only a matter of minutes before three more pickup trucks manned by Triple C riders rolled onto the scene. There was an ample escort to usher the survey crew off the land.

When Jessy reached the main road, more Triple C personnel had converged on the spot, including Ty and Cathleen. While two of the pickups accompanied the surveyor's Jeep to the east gate, the rest stayed to hold an impromptu meeting.

"At a guess, I'd say they were just feeling us out to see how we'd react." Ty supposed their strategy was to find out just how strongly he intended to oppose them, if at all.

"Hey, Ty!" Tiny Yates shouted to him, one row of trucks

back, standing beside the open door of his cab. "I just heard on the CB that they think Ruth Haskell had a heart attack. They're rigging up the plane so they can fly her to the hospital."

"Nanna Ruth!" Cat gasped the name of the woman who had been the nearest thing to a grandmother to her. Her green eyes were huge and liquid when she glanced at her brother.

30

In a grave next to the Calder family plot, they laid Ruth Haskell to rest and the Triple C turned out en masse to pay its final respects to the quiet woman who had been woven into the background of the Calders for so long.

When the graveside services were over, Jessy continued to stand in the shaft of hot sunlight, wearing the same blue dress she'd had on at Maggie Calder's funeral. She remembered sitting with Ruth, remembered Ty's visit to the house. Beyond the heads of the milling throng, she had a clear view of Ty pausing to have a few words with the minister. His arm was around Cat's shoulders, silently comforting the pale and emotionally drained girl. Compassion welled tenderly in her breast for Cat, who had lost the two women she had been closest to, and in such a short span of time.

Moved by this pity for Ty's sister, Jessy worked her way through the crowd to offer her condolences. She approached Ty for no other reason, although her eyes observed the tense, preoccupied lines that made his features appear hard and unforgiving. Rumor had it that Tara had left him because of this pending fight with her father. Since he had offered no explanations for her absence, no one asked. Although Jessy could understand the problem of divided loyalties, she still thought Tara was a fool for leaving Ty when he needed her, if that's what she'd done. But Jessy didn't seek to reestablish her relationship with Ty. That was in the past. He had made his choice and she accepted that.

There was a brief moment when she met his dark eyes; then she turned her attention to his sister. "I'm sorry, Cat," she murmured. "It must seem that something bad happens to everyone you love. But it isn't really that way. Life is just harsh sometimes. But that's what makes the good times better."

"I know." Cat sniffed back the tears that were constantly trembling on the edge of her eyes and managed a small, tight smile. Her eyes made a long, slow swing over the crowd, then returned to her brother. "I really thought Tara would come to the funeral," she said in a low voice that indicated how betrayed she felt.

His gaze flickered briefly to Jessy, the set of his jaw showing a hard pride. "I'm supposed to go after her. It's another one of her games." It was a half-muttered explanation, dry and emotionless.

"Then that's what you'll do." Jessy said it very simply.

Her hazel eyes were equally direct in their regard as Ty looked at her. Finally he slowly nodded. "That's what I'll do," he said.

"Ty." Cat nudged him and looked pointedly at the two men approaching them.

Their arms swung in unison, at first glance concealing the handcuffs that bound one wrist to the other. The prison had permitted Buck Haskell to attend his mother's funeral in the company of a guard. His hat was in his hand, revealing the curly hair that age had silvered, but his features had retained much of their youthful quality, rather like a high-spirited child that refused to grow up. He faced Ty with a humble air.

"I wanted to thank you for lookin' after my mother, and for the real fine funeral you gave her." He glanced at the open grave. "I only wish they'd let me come home while she was alive." The sad look, the smooth words, came too easily to the man.

"As far as I'm concerned, you killed her." Ty could find no pity in his heart for the man. "Every time she visited you in prison, she died a little more inside for what you'd become. If I have my way, you'll rot in that cell."

A sudden blaze of hatred flared in Haskell's blue eyes. "I heard someone's grabbed a bunch of your precious Calder land and there isn't a damned thing you can do about it. You ain't so big anymore."

"You've buried your mother. Now get off my land," Ty ordered coldly.

Haskell took a threatening step toward him, only to be brought up short by the jerk of the handcuffs. The guard said something to him and took hold of his arm. Haskell jerked it free, the metal bracelets clanging, as he glared again at Ty, then turned stiffly to let the guard lead him away.

There wasn't time for the relaxing of tension as the brittle atmosphere was shattered by strident honkings of a horn. Ty swung toward the sound, all his muscles and nerves coiling again. A racing pickup came to a screeching stop, tires skidding on the gravel of the cemetery road.

"They're coming!" Repp Taylor stepped out of the cab as far as the running board to shout the warning. "There's a bunch of them—trucks, road graders, the works!"

Before the second announcement was made, Ty was pushing away from Cathleen and breaking into a run for the closest vehicle. He cursed himself for not guessing Dyson would choose this particular time to make his move while the bulk of the Triple C was attending the funeral of one of their own. He had to stop that equipment while it was on Calder property. Once it reached government land, his chances of getting it removed were substantially lower.

No orders had to be given as men piled into vehicles, scrambling into cabs and truck beds. All were in their best suits and hats and pearl-snapped white shirts. In less than five minutes, the cemetery was choked with dust kicked up by the fast-departing vehicles. The women who stayed behind, including Jessy and Cathleen, were busy organizing themselves into groups. Although theirs was temporarily a waiting lot, they would play a role, depending on the outcome of the confrontation and how quickly it occurred.

A dozen trucks barreled over the road, traveling in a high,

thick dust cloud that limited visibility to the bumper of the truck ahead of it, but there was no slackening of pace as the pickups loaded with men raced blindly to intercept the opposition. With eyes smarting from the dirt particles in the driven air, they strained for a glimpse of anything moving in the distance.

There was a pickup in the ditch, a long, scraping gash dented into its side. A cowboy limped into view beside it and waved his hat, motioning the convoy off the road and up a coulee.

"They just got by me!" he shouted as the trucks slowed and made the turn, each finding its own rough route.

Less than a quarter mile off the road, they came upon the slow-moving vehicles, led by a road grader, still on Calder land. The pickups encircled the elongated band of trucks and machinery, using the high walls of the coulee to box them in and blocking both ends. The road grader ground to a stop and sat idling noisily while the Triple C riders piled out of the trucks.

"You're on private property!" Ty placed himself in clear view of the bunched vehicles. "Back 'em up and clear out!"

"We've got a right to access!" came an answering shout.

The road grader's diesel motor was revved, huffing and snorting like a range bull pawing the ground before a charge. The long, angled blade was inches off the ground, less a battering ram than an effective tool to push obstacles out of its way. It gathered power and began to rumble forward, taking aim on the two pickups in its path, intending to eliminate their barrier the same way it had gotten rid of the pickup they'd passed in the ditch by the road.

Ty retreated behind the first truck in its path. "They're hard of hearing," he said to Wyatt Yates and glanced at the rifle in the wrangler's hand. "Maybe you can open their ears."

The cowboy grinned briefly and began snapping off shots at the oncoming grader, bullets ricocheting off the metal blade with an angry whine. Other cowboys in the front circle joined in the black-powder discussion, armed with rifles from the pickups' gun racks. The minute a bullet came close to the cab

of the road grader, the diesel motor growled into silence as
the driver bolted from the cab and raced back to the other
vehicles. At a signal from Ty, the shooting ceased.

"Go back and tell Dyson he's not crossing my land!" Ty
yelled.

"He'll cross it! Maybe not this time, but he'll cross it!" The
admission of defeat carried a warning.

It became obvious when the last vehicle had been escorted
through the east gate where the ranch lane intersected the
highway that the next confrontation wouldn't be long in
coming. As soon as they left Calder property, the trucks and
machinery began pulling off onto the side of the road and
stopping.

Ty was in the pickup Repp Taylor was driving. Repp turned
to frown at him. "They aren't leaving."

"Neither are we," Ty stated. For the time being, it was a
standoff. But it couldn't last for long. Neither he nor Dyson
could afford to tie up men and machinery for a long period of
time.

All through the afternoon and early evening, the vigil was
maintained. As soon as word of the stalemate was relayed to
the headquarters, the wives gathered at the cookhouse to
send sandwiches, coffee, and desserts. Changes of clothing
began arriving, along with bedrolls.

Ty paid little attention to the comings and goings of
vehicles on his side of the fence. Restlessness pushed at him
as he dragged on his cigarette and expelled the smoke from
his lungs in an impatient rush. He kept watching the activity
around the machinery.

"Ty?" The anxious call of his name disturbed his concentration. He glanced around as Cat came running up to him.
"Are you all right? What's happening?"

"Nothing. What are you doing here?" He gripped her
shoulders to keep her from running pell-mell into him.
"You're supposed to be home."

"I couldn't stay there." The determined lilt in her voice
warned him that she wouldn't be ordered back.

His hard glance flicked past her to take in the sight of Jessy
just coming up to him. Her dress had been replaced by jeans,
boots, and a hat.

"Coffee?" She handed him a cup, steaming fragrantly with the hot brew. "I brought Cat with me," she admitted.

"Since you're here"—his attention reverted to his sister—"make yourself useful and get me a sandwich." He waited until Cat had moved out of hearing before pinching more smoke from the short cigarette. "This is no place for her."

"That's a man's opinion," she returned evenly. "But he usually isn't the one who's sitting home and worrying. Cat was really afraid something was going to happen to you. You're just about all she has left. Besides, I figured it would be just as hard for her to sleep alone in that house as it would be in the back end of one of these trucks."

"Maybe." Ty grudgingly conceded the point, his attention running again to the machinery parked on the roadside. "Were there any calls or messages from Silverton, the attorney?"

"No. Someone at headquarters would have contacted you by radio if there were." Jessy understood that patience was something Ty had learned, but it didn't always ride well with him. Now it was coiling in him.

"Silverton's trying to get some sort of temporary injunction or restraining order barring Dyson from the land. The suit's been refiled, contesting the land title." He explained the things that were being worked on, things out of his hands.

"What do you think Dyson's going to do next?"

"I don't know." The cigarette was smoked down to his fingers. Ty pinched out the fire and ground the butt under his boot. "This might be a diversion to keep us occupied here while he slips in somewhere else." With a turn of his head, he measured her with a glance. "What are you doing here, Jessy?"

The smooth composure of her strong features was beyond a man's reading. So calm and resolute, accepting her fate either good or bad; but still, that was not all he saw in her. There were other things he couldn't name, yet he sensed them, like feeling the vague brush of glory pass close to him after searching long years for it.

"I thought someone should keep an eye on Cat," she said, removing that concern from him.

"Right." An evening star twinkled in the purpling night

sky. It reminded him of Tara. She should be the one looking
after his sister. Jessy noticed the change in his expression, the
faraway look of a man troubled by his dreams. Guiltily, she
moved away.

As darkness settled over the land, the tension diminished.
Voices were pitched softer. Nightwatches were assigned and
bedrolls spread out in and around the pickups. It was nearing
midnight and Jessy was cocooned in a blanket, propped in the
corner of a truck's rear bed. From her vantage point, she
could make out Cathleen's dark shape, sleeping in Repp
Taylor's arms. But Ty had not rested, and she doubted that
he'd try to before morning.

Around midmorning the next day, a horse and rider
cantered in from the north to approach the ranch pickups
clustered around the gate. Ty walked to the edge of the outer
vehicles before ascertaining the rider was Culley O'Rourke
and not one of his men.

"Trouble?" Culley stepped out of the saddle, looking
around.

"Some." Ty nodded shortly, his gaze running over the
man. "Cat mentioned you hadn't been feeling well." He
looked healthy, although he seemed to move with care.

O'Rourke betrayed himself with a startled look for an
instant, then said, "I'm okay. This business with Dyson
coming to a head?"

"It looks that way." There was nothing to be gained by
discussing the situation with his uncle. He angled away from
the man to head back where he could keep watch on the gate.
"Help yourself to some coffee."

"I will." O'Rourke hooked a stirrup on the saddle horn and
tugged to loosen the cinch a notch. He was relieved when he
noticed Cathleen. "So this is where you got to? I been lookin'
all over for you," he declared gruffly.

"Uncle Culley"—her tone was earnest and insistent—
"we've got to tell Ty. He's got to know what we suspect. Both
of us together, we'll be able to convince him."

"It's no use, I been tellin' you that," he reminded her.

"But there's going to be trouble here. There's been some
shooting already. If Dyson and his partner really tried to kill

my father, what's stopping them from trying to get rid of Ty? We have to warn him, just in case."

The shrill wail of a siren wobbled through the air, breaking the quiet that had held the morning. As it approached, growing louder, there was a stirring of movement toward the east gate. Cat grabbed her uncle's hand and pulled him along with her.

A car bearing the sheriff's insignia turned off the highway onto the lane, stopping short of the cattle guard. Ty leaned a shoulder against the tall gatepost that marked the entrance and waited while Blackmore hefted his barrel-chested body out of the car, followed by two uniformed deputies. He hitched his pants up by the waistband, adjusting his holstered gun on his hip, then strolled to the cattle guard with a faint swagger.

"Times have changed, Calder," Blackmore declared with a satisfied look. "You can't have things your way anymore."

"Is that a fact?" Ty didn't change his slouched position as he struck a match head on the rough post and lit a cigarette.

"You've heard of an easement, haven't you? I've got a piece of paper here, all recorded and legal, which says the government has an easement to that property they own west of here." He produced the stamped and sealed document for Ty's inspection. "It gives them and their assigns access across your ranch."

A grimness edged his mouth as Ty unfolded the recorded document. He hadn't thought Dyson would be able to obtain one so soon. Somewhere along the line, he had shortcut the system and eliminated a lot of red tape.

"It's an easement grant, all right," Ty agreed smoothly. "Thirty foot wide, but this legal description doesn't give me a clear idea where it's located. I'm sure you'll agree, Sheriff, that we want this legal. The government wouldn't want its people traveling over a road they don't have a lawful right to be on. I'll hire a surveyor to come out and verify exactly where this easement is located. Of course, that's liable to take some time."

Blood vessels stood out in the sheriff's neck as he struggled with his anger. "You think you're so damned smart, don't you?"

At the moment, all Ty had accomplished was to buy some time. "I'm just abiding by the law."

"A real respectable citizen, aren't you?" the sheriff mocked and turned smug. "In addition to that paper you've got in your pocket, I have another one. It's a warrant for your arrest."

His chin lifted a challenging inch. Behind him, Ty could hear the rumble of protest from his men. "On what charge?" he demanded.

"Assault with a deadly weapon, malicious destruction of property, inciting violence—I have a whole list of them," the sheriff assured him.

"That's a pack of lies," Ty snapped.

"A judge will have to decide that." He smiled. "Now, are you going to come along with me peacefully, or do I have to add resisting an officer to the list?"

"No!" Cat rushed forward, angrily charging between them. "You aren't taking him anywhere!"

"Cat." Ty caught her arm and pulled her out of the way. "They can't hold me. I'll be out on bail within a couple of hours." He pushed her gently into their uncle's waiting hands, then turned to the long, slim woman standing just to the side. "Jessy, call Silverton for me and let him know about this easement and these phony charges."

"I will."

"Ty, you don't understand!" Cat strained to break free of O'Rourke's hands. "Culley, explain to him," she demanded angrily.

"Hush, girl," Culley warned her in a low voice. "Or the sheriff'll end up carting the three of us away. Then what help would you be to your brother?"

She stopped fighting his grip and stood rigid, watching as Ty walked to the police car. The sheriff ordered him to turn around and handcuffed his wrists together behind his back.

"This isn't necessary, Sheriff," Ty muttered at the grate of metal being tightened on his wrists.

"I handcuff all my prisoners. That's the lawful procedure," he chided and pushed Ty's head down as he slid awkwardly into the rear passenger seat.

As the police car pulled away with its prisoner, Cat spun

around to glare at the ranch hands. "Why didn't you do something? Why did you let them take him?" Few of them would look at her.

A mobile-home trailer in Blue Moon had been converted into a payroll and accounting office for the mine. Dyson had commandeered the manager's front office as his base of operations, from which he directed his legal and tactical maneuverings against the Triple C Ranch.

At the end of his phone conversation, he rocked back in the swivel desk chair and eyed the room's other two occupants with a self-satisfied look. "Ty is safely locked away in his jail cell. And the sheriff can hold him for twenty-four hours, actually"—he glanced at his watch—"twenty hours before he has to release him or officially file charges and let him post bail. How opportune that tomorrow is Saturday." The gleam in his eye revealed the timing had been deliberately calculated. "Now, as long as the judge plays his part and sets bail at some outrageously high figure, it will be Monday before Calder can either get it reduced or make arrangements to meet it."

"You don't have to worry about the judge." The calm assurance came from Stricklin, his head slightly bent while he buffed his nails.

Tara broke her statuelike vigil at the small trailer window and swung toward the desk, her eyes dark with appeal. "Is it really necessary for Ty to be in jail?"

"The quickest way to win a battle is to separate a general from his troops. Loyal as they may be, without guidance they aren't going to know what to do," her father explained tolerantly. "I have a little over three days, more than enough time, to force the easement rights to be honored. By Monday, we'll have machinery on the land and it'll all be over but the shouting." There was a slight pause as his expression took on a sternly irritated look. "That impudent husband of yours will be wiser for the experience."

Stricklin rose from his chair, announcing casually, "I'm going to stop by the sheriff's office and make sure everything is going smoothly."

"Suit yourself." Dyson shrugged his indifference, but his

eyes narrowed shrewdly on the man as he left the room. "I don't know what's got into him lately," he murmured. "He's constantly checking and rechecking every detail."

"He's always been particular about everything." Tara saw nothing different in him, her impatience showing for a subject so far removed from her interest.

"Not like this."

"Daddy, what if I went to see Ty?" she suggested somewhat eagerly. "I could talk to him—reason with him."

"Let me explain something to you, Tara Lee." Dyson got up from his chair and walked around the desk to affectionately place his hands on her shoulders. "Right now he's going to be upset and frustrated over being locked up. He wouldn't listen to anything you have to say. But he's going to have three days to do nothing but sit and think. Afterwards, he'll be more than willing to admit the mistake he's made."

"Why did he have to do this?" Tara protested to no one, impatient with Ty's actions and worried, too. There was no doubt in her mind that her father would ultimately triumph, but she didn't want Ty's position to be completely ruined in the process. If they were ever to achieve anything, he had to come out of this with something.

A fly walked across the stubble of his beard as Ty lay on the bare mattress of the jail-cell cot, his hands pillowed under his head and his hat cocked low on his forehead. He shifted, withdrawing one hand to chase the tickling fly from his face. It made a circling buzz over him to pick out its next landing site.

Judging by the vulgar poetry scratched on the wall, the new jail had been suitably christened by former occupants of the cells. Ty had read them all at least twice. The isolation and confinement tore at his nerves. He swung up restlessly to sit on the edge of the cot, rubbing his hands on his thighs.

A door opened in the offices beyond the lockup door, and Ty rose to his feet, moving to the bars. It was hell not knowing what was happening at the ranch or how soon he was going to be released.

"Where's my brother? What have you done with him?" Cat's voice filtered clearly into the cell area. "Why haven't

394 CALDER BORN, CALDER BRED

you let him go?" He didn't hear the murmured answer. He strained, listening for another voice to learn who had come with his sister to obtain his release, but it soon became apparent she was alone. "I want to see him," she demanded, her voice closer to the locked door between the cells and the office.

"I can't allow you to see the prisoner just now—not till we get all the forms processed and the charges filed. Jails aren't a place for young girls anyway," the sheriff insisted. Ty agreed. He didn't want Cat in here.

"How do I know he's all right? How do I know you haven't beat him up?" Cat persisted belligerently.

Stubborn little minx, Ty thought to himself and wondered who had let her come into town by herself . . . not that his little sister was ever very concerned about obtaining permission to do something she wanted.

"Cat! I'm all right!" Ty shouted to make sure she heard him. "Now go on home!"

"No! I'm staying here until they let you go!"

Releasing a long breath of exasperation, Ty shook his head at her stubbornness. He didn't want her hanging around the jail. "I'm out of cigarettes. Go buy me a pack." For a minute, Ty thought she was going to refuse his request.

"I'll be right back." She called the promise to him. Then he heard a door open and shut, and the noises from the outer office became the usual sounds of telephones ringing, and the squawk of the dispatcher's radio, and the pecking of typewriter keys. With an impatient turn of his long body, he walked back to the cot to wait some more.

The powerless feeling had Cat trapped halfway between anger and fear. Everyone knew the sheriff was in Dyson's pocket, and she was afraid for Ty. No matter how wildly she searched, she couldn't come up with an answer.

She charged blindly out of the sheriff's office and onto the new concrete sidewalk. At first, she was too preoccupied to notice the man coming toward her. But her headlong pace slowed the instant she recognized Stricklin. All the bottled-up frustration came to a seething boil when he paused, his glance running past her to the building.

"Have you been to see your brother?" His question was

sharp with interest as his eyes, opaque behind the glasses, studied her.

"They wouldn't let me see him." Cat was all taut and glaring, recklessly abandoning any sense of caution. "Ty isn't the one who belongs behind bars. You are! I can't prove that you murdered my mother yet, but I will!" She hurled the threat at him, then angrily brushed past him to continue toward the pickup truck she had borrowed from one of the ranch hands.

The open accusation had briefly stunned him. He glanced around in alarm, but no one had heard or seen the encounter. A truck door slammed. With the calculating swiftness of a computer, Stricklin weighed his chances. It was unlikely he'd be presented with another opportunity like this, nor could he count on her keeping silent.

As Cat was easing the truck onto the street, the passenger door was jerked open. She jerked around with startled alarm as Stricklin clambered into the cab and shut the door. She started to lift her foot off the accelerator to step on the brake, but his foot came down hard on her boot, pushing the accelerator pedal down. The truck leaped forward with the sudden surge of power. In the first second, her concentration centered on keeping the pickup on a straight course up the street.

"What are you doing? Are you crazy?" She shot the panicked and angry questions at Stricklin, then realized who she was talking to and the implications of his actions.

"Just drive where I say," he ordered.

Cat had no intention of doing anything of the sort. Her first thought was to put the truck in the ditch, but his hand grabbed the wheel before she could whip it to the side and kept it heading straight. Even though the pickup was traveling at a good clip, she tried to open the door so she could jump out and get away from him, but Stricklin easily thwarted that attempt, too, and twisted her arm behind her back. The pain was so intense Cat felt any minute her bones would snap.

"You'll never get away with this," she warned him on a moaning sob of breath, but even she was afraid he could.

He had crowded close to her to have better control of the

vehicle as he turned it onto the highway. Out the side window, Cat noticed the cars and trucks parked in front of Sally's Place and the small grocery store and service station. With her free hand, she tried to slap at the horn and attract somebody's attention, but she missed and the pressure on her arm increased until she cried out.

Too quickly, they were out of town and any chance of someone seeing them was gone. She was frightened, finally realizing how much danger she was in. Except for Ty, nobody even knew she had come to town.

Five miles from town, Stricklin left the two-lane to follow a dirt road, studded with weeds and grass that marked its lack of use. It led to some abandoned buildings, not visible from the highway. The barns and sheds had collapsed in a rubble of wood, but the house was still standing, grayed and weathered, its roof sagging dejectedly.

After he'd stopped the truck, he pushed Cat out the driver's side ahead of him, never relaxing his grip on her arm. A checking jerk stopped her from walking as he paused to look around in a considering manner.

"I remember flying over this place and thinking how utterly forgotten it looked—so far from the highway," he murmured, somewhat pleased with himself for recalling its existence, since it was so ideally suited to his present needs. He changed the pressure on her arm, twisted high on her back, and forced her to back up to the pickup. "Ranch vehicles always seem to be stocked with nearly any item a man might need." A coiled rope was jammed behind the seat. He took it out, then shoved Cat ahead of him toward the ramshackle house.

All the windows were boarded over, although some daylight sifted in through the many cracks. The air was stale and hot inside, rank with old, musty odors and dust. Cobwebs snatched at her face and hair, trying to catch her in their many silken threads. She waved at them with frantic, impatient little gestures of her free arm.

After they had wandered through three rooms of the house, picking their way across the rotten floorboards, Stricklin stopped in the fourth and released her arm with a shove that pushed her into the middle of the room. It appeared to be a bedroom, and the only way out was through the door where Stricklin was standing. Cat eyed him warily and rubbed at the agonizing ache in her arm.

"Who else knows about the plane crash?" he asked with ominous softness.

Her chin lifted defiantly. "No one."

"Liar." It was calmly spoken as his mouth curved faintly in one of those fake smiles that chilled her blood. "But it doesn't matter. It's quite simple to figure it out." He reached inside his suit jacket and took out a pen and a leather-bound note pad. "You're going to write me a note to your boyfriend."

"Repp?" Cat breathed his name in shocked dismay, realizing Stricklin believed she had confided in him. "He doesn't know anything."

"That's very noble of you. Here." He held out the paper and pen.

"No." She took a step backwards. "I'm not writing any note for you."

"I think you will," he murmured.

When the locked door between the twin jail cells and the front offices swung open, Ty rolled to his feet and crossed swiftly to the door of his cell. The tautness ran from him when he recognized the suited man being admitted by the sheriff.

"I wondered when you'd get here," he said.

Silverton flashed him an understanding look, then glanced pointedly at the sheriff, lingering by the door. "I'd like to speak to my client privately." Blackmore shrugged his shoulders and moved away reluctantly. The lawyer faced Ty, a wry smile tugging at one corner of his mouth. "It's lucky your local police weren't out patrolling the highway for speeders, or I'd be in there with you."

"How soon can you get me out of here?"

"There isn't much I can do until they officially file charges, and they're going to drag their feet right up to the deadline, I'm afraid," he replied, cautioning him against expecting to be released any time soon. "I can't do much about arranging bail until I find out what the judge is going to want. You can bet it's not going to be reasonable. They're going to try to keep you in here as long as they can."

"What about the injunction? Any luck?"

"Not so far," Silverton admitted, his mouth tightening in grim sympathy as Ty swore under his breath. "I don't have to tell you what small-town law can be like."

"No." He pulled in a deep breath. "I want you to get hold of Potter. If the judge or any official around here has got old skeletons in their closet, Potter can tell you everything you'd want to know about them and how long since they've been dusted. He's old and sick now, but his mind hasn't gone yet. Let him rattle some bones for us."

31

Long afternoon light laid its angle on the land, stretching out the shadows cast by the mob of pickup trucks that blocked the road from the east gate. Cowboys lounged in the shaded areas, seeking relief from the daylong heat that had baked metal surfaces until they were too hot to touch. The seeming lethargy of the group was a pose, a means of conserving energy. To a man, they were alert, eyes always moving, watching, waiting.

When a dark-colored Chrysler, covered with a film of travel dust, slowed on the highway and turned into the lane, those seated on the ground rolled to their feet and advanced to meet the car before it had clattered across the cattle guard. Their looks of hard suspicion gave way to dawning smiles when Ty Calder climbed out of the passenger side. As the car reversed onto the road, they pressed around him with a hearty, backslapping welcome.

"What's the word, boss?"

"Yeah, what's the word?" another voice echoed. "Are we gonna have to let them through?"

"Silverton"—Ty gestured to indicate the driver of the car just pulling onto the highway—"will have an injunction by morning. So, nothing crosses this range between now and

then—no matter what law-enforcement official orders it."
More talk followed, gradually dying as their curiosity was
satisfied. They began to scatter again, seeking the shade. Ty
poured himself a cup of coffee from the large urn in the back
of a truck, then patted his empty shirt pocket. Repp Taylor
was leaning against the tailgate. "Got a cigarette?" Ty asked,
then lit the one Repp finally offered him after a blank minute.
"I sent Cat to buy me a pack, but she must have forgotten."

"I think something's wrong, Ty." The cowboy's lean-bitten
features looked troubled as he fingered the slip of paper in his
hand. "Some kid came riding up a while ago and said a girl
had asked him to deliver this note to me. It's from Cat." He
unfolded it to look at it again, not reading it verbatim. "She
says she's running away and wants me to meet her tonight."

"Running away?" Furrows ran deep in his brow as Ty
reached for the note.

"Yeah. That's what I couldn't figure out either," Repp
admitted with a gathering frown of concern. "She says she's
tired of the arguing and fighting—and she's upset 'cause you
won't listen to her about the plane crash."

"The plane crash." Ty came to that part in the note and
was equally confused. "I don't know what she's talking
about."

"Neither do I. I know she's still upset over losing her
mother, but—" Repp shrugged, unable to make anything
other than the obvious connection between the two.

"The note also asks you not to tell anyone of her plans."

"I know, but something's not right about this note," Repp
insisted grimly.

"When's the last time anyone on the ranch saw her?"

"I asked around after this note came. Someone thought
they saw her take one of the trucks around noontime." Repp
eyed him with piercing interest. "What do you think?"

"If she's really intending to run away, she's picked a
helluva time for it."

It was difficult not to be irritated with his spoiled sister.
With all the trouble he had on his hands now, the last thing he
needed was for her to pull a disappearing act just to gain his
attention. But he also saw it was a sign of insecurity, a silent
cry for someone to let her know they cared about her. At

sixteen, all the feelings were so intense—pain, pride, love, hate. With their mother's death and now Nanna Ruth's, their father in the hospital for God only knew how much longer, Tara walking out on them, and he, admittedly, too busy lately to give her much of his time, she probably felt completely alone, unwanted and unneeded.

Ty studied the note again. "Since she wants you to meet her tonight, she must be hiding out somewhere. More than likely, she's gone to the same place she went the last time."

"O'Rourke's?"

"When did he leave here?" Ty asked.

"About the same time Cat did—right after the sheriff took you away this morning. He hasn't been back since."

"Come on." Ty returned the note and pushed away from the truck. "We're going over to his place and get her." With luck, things would stay quiet here until he got back.

No time was wasted in the drive to the Shamrock Ranch. They traveled as fast as the condition of the roads would permit. The setting sun was firing the horizon with a cerise hue that grayed to purple where the land met the sky. O'Rourke was on the front stoop to meet them when the truck roared into his ranch yard.

"Tell Cathleen we've come to take her home," Ty announced with firm conviction while he climbed out of the truck.

"Cathleen? She's not here." The denial was startled out of Culley. "The last time I saw her, she was at The Homestead."

"It's no use covering for her, Culley," Ty declared impatiently. "We know she's here. She sent Repp a note, telling him she was running away and asking him to meet her. This is the only place she could hide out."

"I swear she didn't come here." His hand made a vague raking scratch of his head. "She wouldn't run away," he insisted, speaking his thoughts aloud. "Not when she was so worried about what Dyson might do to you while you were in jail. She wouldn't have run."

"In her note, she referred to the plane crash—" Repp started to ask if her uncle knew what she was talking about.

"Did she tell you about that?" His gaze jerked to the cowboy.

"What about it?" Ty demanded.

"About Stricklin tampering with the oil line," Culley answered, then realized neither man had known anything about it. "Oh, no," he groaned suddenly. "You don't suppose Stricklin or Dyson found out she knew what they'd done?" There was a wild sawing of his gaze, racing back and forth. "They've got her." He glanced at Repp. "And they're figuring you saw him, too, that night in the hangar."

"I think you'd better start at the beginning," Ty advised, trying to separate the man's wild rantings from fact.

With the windows boarded shut, the room was pitch-black. Cat's silent, tearless sobs of frustration and self-pity were noisy breaths that stirred the gritty dust caking the floor where she lay, tied hand and foot. Her limbs ached with a tingling numbness from being forced to hold a single position, and the hard floor bruised her bones. Worse, she could feel things crawling all over her.

Floorboards creaked as footsteps approached the door. She held her breath, her heart suddenly leaping with fear. The door opened and a flashlight beam nearly blinded her. She blinked and tried to turn her head away from the glaring light. Stricklin entered the room and bent down to begin unknotting the rope that bound her.

"Your boyfriend will be here shortly."

She had tried everything from shouting and cursing to pleading and reasoning, but nothing had reached him. This time, Cat tried silence.

When she was freed of the ropes, Stricklin helped her to stand up. Her muscles were so sore and stiff she couldn't walk without stumbling. He guided her through the rooms to the front door, the flashlight showing the way. The fresh air smelled sweeter than she remembered as she took her first step into the moonlit night. She drank it in, her senses coming alive to savor the sensation of coolness on her skin and the chirrups of crickets in the weeds by the house. Such simple things. Such beautiful things.

"We'll wait by the truck," he told her. "And when your boyfriend comes, don't get any ideas."

Out of the corner of her eye, she noticed the movement of

his hand that accompanied the warning. A second later, she caught the sheen of metal in the moonlight and realized he had a gun. A tiny run of panic tautened her nerves. Sometime during those long hours she'd been left tied in the house, he'd acquired a pistol.

As they stood in the shadows of the truck, Cat prayed Repp wouldn't come. Her hearing seemed to become more acute, the night sounds appearing to be louder—the rustle of grass from some scurrying animal, the flap of wings overhead, and the shrill music of the crickets and buzzing night insects, all joining the cacophony, and over it all the pounding of her heart.

When she heard the hum of a motor, she tried to pretend it was a vehicle passing on the highway, but a pair of headlight beams grew steadily brighter as they approached the abandoned buildings. Desperately, Cat tried to think of some way to warn him; then she felt the hard circle of the gun's muzzle pressing into her side. She stiffened and watched helplessly as the truck rolled to a stop. Its headlight beams had swept the pickup truck they stood beside but never once invaded the shadows that concealed them.

There was the grinding of metal against metal as the truck door swung open on its hinges, then pushed shut. Cat opened her mouth to shout a warning to him, but the indrawn breath became lodged in her throat when the gun muzzle jabbed her ribs for silence. Footsteps crunched on gravel.

"Cat?" His call broke the silence. "Cat, where are you?"

Stricklin pressed his mouth close to her ear. "Answer him. Tell him to come over here."

Her teeth were clenched together in a mute protest before she finally complied. Between the gun and the brutal grip he had on her arm, she felt helpless to resist.

"Repp, I'm over here." Her voice was unsteady. "On the other side of the pickup."

As Repp came around the hood of the truck, Stricklin shifted his hold on her and forced her to step from the shadows. The gun was pointed at her head. Repp stopped dead still.

"The young lovers meet for their last rendezvous," Stricklin murmured, then motioned Repp to come closer.

"Then it was you Cathleen and I heard in the hangar that night," Repp accused and slowly walked forward until Stricklin signaled him to stop.

Cat stared at him in shock. "Repp, you—"

"It's no use pretending we don't know," he interrupted her quickly, then turned to Stricklin. "You did something to that oil line, didn't you?"

"It was fairly simple." Stricklin was very matter-of-fact about it. "It's unfortunate the two of you happened to be there that night."

"What have you got planned for us?" Repp sounded so calm that Cat wanted to scream.

"It's going to be a very tragic accident—two young lovers parked in some out-of-the-way place, unfortunately overcome by carbon monoxide. A little battery acid on the exhaust hose and you have a leak that allows the fumes to get into the ventilation system. It will be very painless, really." He seemed to offer the comment as assurance. "Of course, afterwards I'll remove the jacks from the front end—I wouldn't want you to attempt to drive away—and I'll reattach the door locks."

"You won't get away with it," Repp countered smoothly.

"No one discovered the last accident—except you two."

"And Dyson—does he know?" It was thrown out as a challenge, faintly contemptuous. "I suppose this was his idea and you just do the dirty work for him."

"Is that an attempt to create friction between myself and E.J.?" There was amusement in Stricklin's voice, as much amusement as ever was allowed into his voice. "It won't work. Dyson has nothing to do with it." He used the gun to motion Repp toward the truck. "Open the door and get in."

There was a long hesitation, as though Repp were weighing his chances of rushing the man. Cat strained toward him, hating the way she was both a pawn and a shield to Stricklin.

"I said, open the door," he repeated the order.

From the shadows of the house, another voice—Ty's voice—answered him. "He's not going to do it, Stricklin."

Stricklin's head jerked in his direction. In that second of distraction, Repp grabbed Cathleen's arm and yanked her out of Stricklin's hold. "Run, Cat! Run!" His hands pushed at her shoulder blades, shoving her into the moonlit darkness as he threw himself at Stricklin.

Cat stumbled the first few steps, trying to get her balance. Her heart was pumping madly, and breath was screaming in her lungs. Something lunged out of the darkness a step behind her, startling a cry from her throat.

Suddenly, all the scuffling noises, the running footsteps, the wild terror pounding in her ears, were shattered by an explosion. Cat spun around. The scene was momentarily freeze-framed. A figure directly in front of her staggered backwards a step. Beyond him, Stricklin stood by the truck, the revolver at the end of his outstretched arm, a trace of white smoke curling from the muzzle.

A second explosion came. It seemed to push Stricklin backwards, a look of shock freezing on his expression as he slid down the side of the truck to the ground. Cat ran forward as the gray-haired man sank onto one knee.

"Uncle Culley." She fell to her knees beside him, her hands reaching to support his sagging frame. Casting a frantic look over her shoulder, she saw Repp being helped to his feet by two men. She didn't know where they came from, but he appeared unharmed. When she looked back to her uncle, she noticed a hand was pressed to his chest. Something wet and dark was oozing from between his fingers. "You've been shot."

"I'll be okay, girl." He patted her hand, leaving the stain of warm, sticky blood on it.

His weight seemed to grow heavier in her arms. She had to use her whole body to support. Then Ty was beside her. "Are you okay?"

"Yes." Before she could draw attention to Culley's chest wound, Ty was unbuttoning the shirt and pressing a folded piece of cloth on the dark purple hole in the flesh.

"There's an ambulance on the way, Culley," he said. "I'm sorry. Repp was in the way and we couldn't get a clear shot at him."

"I . . . I couldn't let him shoot Cathleen. He would have." His voice sounded very tired, although he made an attempt to smile at her. Cat realized he had deliberately placed himself between her and Stricklin. "I've been watchin' after her for a long time. I always tried to know where she was and what she was doin'. 'Cept today . . . I let her down today."

"No, you didn't, Uncle Culley," she declared tightly. "You came. You brought help. And Ty believed you, didn't he?"

"Yeah." He closed his eyes as if to consider that. "A Calder takin' an O'Rourke's word."

"Don't talk anymore," Ty advised. "Just stay quiet."

Sirens wailed eerily through the night. There was a confusion of voices and figures, the bright glare of spotlights and headlamps, and flash cameras taking pictures of Stricklin's lifeless body. Repp joined Cat's vigil at her uncle's side. There was an ugly bruise on his jaw where the revolver had dealt him a glancing blow.

The strong black coffee had a reviving effect on him, and Ty wiped at his mouth with the back of his hand, feeling the scrape of his beard. It was better than thirty-six hours since he'd last shaven and changed clothes—or slept. The weariness had begun pulling at his bones.

"I don't know which Dyson had a harder time swallowing" —Silverton was seated across from him at one of the few occupied tables in Sally's that morning—"discovering Stricklin's treachery or accepting the temporary injunction which bars him from doing any strip-mining on that land, pending a court ruling on the ownership."

"I'm sure both were big blows to him," Ty agreed and lifted the coffee cup to take another sip from it. After spending the last hour giving his account of the night's events to one of the deputies, he didn't feel like talking about Stricklin anymore.

Sally Brogan stopped at the table. "Refill?" The coffeepot was in her hand.

"Not for me," Ty said with a negative turn of his head.

"I was glad to hear that Culley came through his surgery all right," Sally offered while she topped off the attorney's cup.

"The doctors are confident he'll be up and around in no time. The bullet grazed some lung tissue, but luckily it missed the vital organs. Outside of losing a lot of blood, he wasn't critically wounded." He drained the last of his coffee and set the cup on the table. Drawing in a breath, he glanced at the lawyer. "If we've covered everything you wanted to go over, I think I'll be going."

"The rest can wait," Silverton assured him. "You'll be wanting to head home."

"Not right away. I've got a stop to make first," Ty admitted, pushing the chair away from the table to stand up.

"If you're looking for Tara," Sally inserted, "she's been living in one of the company houses, the one with the black shutters on the corner."

"Thanks." He dropped some change on the table for his coffee and left.

It was a square and simple one-story building, the endless dust already dulling the new coat of white paint on its boards. There was a weariness to his slow strides as he left the pickup parked on the side of the street and went up the walk to the front door. Ty paused, feeling the ravel of old excitement— the remembered anticipation he'd always known just before seeing her again. His knuckles rapped lightly on the door.

It opened at once, as if she had been on the other side, waiting for him. She stepped back to admit him, the sunlight making a picture of her dark beauty. She had always possessed the power to stir him—and she had it still.

"Hello, Tara." His whiskered face toughened his looks, darkening the slash of his mustache.

"Ty." The familiar cadence of her voice reached out to him. She turned with a deliberate grace, her glance leaving him although all her attention remained with him. "I heard about the injunction."

"There won't be any coal mined—not on Calder land, not by our generation. I told you that," he said.

"Yes." Her chin dipped slightly. A silence came, pressured by the many things to be said. "I believed my father was right. I believed he would win." She looked at him. "That was my mistake, wasn't it? It will always be there between us. It's all I've thought about for the last three hours, since I heard about the injunction."

"I know, Tara," he said.

"It's true, isn't it?" She came nearer, searching his face with a straining seriousness. "You always believed I was disloyal, choosing to stand by my father instead of you."

"Yes."

Her beauty made it easy for him to stare at her. An eagerness came into her dark eyes, and her lips turned soft. "Ty." She spoke his name in the old way. "Do you remember when we were in college? You were so in love with me then. Life was going to be so wonderful for us. You still feel that way, don't you?"

A feeling of vague surprise glided through him as he glanced away. She had once been his whole life. She had been in his mind wherever he went, the song he heard in the night wind or the desire in his body. He remembered the hot hunger she had once evoked in him, the tumult of wanting, and the way she responded to his heavy urges. But when he tried to bring back those feelings and sensations, it was Jessy's strong image, backlighted by the fireplace, he kept seeing.

Tara stared at him, seeing the emptiness of his regard. "How could you forget?" She breathed out the protest in a pained voice.

"I don't know," he admitted gently. "All I ever asked was for you to stand by my side. But you were always two steps ahead of me, trying to lead me where you wanted to go."

"I was trying to help."

"I know that, too." Ty nodded slowly. "Everything changes, Tara. And you can't bring the old times back, no matter how much you might like to."

"But I loved you." She protested the finality of his words.

"Once I loved you. I'm not blaming you for what you are. There's a man out there somewhere who'll suit you better than I will."

She shut her eyes for an instant; then they flared open, accusing. "It's Jessy, isn't it? I'm sorry, but I hate her." She turned away, hugging her arms tightly. "Maybe because she thrives under this suffocating sky."

Ty hesitated, finding nothing more to say. "Be happy, Tara."

"Oh, yes." Her laugh was slightly brittle. "I'm sure I'll play the role of the gay divorcée very well." Then she sighed. "The next time I won't make the mistake of thinking Daddy's always right."

But it wasn't only that, Ty knew. They had been traveling

separate roads for a long time. He turned and slowly walked to the door.

"I'll keep the ring, Ty." Her soft voice traveled after him, a hint of tears in it. "Part of my might-have-been memories."

The sun was a giant shimmer of white light in the high, summer-blue sky. A wind was picking up speed as it rolled over the undulating plains. When Ty drove away from the house, he didn't look back.

Like an old horse pointed homeward, instinct made all the turns down all the right roads, and Ty didn't have to make them consciously. When he came to the cabin nestled in the trees along the riverbank, he stopped the truck and stumbled out tiredly.

Flies made buzzing attempts to penetrate the mesh of the screen door, but he paid no attention to them as he entered the house. Jessy was sitting at the table, hands folded, waiting. She'd heard him drive up. There was color in her cheeks, but a definite reserve in her posture.

"I don't suppose you have any coffee made," he said, searching for a beginning.

"I'm sure there's plenty of coffee at The Homestead."

"But I like your coffee," he said.

"Now that this business is practically over with Dyson, have you been to see Tara?" She was almost harsh in her demand.

"Yes."

Too much was contained inside for Jessy to remain seated quietly. She pushed out of the chair and took a step into the center of the room, then swung to face him.

"Is she coming back?"

"I didn't ask her to, or I wouldn't be here." There were no words to fit the powerful gentleness that filled him. It lay choked in his throat, holding him against the desire to take her in his arms.

"If you're just here because you're grateful or feel obligated . . ." The pride that was so firmly stamped in her made him smile.

"No, Jessy. It isn't that at all."

Those eyes that had always watched him with such a waiting look now studied him carefully. The wide mouth began to break its severe line to curve with an unsteady smile. "If you're sure . . ." She let out the breath she'd been holding and took a step toward him. "If you're really sure . . ."

"I'm sure, Jessy." There was no doubt in his voice. An emotion deeper than time made a brilliant light in his dark eyes. His arms were opening as she came into them. He bowed his head to kiss her. The sensation of the room spinning was so strong his arms pressed hard around her to keep them from being whirled away.

Epilogue

There was a lean look to the land, which was still wearing its winter colors of faded tan and brown instead of the ripe summer-green. On the endless horizon, ominous storm clouds had rolled into black towers, promising rain after long months of drought.

It had been more than a year since Chase Calder had laid eyes on his home ground, and his hungry gaze had been taking in the sight of it for the last twenty-five miles. All the homesick longings he hadn't permitted himself to feel during the long months in the hospital now rose in his chest. He noticed all the little changes, the subtle differences.

"It looks like those rainclouds are headed this way," he observed somewhat gruffly to the driver.

Ty let his gaze stray from the road to eye the tantalizing closeness of the dark cloudbank. "I hope so. The Lord knows we need it." He flexed the grip of his hands on the steering wheel. "All the operations have been cut back about as much as they can be."

"Anything big is always inefficient; it's the nature of the beast," Chase replied with a trace of wryness. "It's always a battle trying to streamline and modernize the operation.

There's so much paperwork that sometimes the ranching part of it gets lost in the pressure to show a profit. Sometimes you have to suffer some heavy losses in order to win the war."

"Yeah." Ty knew that fact only too well.

"You had quite a baptism of fire." Quietly Chase studied his son, aware of all he'd been through.

"I stumbled a few times," Ty admitted.

"But you stayed with what you knew. Being a Calder means being a cattleman and having a commitment to the land and its people."

"It'll be a few months yet before the court makes a ruling on the disposition of that land," Ty stated, drawing a heavy breath. "Even then it won't be final. Depending on which way the court rules, if Dyson doesn't appeal it, we will."

"I'm not worried." A smile broke across his rugged, lined features.

For an instant, Ty looked at him, then smiled, too. "Neither am I—not with both of us to stop him."

The buildings of the ranch headquarters were in sight and Ty slowed the car. Vehicles crowded the wide yard area and the throng of ranch workers and their families pressed forward to meet the car.

"What's this?" Just for an instant, Chase Calder was a little dazed by the turnout.

Ty's expression gentled as he sat motionless behind the wheel of the stopped car. "I think they want to welcome you home."

After a split-second hesitation, Chase reached for the door handle. A small cheer went up when he stepped from the car unaided. A walking cane was hooked over his arm, but he didn't use it as he moved forward. When a raven-haired girl with eyes as green as Calder grass separated herself from the crowd to run forward to meet him, there was a second when Chase was transported back to another time when a young Maggie had run into his arms. He hugged his daughter tightly, loving her with a special love.

"Welcome home, Dad." Tears were shining in her eyes, happiness radiating from her. She stayed by his side, an arm around him, as if she would never leave him, but Chase was wiser than to believe that. He'd already noticed Repp Taylor standing to one side, and the darkly possessive light in the eyes of the tall, lean cowboy when he looked at Cathleen.

After he had greeted Repp, he looked mockingly from one to the other. "I suppose you two have run off and eloped while I've been gone."

"No, sir. Cat has some growing up to do," he said smoothly, then slid a glance to her. "She's still too spoiled to make a good wife."

"Repp." Her tone of voice sharply reproved him, but Chase merely chuckled at the exchange.

Ty was slower to get out of the car, hanging back to give his father center stage. This was his moment—his homecoming. As he stepped out of the car, he watched his father with Jessy, speaking to her briefly, then moving on to the next person. Then she was swinging across the ground with that long-legged grace to join him by the car. Ty felt his heart lift for this proud, earthy woman.

"It's wonderful, isn't it?" she said, looking back to watch his father.

"Yes." He curved an arm around her waist and drew her against his side. She looked thoughtful. "Is something wrong?"

"No." There was a small shake of her head, accompanied by a faint smile. "When I spoke to him just now, he suggested that I should get in the habit of calling him Dad Calder."

"I haven't told him, but I think he guessed a long time ago that I'd be marrying you as soon as the divorce is final." Ty smiled. "What's between us hasn't exactly been a secret."

"No." Her laugh was soft and her look was pleased. There was a brief silence while their attention went back to the tall, graying man being greeted with a kiss on the cheek by Sally Brogan. "I'm glad she came." She turned a serious look on Ty, as if to warn him. "Your father is a man. There'll come a time when he'll need her, her company and her affection, but it won't mean he'll stop loving your mother or even missing her."

"I know." There was a lot he understood now about human hungers and illusions. But he also knew that they never equaled the solid strength of more enduring things.

As Chase worked his way into the crowd, he almost missed

seeing Culley hovering on the fringe. Stopping, Chase changed direction to seek out Maggie's brother. For a long second, they looked at each other.

"You're looking fit," Culley said at last.

"So are you." Chase nodded.

Then Culley's head dipped as he looked at the ground. "I know how much you loved her. I—"

"We both loved her," Chase cut in quietly. "There may not be anything else, but we'll always share that."

"Yeah—I guess so."

Old friends, men and women he'd worked with and grown up with, pressed around him to welcome Chase home. And the younger ones, to whom the Calder patriarch was someone they knew more by reputation, came to add their reserved words of welcome to the rest. There were a lot of husky male voices, many smiles accompanied by teary eyes.

The gathering was slow to break up, everyone wanting to draw out the moment of reunion for as long as they could. The Yates family was leaving. Chase had just told them goodbye and was turning to walk back to the scattered throng when he heard the remark made by the teenage son of Tiny Yates.

"Ty's old man looks better than I thought he would after being in the hospital for so long."

The phrase stopped him, and his eyes filled with shining tears as he turned them skyward. "Maggie." His voice was choked with emotion. "Did you hear what he said? Ty's old man."

Together you'll face the future,
All the sunlight and shadows ahead,
And you'll raise your children knowing
They'll be Calder born—and Calder bred.